# FIGHTING AIRCRAFT
# OF THE WORLD

# FIGHTING AIRCRAFT
# OF THE WORLD

## OVER 600 FIGHTERS, BOMBERS & TRANSPORTERS

### MICHAEL SHARPE & CHRIS CHANT

**amber**
BOOKS

First published in 2004 by
Amber Books Ltd
Bradley's Close
74–77 White Lion Street
London N1 9PF
www.amberbooks.co.uk

ISBN 1-904687-02-4

Printed in Singapore

Picture credits
Pages 7 and 8 courtesy of TRH Pictures Ltd.
All artworks courtesy of Art-Tech Ltd.

# Contents

# Introduction

It was less than ten years after the Wright Brothers' epic first flight in December 1903 that the first aircraft was used for military purposes. Balloons had long been recognised as ideal for spotting on the battlefield, and the advantages of the aircraft for the military were plain. It was an Italian aircraft that first acted as a weapon in its own right, dropping explosives on the enemy during the Italian–Libyan war of 1911. The arrival of World War I three years later gave military aircraft development a massive boost, and the aircraft in service at the end of the war – the Fokker D.VII, the Sopwith Snipe, and the SPAD S.XIII, to name but three – were far superior to their predecessors.

The frail reconnaissance aircraft of 1914 had developed into faster and stronger machines, armed with machine guns and capable of dramatic air manoeuvres while dogfighting the enemy. Bombers, too, appeared; large, lumbering beasts with a small bombload but with sufficient range to attack strategic targets such as London. However the end of the war saw a cutback in military expenditure and military aviation stagnated even as civil air travel began to boom. The rate of technological advancement slowed dramatically, and there were few advances in military aircraft design until German rearmament began in the early 1930s.

At this point there was a radical change in aircraft design, as fabric-covered biplanes were replaced in civil and then military service by monoplanes covered increasingly

The P-47 Thunderbolt, seen here in D-Day invasion markings, was the most important American fighter-bomber of World War II.

# Introduction

**The MiG-15's appearance in the Korean War destroyed the West's illusion that they were far ahead of the Soviet Union in terms of aviation technology.**

with light alloy skinning. The potential of these new aircraft against ground targets was clearly shown in the German 'Blitzkrieg' campaigns of 1939–41. However World War II demonstrated that command of the air was vital for any effective offensive employment of air assets for strategic bombing and ground support, and was also significant in protecting strategic assets against an enemy's bombers, and safeguarding surface forces against enemy air attacks.

World War II was notable, too, for the emergence of jet propulsion. Germany fielded the first jet aircraft in combat when, in 1944, the Messerschmitt 262 proved itself more than capable of catching the fastest and highest-flying aircraft the Allies could field. Suddenly the piston-engined aircraft was outmoded. After the war Germany was stripped of her jet expertise by the victorious powers. The influence of German research can be seen in the designs of American and Soviet aircraft for the next decade. Perhaps the most significant area of German research was in aerodynamics, particularly the swept wing. By incorporating this with jet propulsion, the gate was opened for a new generation of high-speed, supersonic aircraft.

The military jet earned its spurs in the Korean War. Nothing prepared the United States Air Force for the deep shock of confronting Soviet-built MiG-15s in the skies over Korea. This agile, quick little fighter proved to the West that the Soviets had both the technology and industrial capacity to produce advanced jet aircraft. The war also highlighted some of the deficiencies of jet aircraft. Manoeuvrablity had been sacrificed for speed, take-off runs were much longer, and fuel consumption was too high.

The late 1950s was the heyday of the strategic bomber: large, multi-engined aircraft designed to deliver nuclear or conventional weapons to targets across thousands of miles of ocean. Both the US and USSR fielded jet bombers early in the 1950s – the Boeing B-52 Stratofortress and the Tupolev Tu-16 'Badger' among them. (The B-52 is expected to remain in service until 2038.)

To counter the threat of these strategic jet bombers, both East and West were forced to build a new generation of fast-climbing, radar-equipped aircraft that matched in complexity the bombers they were designed to destroy. Coupled with improving infrared and radar-guided missiles, these aircraft were the forerunners of today's air-superiority fighters. The English Electric Lightning and Lockheed Starfighter were born out of the need to intercept enemy bombers.

In the meantime French mistrust of US foreign policy precluded the purchase of US aircraft, and as a result France rapidly advanced into the jet age on her own. A wide range and diversity of aircraft was produced by French manufacturers during the 1950s and early 1960s. The US, USSR, Britain and France produced the vast majority of military jets during the 1950s and early 1960s, and aircraft produced by these countries were exported widely.

## NEW AIRCRAFT

The late 1960s saw the USSR, which had previously relied on strength in numbers over technical sophistication with regard to its aircraft, produce more advanced types. The MiG-23, -25 and -27 represented a significant step up in Soviet combat capability. The late 1960s also heralded the arrival of a revolutionary new form of aircraft, the Vertical/Short TakeOff and Landing (V/STOL) Hawker Siddley Harrier, which to date has no real equal anywhere in the world.

The Vietnam War caused another rethink. Instances of air-to-air combat were few and far between. By far the greatest threat faced by American pilots were the surface-to-air missiles (SAMs) that many analysts believed would spell the end of the manned fighter aircraft. Warfare again proved the greatest spur to military jet development, forcing the US to adapt and create anti-missile defences for its aircraft.

The end of the Cold War has changed strategic considerations and emphasised the need for rapidly deployable forces and multi-role combat aircraft to police international trouble spots. Stealth technology has emerged as the by-word of modern aviation, but as was demonstrated so forcefully during the 2003 Iraq War, the military jet continues to be the most potent and important symbol of military might.

# AEG C.IV

Allgemeine Elektrizitäts Gesellschaft (AEG) began building aircraft in 1910 and from the outset of World War I was required to build military aircraft for both German air services. The AEG 'C' series began with the C.I, introduced in March 1915 as a two-seat biplane armed reconnaissance aircraft powered by a 150hp (112kW) Benz Bz.III inline engine. Most important of the series was the C.IV, which was fitted with a Mercedes D.III inline engine and a fixed forward-firing machine gun for the pilot. It was built in numbers totalling some 400 aircraft. Development of the C.IV included the IV.N night bomber with increased span wings and Benz Bz.III power, the C.V two-seat reconnaissance prototype and the C.VIII.Dr triplane. Pictured is a C.IV of Fliegerabteilung 'A' (Artillery Cooperation) 224, flying from Chateau Bellingchamp during the spring of 1917.

| Country of origin: | Germany |
| --- | --- |
| Type: | two-seat armed reconnaissance biplane |
| Powerplant: | one 160hp (119kw) Mercedes D.III inline piston engine |
| Performance: | maximum speed 115km/h (71mph); service ceiling 5000m (16,400ft); endurance 4hrs |
| Weights: | empty 800kg (1764lb); maximum take-off weight 1120kg (2469lb) |
| Dimensions: | span 13.45m (44ft 1in); length 7.15m (23ft 5in); height 3.35m (10ft 10in); wing area 39 sq m (420 sq ft) |
| Armament: | one fixed forward-firing 7.92mm LMG 08/15 machine gun; one 7.92mm Parabellum machine gun on ring mounting for observer in rear cockpit |

# AEG G.IV

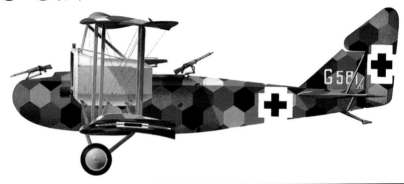

A EG undertook development of bomber aircraft for the German *Kampfstaffel* (battle squadrons) early in World War I. The first of the 'G' series, the G.I, was rather underpowered and only a single example was constructed. The following G.II and G.III suffered from the same problem and were therefore built in very small numbers. Marrying the powerplant of twin Mercedes D.IV engines to the airframe produced a far more effective aircraft in the form of the G.IV, but this did not enter service until the end of 1916. The four crew positions within the steel tube, fabric- and plywood-skinned aircraft were interconnected, enabling crew members to change position in flight as necessary. However, with a maximum bomb load and a crew of three, range was limited. Pictured is a G.IV of Bogohl 4, Staffel 19, stationed at Bazuel in the summer of 1918.

| | |
|---|---|
| **Country of origin:** | Germany |
| **Type:** | four-seat bomber/reconnaissance biplane |
| **Powerplant:** | two 260hp (194kW) Mercedes D.IVa inline engines |
| **Performance:** | maximum speed 165km/h (103mph); service ceiling 4500m (14,765ft); endurance 5hrs |
| **Weights:** | empty 2400kg (5291lb); maximum take-off weight 3630kg (8003lb) |
| **Dimensions:** | span 18.40m (60ft 3in); length 9.7m (31 8in); height 3.9m (12ft 8in); wing area 67 sq m (721 sq ft) |
| **Armament:** | one 7.92mm Parabellum machine gun on ring mounting in forward cockpit; one 7.92mm Parabellum machine gun on rail mounting in aft cockpit; underwing pylons for maximum bomb load of 400kg (882lb) |

# AIDC AT-3A Tzu Chung

In collaboration with Northrop, the Taiwanese Aero Industry Development Center developed a twin-fan military trainer for use by the Chinese Nationalist (Taiwanese) air force. Design of the aircraft began in 1975, and follows a conventional low-wing configuration with tricycle undercarriage, tandem seat cockpit, and twin turbojets mounted in nacelles either side of the fuselage. After design approval in 1978, the first prototypes were ordered in to production and the first of these made its maiden flight in September 1980. Evaluation led to a contract for 60 AT-3A Tzu Chung aircraft for the CNAF. In service the aircraft is operated in the advanced trainer role, and has won praise for its manoeuvrability. Weapons training can also be undertaken, with a wide variety of ordnance. Some 45 of the aircraft have been upgraded to AT-3B standard with radar and a HUD.

| | |
|---|---|
| Country of origin: | Taiwan |
| Type: | two-seat advanced flying and weapons trainer |
| Powerplant: | two 1588kg (3500lb) Garrett TFE731-2-2L turbofans |
| Performance: | maximum speed at 11,000m (36,090ft) 904km/h (562mph); service ceiling 14,650m (48,065ft); range on internal fuel 2280km (1417 miles) |
| Weights: | empty 3855kg (8500lb); maximum take-off 7940kg (17,505lb) |
| Dimensions: | wingspan 10.46m (34ft 3.75in); length (including probe) 12.9m (42ft 4in); height 4.36m (14ft 3.75in); wing area 21.93sq m (236.05sq ft) |
| Armament: | provision for two 0.5in machine-guns in ventral pack; two wingtip rails for two AIM-9 Sidewinder air-to-air missiles; five other hardpoints with provision for up to 2720kg (5998lb) of stores, including air-to-surface missiles, cannon and machine-gun pods, rocket-launcher pods, bombs, and cluster bombs |

# AIDC Ching-Kuo IDF

The Ching-Kuo was developed in Taiwan to help that country overcome the considerable restrictions placed on foreign imports. The country had intended replacing its ageing fleet of F-104 Starfighters with the Northrop F-20 Tigershark, but this proved impossible when the US government placed an embargo on this and any other comparable advanced fighter. American expertise was therefore bought in from General Dynamics, Garrett, Westinghouse, Bendix/King and Lear who helped to finalise a design in 1985. The first prototype flew on May 28, 1989; from the outset, it was obvious that the production aircraft would bear many design characteristics familiar to the F-16 and F-18. The first aircraft was delivered to the Chinese Nationalist Air Force in 1994, although sales of the F-16 Fighting Falcon to Taiwan in 1992 reduced its production to a mere 130 aircraft.

| | |
|---|---|
| Country of origin: | Taiwan |
| Type: | lightweight air-defence fighter with anti-ship capability |
| Powerplant: | two 4291kg (9460lb) ITEC (Garrett/AIDC) TFE1042-70 turbofans |
| Performance: | maximum speed at 10,975m (36,000ft) 1275km/h (792mph); service ceiling 16,760m (55,000ft) |
| Weights: | normal take-off weight 9072kg (20,000lb) |
| Dimensions: | wingspan 9.00m (29ft 6in) over missile rails; length 14.48m (47ft 6in) |
| Armament: | one 20mm General Electric M61A1 Vulcan rotary six-barrel cannon, six external pylons with provision for four Tien Chien 1 short range air-to-air missiles, or two Tien Chien 2 medium range air-to-air missiles, or four Tien Chien 1 and two Tien Chien 2, or three Hsiung Feng II anti-ship missiles and two Tien Chien 1 AAMs, or AGMs, or various combinations of rocket or cannon pods |

# AMX International AMX

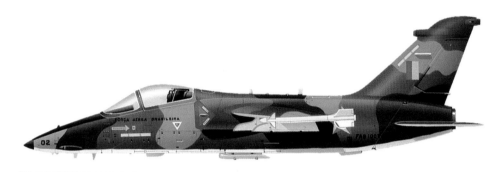

The AMX International AMX is the product of a collaboration between the Italian companies of Aeritalia and Aermacchi, and the Brazilian EMBRAER company. It was born out of a requirement that the indigenous air forces of both countries had in the early 1980s for a small tactical fighter bomber, to replace Fiat G91s and F104Gs, and EMBRAER AT-26 Xavantes respectively. A Piaggio built Rolls-Royce tubofan was chosen as the powerplant for the compact and attractive little fighter. The first prototype flew in May 1984 and by 1990 the seven development aircraft had accumulated more than 2,500 hours. Aeritalia are responsible for approximately 50 percent of the work, including the major assemblies, with the other two partners completing all other sections. The aircraft entered service with the Aeronautica Italia Militare in April 1989.

| | |
|---|---|
| Country of origin: | Italy and Brazil |
| Type: | single-seat multi-role combat aircraft |
| Powerplant: | One 5003kg (11,030lb) Fiat/Piaggio/Alfa Romeo (Rolls Royce) Spey Mk 807 turbofan |
| Performance: | maximum speed 1047km/h (651mph); service ceiling 13,000m (42,650ft); combat radius at low level 556km (345 miles) |
| Weights: | empty 6700kg (14,771lb); maximum take-off 13,000kg (28,660lb) |
| Dimensions: | wingspan 8.87m (29ft 1.5in); length 13.23m (43ft 5in); height 4.55m (14ft 11.25in); wing area 21sq m (226.04sq ft) |
| Armament: | one 20mm General Dynamics M61A1 cannon or two 30mm DEFA cannon (on Brazilian version); five exernal hardpoints with provision for up to 3800kg (8377lb) of stores; two wing tip rails for Sidewinder or similar air-to-air missiles |

# Aeritalia G91R/1A

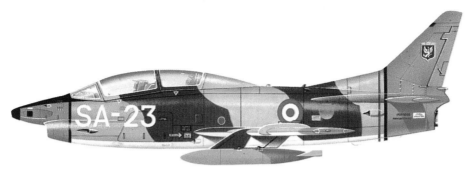

The original G91 models were built by Fiat, who submitted the successful design to a NATO specification issued to European manufacturers in 1954. It was envisaged that the G91 would become standard equipment with member nations' air forces, but this aim was never realised. The program had an early setback when the first prototype was lost on the inaugural flight due to problems in the design of the vertical stabiliser. Despite this the aircraft was built in substantial numbers, equipping both the Italian Air Force and the Luftwaffe. First entering service in 1958, there are only a handful now left in service around the world. The G91 gained a reputation for being reliable and easy to fly. The manufacturers were quick to realise the suitability of the machine as a tactical reconnaissance aircraft, leading to the 'R' series.

| Country of origin: | Italy |
| --- | --- |
| Type: | single-seat tactical reconnaissance aircraft |
| Powerplant: | one 2268kg (5000lb) Fiat built Bristol Siddeley Orpheus 803 turbojet |
| Performance: | maximum level speed at 1520m (5000ft) 1086km/h (675mph) or Mach 0.87; service ceiling 13100m (42,978ft); operational radius (standard fuel) 320km (200 miles) |
| Weights: | empty 3100kg (6835lb); maximum takeoff weight 5500kg (12,125lb) |
| Dimensions: | wingspan 8.56m (28ft 1in); length overall 10.30m (33ft 9.25in); height overall 4.00m (13ft 1.25in); wing area 16.42sq m (176.64sq ft) |
| Armament: | four 12.7mm machine guns; three 70mm Vinten cameras; four underwing pylons for two 227kg (500lb) bombs, tactical nuclear weapons, Nord 5103 air-to-air guided missiles, clusters of six 76mm (3in) air-to-air rockets, hon eycomb packs of 31 air-to-ground folding fin rockets, machine gun pods containing one 12.7mm (0.5in) machine gun with 250 rounds |

# Aermacchi M.B.326B

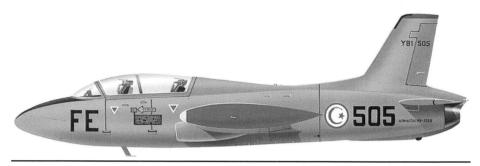

The 326B is one of the most important light attack and trainer aircraft to have emerged in the past four decades. The initial prototype flew in 1957; the basic airframe designed by Ermanno Bazzocchi of Aermacchi around a Rolls Royce Viper turbojet is conventional, with a well equipped tandem cockpit ahead of a slightly swept leading edge low/mid wing monoplane. The Aeronautica Militare Italia received the first of 85 M.B.326s in February of 1962. Vice free and predictable handling characteristics enabled the service to use the aircraft for all stages of flying training. In the training role, the M.B.326 has provided the AMI with a superb crossover trainer which provided countless pilots with jet experience prior to moving on to faster jets. Tunisia purchased eight armed trainer M.B.326s in 1965, which are painted in high-visibility orange.

| Country of origin: | Italy |
|---|---|
| Type: | two-seat basic/advanced trainer |
| Powerplant: | one 1134kg (2500lb) Rolls Royce Viper 11 turbojet |
| Performance: | maximum speed 806km/h (501mph); standard range 1665km (1,035 miles) |
| Weights: | empty 2237kg (4930lb) maximum take-off 3765kg (8300lb) |
| Dimensions: | span over tip tanks 10.56m (34ft 8in); length 10.65m (34ft 11.25in); height 3.72m (12ft 2in); wing area 19sq m (204.5sq ft) |
| Armament: | two optional 7.7mm machine guns, six underwing pylons with provision for machine gun pods, rockets and/or bombs, or camera pods, up to a maximum of 907kg (2000lb) |

# Aermacchi M.B.326K

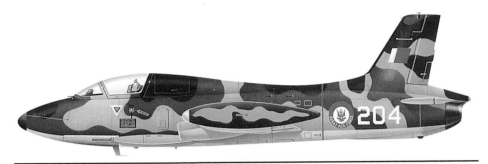

Having already proved the soundness of the basic 326 design and its usefulness as a weapons platform, it took Aermacchi a surprising length of time to finalise a design for a single-seat version. A primary goal of the design team was to provide the aircraft with more power, and the second prototype was equipped with the 1814kg (4000lb) Rolls Royce Viper 632-43 which became the standard fit on all production models. The installation of two electrically operated cannon in the lower forward fuselage in the MB.326K increased offensive capability of the aircraft, and maximum permitted weapons load was also increased. The space previously occupied by the rear cockpit now houses the cannon ammunition drums, the avionics suite, and an additional fuel tank. Export customers include South Africa, Dubai, Ghana, and Tunisia.

| | |
|---|---|
| **Country of origin:** | Italy |
| **Type:** | single-seat close air support or tactical reconnaissance aircraft, and limited air-to-air interceptor |
| **Powerplant:** | one 1814kg (4000lb) Rolls Royce Viper 632-43 turbojet |
| **Performance:** | maximum speed at 1525m (5000ft) 890km/h (553mph); combat radius at low level with maximum armament 268km (167 miles) |
| **Weights:** | empty 3123kg (6885lb) maximum take-off 5895kg (13,000lb) |
| **Dimensions:** | span over tip tanks 10.85m (35ft 7.25in); length 10.67m (35ft 0.25in); height 3.72m (12ft 2in); wing area 19.35sq m (208.3sq ft) |
| **Armament:** | two 30mm DEFA 553 cannon with 125rpg, six underwing points with provision for machine gun pods, launchers for 37mm, 68mm, 100mm, 2.75in or 5in rockets, Matra 550 Magic air-to-air missiles, and/or bombs, or (on inboard pylon) four-camera reconnaissance pod; maximum external load 1814 kg (4000 lb) |

# Aero A.18

A ero Tovarna Letadel Dr Kabes was formed in Prague just after World War I, at a time when the majority of European aircraft manufacturers were closing down. The A.18 was the company's successful submission to a Czech Air Force competition for a new single-seat fighter aircraft. The A.18 was a smaller, single-seat version of the A.11, and followed that aircraft's single-bay, unequal-span biplane wing planform. The powerplant was sourced from the Bayerne MotorischeWerke and the twin machine guns, synchronised to fire through the propeller disc, came from Vickers. Some 20 aircraft were supplied to the Czech Air Force; development continued with the A.18B with a reduced wing span, victor by default of a national aircraft race in 1923 when the two other competitors crashed, and the A.18C with a 300hp (224kW) Walter W-IV engine. Shown here is an A.18 of the 2nd Air Regiment, Czech Air Force, stationed at Oloumouc in the mid-1920s.

| | |
|---|---|
| Country of origin: | Czechoslovakia |
| Type: | single-seat fighter biplane |
| Powerplant: | one 185hp (138kW) BMW IIIa inline piston engine |
| Performance: | maximum speed 229km/h (142mph); service ceiling 9000m (29,530ft); range 400km (249 miles) |
| Weights: | empty 637kg (1404lb); maximum take-off weight 862kg (1900lb) |
| Dimensions: | span 7.6m (24ft 11in); length 5.9m (19ft 4in); height 2.9m (9ft 6in); wing area 15.9 sq m (171 sq ft) |
| Armament: | two fixed forward-firing synchronised machine guns |

# Aero A.100

The success of its A.11 encouraged Aero to fund further development of the basic airframe. However, installing a more powerful 450hp (336kW) Lorraine-Dietrich engine proved unsatisfactory and substantial revisions to the structure were necessary before the resulting A.30 could enter production. From the A.30 was spawned the A.430 prototype, a single example of which was built with a 650hp (485kW) Avia engine and oleo-pneumatic shock-struts for the main landing gear units. This aircraft offered significantly improved performance over the A.30. Redesignated as the A.100, it was offered to the Czech Air Ministry and selected for production in 1933. Some 44 aircraft were produced for the Czech Air Force. Two bomber versions were the A.101 with an 800hp (596kW) Praga engine, and the Ab.101, with a 750hp (559kW) Hispano-Suiza 12Ydrs engine. Pictured is an A.100 of the 3rd Air Regiment, Czech Air Force, based at Piestany in the mid-1930s.

| Country of origin: | Czechoslovakia |
| --- | --- |
| Type: | two-seat long-range reconnaissance biplane |
| Powerplant: | one 650hp (485kW) Avia Vr-36 inline piston engine |
| Performance: | maximum speed 270km/h (168mph); service ceiling 6500m (21,325ft); endurance 4hrs |
| Weights: | empty 2040kg (4497lb); maximum take-off weight 3220kg (7099lb) |
| Dimensions: | span 14.7m (48ft 2in); length 10.6m (34ft 9in); height 3.5m (11ft 5in); wing area 44.3 sq m (477 sq ft) |
| Armament: | two fixed forward-firing 0.303in Vickers machine guns; two Lewis guns on flexible mount in rear cockpit; external pylons for a maximum bomb load of 600kg (1322lb) |

# Aero L-29 Delfin

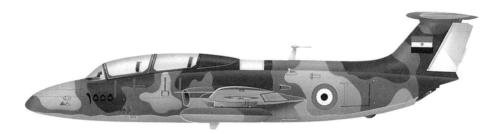

The Czech designed L-29 Delfin was selected in 1961 as the basic jet trainer of the USSR in whose service the aircraft gained the NATO reporting name 'Maya'. Total production by Aero Vodochodny Narodni Podnik exceeded 3600. The L-29 is a simple, rugged aircraft that can be operated from grass, sand, or waterlogged airstrips. First entering service in 1963, the production lines remained in operation for the next 11 years. The Soviets took more than 2000 of the production total; deliveries were also made to almost every Communist Bloc air force. Many were exported to Soviet allies in the Middle East and Africa, where they are still in service. This aircraft wears the desert scheme of the Egyptian air force. The Egyptian aircraft can be configured for use in the attack role, and are fitted with equipment to suit.

| | |
|---|---|
| Country of origin: | Czechoslovakia |
| Type: | two-seat basic and advanced trainer |
| Powerplant: | one 890kg (1960lb) Motorlet M 701 VC-150 turbojet |
| Performance: | maximum speed at 5000m (16,400ft) 655km/h (407mph); service ceiling 11,000m (36,100ft); standard range 640km (397 miles) |
| Weights: | empty 2280kg (5027lb); maximum take-off 3280kg (7231lb) |
| Dimensions: | wingspan 10.29m (33ft 8in); length 10.81m (35ft 5.5in); height 3.13m (10ft 3in); wing area 19.80sq m (213.1sq ft) |

# Aero L-39C Albatros

First entering service in 1974 with the Czech air force, the L-39 succeeded the L-29 as the standard jet trainer for the air forces of Czechoslovakia, the USSR, and East Germany. The aircraft continues in this role today in the air forces of many former Eastern Bloc countries. The prototype L-39 first flew in November 1968 and it was obvious from the trials that vastly improved performance over the L-29 had been achieved. This was due mainly to the adoption of the Ivchyenko I-25 turbofan engine, which produced nearly double the power of the L-29s Motorlet unit. Throughout the design process, emphasis was placed on ease of maintenance. An auxiliary power unit allows the aircraft to operate independently of ground facilities. The L-39C is the basic trainer variant. Many have been sold on the private market, and are a common sight at aviation meets.

| Country of origin: | Czechoslovakia |
|---|---|
| Type: | two-seat basic and advanced trainer |
| Powerplant: | one 1720kg (3792lb) Ivchyenko AI-25TL turbofan |
| Performance: | maximum speed at 6000m (19,685ft) 780km/h (435mph); service ceiling 11,500m (37,730ft); standard range 1100km (683 miles) |
| Weights: | empty 3330kg (7341lb); maximum take-off 4700kg (10,632lb) |
| Dimensions: | wingspan 9.46m (31ft 0.5in); length 12.13m (39ft 9.5in); height 4.77m (15ft 7.75in); wing area 18.80sq m (202.36sq ft) |

# Aero L-39ZA Albatros

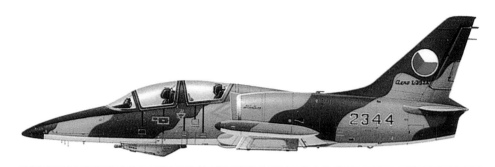

From the basic L-39 airframe Aero created four variants. By far the most numerous was the L-39C trainer model, but the success of this aircraft encouraged the Czech manufacturer to produce three subvariants. Part of the reason for the success was the the ease of maintenance afforded by the L-39s modular airframe, which can be readily broken down into three major subassemblies: wing, fuselage, and rear fuselage. To allow easy access to the engine, the rear fuselage can be removed in one piece. The L-39ZO is a single-seat version, featuring reinforced wings to facilitate the carriage of a variety of weapons on four underwing stations. Both Iraq and Libya have bought this aircraft and utilise it in the light attack role. More numerous is the L-39ZA, which retains the twin seat configuration of the trainer.

| Country of origin: | Czechoslovakia |
|---|---|
| Type: | single-seat light ground attack aircraft (ZO) |
| Powerplant: | one 1720kg (3792lb) Ivchyenko AI-25TL turbofan |
| Performance: | maximum speed at 5000m (16,404ft) 630km/h (391mph); service ceiling 9000m (29,525ft); standard range 1750km (1087 miles) |
| Weights: | empty 3330kg (7341lb); maximum take-off 5270kg (11,618lb) |
| Dimensions: | wingspan 9.46m (31ft); length 12.32m (40ft 5in); height 4.72m (15ft 5.5in); wing area 18.80sq m (202.36 q ft) |
| Armament: | one 23-mm GSh-23L two barrel cannon with 150 rounds; four underwing pylons with provision for pods of 57 or 130mm rockets, gun pods, a single five camera pack, AA-2 Atoll air-to-air missiles, bombs up to 500kg (1102lb); maximum external load of 1100kg (2425lb) |

# Aeronca L-3 Grasshopper

A fter using converted biplane attack aircraft as its observation types for many years, the US Army Air Corps decided to adopt larger and more capable purpose-designed aircraft but then came to the conclusion in the early 1940s that minimum-change adaptations of two-seat civil lightplane types offered considerably greater advantages. Such aircraft were cheap to buy and operate, could fly in the liaison as well as observation roles, and as a result of their low observability and high agility were less vulnerable to ground defences. Short-field performance was particularly impressive, making the aircraft a useful asset to ground commanders. The USAAC and its successor, the US Army Air Forces, therefore procured large numbers of these aircraft in several types, all characterised by an enclosed cabin, high-set braced wing and fixed tailwheel landing gear. The Aeronca Model 65 was typical of the breed, 1740 being procured in L-3 to L-3J variants.

| | |
|---|---|
| Country of origin: | USA |
| Type: | (L-3) two-seat light liaison and observation aeroplane |
| Powerplant: | one 65hp (48.5kW) Continental O-170-3 flat-four engine |
| Performance: | maximum speed 140km/h (87mph); initial climb rate 123m (405ft) per minute; service ceiling 2360m (7750ft); range 351km (218 miles) |
| Weights: | empty 379kg (835lb); maximum take-off 590kg (1300lb) |
| Dimensions: | span 10.67m (35ft 0in); length 6.40m (21ft 0in); height 2.34m (7ft 8in) |
| Armament: | none |

# Aerospatiale (Fouga) CM.170 Magister

**O**ne of the most successful and widely used trainer aircraft in the world, the Magister was conceived and designed by Castello and Mauboussin for Fouga in 1950. It was the first purpose built jet trainer in the world. Despite the unusual butterfly type tail, it proved a delight to fly. After prolonged testing, the Magister was put into production for the Armée de l'Air. Total production of this and the hooked navalised version (CM.75 Zephyr) was 437. Fouga was absorbed into the Potez company in 1958, which continued to produce a number of variants for international customers. In 1967, the Magister saw action during the Six-Day War with the Israeli Air Force. It was also previously the mount of the French national aerobatic team, the 'Patrouille de France'. The team now uses the Dassault/Dornier Alpha jet.

| | |
|---|---|
| **Country of origin:** | France |
| **Type:** | two-seat trainer and light attack aircraft |
| **Powerplant:** | two 400kg (882lb) Turbomeca Marbore IIA turbojets |
| **Performance:** | maximum speed at 9150m (30,000ft) 715km/h (444mph); service ceiling 11,000m (36,090ft); range 925km (575 miles) |
| **Weights:** | empty equipped 2150kg (4740lb); maximum takeoff 3200kg (7055lb) |
| **Dimensions:** | over tip tanks 12.12m (39ft 10in); length 10.06m (33ft); height 2.80m (9ft 2in); wing area 17.30sq m (186.1sq ft) |
| **Armament:** | two 7.5mm (0.295in) or 7.62mm machine guns; rockets, bombs or Nord AS.11 missiles on underwing pylons |

# Aichi D1A 'Susie'

In response to a 1932 requirement for an advanced carrierborne dive-bomber for the Japanese Navy, Nakajima adapted the Heinkel He 66, of which a single example had been imported from Germany, with a Japanese engine to create the Aichi Special Bomber prototype. Late in 1934 the Imperial Japanese navy air force ordered Aichi to proceed with the finalisation of its AB-9 design for production as the D1A1 with the 580hp (432.5kW) Nakajima Kotobuki 2 Kai 1 or Kotobuki 3 radial engine. Deliveries of this initial model totalled 162 aircraft. The company then built 428 of the improved D1A2 model with spatted wheels and an uprated engine. The D1A saw widespread service during the Sino-Japanese war, but by the time of Japan's entry into World War II in 1941, all surviving D1A1 and most D1A2 aircraft had been relegated to training units, with a mere 68 D1A2 machines operating in second-line roles until 1942.

| Country of origin: | Japan |
|---|---|
| Type: | (D1A2) two-seat carrierborne and land-based dive-bomber |
| Powerplant: | one 730hp (544kW) Nakajima Hikari 1 nine-cylinder single-row radial engine |
| Performance: | maximum speed 309km/h (192mph); climb to 3000m (9845ft) in 7 minutes 51 seconds; service ceiling 6980m (22,900ft); range 927km (576 miles) |
| Weights: | empty 1516kg (3342lb); maximum take-off 2610kg (5754lb) |
| Dimensions: | span 11.40m (37ft 4.75in); length 9.30m (30ft 6.125in); height 3.41m (11ft 2.25in) |
| Armament: | two 7.7mm fixed forward-firing machine guns in the upper part of the forward fuselage, and one 7.7mm trainable rearward-firing machine gun in the rear cockpit, plus an external bomb load of 310kg (683lb) |

# Aichi D3A 'Val'

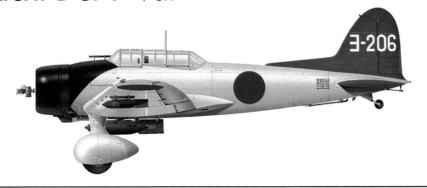

**B**est remembered as one of the two main attack types involved in the Japanese attack on Pearl Harbor in December 1941, the D3A resulted from a 1936 requirement for a D1A successor and was a trim low-wing monoplane with enclosed accommodation but fixed and nicely faired landing gear. The first of eight prototype and service trials aircraft flew in January 1938, and there followed production of 470 D3A1 aircraft with the 1000hp (746kW) Mitsubishi Kinsei 43 or 1070hp (898kW) Kinsei 44 engine. It was this type that was the Japanese navy's mainstay early in World War II. The improved D3A2 (1016 aircraft) entered service in the autumn of 1942. By this time the type was obsolescent, however, and from 1943 most of the surviving aircraft were adapted as D3A2-K trainers. Many were later used for *kamikaze* attacks on Allied shipping. The aircraft pictured is a D3A1 of the Yokosuka Kokota, in 1940 colours.

| Country of origin: | Japan |
|---|---|
| Type | (D3A2) two-seat carrierborne and land-based dive-bomber |
| Powerplant: | one 1300hp (969kW) Mitsubishi Kinsei 54 14-cylinder two-row radial engine |
| Performance | maximum speed 430km/h (267mph); climb to 3000m (9845ft) in 5 minutes 48 seconds; service ceiling 10,500m (34,450ft); range 1352km (840 miles) |
| Weights | empty 2570kg (5666lb); maximum take-off 4122kg (9100lb) |
| Dimensions: | span 14.37m (47ft 2in); length 10.20m (33ft 5.4in); height 3.8m (12ft 7.5in) |
| Armament: | two 7.7mm fixed forward-firing machine guns in the upper part of the forward fuselage, and one 7.7mm trainable rearward-firing machine gun in the rear cockpit, plus an external bomb load of 370kg (816lb) |

# Aichi E13A 'Jake'

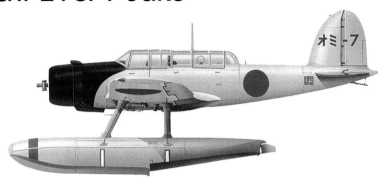

The E13A resulted from a 1937 requirement for a long-range reconnaissance floatplane and first flew in prototype form during 1940. This paved the way for the E13A1 initial production model that entered service late in 1941. Production by three manufacturers totalled 1418 including an unknown number of prototypes, and these machines were delivered in variants such as the E13A1 baseline model, E13A1-K dual-control trainer, E13A1a with detail improvements as well as exhaust flame-dampers in a nocturnal subvariant, and E13A1b with air-to-surface radar. Numbers of E13A1a and E13A1b floatplanes were later adapted to the light anti-ship role with a 20mm cannon in a trainable downward-firing installation. The aircraft in Imperial Japanese Navy service regularly undertook patrol sorties lasting up to 15 hours, but many came to a rather ignominious end during the latter stages of the war on *kamikaze* operations.

| | |
|---|---|
| **Country of origin:** | Japan |
| **Type:** | (E13A1a) three-seat reconnaissance floatplane |
| **Powerplant:** | one 1080hp (805kW) Mitsubishi Kinsei 43 14-cylinder two-row radial engine |
| **Performance:** | maximum speed 377km/h (234mph); climb to 3000m (9845ft) in 6 minutes 5 seconds; service ceiling 8730m (28,640ft); range 2089 km (1298 miles) |
| **Weights:** | empty 2642kg (5825lb); maximum take-off 4000kg (8818lb) |
| **Dimensions:** | span 14.50m (47ft 7in); length 11.30m (37ft 1in); height 4.70m (15ft 5in) |
| **Armament:** | one 20mm trainable downward-firing cannon in the ventral position (field modification on late-production floatplanes), and one 7.7mm trainable rearward-firing machine gun in the rear of the cockpit, plus an external bomb load of 250kg (551lb) |

27

# Aichi B7A Ryusei 'Grace'

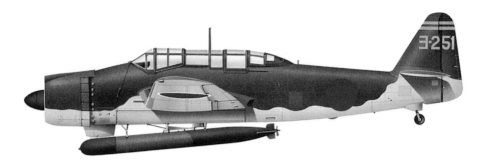

In 1941 the Imperial Japanese navy air force issued an exacting requirement for a carrierborne attack bomber to replace the Nakajima B6N torpedo bomber and Yokosuka D4Y dive-bomber. Aichi's response was the AM-23 design, and the first of nine B7A1 prototypes flew in May 1942. The development programme was constantly delayed by engine teething problems, and it was April 1944 before the type entered production as the B7A2, which offered very good handling and excellent performance. Although production in three factories was planned, only two in fact came on stream and production totalled a mere 105 aircraft (80 from Aichi and 25 from the 21st Naval Air Arsenal). These had to operate from land bases as the Japanese navy had no operational aircraft carriers by this time. The aircraft pictured is a B7A2 of the Yokosuka Kokutai and is carrying a 'Long Lance' torpedo, one of the most effective weapons of its type.

| Country of origin: | Japan |
|---|---|
| Type: | (B7A2) two-seat carrierborne and land-based torpedo bomber and dive-bomber |
| Powerplant: | one 2000hp (1491kW) Nakajima NK9C Homare 12 18-cylinder two-row radial engine |
| Performance | maximum speed 566.5km/h (352mph); climb to 4000m (13,125ft) in 6 minutes 55 seconds; service ceiling 11,250m (36,910ft); range 3038km (1888 miles ) |
| Weights: | empty 3810kg (8400lb); maximum take-off 6500kg (14,330lb) |
| Dimensions: | span 14.40m (47ft 3in); length 11.49m (37ft 8.33in); height 4.07m (13ft 4.5in) |
| Armament: | two 20mm fixed forward-firing cannon in wing l.e, and one 13mm trainable rearward-firing machine gun in the rear cockpit, plus an internal bomb and torpedo load of 800kg (1764lb) |

# Airco D.H.2

The Aircraft Manufacturing Company (Airco) was established at Hendon in early 1912 and while still in its infancy nurtured the talents of one of Britain's greatest aircraft designers, Geoffrey de Havilland. De Havilland designed the D.H.2 as a smaller version of the earlier D.H.1, a single-seat pusher reconnaissance/fighter biplane of wood-and-fabric construction. With no interrupter gear available to British aircraft designers the unusual pusher layout was considered essential. The D.H.2 mounted a Lewis gun in the front cockpit, its field of fire unencumbered by the need to avoid the propeller. Controlling the aircraft while operating the gun was tricky, but the D.H.2 was the best fighter available to the British in mid-1916 and did much to counter the superiority of the Fokker monoplanes. A total of 400 were built, but by early 1917 the D.H.2 had been eclipsed by the Albatros D.I and D.II and was withdrawn from service on the Western Front and reallocated to less demanding theatres.

| | |
|---|---|
| Country of origin: | United Kingdom |
| Type: | single-seat scout fighter biplane |
| Powerplant: | one 100hp (75kW) Gnome Monosoupape rotary piston engine; later examples had 110hp (82kW) Le Rhône rotary |
| Performance: | maximum speed 150km/h (93mph); service ceiling 1300m (4265ft); endurance 2hrs 45mins |
| Weights: | empty 428kg (943lb); maximum take-off weight 654kg (1441lb) |
| Dimensions: | span 8.61m (28ft 3in); length 7.68m (25ft 2in); height 2.91m (9ft 6.5in); wing area 23.13 sq m (249 sq ft) |
| Armament: | one forward-firing .303in Lewis gun on flexible mounting (pilots often fixed this to fire straight ahead, preferring instead to bring the gun to bear by aiming the aircraft) |

# Airco D.H.4

De Havilland designed the Airco D.H.4 around the 200 BHP (Beardmore-Halford-Pullinger) engine in response to an Air Ministry request for a new day bomber. In this role the D.H.4 was the best aircraft in its class during the war. Using an inline piston engine, de Havilland employed a clean tractor layout, breaking away from the traditional use of the rotary engine, but the wide separation between pilot and observer was a controversial and potentially dangerous feature as it hampered communication in the air. The 1449 British-built aircraft was manufactured by various sub-contractors, although delayed production of the BHP engine meant that other engines were employed on production aircraft. By spring 1918 the D.H.4 equipped nine RAF squadrons and was also in service with the Royal Naval Air Service. D.H.4s were engaged in the destruction of the flagship Zeppelin L.70. Pictured is a Rolls Royce Eagle VI-engined aircraft of No 5 (Naval) Squadron, RNAS.

| | |
|---|---|
| Country of origin: | United Kingdom |
| Type: | two-seat day bomber biplane (Westland-built, Eagle VI engine) |
| Powerplant: | one 250hp (186kW) Rolls-Royce Eagle VI inline piston engine |
| Performance: | maximum speed 230km/h (143mph); service ceiling 6705m (22,000ft); endurance 3hrs 45mins |
| Weights: | empty 1083kg (2387lb); maximum take-off weight 1575kg (3742lb) |
| Dimensions: | span 12.92m (42ft 4in); length 9.35m (30ft 8in); height 3.35m (11ft); wing area 40.32 sq m (434 sq ft) |
| Armament: | two fixed forward-firing .303in Vickers machine guns and two .303in Vickers machine guns in rear cockpit; external pylons; provision for 209kg (460lb) of bombs |

# Airco DH-4 'Liberty Plane'

America showed great interest in the D.H.4, and from mid-1917 licensed manufacture of the aircraft was undertaken by three US companies – Dayton-Wright (3106 aircraft), Fisher Body Corporation (1600 aircraft) and the Standard Aircraft Corporation (140 aircraft). The first American-manufactured machines had the baseline American Liberty 12 engine that produced some 400hp (298kW). Many of the aircraft passed to civilian operators after the war and in post-war USA the D.H-4 (as it was known locally) flourished. No fewer than 60 separate versions were evolved for roles as diverse as crop-dusting and aerial mapping, using developments of the Liberty engine. Pictured is a DH-4B that served with the 168th Aero Squadron as part of the American Expeditionary Force, one of 13 squadrons equipped with the aircraft. The winged skull badge adopted by the squadron is painted on the fuselage.

| Country of origin: | USA (United Kingdom) |
| --- | --- |
| Type: | two-seat day bomber biplane (US-built American Liberty engine) |
| Powerplant: | one 400hp (298kW) Packard Liberty 12 inline piston engine |
| Performance: | maximum speed 230km/h (143mph); service ceiling 5000m (17,400ft); endurance 3hrs 45mins |
| Weights: | empty 1083kg (2387lb); maximum take-off weight 1575kg (3742lb) |
| Dimensions: | span 12.92m (42ft 4in); length 9.35m (30ft 8in); height 3.35m (11ft); wing area 40.32 sq m (434 sq ft) |
| Armament: | one fixed forward-firing .303in Vickers machine gun and one .303in Lewis machine gun in rear cockpit; external pylons with provision for 209kg (460lb) of bombs |

# Airco D.H.9A

**P**ersistent German raids on Britain during World War I prompted a doubling in the size of the Royal Flying Corps, with most of the new squadrons equipped with day bombers. The D.H.4 was the expected type, but de Havilland had already attempted to rectify a glaring weakness of this aircraft by designing a modified version designated D.H.9 with the pilot and observer accommodated in back-to-back seating. This had a Siddeley Puma engine that could only produce 230hp (172kW), and performance of the early production D.H.9s was decidedly inferior to the D.H.4. In service with the RNAS and RFC from December 1917, the Puma engine was chronically unreliable and, furthermore, the new aircraft that it powered had a much reduced ceiling of 3960m (13,000ft). A much improved version of the aircraft, the D.H.9A, with a 400hp (298kW) Liberty engine was produced after the war and became an important tool of RAF operations in the Middle East during the 1920s.

| | |
|---|---|
| **Country of origin:** | United Kingdom |
| **Type:** | two-seat day bomber biplane (American Liberty engine) |
| **Powerplant:** | one 420hp (313kW) Packard Liberty 12 vee-12 piston engine |
| **Performance:** | maximum speed 198km/h (123mph); service ceiling 5105m (16,750ft); endurance 5hrs 15mins |
| **Weights:** | empty 1270kg (2800lb); maximum take-off weight 2107kg (4645lb) |
| **Dimensions:** | span 14.01m (45ft 11in); length 9.22m (30ft 3in); height 3.45m (11ft 4in); wing area 45.22 sq m (487 sq ft) |
| **Armament:** | one fixed forward-firing .303in Vickers machine gun and one or two .303in Lewis machine guns on Scarff ring in rear cockpit; external pylons with provision for 299kg (660lb) of bombs |

# Airco D.H.10 Amiens

In 1916 de Havilland produced his first twin-engine aircraft for Airco, a bomber powered by two pusher Beardmore engines mounted midway between the biplane wings. This D.H.3 was never put into production, but during 1917 de Havilland redesigned it for greater power in response to the urgent need for a retaliatory weapon to counter German bomber raids. The first prototype D.H.10 Amiens flew in March 1918 with 230hp (171kW) BHP pusher engines, however the other two prototypes – the Amiens II with 360hp (268kW) Rolls Royce Eagle VIII and Amiens III with 400hp (298kW) Liberty 12 engines – had their engines installed in a tractor configuration. The fourth prototype mounted the engines directly on to the lower wing, and in this form was produced as the Amiens D.H.10A. A total of 1291 were ordered by 7 manufacturers but were delivered too late to see service in World War I. At least 220 were completed for the RAF and these served with distinction in Britain, Egypt and India until 1927.

| Country of origin: | United Kingdom |
| --- | --- |
| Type: | three-seat day bomber biplane |
| Powerplant: | one 400hp (313kW) Packard Liberty 12 vee-12 piston engine |
| Performance: | maximum speed 180km/h (112mph); service ceiling 5030m (16,500ft); endurance hrs 45mins |
| Weights: | empty 2533kg (5585lb); maximum take-off weight 4082kg (9000lb) |
| Dimensions: | span 19.96m (65ft 6in); length 12.08m (39ft 7in); height 4.42m (14ft 6in); wing area 77.79 sq m (837 sq ft) |
| Armament: | single or twin .303in Lewis guns on Scarff ring mounting in nose and midships cockpits; external pylons with provision for a maximum bomb load of 408kg (900lb) |

# Albatros B.III

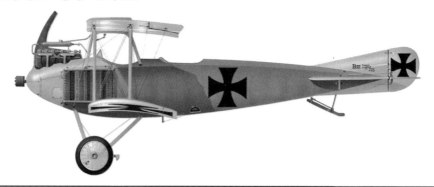

A lbatros Flugzeugwerke GmbH was established in early 1909 and in 1913 collaborated with Ernst Heinkel to produce the B.I, a two-seat reconnaissance aircraft for the German Air Service. Development of the aircraft continued with the B.II series that had reduced span wings and various engines in the 100–120hp (75–89kW) range. This aircraft established Albatros' name as an aircraft manufacturer, and was built in some numbers. Accommodation for the pilot and observer was in tandem cockpits with the pilot seated aft, a configuration that somewhat hampered the downward view of the observer. The B.II-W (Albatros W.1) was a floatplane variant and the B.IIa a trainer with slightly increased span and either a Mercedes D.II or Argus As.II. Pictured is a B.III, a variant built in small numbers in 1915, that served with Fliegersatzabteilung (FEA) 1 at Döberitz during the winter of 1916–17.

| | |
|---|---|
| **Country of origin:** | Germany |
| **Type:** | two-seat reconnaissance biplane |
| **Powerplant:** | one 120hp (89kW) Mercedes D.II inline piston engine |
| **Performance:** | maximum speed 120km/h (75mph); service ceiling 3000m (9840ft); endurance about 4hrs |
| **Weights:** | empty 723kg (1594lb); maximum take-off weight 1071kg (2361lb) |
| **Dimensions:** | span 11m (36ft 1in); length 7.8m (25ft 7in); height 3.15m (10ft 4in); wing area (B.II) 40.12 sq m (432 sq ft) |

# Albatros J.I

Infantry close support was pioneered by the German Army Air Service in 1916 with the introduction of *Infantrie-flieger* (infantry contact patrol) units for the Battle of Verdun. This role became an increasingly important aspect of air operations and in response Albatros developed the J.I which adopted the wing of the C.XII two-seat reconnaissance aircraft mated to a fuselage of completely new design. The hazards associated with low-level operations called for some measure of armoured protection to the cockpit floor and sides, but the added weight (490kg/1080lb) of this armour, coupled with the decision to use the Benz Bz.IV engine rather than the more powerful Mercedes D.IVa of the Albatros C.XII, had an inevitably detrimental effect on performance. Entering service in late 1917, the J.I enjoyed some measure of success despite its shortcomings and may be considered as a truly pioneering aircraft. Pictured is a J.I of the post-war Polish Air Force.

| Country of origin: | Germany |
| --- | --- |
| Type: | two-seat close-support biplane |
| Powerplant: | one 200hp (149kW) Benz Bz.IV inline piston engine |
| Performance: | maximum speed 140km/h (87mph); service ceiling 4000m (13,120ft); endurance about 2hrs 30mins |
| Weights: | empty 1398kg (3082lb); maximum take-off weight 1808kg (3986lb) |
| Dimensions: | span 14.14m (46ft 4in); length 8.83m (28ft 11in); height 3.37m (11ft); wing area 42.82 sq m (461 sq ft) |
| Armament: | two fixed downward-firing 7.92mm LMG 08/15 machine guns; one 7.92mm Parabellum machine gun on movable mount in rear cockpit |

# Albatros C.III

A natural development of the B.III was the C.I, which had a more powerful engine and revised accommodation which placed the observer aft of the pilot where he was provided with a machine gun on a movable mount. The C.II never reached production, but the Albatros C.III, which first entered service in late 1916, was the company's most prolific two-seater of the war. This followed a generally similar configuration to the C.I series, but had a number of important revisions including a redesigned tail, which prefigured the more rounded versions of later Albatros types. Later aircraft were equipped with a synchronised forward-firing machine gun and had a small bay between the two crew for the stowage of small bombs. These features greatly increased the offensive capabilities of the aircraft. Pictured is the C.III of Lieutenant Bruno Maas (hence the stylised insignia on the fuselage) of Fliegerabteilung 14, flying on the Eastern Front in January 1917.

| | |
|---|---|
| Country of origin: | Germany |
| Type: | two-seat general purpose biplane |
| Powerplant: | one 150hp (112kW) Benz Bz.III or 160hp (119kW) Mercedes D.III inline piston engine |
| Performance: | maximum speed 140km/h (87mph); service ceiling 3350m (11,000ft); endurance about 4hrs |
| Weights: | empty 851kg (1876lb); maximum take-off weight 1353kg (2983lb) |
| Dimensions: | span 11.69m (38ft 4in); length 8.0m (26ft 3in); height with Benz engine 3.07m (10ft); Mercedes engine 3.10m (10ft 2in); wing area 36.91 sq m (397.31 sq ft) |
| Armament: | one 7.92mm Parabellum machine gun on flexible mount in rear cockpit; later aircraft had one 7.92mm LMG 08/15 fixed forward-firing machine gun, plus a small internal bomb bay |

# Albatros D.V

First of the 'D' series of Albatros fighter scouts, the D.I was introduced in early 1917 and was for some time the best aircraft in its class. Designed by Robert Thelen and first demonstrated in prototype form in August 1916, the D.I followed a familiar single-bay, staggered biplane wing planform but introduced the distinctive elliptical fuselage of monocoque structure that is characteristic to all of the 'D' series aircraft. This proved expensive to produce but the aircraft became the favoured mount of Böelcke and Richtofen. For the improved D.II the wing was remounted nearer to the top fuselage to facilitate a better view for the pilot. The D.III was the result of Thelen's attempt to improve the manoeuvrability of the D.II, by revising the wing configuration to a lower-chord lower and increased-chord upper wing. However rapid improvements in Allied fighter capability prompted the development of the D.V, pictured above.

| Country of origin: | Germany |
|---|---|
| Type: | single-seat scout fighter |
| Powerplant: | one 180/200hp (134/149kW) Mercedes D.II inline piston engine |
| Performance: | maximum speed 186km/h (116mph); service ceiling 5700m (18,700ft); endurance about 2hrs |
| Weights: | empty 687kg (1515lb); maximum take-off weight 937kg (2066lb) |
| Dimensions: | span 9.05m (29ft 7in); length 7.33m (24ft); height 2.70m (8ft 10in); wing area 21.20 sq m (228 sq ft) |
| Armament: | two fixed forward-firing 7.92mm LMG 08/15 machine guns |

# Albatros D.Va

**D**evelopment of the D.IV began in early 1917, in response to the emergence of much improved Allied fighters, but was plagued by problems associated with the experimental Mercedes D.III engine chosen for the powerplant and never entered production. The D.V reverted to the D.IIIa engine mounted in a deeper fuselage that improved streamlining and thus reduced drag. The gap between the wing and upper fuselage was further reduced, rudder area was increased and the aileron controls were revised. The D.V entered service in May 1917 and was quickly followed by the D.Va which reverted to the the upper wing and aileron control system of the D.III. Production of the two versions was in excess of 3000 aircraft, with 1512 in service on the Western Front in May 1918, by which time they had been outclassed by the latest scout aircraft of both sides. Pictured is the D.Va of Lieutenant H.J. von Hippel, serving with Jagdstaffel 5 in the spring of 1918.

| | |
|---|---|
| **Country of origin:** | Germany |
| **Type:** | single-seat scout fighter |
| **Powerplant:** | one 180/200hp (134/149kW) Mercedes D.II inline piston engine |
| **Performance:** | maximum speed 186km/h (116mph); service ceiling 5700m (18,700ft); endurance about 2hrs |
| **Weights:** | empty 687kg (1515lb); maximum take-off weight 937kg (2066lb) |
| **Dimensions:** | span 9.05m (29ft 8in); length 7.33m (24ft); height 2.70m (8ft 10in); wing area 21.20 sq m (228 sq ft) |
| **Armament:** | two fixed forward-firing 7.92mm LMG 08/15 machine guns |

# Amiot 143

First flown in April 1931, the Amiot 140 was designed to meet a 1928 requirement for a day and night bomber, long-range reconnaissance, and bomber escort type. Ordered into production in November 1934 with Lorraine W-type engines, the type became the Amiot 143 with the powerplant changed to Gnome-Rhòne engines. The Amiot 143M.4 entered service in 1935, and production totalled 138 aircraft, the later examples with 7.5mm MAC 1934 machine guns in place of the original Lewis guns, a longer nose, and fixed rather than jettisonable auxiliary fuel tanks. This obsolete type still equipped six *groupes de bombardement* at the start of World War II but suffered heavy losses when switched from night to day operations. The surviving aircraft were operated as transports to Vichy French forces in North Africa until 1944. The aircraft pictured is a 143M, the 78th production aircraft, of the 3rd Escadrille of GB II/35, based at Pontarlier in September 1939.

| Country of origin: | France |
| --- | --- |
| Type: | (Amiot 143M.4) four/six-seat night bomber and reconnaissance warplane |
| Powerplant: | two 870hp (640kW) Gnome-Rhòne 14Kirs/Kjrs Mistral-Major 14-cylinder two-row radial engines |
| Performance: | maximum speed 310km/h (193mph); climb to 4000m (13,125ft) in 14 minutes 20 seconds; service ceiling 7900m (25,920ft); range 2000km (1243 miles) |
| Weights: | empty 6100kg (13,448lb); maximum take-off 9700kg (21,385lb) |
| Dimensions: | span 24.53m (80ft 5.75in); length 18.26m (59ft 11in); height 5.68m (18ft 7.75in) |
| Armament: | up to six 7.5mm machine guns, plus an internal and external bomb load of 1600kg (3527lb) |

# Amiot 354

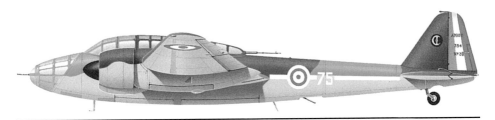

Having produced the extraordinarily ungraceful Amiot 143 during the late 1920s, in the early 1930s the Amiot design team then acquired a flair for graceful design and evolved the beautiful Amiot 341 long-range mailplane. This aircraft paved the way for the Amiot 340 bomber prototype that developed by a number of steps into the Amiot 354B.4 production bomber. The 354B.4 was one of the best aircraft of its type to enter production before World War II. Some 900 of this type were ordered and offered good performance and potent defensive firepower. However, development and production delays meant that only about 45 had been completed before the fall of France in June 1940. The survivors were used mainly as high-speed transports, four being taken over by the Luftwaffe for clandestine operations. The aircraft pictured was the 39th delivered to the Armée de l'Air. After the war the sole surviving aircraft was operated by the French Air Ministry.

| Country of origin: | France |
| --- | --- |
| Type: | (Amiot 354B.4) four-seat medium bomber |
| Powerplant: | two 1060hp (790kW) Gnome-Rhòne 14N-48/49 14-cylinder two-row radial engines |
| Performance: | maximum speed 480km/h (298mph); climb to 4000m (13,125ft) in 8 minutes 42 seconds; service ceiling 10,000 m (32,810ft); range 3500km (2175 miles ) with an 800kg (1764lb) bomb load |
| Weights: | empty 4725kg (10,417lb); maximum take-off 11,300kg (24,912lb) |
| Dimensions: | span 22.83m (74ft 10.75in); length 14.50m (47ft 6.75in); height 4.08m (13ft 4.5in) |
| Armament: | one 20mm trainable rearward-firing cannon in the dorsal position, one 7.5mm trainable forward-firing machine gun in the nose, and one 7.5mm trainable rearward-firing machine gun in a ventral mounting, plus an internal bomb load of 1200kg (2646lb) |

# Antonov An-72 'Coaler-C'

The design of the An-72 'Coaler' is optimised for STOL capability, with a variety of high lift features to permit short filed operation. The most noticeable of these is the positioning of the twin powerplants, at a position high up and well forward on the wing. When the inboard flaps are deployed, the engine exhaust is deflected over them producing greatly increased lift. The cabin design follows accepted convention, with a rear tailgate and broadly spaced main gear pods to optimise internal cargo space. The aircraft first flew on December 22, 1977, although it was first seen in the West at the Paris airshow of 1979. The aircraft has been adapted for a number of roles, including AEW. A development of the basic airframe known as the An-74 is designed for operations in the Antarctic, with de-icing equipment, improved avionics, and provision for fitting skis.

| | |
|---|---|
| **Country of origin:** | USSR (Ukraine) |
| **Type:** | STOL transport |
| **Powerplant:** | two 6500kg (14,330lb) Zaporozhye/Lotarev D-36 turbofans |
| **Performance:** | maximum speed 705km/h (438mph) at 10,000m (32,810ft); service ceiling 11,800m (38,715ft); range 800km (497 miles) with maximum payload |
| **Weights:** | empty 19,050kg (41,997lb); maximum take-off weight 34,500kg (76,059lb) |
| **Dimensions:** | wingspan 31.89m (104ft 7.5in); length 28.07m (92ft 1in); height 8.65m (28ft 4.5in); wing area 98.62sq m (1,062sq ft) |

# Arado Ar 65F

A rado Handelgessellschaft GmbH was founded in 1925 from the remnants of the wartime AGO company, and took over the premises of the Werft Warnemünde der Flugzeugbau Friedrichhafen GmbH. Because of the ban on military aircraft production imposed by the Armistice, development of the SD I and II fighter aircraft in the late 1920s for the *Reichswehrministerium* was undertaken under great secrecy. These aircraft formed the basis for the Ar 64, intended as a replacement for the Fokker DXIII then equipping the secret German flying training school at Lipetsk in the Soviet Union. This aircraft gestated into the Ar 65, modelled closely on the 64 but with a more powerful engine. The first production version was the Ar 65E, which was followed by the 65F with improved communications equipment. Used only for a short time in the fighter role, Ar 65Es and Ar 65-Fs were used as fighter trainers until 1936.

| | |
|---|---|
| **Country of origin:** | Germany |
| **Type:** | single-seat fighter trainer |
| **Powerplant:** | one 750hp (560kW) BMW V1 7.3 Vee-12 piston engine |
| **Performance:** | maximum speed 300km/h (186mph); service ceiling 7600m (24,935ft) |
| **Weights:** | empty 1550kg (3418lb); maximum take-off weight 1970kg (4344lb) |
| **Dimensions:** | span 11.2m (36ft 9in); length 8.4m (27ft 6in); height 3.42m (11ft 2in); wing area 23 sq m (248 sq ft) |
| **Armament:** | two fixed forward-firing 7.92mm MG 17 machine guns with 500 rpg |

# Arado Ar 68

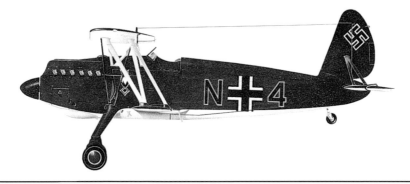

The Ar 68 was Germany's last biplane fighter, and entered service in the summer of 1936 as successor to the Heinkel He 51. The Ar 68 was typical of late-generation biplane fighters in its clean design, comparatively high-powered engine and cantilever main landing gear units, but survived in first-line service only to 1938, by which time it had been superseded by the Messerschmitt Bf 109. The two main models, in order of their entry into service, were the Ar 68F-1 with the 750hp (559kW) BMW VI Vee engine, and the Ar 68E-1 that was the main production variant with the revised powerplant of one Junkers engine. By the start of World War II the Ar 68 was serving as an interim night-fighter, but by the spring of 1940 was used only for the advanced flying and fighter lead-in training roles. Pictured is an Arado Ar 68F night fighter of 10 (Nacht) JG 53 based at Oedheim/Heilbron during September 1939.

| | |
|---|---|
| **Country of origin:** | Germany |
| **Type:** | (Ar 68E-1) single-seat fighter |
| **Powerplant:** | one 690hp (515kW) Junkers Jumo 210Ea 12-cylinder Vee engine |
| **Performance:** | maximum speed 335km/h (208mph); climb to 6000m (19,685ft) in 10 minutes 0 seconds; service ceiling 8100m (26,575ft); range 415km (258 miles) |
| **Weights:** | empty 1840kg (4057lb); maximum take-off 2475kg (5457lb) |
| **Dimensions:** | span 11.00m (36ft 1in); length 9.50m (31ft 2in); height 3.28m (10ft 9in) |
| **Armament:** | two 7.92mm fixed forward-firing machine guns in the upper side of the forward fuselage, plus an external bomb load of 60kg (132lb) |

# Arado Ar 95A-1

A rado Chief Engineer Walter Blume designed the Ar 95 two-seat twin-float seaplane in
1935 to meet a Luftwaffe requirement for a coastal patrol and light-attack aircraft. Two
prototypes had, respectively, the 880hp (656kW) BMW 132De 9-cylinder radial engine and
690hp (515kW) Junkers Jumo 210 12-cylinder inline piston engine, and the first of these
flew in 1937. After evaluation with the Focke-Wulf Fw 62 seaplane, the BMW-powered Ar
95V2 was further developed. Twelve aircraft were sent to Spain for evaluation, but the
Luftwaffe showed a marked indifference to the aircraft and Arado offered it for export as
the Ar 95W, and with fixed landing gear as the Ar 95L. A Turkish order for the Ar 95W was
diverted to the Luftwaffe *Seeaufklärungsgruppe* (coastal reconnaissance units) at the
outbreak of World War II and given the designation Ar 95A. Pictured is aircraft F, an Ar
95A-I of the 3rd Staffel of Seeaufklärungsgruppe 125 operating in the Baltic during 1941.

| | |
|---|---|
| Country of origin: | Germany |
| Type: | two-seat coastal patrol and light attack aircraft |
| Powerplant: | one 880hp (656kW) BMW 132De 9-cylinder radial engine |
| Performance: | maximum speed 310km/h (193mph); service ceiling 7300m (23,945ft); range 1100km (683 miles) |
| Weights: | empty 2450kg (5402lb); maximum take-off weight 3560kg (7870lb) |
| Dimensions: | span 12.5m (41ft); length 11.1m (36ft 5in); height 3.6m (11ft 9in); wing area 45.40 sq m (489 sq ft) |
| Armament: | one fixed forward-firing 7.92mm MG 17 machine gun, one 7.92mm MG 15 on flexible mounting in rear cockpit; underfuselage rack with provision for an 800kg (1764lb) torpedo or 500kg (1102lb) bomb |

# Arado Ar 196

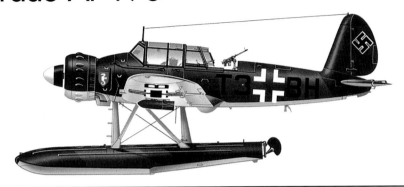

The Ar 196 was designed from late 1936 as a successor to the Heinkel He 50, the catapult-launched spotter and reconnaissance floatplane carried by German warships. The Ar 196 was initially built to the extent of five prototypes (three and two with single- and twin-float alighting gear respectively), of which the first flew in the summer of 1938. The twin-float arrangement was selected for the Ar 196A production model (536 aircraft) that entered service in the autumn of 1939 in variants such as the Ar 196A-0 pre-production model, Ar 196A-1 baseline model with two fixed forward-firing machine guns, Ar 196A-2 improved model with two 20mm fixed forward-firing cannon added, Ar 196A-3 structurally strengthened major production model, Ar 196A-4 with extra radio equipment, Ar 195A-5 with revised armament. There were also five Ar 196B-0 pre-production aircraft with single-float alighting gear.

| | |
|---|---|
| **Country of origin:** | Germany |
| **Type:** | (Ar 196A-3) two-seat reconnaissance and light attack floatplane |
| **Powerplant:** | one 970hp (723kW) BMW 132K nine-cylinder single-row radial engine |
| **Performance:** | maximum speed 320km/h (199mph); initial climb rate 415m (1362ft) per minute; service ceiling 7000m (22,960ft); range 1070 km (665 miles) |
| **Weights:** | empty 2572kg (5670lb); maximum take-off 3730kg (8223lb) |
| **Dimensions:** | span 12.40m (50ft 9.5in); length 11.00m (36ft 0.5in); height 4.45m (14ft 7.25in) |
| **Armament:** | two 20mm fixed forward-firing cannon in wing, i.e one 7.92mm fixed forward-firing machine gun in starboard side of forward fuselage, and one 7.92mm trainable rearward-firing machine gun in rear of cockpit, plus an external bomb load of 220lb (100kg) |

# Arado Ar 232

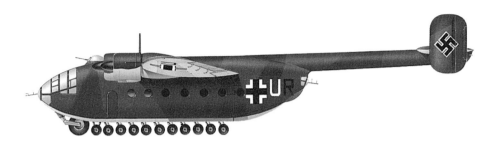

The Ar 232 was designed as a general-purpose transport with multi-wheel landing gear for operation into front-line airfields. The aircraft first flew in prototype during the summer of 1941 with a powerplant of two 1600hp (1193kW) BMW 801MA radial engines. The design incorporated innovative features with provision for easy loading into and unloading from the pod-like main section of the fuselage. BMW 801 engines were required more urgently for combat aircraft, such as the Focke Wulf 190, and the third prototype introduced the powerplant of four BMW Bramo 323 radial engines on the leading edges of a centre section of increased span. This basic configuration was retained for the 19 or so Ar 232B production aircraft that were completed (one of them fitted with captured French Gnome-Rhône engines) for intensive service between 1942 and 1945. Most of these aircraft served with KG 200, the Luftwaffe's special operations unit.

| | |
|---|---|
| Country of origin: | Germany |
| Type: | (Ar 232B-0) Four-seat medium transport |
| Powerplant: | four 1200hp (895kW) BMW Bramo 323R-2 Fafnir nine-cylinder single-row radial engines |
| Performance | maximum speed 340km/h (211mph); climb to 4000m (13,125ft) in 15 minutes 48 seconds; service ceiling 6900m (22,640ft); range 1335km (830 miles) |
| Weights: | empty 12,800kg (28,219lb); maximum take-off 21,160kg (46,649lb) |
| Dimensions: | span 33.50m (109ft 10.75in); length 23.52m (77ft 2in); height 5.70m (18ft 8.25in) |
| Armament: | one 20mm trainable cannon in the dorsal turret, one 13mm trainable forward-firing machine gun in the nose position, and one or two 13mm trainable rearward/downward-firing machine guns in the rear of the fuselage pod |

# Arado Ar 234 Blitz

The Blitz (lightning) was the only turbojet-powered bomber to achieve operational status in World War II, and as such was an important milestone in the development of military aviation. The origins of the type can be traced to a 1940 requirement issued by the German air ministry for a turbojet-powered fast reconnaissance aeroplane. An intensive programme of design and development resulted in no fewer than 18 prototypes with a powerplant of two Junkers 004 or four BMW 003 turbojets, provision for rocket-assisted take-off units, a cabin with or without pressurisation and a pilot's ejection seat, and a clumsy combination of a drop-away trolley for take-off and extendable skids for landing. Four B-1s were operated by Sonderkommando Götz based at Rheine from July 1944 for the reconnaissance role, and from early October reconnaissance missions were being flown over Allied-occupied Europe and the British Isles.

| | |
|---|---|
| Country of origin: | Germany |
| Type: | (Ar 232 V3) single-seat reconnaissance aeroplane |
| Powerplant: | two 1852lb (8.24kN) Junkers Jumo 109-004A-0 turbojet engines |
| Performance: | (estimated) maximum speed 780km/h (485mph); service ceiling 16,370m (36,090ft); range 2000km (1243 miles) |
| Weights: | empty 4800kg (10,580lb); maximum take-off 8000kg (17,637lb) |
| Dimensions: | span 14.40m (47ft 3.25in); length 12.65m (41ft 5.5in) |
| Armament: | none |

# Armstrong Whitworth F.K.3

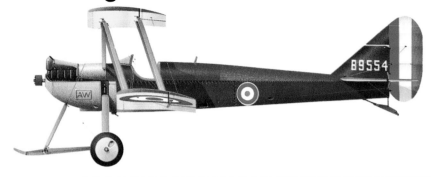

The talented Dutchman Frederick Koolhoven began designing aircraft in 1910, and in 1914 joined Armstrong Whitworth of Coventry. He produced a number of designs for the company that bore his initials, the first of them the Royal Aircraft Factory B.E.2C-derived F.K.3. The prototype for this aircraft had a 70hp (52kW) Renault engine, although production models had a more powerful Royal Aircraft Factory IA which considerably improved performance. The F.K.3 and B.E.2C were evaluated at Upavon with the former aircraft demonstrating speed and height advantage. Production totalled some 493 aircraft, 150 by Armstrong Whitworth and a further 300 by Hewlett & Blondeau Ltd. The aircraft, dubbed 'Little Ack' by servicemen, served at Salonika with No 47 Squadron, but was used mainly for training duties until replaced by the Avro 504K.

| | |
|---|---|
| Country of origin: | United Kingdom |
| Type: | two-seat general purpose aircraft |
| Powerplant: | one 90hp (67kW) Royal Aircraft Factory. IA inline piston engine |
| Performance: | maximum speed 143km/h (89mph); service ceiling 3660m (12,000ft); endurance 3 hours |
| Weights: | empty 629kg (1,386lb); maximum take-off weight 983kg (2,056lb) |
| Dimensions: | span 12.19m (40ft); length 8.84m (29ft); height 3.63m (11ft 11in); wing area 42.46 sq m (457 sq ft) |
| Armament: | one .303 Vickers machine gun on flexible mount in rear cockpit |

# Armstrong Whitworth F.K.8

The increasing importance of the army co-operation role from 1916 prompted development of a larger version of the F.K.3 designated the F.K.8. Koolhoven designed this with a sturdier fuselage to accommodate a more powerful engine, allowing for a bomb load of up to 72kg (160lb). The F.K.8 is roughly comparable to the Royal Aircraft Factory R.E.8 that was produced at the same time and although a superior aircraft, for political reasons it was never produced in the same numbers. Armstrong Whitworth built 700 between August 1916 and July 1918, and thereafter production passed to the Angus Sanderson & Co. company which built a further 700 aircraft. The 'Big Ack' gained a reputation for being strong and reliable, and did every kind of reconnaissance, bombing and strafing mission on the Western Front, in Macedonia and in Palestine. Two aircraft were used in Australia post-war by Queensland and Northern Territory Aerial Services Ltd (later QANTAS).

| | |
|---|---|
| **Country of origin:** | United Kingdom |
| **Type:** | two-seat general-purpose aircraft |
| **Powerplant:** | one 160hp (119kW) Beardmore, 150hp (112kW) Lorraine-Dietrich or 150hp (112kW) Royal Aircraft Factory.4A inline piston engine |
| **Performance:** | maximum speed 153km/h (95mph); service ceiling 3690m (13,000ft); endurance 3hrs |
| **Weights:** | empty 869kg (1916lb); maximum take-off weight 1275kg (2811lb) |
| **Dimensions:** | span 13.26m (43ft 6in); length 9.58m (31ft 5in); height 3.33m (10ft 11in); wing area 50.17 sq m (540 sq ft) |
| **Armament:** | one fixed forward-firing .303in Vickers machine gun; one .303in Lewis machine gun on flexible mount in rear cockpit |

# Armstrong Whitworth Siskin IIIA

This aircraft has its origins in the Siddeley S.R.2 Siskin, produced by the Siddeley-Deasy Motor Car Company in 1918 for the 300hp (224kW) Royal Aircraft Factory RAF.8 engine but which in fact first flew with the 320hp (239kW) ABC Dragonfly. The poor performance of this latter engine prompted Armstrong Siddeley to equip the aircraft with its own 325hp (242kW) Jaguar engine, and after the aircraft had been redesigned in line with Air Ministry policy with an all-metal structure it was ordered for the RAF in 1923 as the Siskin Mk IIIA. Some 360 were delivered by Armstrong Whitworth Aircraft at Coventry, and by Bristol, Vickers, Gloster and Blackburn. This superbly aerobatic aircraft formed the vanguard of Britain's home-defence squadrons from March 1927 but faded swiftly in the 1930s as technology developed and newer types such as the Bristol Bulldog. Pictured is a Siskin IIIA of No 43 Squadron in 1929.

| | |
|---|---|
| Country of origin: | United Kingdom |
| Type: | single-seat fighter biplane |
| Powerplant: | one 420hp (313kW) Armstrong Siddeley Jaguar IV radial engine |
| Performance: | maximum speed 251km/h (156mph); service ceiling 8230m (27,000ft); endurance 3hrs |
| Weights: | empty 935kg (2061lb); maximum take-off weight 1366kg (3012lb) |
| Dimensions: | span 10.11m (33ft 2in); length 7.72m (25ft 4in); height 3.10m (10ft 2in); wing area 27.22 sq m (293 sq ft) |
| Armament: | two fixed forward-firing .303in Vickers machine guns in forward fuselage; underwing racks with provision for up to four 9kg (20lb) Cooper practice bombs |

# Armstrong Whitworth Whitley

Obsolescent at the beginning of World War II, the Whitley was nonetheless one of Bomber Command's mainstays in 1939 and enjoyed an important role in the early days of the war as a night bomber before passing to Coastal Command as a patrol and anti-submarine type and ending its days as a glider-towing and paratroop training machine. The Whitley Mk I (34 aircraft) entered service in March 1937 with Armstrong Siddeley Tiger radial engines, which were retained in the 126 improved Mk II and Mk III aircraft, while the 33 Whitley Mk IV bombers switched to Rolls-Royce Merlin engines and introduced a powered tail turret. The main variant was the Mk V with a longer rear fuselage, revised tail unit and greater fuel capacity, and these 1,466 aircraft were followed by the 146 Mk VII aircraft for Coastal Command with air-to-surface search radar. The aircraft pictured wears pre-war insignia and was operated by No 10 Squadron, RAF, from Dishworth in 1937.

| | |
|---|---|
| **Country of origin:** | United Kingdom |
| **Type:** | (Whitley Mk V) five-man long-range night bomber |
| **Powerplant:** | two 1145hp (854kW) Rolls-Royce Merlin X 12-cylinder Vee engines |
| **Performance:** | maximum speed 370km/h (230mph); climb to 4570m (15,000ft) in 16 minutes 0 seconds; service ceiling 7925m (26,000ft); range 2655km (1650 miles ) with standard fuel and a 1361kg (3000lb) bomb load |
| **Weights:** | empty 8777kg (19,350lb); maximum take-off 15,195kg (33,500lb) |
| **Dimensions:** | span 25.60m (84ft 0in); length 21.49m (70ft 6in); height 4.57m (15ft 0in) |
| **Armament:** | one 0.303in trainable forward-firing machine gun in the nose turret, and four 0.303in trainable rearward-firing machine guns in the tail turret, plus an internal bomb load of 7000lb (3175kg) |

# Armstrong Whitworth Albemarle

The Albemarle medium bomber was designed by Bristol during 1939, but production was transferred to Armstrong Whitworth when it became clear that the latter had spare design and production capacity. Subsequently the Albemarle was redesigned as a reconnaissance bomber with an airframe of steel and wood (thereby reducing demand on strategic light alloys) that could be produced largely by subcontractors for assembly on a single line. The first of two prototypes flew in March 1940, and was a poor performer as a result of its great structural weight. Production of 600 aircraft was then undertaken in the revised airborne forces support role for service from January 1943 as the first British operational aeroplane with tricycle landing gear. The Mks I, II and VI differed only in details and were completed as paratroop transports and glider tugs, while the Mk V was only a glider tug.

| | |
|---|---|
| Country of origin: | United Kingdom |
| Type: | (Albemarle Mk II) three-seat paratroop transport and glider tug |
| Powerplant: | two 1590hp (1186kW) Bristol Hercules XI 14-cylinder two-row radial engine |
| Performance: | maximum speed 426km/h (265mph); initial climb rate 279m (980ft) per minute; service ceiling 5485m (18,000ft); range 2092km (1300 miles) |
| Weights: | empty 11,497kg (25,347lb); maximum take-off 16,556kg (36,500lb) |
| Dimensions: | span 23.47m (77ft); length 18.26m (59ft 11in); height 4.75m (15ft 7in); wing area 74.65 sq m (803.5 sq ft) |
| Armament: | two 0.303in trainable machine guns in the dorsal position |

# Atlas Cheetah

**B**earing a strong resemblance to the Israeli Kfir, the Atlas Cheetah is in fact the South African answer to an international arms embargo imposed on the country in 1977, which prevented the SAAF from importing a replacement for its ageing fleet of Mirage IIIs. The programme involved replacing nearly 50 percent of the airframe, and adding a host of improved features. Externally, a number of aerodynamic changes were made to the original airframe, the most obvious of which are the small inlet mounted canard foreplanes. The first aircraft was modified from a two-seat Mirage IIID2; production aircraft are modified from both single-seaters and twin seaters, the twin seaters possessing more advanced systems; all variants are configured to carry a host of indigenously produced weapons. The aircraft is now known as the Denel Cheetah.

| Country of origin: | South Africa |
|---|---|
| Type: | one/two-seat combat and training aircraft |
| Powerplant: | one 7200kg (15,873lb) SNECMA Atar 9K-50 turbojet |
| Performance: | maximum speed above 12,000m (39,370ft) 2337 km/h (1452mph); service ceiling 17,000m (55,775ft) |
| Weights: | not revealed |
| Dimensions: | wingspan 8.22m (26ft 11.5in); length 15.40m (50ft 6.5in); height 4.25m (13ft 11.5in); wing area 35sq m (376.75sq ft) |
| Armament: | two 30mm DEFA cannon, Armscor V3B and V3C Kukri air-to-air missiles, provision for external stores such as cluster bombs, laser designator pods, and rockets |

# Avia BH.21

The Avia company (Avia ack. spolecnost pro prumsyl letecky) was founded in 1919 and established workshops near Cakovice in the newly-formed republic of Czechoslovakia. The chief engineers of the company, until their move to Praga in 1927, were Pavel Benes and Miroslav Hajn. The BH.21 traced its lineage to the BH-17 biplane fighter of 1924, and had revised forward upper fuselage for improved pilot view, single underfuselage radiator to replace the twin mainwheel leg mounted units of the BH.17, and single-bay 'N' interplane struts. Some 137 aircraft were acquired by the Czech Air Force and, with the designation B.21, these served until the early 1930s when they were replaced in service by the Avia B.33. After a competition in 1925 SABCA and SEGA in Belgium licence-built 44 and 39 respectively for the Belgian Air Force. Pictured above is a B.21 of the 3rd Air Regiment of the Czech Air Force.

| Country of origin: | Czechoslovakia |
| --- | --- |
| Type: | single-seat fighter biplane |
| Powerplant: | one 310hp (231kW) Avia (license-built Hispano-Suiza) 8Fb inline piston engine |
| Performance: | maximum speed 245km/h (152mph); service ceiling 5500m (18,045ft); range 550km (342 miles) |
| Weights: | empty 720kg (1587lb); maximum take-off weight 1084kg (2390lb) |
| Dimensions: | span 8.9m (29ft 2in); length 6.87m (22ft 6in); height 2.74m (8ft 11in); wing area 21.96 sq m (236 sq ft) |
| Armament: | two fixed forward-firing .303in Vickers machine guns in forward fuselage |

# Avia BH.26

The prototype for the BH.26 two-seat fighter reconnaissance aircraft first flew in 1927. In common with previous Benes and Hajn designs the aircraft had a slab-sided fuselage, single-bay unequal-span biplane wing planform, a rudder but no fixed vertical tail fin. Early flight testing revealed the inadequacy of this configuration and the design was revised to include the fin and rudder assembly that appeared on production aircraft. Only a very limited production run of eight aircraft was completed for the Czech Air Force, and these served under the designation B.26. A development of the BH.26 was the BH.28 with the powerplant of a single 385hp (287kW) Armstrong Siddeley Jaguar radial engine, but this did not progress beyond the prototype stage. Pictured is an Avia B.26 of the Czech Central Flying School.

| Country of origin: | Czechoslovakia |
| --- | --- |
| Type: | two-seater fighter reconnaissance biplane |
| Powerplant: | one 450hp (336kW) Walter (licence-built Bristol Jupiter IV) 9-cylinder radial piston engine |
| Performance: | maximum speed 242km/h (150mph); service ceiling 8500m (27,885ft); range 530km (329 miles) |
| Weights: | empty 1030kg (2721lb); maximum take-off weight 1630kg (3594lb) |
| Dimensions: | span 10.8m (35ft 5in); length 8.85m (29ft); height 3.35m (10ft 11in); wing area 31 sq m (334 sq ft) |
| Armament: | two fixed forward-firing .303in Vickers machine guns in forward fuselage; two .303in Lewis machine guns on Skoda mount over rear cockpit |

# Avia B-534

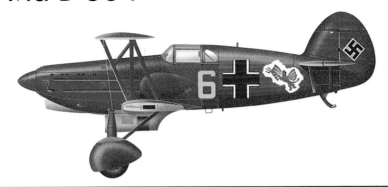

Avia developed the last Czechoslovak fighter biplane to enter service, the B-534, from the earlier B-34. The B-534 first flew in 1933; for its time it was one of the best fighters in the world. The type was developed through five main variants, namely the B-534-I (47 with pairs of 7.7mm machine guns in the fuselage and lower wing), B-534-II (99 with four 7.7mm machine guns in the fuselage), B-534-III (46 including Greek and Yugoslav orders with spatted wheels and enlarged supercharger inlet), B-534-IV (272 with an enclosed cockpit) and Bk-534 (35 with one 7.7mm machine gun firing through the propeller shaft and provision for this weapon to be replaced by a 20mm cannon). After Germany's seizure of Czechoslovakia in 1939 some of the aircraft were allocated to the puppet Slovak regime and they continued in service until 1944, but the majority were used by Germany as advanced trainers for the Luftwaffe.

| Country of origin: | Czechoslovakia |
| --- | --- |
| Type: | (B-534-IV) single-seat fighter |
| Powerplant: | one 830hp (619kW) Avia (Hispano-Suiza) 12Ydrs 12-cylinder Vee engine |
| Performance: | maximum speed 415km/h (251.5mph); climb to 5000m (16,405ft) in 4 minutes 28 seconds; service ceiling 10,600m (34,775ft); range 580km (360 miles) |
| Weights: | empty 1460kg (3219lb); normal take-off 1980kg (4365lb); maximum take-off 2120kg (4674lb) |
| Dimensions: | span 9.40m (30ft 10in); length 8.20m (26ft 10.8in); height 3.10m (10ft 2in) |
| Armament: | four 7.7mm or 7.92mm fixed forward-firing machine guns, plus an external bomb load of 120kg (265lb) |

# Aviatik B.II

The early products of Automobil und Aviatik AG were copies of French designs, however with the experience gained the Mulhausen-based company was soon able to produce its own original designs. The B.I two-seat reconnaissance aircraft that appeared in service in 1914 was developed from a 1913 design for a racing biplane, and in common with contemporary unarmed reconnaissance machines the observer was accommodated in the forward cockpit. Power for this three-bay reconnaissance biplane was provided by a 100hp (75kW) Mercedes D.I engine, and the cooling was provided by a radiator mounted on the lower wing inboard of the inner starboard strut. The B.II appeared in 1915 and had a lightened and stronger rudder and elevator structure, as well as a more powerful Mercedes engine. Pictured is an Aviatik B.II of the *Beobachterschule* (Observers' School) based at Köln-Butzweilerhof in 1916.

| Country of origin: | Germany |
| --- | --- |
| Type: | two-seat reconnaissance biplane |
| Powerplant: | one 120hp (89kW) Mercedes D.III 6-cylinder inline piston engine |
| Performance: | maximum speed 100km/h (62mph); endurance 4hrs |
| Weights: | 1088kg (2400lb) |
| Dimensions: | span 13.97m (45ft 10in); length 7.97m (26ft 2in); height 3.3m (10ft 10in) |

# Aviatik C.Ia

The first Aviatik aircraft designed from the outset for military use was the C.I. This aircraft bore a marked resemblance to the earlier B series, and although the observer in the forward cockpit was provided with a machine gun, his field of fire was severely restricted. In the C.Ia this layout was reversed and resulted in a much more potent aircraft. Construction was of wood and fabric, with an aluminium engine bay and tailskid landing gear. Power was provided by a Mercedes D.III producing some 160hp (119kW). Only a small number of C.Ia aircraft were built before production switched to the C.II with 200hp (149kW) Benz Bz.IV power and significantly revised tail surfaces. Most widely produced was the C.III, which had reduced span wings, streamlined nose, improved exhaust system, and armament uprated to two machine guns. Pictured above is a C.Ia aircraft serving on the Eastern Front.

| Country of origin: | Germany |
| --- | --- |
| Type: | two-seat reconnaissance biplane |
| Powerplant: | one 120hp (89kW) Mercedes D.II 6-cylinder inline piston engine |
| Performance: | maximum speed 142km/h (89mph); service ceiling 3500m (11,480ft) endurance 3hrs |
| Weights: | empty 980kg (2161lb); maximum take-off weight 1340kg (2954lb) |
| Dimensions: | span 12.5m (41ft); length 7.92m (26ft); height 2.95m (9ft 8in) |
| Armament: | one 7.92mm Parabellum machine gun on flexible mount in rear cockpit |

# Avions Fairey Fox VI

A fter a thrilling programme of competitive fly-offs with rival designs, the Belgian Government selected an all-metal version of the Fairey Fox for licensed manufacture by Belgian subsidiary Avions Fairey at Gosselies as the Fox IIM. This aircraft was powered by a 480hp (385kW) engine, and the first of 31 examples entered service in 1933 with the Aéronautique Militaire. Avions Fairey developed a number of versions, including the Fox III reconnaissance fighter with Armstrong Siddeley Serval radial power, Fox IIIC with enclosed cockpits and Rolls Royce Kestrel engine (47 aircraft built), Fox IIICS dual-control variant (1), Fox IIIS dual-control trainer (4), Fox V prototype for the Fox VI with Hispano-Suiza 12Ydrs engine (1), and the Fox VI with this latter engine (94). Pictured is a Fox VI of 6/III, 2e Regiment d'Aéronautique, based at Le Zoute on the eve of the German invasion on 10 May 1940.

| Country of origin: | Belgium |
|---|---|
| Type: | two-seat reconnaissance fighter biplane |
| Powerplant: | one 860hp (641kW) Hispano-Suiza 12Ydrs inline piston engine |
| Performance: | maximum speed 365km/h (227mph); service ceiling 11,200m (36,745ft); range 600km (373 miles) |
| Weights: | empty 1361kg (3000lb); maximum take-off weight 2245kg (4950lb) |
| Dimensions: | span 11.58m (38ft); length 9.17m (30ft 1in); height 3.35m (9ft 8in) |
| Armament: | two fixed forward-firing 7.5mm FN machine guns in forward fuselage; one .303in Lewis on flexible mount in rear cockpit; underwing racks with provision for 240kg (528lb) bomb load |

# Avro 504K

When A.V. Roe built the first Avro 504 in the pioneer days more than a year before World War I, he could not have envisaged that the aircraft would still be in production in 1933. Production in wartime alone totalled around 8340 aircraft. In the summer of 1913 the War Ministry placed an order for 12 of the Avro 504 production aircraft for the Royal Flying Corps, and these were followed into service by examples for the Royal Naval Air Service. Sixty-three of the basic version were produced and although these saw limited active service, including the famous raid on the Zeppelin sheds at Friedrichshafen on 21 November 1914, the type saw far more widespread use in the training role. Some 504Ks were used for testing at RAE Farnborough. Pictured is a 504K built by Hewlett & Blondeau, of No 8 Training Squadron, Royal Air Force, in 1918. Other major sub-contractors were Harland & Wolff, Frederic Sage, Humber Motor Co, and Sunbeam.

| Country of origin: | United Kingdom |
| --- | --- |
| Type: | (504K) two-seat elementary trainer |
| Powerplant: | one 110hp (82kW) Le Rhône rotary piston engine |
| Performance: | maximum speed 153km/h (95mph); service ceiling 4875m (16,000ft); range 402km (250 miles) |
| Weights: | empty 558kg (1230lb); maximum take-off weight 830kg (1829lb) |
| Dimensions: | span 10.97m (36ft); length 8.97m (29ft 5in); height 3.17m (10ft 5in); wing area 30.66 sq m (330 sq ft) |

# Avro 529A

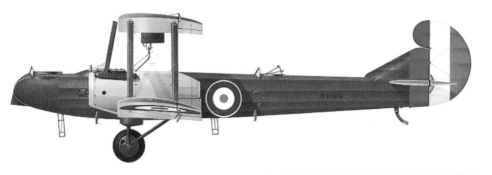

A fter failing to win a production order from the Admiralty for the promising Avro 523 Pike long-range escort/reconnaissance aircraft, Avro was requested to construct a modified and enlarged version for evaluation in the long-range bombing role. Roy Chadwick, the Avro chief designer who had designed the 523 and went on to lead the Lancaster team, created a prototype for the new aircraft, designated Avro 529, by simply stretching the dimensions of his original design. Other changes were wings that hinged outboard of the engines, revised tail unit, and twin Rolls Royce Falcon engines in a tractor rather than pusher installation. The second prototype (pictured) substituted 230hp (172kW) BHP engines and had a revised fuel system. Communication between the crew positions by the Gosport tube system was an innovative feature, but no production order was made.

| | |
|---|---|
| **Country of origin:** | United Kingdom |
| **Type:** | three-seat long-range bomber |
| **Powerplant:** | two 230hp (172kW) BHP inline piston engines |
| **Performance:** | maximum speed 153km/h (95mph); service ceiling 4115m (13,500ft); endurance 5hrs |
| **Weights:** | empty 2148kg (4736lb); maximum take-off weight 2862kg (6309lb) |
| **Dimensions:** | span 19.2m (63ft); length 12.09m (39ft 8in); height 3.96m (13ft); wing area 85.7 sq m (922 sq ft) |
| **Armament:** | one .303in Lewis gun on Scarff ring mounting in front cockpit; one .303in Lewis gun on Scarff ring mounting in rear cockpit; internal bay with provision for up to twenty 23kg (50lb) bombs |

# Avro 533 Manchester Mk I

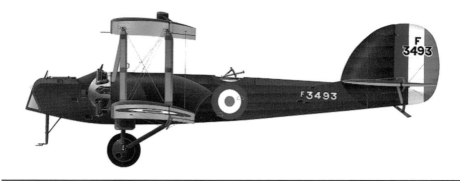

R ather less famous than the later Manchester Mk II, the Avro 533 Manchester of 1918 represented the final development of the 523/529 concept. The new design incorporated a number of changes including deeper fuselage, balanced ailerons, larger fin and horizontal stabiliser, and enlarged bomb aimer/front gunners position. It was designed around the ABC Dragonfly, the engine that was supposed to bring some measure of standardisation to the wartime British aircraft industry, but protracted development problems with this engine meant that Avro was forced to substitute 300hp (224kW) Siddeley Puma engines to produce the Avro 533 Manchester Mk II. By the time this flew in December 1918, a month after the Armistice, the 533 was an aircraft without a purpose. A year later the Mk I, pictured here, finally flew under the power of the much delayed and troublesome Dragonfly engines. No production orders were received.

| | |
|---|---|
| **Country of origin:** | United Kingdom |
| **Type:** | three-seat long-range bomber |
| **Powerplant:** | two 320hp (239kW) ABC Dragonfly radial piston engines |
| **Performance:** | maximum speed 185km/h (115mph); service ceiling 5790m (19,000ft); endurance 5hrs 45 mins |
| **Weights:** | empty 2217kg (4887lb); maximum take-off weight 3352kg (7390lb) |
| **Dimensions:** | span 18.29m (60ft); length 11.28m (37ft); height 3.81m (12ft 6in); wing area 75.90 sq m (817 sq ft) |
| **Armament:** | one .303in Lewis gun on Scarff ring mounting in front cockpit; one .303in Lewis gun on Scarff ring mounting in rear cockpit; internal bay with provision for up to 339kg (880lb) of bombs |

# Avro 549 Aldershot III

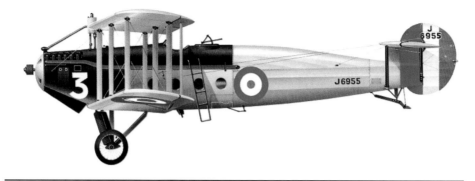

In 1920 Avro and de Havilland submitted proposals to Air Ministry Specification 2/20, which called for a long-range day bomber. Avro's submission, the Type 549 Aldershot, was the company's first post-war military aircraft, a three-bay unequal-span biplane with all-metal fuselage (the first built by the company) and Rolls Royce Condor engine. After competitive trials with the de Havilland Derby the Type 549 won an order for two prototypes. The first of these flew at Hamble in 1922 and after a 1.8m (6-ft) fillet had been added to the fuselage the aircraft was demonstrated at the Hendon RAF display in June 1922. In 1923 this aircraft was ordered as the Aldershot III. Around 15 were supplied and all were operated by No 99 Squadron, from April 1924, until they were replaced by the Handley Page Hyderabad at the end of 1925.

| Country of origin: | United Kingdom |
|---|---|
| Type: | three-seat heavy bomber |
| Powerplant: | one 650hp (485kW) Rolls Royce Condor III inline piston engine |
| Performance: | maximum speed 177km/h (110mph); service ceiling 4420m (14,500ft); range 1006km (625 miles) |
| Weights: | empty 649kg (1431lb); maximum take-off weight 1010kg (2226lb) |
| Dimensions: | span 11.20m (36ft 9in); length 9.02m (29ft 5in); height 3.17m (10ft 5in); wing area 31.12 sq m (335 sq ft) |

# Avro 555 Bison

Avro produced very few naval aircraft, a notable exception being the Type 555 Bison of 1921. This aircraft was designed to Admiralty Specification 3/11 that called for a carrier-based fleet spotter and reconnaissance aircraft. The first prototype was flown in 1921, followed by a second with raised upper wing, and a third in 1923. The first production aircraft were built to the standard of the second prototype and became Bison IAs in Royal Navy service. Orders for a further 35 aircraft (Bison II) were received between July 1924 and February 1927. The Bison IA entered service with No 3 Squadron, Royal Air Force, at Gosport, and it first went to sea with No 423 Fleet Spotter Flight embarked on HMS *Eagle*, on patrol in the Mediterranean. After serving aboard several other Royal Navy carriers and with shore-based units the Bison was replaced by the Fairey IIIF and retired in 1929. An attempted seaplane conversion was not a success.

| | |
|---|---|
| **Country of origin:** | United Kingdom |
| **Type:** | three/four-seat fleet spotter biplane |
| **Powerplant:** | one 450hp (336kW) Napier Lion inline piston engine |
| **Performance:** | maximum speed 177km/h (110mph); service ceiling 4265m (14,000ft); range 547km (340 miles) |
| **Weights:** | empty 1887kg (4160lb); maximum take-off weight 2631kg (5800lb) |
| **Dimensions:** | span 14.02m (46ft); length 10.97m (36ft); height 4.22m (13ft 10in); wing area 57.6 sq m (620 sq ft) |
| **Armament:** | one .303 Lewis machine gun on flexible mount in aft cockpit |

# Avro 621 Tutor

Roy Chadwick, the Avro designer, realised that the aircraft built to succeed the Avro 504N would have to be special, and in the 621 Tutor he designed an aircraft with the excellent handling characteristics of its predecessor. The prototype was evaluated at the Aircraft and Armament Experimental Establishment at Martlesham Heath in December 1929 before being selected for production in 1930. The production aircraft had the 240hp (179kW) Armstrong Siddeley Lynx IVC radial piston engine. Delivery of the first of an eventual 394 aircraft (from the production total of 795) for the RAF flying schools was made in 1933. Export orders to Canada (7 aircraft), Eire (3), Greece (30), Denmark (3) and China (5) were fulfilled before the line closed in 1936; licensed manufacture was undertaken in South Africa (57). In the late 1930s the Tutor was phased out from its position as main Royal Air Force elementary trainer in favour of the Miles Magister, a low-wing monoplane.

| | |
|---|---|
| **Country of origin:** | United Kingdom |
| **Type:** | two-seat elementary trainer biplane |
| **Powerplant:** | one 240hp (179kW) Armstrong Siddeley Lynx IVC radial piston engine |
| **Performance:** | maximum speed 196km/h (122mph); service ceiling 4940m (16,200ft); range 402km (250 miles) |
| **Weights:** | empty 839kg (1844lb); maximum take-off weight 1115kg (2458lb) |
| **Dimensions:** | span 10.36m (34ft); length 8.08m (26ft 6in); height 2.92m (9ft 7in); wing area 27.96 sq m (301 sq ft) |

# Avro 626 Prefect

In an attempt to wring the maximum potential from the Avro 621 Tutor airframe and to maximise its sales potential to foreign clients, Avro developed the 626 specifically for export. This involved a number of changes to the basic airframe to incorporate a tailwheel and a gunner's position behind the aft cockpit. As supplied to foreign clients with special conversion kits the 626 could be used for a wide variety of training roles. A successful tour of South America was undertaken in 1931, and the aircraft subsequently served with the air arms of Argentina, Belgium, Brazil, Canada, Chile, China, Eire, Egypt, Estonia, Greece, Lithuania, New Zealand, Portugal, and the UK. The Royal Air Force and Royal New Zealand Air Force aircraft was known as the Prefect. Pictured here is one of the RNZAF aircraft, as can be seen from its registration number.

| Country of origin: | United Kingdom |
| --- | --- |
| Type: | two/three-seat elementary trainer biplane |
| Powerplant: | one 240hp (179kW) Armstrong Siddeley Lynx IVC radial piston engine |
| Performance: | maximum speed 180km/h (112mph); service ceiling 4510m (14,800ft); range 354km (220 miles) |
| Weights: | empty 801kg (1765lb); maximum take-off weight 1247kg (2750lb) |
| Dimensions: | span 10.36m (34ft); length 8.08m (26ft 6in); height 2.92m (9ft 7in); wing area 27.87 sq m (300 sq ft) |

# Avro 643 Mk II Cadet

Essentially a scaled-down version of the Avro 621 Tutor, the Cadet was produced in three versions for civilian and military customers. The 631 Cadet first flew in 1931, and 35 aircraft were eventually built for private customers and the Irish Air Corps. In 1934 the 634 Cadet was introduced, retaining the uncowled 135hp (101kW) Armstrong Siddeley Genet Major of the 631. A sub-variant, the 643 Mk II, had minor modifications and an uprated 150hp (112kW) Genet. This was the most extensively produced model with 4 supplied to private clients, 20 to Air Service Training and 34 for the Royal Australian Air Force. These last aircraft soldiered on until the 1950s under civilian ownership. One was converted as a single-seat crop-spraying aircraft with a chemical hopper in the forward cockpit and a 220hp (164kW) Jacobs R-755 radial piston engine.

| Country of origin: | United Kingdom |
|---|---|
| Type: | two-seat elementary trainer biplane |
| Powerplant: | one 150hp (112kW) Armstrong Genet Major IA radial piston engine |
| Performance: | maximum speed 187km/h (116mph); service ceiling 3660m (12,000ft); range 523km (325 miles) |
| Weights: | empty 839kg (1844lb); maximum take-off weight 1115kg (2458lb) |
| Dimensions: | span 9.19m (30ft 2in); length 7.54m (24ft 9in); height 2.69m (8ft 10in); wing area 24.34 sq m (262 sq ft) |

# Avro Anson Mk I

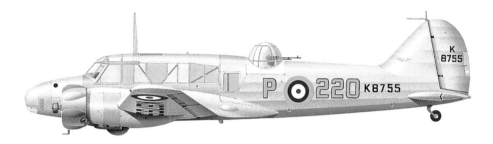

Enjoying a production run that lasted from 1934 to 1952, the Anson was built in larger numbers than any other British aeroplane except the Hawker Hurricane and Supermarine Spitfire. The type was initially schemed as a light transport but then adapted as a coastal reconnaissance type to meet a May 1934 requirement. The prototype first flew in March 1935, and the type was ordered into production as the Anson Mk I (later Anson GR.Mk I) with a revised tail unit, a larger cabin window area, Cheetah IX radial engines, and full military equipment. The first of these aircraft flew in December 1935, and the type entered service in March of the following year at the start of a programme that saw the delivery of 6915 aircraft, the later aircraft completed to a five-seat trainer standard with dual controls and different equipment. Pictured is an Anson Mk 1 of No 220 Squadron, RAF Coastal Command. The aircraft has a typical pre-war silver finish.

| | |
|---|---|
| Country of origin: | United Kingdom |
| Type: | (Anson Mk I) three/five-seat coastal reconnaissance aeroplane or multi-role trainer |
| Powerplant: | two 335hp (250kW) Armstrong Siddeley Cheetah IX or, in later aircraft, 395hp (295kW) Cheetah XIX seven-cylinder single-row radial engines |
| Performance: | maximum speed 302.5km/h (188mph); initial climb rate 293m (960ft) per minute; service ceiling 5790m (19,000ft); range 1271 km (790km) |
| Weights: | empty 2438kg (5375lb); maximum take-off 4218kg (9300lb) |
| Dimensions: | span 17.22m (56ft 6in); length 12.88m (42ft 3in); height 3.99m (13ft 1in) |
| Armament: | up to four 0.303in machine guns on cabin mountings (or in dorsal turret for the trainer model), plus a 227kg (500lb) internal bomb load |

# Avro Manchester

**B**y the mid-1930s the steady improvement in aeronautical design allowed the Air Ministry to plan a new generation of advanced medium bombers, and in 1936 issued a requirement that elicited responses from both Avro and Handley Page. Both companies received prototype orders although the Handley Page did not progress beyond the drawing board. The Avro type was the Manchester medium bomber that first flew in July 1939 after an initial order for 200 aircraft had been built. The Manchester Mk I became operational in November 1940, and these 20 aircraft were followed by 180 examples of the Manchester Mk IA with larger endplate vertical surfaces on the tail, allowing the removal of the Mk I's centreline surface. The Manchester had an ideal airframe, but was rendered a failure by its wholly unreliable Vulture engines and finally retired in June 1942. Pictured is a Mk 1 of No 207 Squadron, RAF Bomber Command in early 1941.

| | |
|---|---|
| **Country of origin:** | United Kingdom |
| **Type:** | (Manchester Mk I) seven-seat medium bomber |
| **Powerplant:** | two 1760hp (1312kW) Rolls-Royce Vulture I 24-cylinder X-type engines |
| **Performance:** | maximum speed 426km/h (265mph); service ceiling 5850m (19,200ft); range 2623km (1630 miles) with 3674kg (8100lb) of bombs |
| **Weights:** | empty 13,350kg (29,432lb); maximum take-off 25,402kg (56,000lb) |
| **Dimensions:** | span 27.46m (90ft 1in); length 21.14m (69ft 4.25in); height 5.94m (19ft 6in) |
| **Armament:** | two 0.303in trainable forward-firing machine guns in the nose turret, two 0.303in trainable machine guns in a ventral turret later replaced by a dorsal turret, and four 0.303in trainable rearward-firing machine guns in the tail turret, plus an internal bomb load of 10,350lb (4695kg) |

# Avro Lancaster Mk I

The most successful and celebrated heavy night bomber used by the Royal Air Force in World War II, the Lancaster was a development of the Manchester with the revised powerplant of four Rolls-Royce Merlin Vee engines. The Lancaster first flew on January 9, 1941, and entered service from the beginning of 1942. The original Lancaster Mk I soon developed an enviable reputation as a sturdy aeroplane that handled well in the air, possessed moderately good performance and had good defensive and offensive firepower. The fact that the type was essentially 'right' from its beginning is indicated that few changes were made other than minor engine and equipment details in the course of a long production run that saw the delivery of 7378 aircraft including 3,294 examples of the Lancaster Mk I (later Lancaster B.Mk I and finally B.Mk X). Pictured is a Lancaster Mk 1 of No 463 Squadron, RAF, based at Waddington in spring 1945.

| Country of origin: | United Kingdom |
| --- | --- |
| Type: | (Lancaster Mk I) seven-seat heavy night bomber |
| Powerplant: | four 1640hp (1223kW) Rolls-Royce Merlin XX, 22 or 24 12-cylinder Vee engines |
| Performance: | maximum speed 462km/h (287mph); initial climb rate 76m (250ft) per minute; service ceiling 5790m(19,000ft); range 2784km (1730 miles) with a 5443kg (12,000lb) bomb load |
| Weights: | empty 16,783kg (37,000lb); maximum take-off 29,484kg (65,000lb) |
| Dimensions: | span 31.09m (102ft); length 21.18m (69ft 6in); height 6.25m (20ft 6in) |
| Armament: | two 0.303in trainable machine guns in the nose turret, two 0.303in trainable machine guns in the dorsal turret, four 0.303in trainable machine guns in the tail turret, and provision for one 0.303in trainable machine gun in a ventral turret, plus an internal bomb load of 8165kg (18,000lb) |

# Avro Lancaster Mk III and Mk X

When it became clear that production by Rolls-Royce of its great Merlin engine would not be able to keep pace with the manufacture of the airframes designed to use it, the decision was made to use the American licence-built version, namely the Packard V-1650 in its Merlin 28, 38 or 224 forms. When this engine was installed in the Lancaster Mk I, the aeroplane was known as the Lancaster Mk III (later B.Mk III and finally B.Mk 3), and deliveries of this model totalled 3020 aircraft. The Lancaster Mk III was also selected for production in Canada by Victory Aircraft Ltd. of Toronto, which delivered 430 examples of the Lancaster Mk X (later B.Mk X and finally B.Mk 10) that were identical in all important respects to the Mk III machines. KB861 was one of a batch of 300 aircraft built as Lancaster Mk Xs by Victory Aircraft, with Packard engines and the Martin 250-CE23 electrically driven mid-upper turret with 0.5in guns.

| | |
|---|---|
| Country of origin: | United Kingdom |
| Type: | (Lancaster Mk III) seven-seat heavy night bomber |
| Powerplant: | four 1640hp (1223kW) Packard (Rolls-Royce) Merlin 28, 38 or 224 12-cylinder Vee engines |
| Performance: | maximum speed 462km/h(287mph); initial climb rate 76m (250ft) per minute; service ceiling 5790m (19,000ft); range 2784km (1730 miles ) with a 5443kg (12,000lb) bomb load |
| Weights: | empty 16,783kg (37,000lb); maximum take-off 29,484kg (65,000lb) |
| Dimensions: | span 31.09m (102ft 0in); length 21.18m (69ft 6in); height 6.25m (20ft 6in) |
| Armament: | two 0.303in trainable machine guns in the nose, turret, two 0.303-in trainable machine guns in the dorsal turret and four 0.303in trainable machine guns in the tail turret, plus an internal bomb load of 8165kg (18,000lb) |

# Avro Vulcan B.Mk 2

In the early 1950s, the Royal Air Force issued Specification B.14/46, which called for an aircraft that could deliver nuclear weapons from any of its bases in the world. The Avro Vulcan was thus designed ostensibly as a high level nuclear bomber. The first production aircraft were designated B. Mk 1 and entered service in this role in 1956 with the V-bomber force. The B.Mk 1 was joined in service in 1960 by the improved Vulcan B.Mk 2. These aircraft were furnished with inflight refuelling equipment. It was also intended that this variant would carry the Blue Steel or American Skybolt stand-off nuclear weapons, but, with the adoption of Polaris, these plans never materialised. Existing Vulcan squadrons converted to the B.Mk 2A in 1962-64. This aircraft wears the bat emblem of No. 9 Squadron, and was later converted to B.Mk 2A standard.

| | |
|---|---|
| **Country of origin:** | United Kingdom |
| **Type:** | long-range strategic bomber |
| **Powerplant:** | four 7711kg (17,000lb) Rolls-Royce Olympus 201 turbojets |
| **Perfomance:** | maximum speed at altitude 1038km/h (645mph); service ceiling 19,810m (65,000ft); range with normal bomb load 7403km (4600 miles) |
| **Weights:** | maximum takeoff weight 113,398kg (250,000lb) |
| **Dimensions:** | wingspan 33.83m (111 ft); length 30.45m (99ft 11in); height 8.28 m (27 ft 2in); wing area 368.26sq m (3964 sq ft) |
| **Armament:** | internal bay with provision for up to 21,454kg (47,198lb) of bombs |

# Avro Canada CF-105 Arrow

The story of the Arrow bears a startling similarity to that of the BAC TSR.2. Both projects showed great promise during the early stages of development in the mid-1950s, and both were destroyed by the misguided decisions of politicians who were convinced that the days of the manned interceptor were numbered. The first stages of development of the Arrow, a two-seat all-weather interceptor, began in 1953, with planned entry into service as a replacement for the same company's CF-100 a decade later. Production of the first five prototypes began in April 1954. The design incorporated a huge high-set delta wing. The first flight of the aircraft was made on March 25, 1958, but a little under 10 months later, the whole project was cancelled. All the prototypes were destroyed in what must rank as one of the most short-sighted decisions made by any Canadian government.

| | |
|---|---|
| **Country of origin:** | Canada |
| **Type:** | two-seat all-weather long range supersonic interceptor |
| **Powerplant:** | two 10,659kg (23,500lb) Pratt and Whitney J75-P-3 turbojets |
| **Performance:** | Mach 2.3 recorded during tests |
| **Weights:** | empty 22,244kg (49,040lb); average take-off during trials 25,855kg (57,000lb) |
| **Dimensions:** | wingspan 15.24m (50ft); length 23.72m (77ft 9.75in); height 6.48m (21ft 3in); wing area 113.8sq m (1,225sq ft) |
| **Armament:** | eight Sparrow air-to-air missiles in internal bay |

# BAC TSR.2

At the time, the cancellation of the TSR.2 program was widely regarded within the aviation industry as the greatest disaster to befall the post war British aviation industry. In retrospect it is clear that much of the pioneering research carried out by the project team was of great benefit during the development of Concorde. Conceived as a replacement for the English Electric Canberra, the aircraft was designed by a combined English Electric and Vickers Armstrong to an RAF requirement issued in 1957 for a high-speed low-level tactical strike and reconnaissance aircraft. In January 1959 it was decided to proceed with development. The aircraft that emerged represented a huge leap in airframe, avionics, engine, and equipment technology; XR219 first flew on 27 September 1964. Just four were built, although XR219 was the only example to fly.

| | |
|---|---|
| Country of origin: | United Kingdom |
| Type: | two-seat strike/reconnaissance aircraft |
| Powerplant: | two 13884kg (30,610lb) thrust Bristol Siddeley Olympus 320 turbojets |
| Performance: | maximum speed at altitude 2390km/h (1485mph); maximum speed 1345km/h (836mph) at 61m (200ft);operating ceiling 16,460m (54,000ft); range at low level 1287km (800 miles) |
| Weights: | average mission take-off weight 36,287kg (80,000lb); maximum take-off weight 43,545kg (96,000lb) |
| Dimensions: | wingspan 11.28m (37ft); length 27.13m (89ft); height 7.32m (24ft); wing area 65.03sq m (700sq ft) |
| Armament: | (planned) up to 2722kg (6000lb) of conventional or nuclear weapons in an internal weapons bay; four underwing pylons for up to 1814kg (4000lb) of weapons |

# BAC (English Electric) Canberra B.Mk 2

**B**efore he left Westland aircraft, the company established by his family in 1915, W.E.W. Petter already had a scheme for a jet bomber. To meet specification B.3/45 he eventually planned a straightforward unswept aircraft with a broad wing for good behaviour at high altitude. Like the Mosquito the A.1 bomber was to be fast enough to escape interception. whilst carrying a 2727kg (6000lb) bomb load over a radius of 750 nautical miles. It was to have a radar sight for blind attacks in all conditions. The prototype, which flew for the first time on 13 May 1949 at the hands of Roland 'Bee' Beaumont, amazed everybody with its low-level manoeuvrability. Delays in the development of the bombsight resulted in an initial order for a tactical day bomber, designated B.Mk 2. The first of these entered service with No. 101 Squadron on 25 May 1951.

| | |
|---|---|
| **Country of origin:** | United Kingdom |
| **Type:** | two-seat interdictor aircraft |
| **Powerplant:** | two 2948kg (6500lb) Rolls Royce Avon Mk 101 turbojets |
| **Performance:** | maximum speed at 12,192m (40,000ft) 917km/h (570mph); service ceiling 14,630m (48,000ft); range 4274km (2656 miles) |
| **Weights:** | empty not published approx 11,790kg (26,000lb); maximum take-off 24,925kg (54,950lb) |
| **Dimensions:** | wingspan 29.49m (63ft 11in); length 19.96m (65ft 6in); height 4.78m (15ft 8in); wing area 97.08sq m (1045sq ft) |
| **Armament:** | internal bomb bay with provision for up to 2727kg (6000lb) of bombs, plus an additional 909kg (2000lb) of underwing pylons |

# BAC (English Electric) Canberra PR.Mk 9

The Canberra jet bomber was designed originally by Teddy Petter for the English Electric company. The aircraft they subsequently produced served for over 40 years around the world in countless different variants. The PR. Mk 9 is an extensively modified high altitude reconnaissance version of the aircraft, with increased wing span, uprated Rolls Royce Avon engines, and redesigned cockpit. Development work was carried out by the Short company, one of the main subcontractors of English Electric. As an aid to high altitude reconnaissance flying, the 23 production aircraft were equipped with powered controls, increased internal fuel, and much modified avionics and EW equipment. The aircraft served with No.1 PRU, and Nos. 58 and 39 Squadrons until 1983, but five aircraft underwent a further modification to equip them for classified electronic intelligence and reconnaissance operations.

| Country of origin: | United Kingdom |
|---|---|
| Type: | photo-reconnaissance aircraft |
| Powerplant: | two 4763kg (10,500lb) Rolls Royce Avon Mk 206 turbojets |
| Performance: | maximum speed about 650mph (1050km/h) at medium altitude; service ceiling 14,630m (48,000ft); range 5842km (3630 miles) |
| Weights: | empty not published approx 11,790kg (26,000lb); maximum take-off 24,925kg (54,950lb) |
| Dimensions: | wingspan 20.68m (67ft 10in); length 20.32m (66ft 8in); height 4.78m (15ft 8in); wing area 97.08sq m (1045sq ft) |

# BAC (English Electric) Lightning F.Mk 1A

W.E.W. 'Teddy' Petter was again the driving force behind the aircraft that was for a period during the 1960s the most formidable interceptor in the world. The Lightning developed from a prototype built by English Electric, called the P.1, which first flew in August 1954. The P.1 was powered by two Bristol Siddeley Sapphire engines mounted 'under and over', and fed by a common inlet. P.1B was a completely redesigned version to meet the British government Specification F.23/49, with a two-shock intake. With Avon engines fitted, Mach 2 was attained in November 1958. Twenty pre-production aircraft were built before the first F.Mk 1 entered service in 1960. The F.Mk 1A had provision for flight refuelling and UHF radio. The Lightning was a complicated aircraft for its time, and maintenance time per flying hour was high.

| | |
|---|---|
| Country of origin: | United Kingdom |
| Type: | single-seat all-weather interceptor |
| Powerplant: | two 6545kg (14,430lb) Rolls Royce Avon turbojets |
| Performance: | maximum speed at 10.970m (36,000ft) 2,414km/h (1,500mph); service ceiling 18,920m (60,000ft); range 1440km (895 miles) |
| Weights: | empty 12,700kg (28,000lb); maximum take-off 22,680kg (50,000lb) |
| Dimensions: | wingspan 10.6m (34ft 10in); length 16.25m (53ft 3in); height 5.95m (19ft 7in); wing area 35.31sq m (380.1sq ft) |
| Armament: | interchangeable packs of two all-attitude Red Top or stern chase Firestreak air-to-air missiles or two 30mm Aden guns, in forward part of belly tank |

# BAC (English Electric) Lightning F.Mk 6

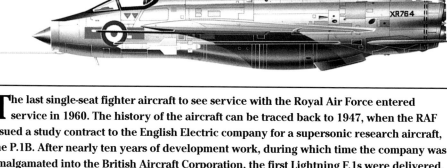

The last single-seat fighter aircraft to see service with the Royal Air Force entered service in 1960. The history of the aircraft can be traced back to 1947, when the RAF issued a study contract to the English Electric company for a supersonic research aircraft, the P.1B. After nearly ten years of development work, during which time the company was amalgamated into the British Aircraft Corporation, the first Lightning F.1s were delivered. In service the aircraft proved to be as good as any all-weather interceptor then available, with a phenomenal top speed and rate of climb. However, it was hampered by poor duration. On the recommendation of BAC the RAF decided to modify the much improved F.3 to F.6 standard in 1965. The F.6 featured and extensively modified ventral tank and a cambered, kinked wing leading edge, to allow operations at greater weights.

| | |
|---|---|
| Country of origin: | United Kingdom |
| Type: | supersonic all-weather interceptor, strike and reconnaissance aircraft |
| Powerplant: | two 7112kg (15,680lb) rolls Royce Avon 302 afterburning turbojets |
| Perfomance: | maximum speed 2415km/h (1500mph, Mach 2.3) at 12,190m (40,000ft); standard range 1287km (800miles); initial rate of climb 15,240m (50,000ft) per minute |
| Weights: | empty equipped 12,700kg (28,000lb); maximum take-off 22,680kg (50,000lb) |
| Dimensions: | wingspan 10.61m (34ft 10in); length 16.84 m (55ft 3in); height 5.97m (19ft 7in); wing area 35.31sq m (380.1 q ft) |
| Armament: | two 30mm Aden guns in ventral pack (120 rounds), two Fire Streak or Red Top air-to-air missiles, or five Vinten 360 70mm cameras, or night recon naissance cameras and linescan equipment and underwing flares; under wing/overwing pylons for up to 144 rockets or six 454kg (1000lb) bombs |

# BAC (Vickers) VC-10 K.Mk 2

The RAF received 14 VC-10 C. Mk 1 aircraft, which were derived from the civil VC-10 and Super VC-10. The aircraft had the short fuselage of the VC.10 and many of the features of the 'Super' including uprated engines, a stronger structure, wet (integral tank) fin, extended leading edge, and increased gross weight. The RAF requirement also specified an Auxiliary Power Unit in the tail, a strengthened cabin floor and large cargo door for heavy freight. The aircraft cabin can be laid out for 150 rear facing seats, or mixed passenger/cargo, or all cargo use, or casevac use with provision for up to 78 litters. The 13 surviving aircraft were fitted with an inflight refuelling probe, and between 1990 and 1992 13 ex-commercial (BA and East African Airways aircraft) were rebuilt as tanker aircraft. The aircraft are designated VC-10 K.Mk 2 and Mk 3 respectively.

| | |
|---|---|
| **Country of origin:** | United Kingdom |
| **Type:** | long-range transport and/or tanker aircraft |
| **Powerplant:** | four 9888kg (21,800lb) Rolls Royce Conway turbofans |
| **Performance:** | cruising speed at 30,000ft (9145m) 684km/h (425mph); service ceiling 12,800m (42,000ft); range with maximum payload 6276km (3900 miles) |
| **Weights:** | empty 66,224kg (146,000lb); maximum take-off 146,510kg (323,000lb) |
| **Dimensions:** | wingspan 44.55m (146ft 2in); length 48.36m (158ft 8in); height 12.04m (39ft 6in); wing area 272.38sq m (2,932sq ft) |

# BAe Sea Harrier FRS.Mk 1

The Sea Harrier FRS.Mk 1 was ordered to equip the three Royal Navy 'through-deck cruisers' (a strange name dreamed up by defence staff for the Invincible-class carriers) in fighter, anti-submarine and surface-attack roles, with Blue Fox radar and other weapons. Official policy during the time of the land-based Harrier's gestation was that all future Royal Navy combat aircraft must be helicopters, and this delayed development of its carrier borne equivalent until 1975. Installing the Blue Fox radar meant lengthening the nose, and the cockpit was raised to accommodate a more substantial avionics suite and to afford the pilot a better all-round view. Introduced into service shortly before the Falklands War, the aircraft proved an incalculably important asset during that conflict. The aircraft has pictured three of its Argentine victims stencilled on its nose.

| | |
|---|---|
| Country of origin: | United Kingdom |
| Type: | shipborne multi-role combat aircraft |
| Powerplant: | one 9752kg (21,500lb) Rolls-Royce Pegasus Mk.104 vectored thrust turbofan |
| Performance: | maximum speed at sea level 1110km/h (690mph) with maximum AAM load; service ceiling 15,545m (51,000ft); intercept radius 740km (460 miles) on high level mission with full combat reserve |
| Weights: | empty 5942kg (13,100lb); maximum take-off 11,884kg (26,200lb) |
| Dimensions: | wingspan 7.7m (25ft 3in); length 14.5m (47ft 7in); height 3.71m (12ft 2in); wing area 18.68sq m (201.1sq ft) |
| Armament: | two 30mm Aden cannon with 150 rounds, five external pylons with provision for AIM-9 Sidewinder or Matra Magic air-to-air missiles, and two Harpoon or Sea Eagle anti-shipping missiles, up to a total of 3629kg (8000lb) |

# BAe Sea Harrier FRS.Mk 2

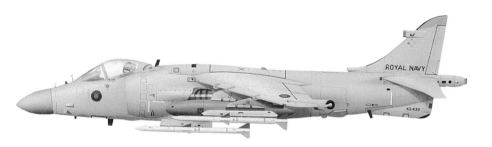

In 1985, on orders from the Ministry of Defence and the Fleet Air Arm, British Aerospace began the development of an upgrade programme to modernise the fleet of FRS. Mk 1s. The primary aim of the program was to give the Sea Harrier the ability to engage multiple beyond-visual-range targets with the new AIM-120 AMRAAM medium-range air-to-air missile. The most obvious difference is to the shape of the forward fuselage, which accommodates the new Ferranti Blue Vixen pulse-Doppler track-while-scan radar. Further upgrades to the avionics include a MIL 1553B digital databus, redesigned HUD and dual head-down displays, Marconi Sky Guardian Radar Warning Receiver, and a secure data and voice link system. Two additional missile launch rails and the Aden 25 cannon complete the package. Deliveries of the 33 converted aircraft commenced in April 1992.

| | |
|---|---|
| **Country of origin:** | United Kingdom |
| **Type:** | shipborne multi-role combat aircraft |
| **Powerplant:** | one 9752kg (21,500lb) Rolls-Royce Pegasus Mk 106 vectored thrust turbofan |
| **Performance:** | maximum speed at sea level 1185km/h (736mph) at sea level with maximum AAM load; service ceiling 15,545m (51,000ft); intercept radius 185km (115 miles) on hi-hi-hi CAP with 90 minuted loiter on station |
| **Weights:** | empty 5942kg (13,100lb); maximum take-off 11,884kg (26,200lb) |
| **Dimensions:** | wingspan 7.7m (25ft 3in); length 14.17m (46ft 6in); height 3.71m (12ft 2in); wing area 18.68sq m (201.1sq ft) |
| **Armament:** | two 25mm Aden cannon with 150 rounds, five external pylons with provision for AIM-9 Sidewinder, AIM-120 AMRAAM, and two Harpoon or Sea Eagle anti-shipping missiles, up to a total of 3629kg (8000lb) |

# BAe (BAC) 167 Strikemaster

The Strikemaster was originally developed from the Jet Provost trainer designed by Hunting. BAC absorbed Hunting in 1961, and refined the strike/attack BAC 145 into the more potent Strikemaster. With a more powerful Rolls-Royce Viper engine, the Strikemaster proved to be a great worldwide success. It had side by side ejector seats, and the ability to operate from the roughest airstrip whilst carrying an impressive load. The first customers were Saudi Arabia, South Yemen People's Republic, Sultanate of Oman (where the aircraft saw action against rebel forces), Kuwait, Singapore, Kenya, New Zealand and Ecuador. The aircraft has a considerably reinforced structure, making it extremely durable. Pictured is one of the Kuwaiti Air Force Mk. 83s equipped with a centreline drop tank and underwing rocket pods.

| | |
|---|---|
| Country of origin: | United Kingdom |
| Type: | two seat light tactical aircraft and trainer |
| Engine: | one 1547kg (3410lb) Rolls Royce Viper |
| Performance: | maximum speed 774 km/h (481mph); service ceiling 13,410m (44,000ft); combat radius with 3300lb load 233km (145 miles) |
| Weights: | empty 2840kg (6270lb); maximum 5210kg (11,500lb) |
| Dimensions: | wingspan 11.23m (36ft 10in); length 10.27m (33ft 8.5in); height 3.34m (10ft 11.5in) |
| Armament: | two 7.62mm FN machine guns with 550rpg; four underwing hardpoints with provision for up to 1360kg (3000lb) of stores, including rockets, bombs and air-to-ground missiles, and drop tanks |

# BAe (HS) Harrier GR.Mk 3

The GR.Mk 3 Harrier is essentially the same as the GR.Mk 1, but with a retrofitted 9753kg (21,500lb) Rolls Royce Pegasus 103 turbofan. In operational service it was discovered that the Gr.Mk 1 used up a great deal of fuel in vertical take-off with full weapons load operations, so it was more common for the Harrier to be operated as a V/STOL aircraft. Standard equipment on the GR.Mk 3 included inflight refuelling equipment, head-up display, and a laser range finder. From 1970 the aircraft equipped one RAF squadron in the UK and three in Germany. The final units to operate the GR.Mk 3 were the Operational Conversion Unit and a flight stationed in Belize. After nearly 20 years' service in the RAF, they have been replaced by the GR7, which itself will soon be replaced by the GR9 and GR9a, with uprated Pegasus 107 engines, a strengthened rear fuselage, improved avionics and the ability to carry a wider range of weapons such as the Maverick ASM.

| | |
|---|---|
| Country of origin: | United Kingdom |
| Type: | V/STOL close support and reconnaissance aircraft |
| Powerplant: | one 9752kg (21,500lb) Rolls Royce Pegasus 103 vectored thrust turbofan |
| Performance: | maximum speed at low altitude over 1186km/h (737mph); service ceiling over 15,240m (50,000ft); range with one inflight refuelling 5,560 km (3,455 miles) |
| Weights: | basic operating empty 5579kg (12,300lb); maximum take-off 11,340kg (25,000lb) |
| Dimensions: | wingspan 7.7m (25ft 3in); length 13.87m (45ft 6in); height 3.45m (11ft 4in); wing area 18.68sq m (201.1sq ft) |
| Armament: | maximum of 2268kg (5000lb) of stores on underfuselage and underwing points; one 30mm Aden gun or similar gun, with 150 rounds, rockets, bombs |

# BAe (HS) Hawk T.Mk 1

The Hawk has been one of the truly outstanding successes of the British aerospace industry in the past three decades. Much of this success is due to the exceptional service life of the airframe, low maintenance requirements (the lowest per flight hour of any jet aircraft in the world), relatively inexpensive purchase price when originally offered for export, large optional payload, and its ability to operate in the medium range attack and air superiority role for a fraction of the cost of more powerful types. The Hawk was the only entirely new all-British military aircraft for 15 years in 1980. The first prototype flew in August 1974, and the first two operational aircraft were handed over in November 1976. Construction of the efficient Adour turbofan is modular, enabling easy maintenance. The basic RAF advanced trainer is designated the T Mk 1.

| Country of origin: | United Kingdom |
|---|---|
| Type: | two-seat basic and advanced jet trainer |
| Powerplant: | one 2359kg (5200lb) Rolls Royce/Turbomeca Adour Mk 151 turbofan |
| Performance: | maximum speed 1038km/h (645mph); service ceiling 15,240m (50,000ft); endurance 4 hours |
| Weights: | empty 3647kg (8040lb); maximum take-off 7750kg (17,085lb) |
| Dimensions: | wingspan 9.39m (30ft 9.75in); length 11.17m (36ft 7.75in); height 3.99m (13ft 1.75in); wing area 16.69sq m (179.64sq ft) |
| Armament: | underfuselage/wing hardpoints with provision for up to 2567kg (5660lb) of stores |

# BAe (HS) Nimrod MR2

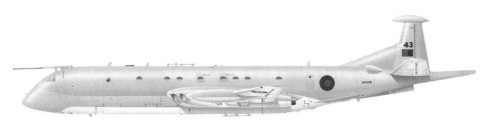

**H**awker Siddeley began the design of the Nimrod in 1964, using the Comet 4C airliner as the basis for a new aircraft to replace the Avro Shackelton in the maritime patrol and anti-submarine warfare role with the Royal Air Force. The aircraft's basic fuselage was retained but an additional fuselage fairing covering almost the entire length of the lower fuselage was added to accommodate radar, weapons bay and various other systems. The aircraft began entering service in 1969, and were significantly updated to MR2 standard from 1979 with improved avionics and weapons systems. Nimrods were very active during the Falklands War; inflight refuelling equipment was hastily added to a number of aircraft to allow them to operate from Ascension Island. The MR2 is the version currently in RAF service, but they will soon be replaced by the updated Nimrod MRA4.

| | |
|---|---|
| **Country of origin:** | United Kingdom |
| **Type:** | maritime patrol and anti-submarine warfare aircraft |
| **Powerplant:** | four 5507kg (12,140lb) Rolls Royce Spey Mk 250 turbofans |
| **Performance:** | maximum speed 925km/h (575mph); service ceiling 12,800m (42,000ft); range on internal fuel 9262km (5,755 miles) |
| **Weights:** | empty 39,010kg (86,000lb); maximum take-off 87,090kg (192,000lb) |
| **Dimensions:** | wingspan 35.0m (114ft 10in) excluding wingtip ESM pods; length 39.34m (129ft 1in); height 9.08m (29ft 9.5in); wing area 197.04sq m (2,121sq ft) |
| **Armament:** | internal bay with provision for 6123kg (13,500lb) of stores, including nine torpedoes and/or depth charges; underwing pylons for Harpoon anti-ship missiles or pairs of Sidewinder air-to-air missiles |

# BAe/McDonnell Douglas AV-8B Harrier II

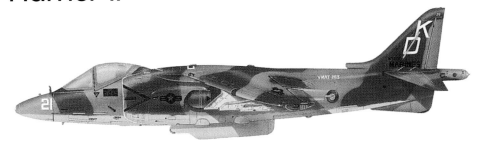

The AV-8B version of the Harrier was developed for the US Marine Corps, who had a requirement for a single-seat close support aircraft to supersede the AV-8A Harriers in service from the mid-1970s. The design resulted from a collaboration between the two companies, who had individually sought to improve on the Harrier design. The first of four full-scale development aircraft was flown on 5 November 1981. The design team made significant improvements by using carbon fibre in many of the major structural components, by introducing a range of lift augmenting devices, by redesigning the control surface, redesigning the cockpit/forward fuselage, and by adding two additional wing hard points. The aircraft entered service with the Marine Corps in January 1985. The RAF's GR7 Harriers are essentially AV-8Bs with RAF electronics and weapons fit. The Spanish navy operate a version of the AV-8A, designated AV-8G Matador.

| | |
|---|---|
| Country of origin: | USA and UK |
| Type: | V/STOL close-support aircraft |
| Powerplant: | one 10,796kg (23,800lb) Rolls Royce F402-RR-408 Pegasus vectored thrust turbofan |
| Performance: | maximum speed at sea level 1065km/h (661mph); service ceiling more than 15,240m (50,000ft); combat radius with 2722kg (6000lb) bombload 277km (172 miles) |
| Weights: | empty 5936kg (13,086lb); maximum take-off 14,061kg (31,000lb) |
| Dimensions: | wingspan 9.25m (30ft 4in); length 14.12m (46ft 4in); height 3.55m (11ft 7.75in); wing area 21.37sq m (230sq ft) |
| Armament: | one 25mm GAU-12U cannon; six external hardpoints with provision for up to 7711kg (17,000lb) (Short take-off) or 3175kg (7000lb) (Vertical take-off) of stores, including AAMs, ASMs, freefall or guided bombs, cluster bombs, dispenser weapons, napalm tanks, rocket launchers and ECM pods |

# BAe/McDonnell Douglas T-45A Goshawk

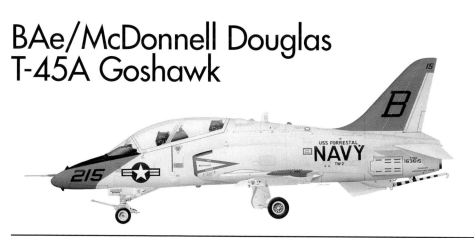

The Goshawk is a development of the highly successful BAe (HS) Hawk trainer for the US Navy. A joint McDonnell Douglas/BAe venture based Hawk emerged as the winner of a competition announced by the US Navy in the late 1970s for a carrier-equipped naval pilot trainer to replace the Rockwell T-2 Buckeye. The aircraft is significantly different from the Hawk, with strong twin-wheel nose gear, strengthened long-stroke main gear legs, an arrestor hook, and twin lateral airbrakes. Other changes include US Navy-style cockpit and avionics, and US Navy standard avionics. Emphasis was placed on the need for operational economy, and the Rolls-Royce/Turbomeca engine has been designed with this in mind. The aircraft, which are built by McDonnell in Missouri, entered service in 1990. Pictured is a T-45A Goshawk of Training Wing Two at Kingsville, Texas.

| Country of origin: | USA |
|---|---|
| Type: | tandem-seat carrier-equipped naval pilot trainer |
| Powerplant: | one 2651kg (5845lb) Rolls Royce/Turbomeca F-405-RR-401 turbofan |
| Performance: | maximum speed at 2440m (8000ft) 997km/h (620mph); service ceiling 12,875m (42,250ft); range on internal fuel 1850km (1150 miles) |
| Weights: | empty 4263kg (9399lb); maximum take-off 5787kg (12,758lb) |
| Dimensions: | wingspan 9.39m (30ft 9.75in); length 11.97m (39ft 3.125in); height 4.27m (14ft); wing area 16.69sq m (179.6sq ft) |

# BAT F.K.23 Bantam

In 1917 Frederick Koolhoven left Armstrong Whitworth and took his services to the British Aerial Transport Co Ltd (BAT). His first design for the company was the F.K. 22, a single-seat two-bay biplane of wooden construction and monocoque fuselage housing a 170hp (127kW) ABC Wasp I. Six prototypes were constructed under the development contract, the final three designated F.K. 23 Bantam I. Flight tests of the Bantam I commenced in May 1918 and revealed unsatisfactory spin characteristics. Development of a further two slightly larger prototypes and nine pre-production aircraft was undertaken, and by the time the aircraft was ready for production the problems had been eradicated. In the event, a combination of a lengthy development process and post-war contraction of the Royal Air Force meant that no orders for the aircraft were forthcoming, although at least one ended up substantially modified for the air races at Hendon.

| | |
|---|---|
| Country of origin: | United Kingdom |
| Type: | single-seat fighter biplane |
| Powerplant: | one 170hp (127kW) ABC Wasp I radial piston engine |
| Performance: | maximum speed 206km/h (128mph); service ceiling 6100m (20,000ft); endurance 2hrs 30mins |
| Weights: | empty 378kg (833lb); maximum take-off weight 599kg (1321lb) |
| Dimensions: | span 7.62m (25ft); length 5.61m (18ft 5in); height 2.06m (6ft 9in); wing area 17.19 sq m (185 sq ft) |

# Barling XNBL-1

This enormous and curiously formed machine was designed by Walter Barling of the Army Air Services' Engineering Division in response to a request from US Chiefs of Staff for a strategic bomber. It was built by the Witteman-Lewis Aircraft Corporation of Newark, New Jersey. The XNBL-1 (Experimental Night Bomber Long-range), which first flew in August 1923, was at that time the world's largest aircraft with triplane wings spanning some 36.6m (120ft), ten wheel main gear, and positions for seven machine guns in five separate locations around the capacious fuselage. All this made for a heavy aircraft, and during flight testing the six Liberty engines driving a total of ten propellers (including four pushers) proved insufficient for the excessive demands placed on them. Development was abandoned in 1925, and no funds were made available for the improved XNBL-2.

| | |
|---|---|
| **Country of origin:** | United States |
| **Type:** | experimental long-range bomber |
| **Powerplant:** | six 420hp (313kW) Liberty inline piston engines |
| **Performance:** | maximum speed 154km/h (96mph); service ceiling 2355m (7725ft); range with 2268kg (5000lb) 274km (170 miles) |
| **Weights:** | empty 12,566kg (27,703lb); maximum take-off weight 19,309kg (42,569lb) |
| **Dimensions:** | span 36.58m (120ft); length 19.81m (65ft); height 8.23m (27ft); wing area 390.18 sq m (4200 sq ft) |
| **Armament:** | seven .3in machine guns on flexible mountings, plus up to 2268kg (5000lb) of bombs |

# Beardmore W.B.III

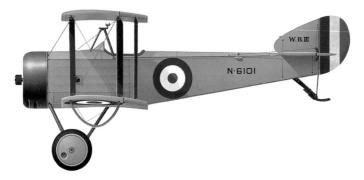

One of the many licensed wartime manufacturers of the Sopwith Pup was William Beardmore and Co Ltd of Balmuir, which developed a prototype version, the Beardmore W.B.III, for carrier operations. This had folding landing gear, folding, unstaggered wings, a lengthened fuselage carrying emergency flotation gear, a modified interplane strut configuration, and rod-operated ailerons with inter-aileron struts fitted to the upper and lower mainplanes. Some 100 production aircraft were ordered under the designation Beardmore S.B.3, and a number served aboard the carriers HMS *Furious*, *Nariana* and *Pegasus*. The first 13 aircraft (S.B.D.3F) had a tripod-mounted Lewis gun fired upwards through a centre section cut-out; in later S.B.D. aircraft the Lewis gun was mounted above the wing-centre section, the rod-operated ailerons were replaced by a conventional cable system, the wing-root interplane struts were deleted and a jettisonable undercarriage was provided.

| Country of origin: | United Kingdom |
|---|---|
| Type: | single-seat shipboard fighter |
| Powerplant: | one 80hp (60kW) Le Rhône 9C or Clerget rotary piston engine |
| Performance: | maximum speed 166km/h (103mph); service ceiling 3780m (12,400ft); endurance 2hrs 45mins |
| Weights: | empty 404kg (890lb); maximum take-off weight 585kg (1289lb) |
| Dimensions: | span 7.62m (25ft); length 6.16m (20ft); height 2.47m (8ft 1in); wing area 22.57 sq m (243 sq ft) |
| Armament: | one .303in Lewis machine gun |

# Bell P-39 Airacobra

The P-39 was a bold attempt to create an advanced fighter by locating the engine in the fuselage behind the cockpit, from where it drove the tractor propeller by means of a long extension shaft. This was intended to leave the nose free for a concentrated forward-firing battery of guns, improve agility by locating the engine nearer the centre of gravity than was common, and facilitate the use of tricycle landing gear. The XP-39 prototype first flew in April 1938, and a number of prototype and pre-production standards appeared before the P-39D entered service as the first operational model. Despite the fact that it served with 13 groups, the US Army never deemed the P-39 genuinely successful, and 4924 of the 9590 aircraft were shipped to the USSR for use mainly in the ground-attack role. The other main variants were the P-39F, J, K, L, M, N and Q. This Airacobra Mk 101 wears the colours on No 601 Squadron, the only operational RAF unit to fly the type.

| Country of origin: | USA |
| --- | --- |
| Type: | (P-39N) single-seat fighter and fighter-bomber |
| Powerplant: | one 1125hp (839kW) Allison V-1710-85 12-cylinder Vee engine |
| Performance: | maximum speed 605km/h (376mph); climb to 4570m (15,000ft) in 6 minutes 6 seconds; service ceiling 11,665m (38,270ft); range 1569km (975 miles) |
| Weights: | empty 2903kg (6400lb); maximum take-off 3992kg (8800lb) |
| Dimensions: | span 10.36m (34ft); length 9.2m (30ft 2in); height 3.79m (12ft 5in) |
| Armament: | one 37mm fixed forward-firing cannon and two 0.5in fixed forward-firing machine guns in the nose, and four 0.3in fixed forward-firing machine guns in the leading edges of the wing, plus an external bomb load of 227kg (500lb) |

# Bell P-59 Airacomet

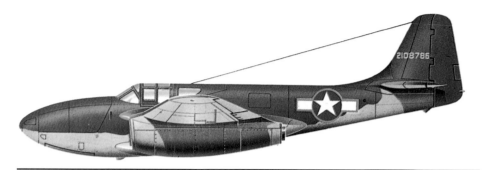

The Airacomet was the first American-designed aeroplane to fly with a turbojet-engine and was also the first Allied warplane of World War II to take to the air after being designed from the outset for turbine power. The first of three XP-59A prototypes made its maiden flight in October 1942 with General Electric I-A turbojets derived from a British engine, the Whittle W.2. There followed 13 YP-59A service test aircraft with uprated I-16 (J31) engines and armament, but flight trials highlighted indifferent performance and handling and persuaded the US Army that the production variant could be used only as a fighter trainer. The two production models were the P-59A and P-59B: the 20 P-59A aircraft delivered from the autumn of 1944 had J31-GE-5 engines and a lengthened fuselage. Illustrated is the third and last prototype, in USAAF markings whilst undergoing evaluation at Muroc Dry Lake in summer 1943.

| | |
|---|---|
| Country of origin: | USA |
| Type: | (P-59A) single-seat fighter and fighter-bomber |
| Powerplant: | two General Electric J31-GE-3 turbojets |
| Performance: | maximum speed 664.5km/h (413mph); climb to 6095m (20,000ft) in 7 minutes 24 seconds; service ceiling 14,080m (46,200ft); range 837km (520 miles) |
| Weights: | empty 3704kg (8165lb); normal take-off 5008kg (11,040lb); maximum take-off 6214kg (13,700lb) |
| Dimensions: | span 13.87m (45ft 6in); length 11.62m (38ft 1.5in); height 3.66m(12ft) |
| Armament: | one 37mm fixed forward-firing cannon and three 0.5in fixed forward-firing machine guns in the nose, plus an external; bomb and rocket load of 907kg (2,000lb) |

# Beriev MBR-2

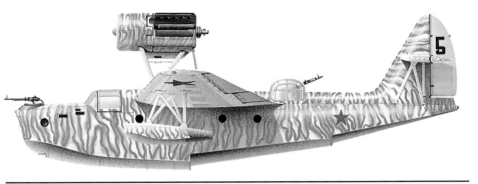

The MBR-2 was intended to provide the Soviet naval air arm with a coastal flying boat for the reconnaissance bomber role, and first flew in prototype form during October 1932. Trials revealed structural strength, good performance, and problem-free handling on the water and in the air, and the type was therefore ordered into production. The first of an initial 100 or so MBR-2/M-17 boats was delivered in the spring of 1934 with the M-17 Vee engine rated at 500hp (373kW). Beriev then developed the type into the MBR-2/M-34 with the uprated M-34NB engine, structural strengthening for greater weights and higher speeds, a revised tail unit with curved rather than angular outlines, a deepened hull, a revised cockpit of the enclosed type, and improved defensive armament. Production of some 1200 boats lasted to 1942. This MBR-2 has sea green streaking camouflage. The type served for nearly a decade after World War II on fishery patrol duties.

| Country of origin: | USSR |
| --- | --- |
| Type: | (MBR-2/M-34) four-seat coastal reconnaissance and bomber flying boat |
| Powerplant: | one 860hp (641kW) Mikulin M-34NB 12-cylinder Vee engine |
| Performance: | maximum speed 238km/h (148mph); initial climb rate not available; service ceiling 7900m (25,920ft); range 800km (497 miles) |
| Weights: | empty 2718kg (5992lb); normal take-off 4100kg (9039lb); maximum take-off 4000kg (9921lb) |
| Dimensions: | span 19.00m (62ft 4in); length 13.50m (44ft 3.75in); height not available |
| Armament: | one 7.62mm trainable forward-firing machine gun in the bow position, and one 7.62mm trainable machine gun in the dorsal turret, plus an external bomb load of 500kg (1102lb) |

# Beriev KOR-2 (Be-4)

The KOR-1 was designed in 1934-35 by Beriev as successor to the Heinkel HD 55 floatplane carried by catapult-equipped Soviet warships. The aircraft first flew in prototype form in around April 1936. The type entered service in the following year, and despite the fact that its utility was hampered by seaworthiness problems as well as a lack of structural rigidity on the water and during catapult launches, the type remained in production (about 300 aircraft) up to 1940. As Beriev sought to rectify the KOR-1's structural problems, most of the early aircraft were restricted to shore-based operations. It was only in 1939, when it had received the updated designation KOR-2, that the type was granted full release for naval use, and then only without armament and with a restriction to water take-off rather than catapult launch. Only a small number of the aircraft had been completed before the Beriev factory at Taganrog was overrun by German troops in the autumn of 1941.

| | |
|---|---|
| Country of origin: | USSR |
| Type: | (KOR-1) two-seat reconnaissance floatplane |
| Powerplant: | one  900hp (671kW) M-25A nine-cylinder single-row radial engine |
| Performance: | maximum speed 360km/h (223mph); climb to 1000m (3280ft) in 3 minutes 12 seconds; service ceiling 8100m (26,575ft); range 950km (590 miles) |
| Weights: | empty 2055kg (4530lb); normal take-off 2486kg (5480lb); maximum take-off 2760kg (6085lb) |
| Dimensions: | span 12.00m (39ft 4.5in); length 10.5m (34ft 5.25in); height 4.05m (13ft 3in) |
| Armament: | one 7.62mm trainable machine gun in aft cockpit, plus an external bomb load of 300kg (661lb) |

# Berliner-Joyce P-16

The Berliner-Joyce Aircraft Corporation was established in February 1929 with the intention of producing the Berliner Monoplane, but when the Army announced its intention to purchase a new two-seat fighter the company entered the competition. Boeing and Curtiss also submitted designs and in June a prototype contract was awarded for the Berliner-Joyce XP-16. This gull-winged biplane had tandem open cockpits and was powered by a supercharged Curtiss V-1570-25 Conqueror engine. Flight trials commenced in October 1929, and 25 service-test aircraft were ordered in March 1931. The production PB-16 (later PB-1), with three-blade airscrew and unsupercharged engine, entered service in 1933 with the 27th and 94th Pursuit Squadrons (pictured). However, it exhibited a number of defects, including a tendency to nose-over on landing and poor manoeuvrability, and was withdrawn at the end of January 1934.

| Country of origin: | USA |
| --- | --- |
| Type: | two-seat fighter biplane |
| Powerplant: | one 600hp (447kW) Curtiss V-1570-25 Conqueror vee piston engine |
| Performance: | maximum speed 282km/h (175mph); service ceiling 6588m (21,600ft); range 1046km (650 miles) |
| Weights: | empty 1271kg (2803lb); maximum take-off weight 1813kg (3996lb) |
| Dimensions: | span 10.36m (34ft); length 8.59m (28ft 2in); height 2.74m (9ft); wing area 25.92 sq m (279 sq ft) |
| Armament: | two fixed forward-firing .3in machine guns; one .3in machine gun on flexible mount in rear cockpit; underwing racks with provision for up to 102kg (224lb) of bombs |

# Berliner-Joyce OJ-2

The US Bureau of Aeronautics, established in 1921, was able to win for the Naval Flying Corps a healthy portion of the scant resources allocated by the Department of Defence to military flying in the interwar years. In 1930 the Bureau announced a competition for a lightweight observation aircraft for the US Navy and after trials the Berliner-Joyce XOJ-1 prototype was selected over the Keystone Aircraft Corporation submission. The winning design was a conventional two-seat biplane with fabric-covered fuselage, staggered wings and strut-braced tailplane, powered by a Pratt & Whitney Wasp radial engine. Catapult launch gear was fitted to a number of the 39 OJ-2 aircraft delivered to the US Navy, the first of them entering service with VS-5B and VS-6B in 1933. They were in service for only a short time, as the type was withdrawn in 1935. Pictured is is an OJ-2 of VS-6B, based in Cincinnati in 1933.

| | |
|---|---|
| Country of origin: | USA |
| Type: | two-seat observation biplane |
| Powerplant: | one 400hp (298kW) Pratt & Whitney R-985-A Wasp radial piston engine |
| Performance: | maximum speed 243km/h (151mph) |
| Weights: | maximum take-off weight 1646kg (3629lb) |
| Dimensions: | span 10.26m (33ft 8in); length 7.82m (25ft 8in) |

# Besson MB.35

**F**rench aviation pioneer Marcel Besson collaborated with Georges Lévy from 1915 to produce a series of flying boats that appeared between 1917 and 1919 with the LB designation. The partnership did not endure the war, although Besson continued to produce new designs for marine aircraft throughout the 1920s and early 1930s. The ungainly MB.35 twin-float reconnaissance and observation monoplane-winged floatplane was intended for service on board a proposed new class of French ocean-going submarines, and was by necessity of compact, easily disassembled design to allow it to be accommodated in a sealed deck hangar. This can clearly be seen in the 'upside-down' tailplane, to allow the hangar roof to be as low as possible. The first flight was made in 1926, but the two machines that were built served on surface vessels during their short service careers, and failed to win export orders.

| | |
|---|---|
| **Country of origin:** | France |
| **Type:** | two-seat spotter and observation floatplane |
| **Powerplant:** | one 120hp (89kW) Salmson 9Ac radial piston engine |
| **Performance:** | maximum speed 160km/h (99mph); service ceiling 4800m (15,750ft); range 300km (186 miles) |
| **Weights:** | empty 540kg (1190lb); maximum take-off weight 765kg (1687lb) |
| **Dimensions:** | span 9.82m (32ft 2in); length 7m (22ft 11in); height 2.45m (8ft); wing area 16.5 sq m (178 sq ft) |
| **Armament:** | (intended) one light machine gun on ring mounting in rear cockpit |

# Besson MB.411

This small floatplane was specifically designed for disassembled carriage (in the watertight cylindrical hangar abaft the conning tower of the submarine cruiser *Surcouf*) before rapid assembly and launch as a reconnaissance type or as a spotter for the submarine's pair of 8in guns. Early trials had involved the MB.35 and MB.410 floatplanes, the latter paving the way for the MB.410 that first flew in June 1935 as a low-wing monoplane with single-float alighting gear. Only one other MB.411 was built, and the concept of their operation proved practical if not actually very effective as a result of the time it took to assemble and then disassemble the type before and after any mission. Neither of the two floatplanes was on board the submarine when it was lost in February 1942, after being rammed in darkness by an American freighter. Plans to operate the MB.411 from a British merchant ship never came to fruition.

| | |
|---|---|
| **Country of origin:** | France |
| **Type:** | (MB.411) two-seat submarine-borne reconnaissance and observation floatplane |
| **Powerplant:** | one 175hp (130kW) Salmson 9Nd nine-cylinder single-row radial engine |
| **Performance:** | maximum speed 190km/h (118mph); initial climb rate not available; service ceiling 5000m (16,405ft); range 650 km (404 miles) |
| **Weights:** | empty 760kg (1676lb); maximum take-off 1140kg (2513lb) |
| **Dimensions:** | span 12.00m (39ft 4.5in); length 8.25m (27ft 0.75in); height 2.85m (9ft 4.25in) |
| **Armament:** | none |

# Blackburn R.B.1 Iris

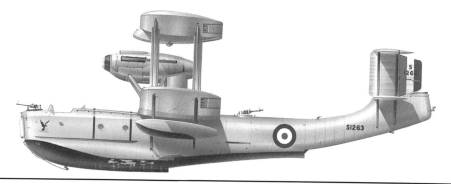

**R**obert Blackburn was among the first generation of British aviation pioneers, and produced his first aircraft, a monoplane, in April 1909. There followed a successful series of monoplanes and military biplanes before Blackburn responded to Air Ministry Specification R.14/24, which called for a long-range reconnaissance aircraft, with the R.B.1 design. The wooden-hulled prototype first flew in June 1926 and undertook flying and sea trials at Felixstowe that summer. Refitted at the factory with a metal hull and Rolls Royce Condor IIIA engines the aircraft undertook a successful overseas tour and in this form was ordered as the Blackburn R.B.1B Iris Mk III. The first of three aircraft was delivered in November 1929, all of which served with No 209 Squadron. The survivors were re-engined with 825hp (615kW) Rolls-Royce Buzzard IIMS engines in 1932, becoming R.B.1D Iris Vs.

| | |
|---|---|
| **Country of origin:** | United Kingdom |
| **Type:** | five-seat long-range reconnaissance flying-boat |
| **Powerplant:** | three 675hp (503kW) Rolls Royce Condor IIIB inline piston engines |
| **Performance:** | maximum speed 190km/h (118mph); service ceiling 3230m (10,600ft); range 1287km (800 miles) |
| **Weights:** | empty 8640kg (19,048lb); maximum take-off weight 13,376kg (29,489lb) |
| **Dimensions:** | span 29.57m (97ft); length 20.54m (67ft 4in); height 7.77m (25ft 6in); wing area 207.07 sq m (2229 sq ft) |
| **Armament:** | one .303in Lewis machine gun in nose position; one .303in Lewis machine gun in mid-ships position; one .303in Lewis machine gun in tail position; underwing racks with provision for up to 907kg (2000lb) of bombs |

# Blackburn Baffin

After the Finnish Air Force had replaced the Napier Lion W-type engine with a radial engine in most of its licence-built Blackburn Ripon torpedo bombers, Blackburn followed a similar course to create the two T.5J (Ripon Mk V) private-venture prototypes. These aircraft were then redesigned as the B-4 and B-5 with 650hp (485kW) Armstrong Siddeley Tiger I and 545hp (406kW) Bristol Pegasus IMS radial engines respectively. The prototypes flew in 1932, and there followed two Pegasus IM3-powered T.8 pre-production aircraft. These paved the way for the Baffin Mk I, of which 97 were delivered up to June 1935 in the form of 38 and 30 Ripon Mk IIA and Mk IIC conversions as well as 29 new-build aircraft. The Baffin was declared obsolete in September 1937, and this allowed New Zealand to buy 19 aircraft for coastal patrol service up to 1942. Pictured is one of the B-5 aircraft operated by the Finnish Air Force

| Country of origin: | United Kingdom |
| --- | --- |
| Type: | (Baffin Mk I) two-seat carrierborne and land-based torpedo and level bomber |
| Powerplant: | one 565hp (421kW) Bristol Pegasus IM3 nine-cylinder single-row radial engine |
| Performance: | maximum speed 219km/h (136mph); initial climb rate 146m (480ft) per minute; service ceiling 4570m (15,000ft); range 869km (450 miles) |
| Weights: | empty 1452kg (3200lb); maximum take-off 3452kg (7610lb) |
| Dimensions: | span 13.88m (45ft 6.5in); length 11.68m (38ft 3.75in); height 3.91m (12ft 10in) |
| Armament: | one 0.303in fixed forward-firing machine gun in the upper port side of the forward fuselage, and one 0.303in trainable rearward-firing machine gun in the rear cockpit, plus an external torpedo and bomb load of 907kg (2000lb) |

# Blackburn Botha

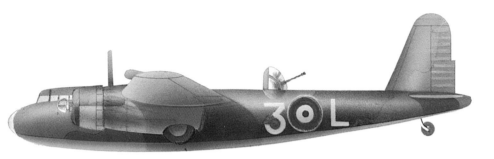

Designed to meet a 1935 requirement for a twin-engined reconnaissance bomber with a bomb bay large enough to accommodate an 18in (457mm) torpedo, the Botha first flew in prototype form during December 1938. Trials revealed that the type had a number of handling problems and was also seriously underpowered, but the handling problems were cured and the type was placed in production (580 aircraft) with the option of marginally uprated engines. The first aircraft to be delivered to the RAF was the third aircraft off the Dumbarton production line, which arrived at No 12 Maintenance Unit, Kemble, in December 1939. Entering service in May 1940, the Botha proved so inadequate for coastal reconnaissance and attack purposes that only two operational squadrons converted to the type, which was soon relegated to second-line duties. The Botha survived as a navigation and gunnery trainer into 1944, and was unsuccessful even in this secondary role.

| | |
|---|---|
| **Country of origin:** | United Kingdom |
| **Type:** | (Botha Mk I) four-seat reconnaissance and torpedo bomber used mainly for training and communications |
| **Powerplant:** | two 930hp (694kW) Bristol Perseus XA nine-cylinder single-row radial engine |
| **Performance:** | maximum speed 401km/h (249mph); initial climb rate 300m (985ft) per minute; service ceiling 5610m (18,400ft); range 2044km (1270 miles) |
| **Weights:** | empty 5366kg (11,830lb); maximum take-off 8369kg (18,450lb) |
| **Dimensions:** | span 17.98m (59ft 0in); length 15.56m (51ft 0.5in); height 4.46m (14ft 7.5in) |
| **Armament:** | one 0.303in fixed forward-firing machine gun in the nose, and two 0.303in trainable machine guns in the dorsal turret, plus an internal bomb and torpedo load of 907kg (2000lb) |

# Blackburn Firebrand

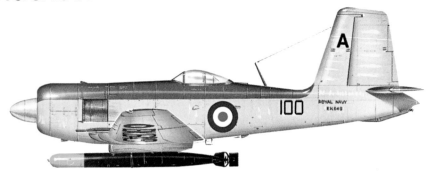

In March 1939 the Admiralty issued a requirement for a two-seat fleet-defence fighter with an armament of four 20mm wing-mounted cannon, later revised to cover a single-seat type. The Blackburn design was deemed more promising than Hawker's navalised Typhoon concept, and the first of three Firebrand prototypes made its maiden flight in February 1942. By this time the Supermarine Seafire had been accepted for service, and plans were then made for the Firebrand to be used as torpedo fighter. The first nine aircraft were too advanced in construction for adaptation, however, and were completed as Firebrand F.Mk I fighters before the advent of the Firebrand TF.Mk II with external carriage of one torpedo. Only 12 aircraft were completed before the type was revised for post-war production with the Bristol Centaurus radial engine. Illustrated is a Firebrand TF.5 of No 813 Squadron, with torpedo carrying MAT Mk IV directional stablising fins.

| | |
|---|---|
| **Country of origin:** | United Kingdom |
| **Type:** | (Firebrand Mk II) single-seat carrierborne and land-based torpedo fighter |
| **Powerplant:** | one 2305hp (1719kW) Napier Sabre III 24-cylinder h-type engine |
| **Performance:** | maximum speed 571km/h (355mph); initial climb rate 701m (2300ft) per minute; service ceiling not available; range 1239km (770 miles) |
| **Weights:** | empty 5368kg (11,835lb); maximum take-off 6826kg (15,049lb) |
| **Dimensions:** | span 15.63m (51ft 3.5in); length 11.63m (38ft 2in); height 4.06m (13ft 4in) |
| **Armament:** | four 20mm fixed forward-firing cannon in the leading edges of the wing, and an external torpedo or bomb load of 839kg (1850lb) |

# Blackburn Buccaneer S.2B

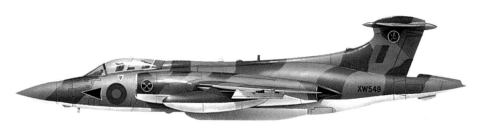

After the Defence White Paper of April 1957, which proclaimed manned combat aircraft obsolete, the only British aircraft which avoided cancellation was the Blackburn B.103. Development of this aircraft, the first to be designed specifically for carrier-borne strike operations at below radar level. The S.1 was marginal on power, but the greatly improved S.2 was a reliable and formidable aircraft. The first 84 were ordered by the Royal Navy, and after giving good service, most were transferred to the Royal Air Force from 1969. A program of substantial modification was carried out on the existing S.2 fleet, with a further 43 aircraft delivered from new. The primary difference with these aircraft, designated S.2B, was the provision to carry the Martel anti-radar missile. Some were equipped with a TIALD (Thermal Imaging And Laser Designation Pod) and deployed to the Gulf, where they gave good service. The S.2 was retired in the mid-1990s.

| | |
|---|---|
| **Country of origin:** | United Kingdom |
| **Type:** | two-seat attack aircraft |
| **Powerplant:** | two 5105kg (11,255lb) Rolls Royce RB.168 Spey Mk 101 turbofans |
| **Performance:** | maximum speed at 61m (200ft) 1040km/h (646mph); service ceiling over 12,190m (40,000ft); combat range with typical weapons load 3701km (2300 miles) |
| **Weights:** | empty 13,608kg (30,000lb); maximum take-off 28,123kg (62,000lb) |
| **Dimensions:** | wingspan 13.41 (44ft); length 19.33m (63ft 5in); height 4.97m (16ft 3in); wing area 47.82sq m (514.7sq ft) |
| **Armament:** | four 454kg (1000lb) bombs, fuel tank, or reconnaissance pack on inside of rotary bomb door, four underwing pylons with provision for up to 5443kg (12,000lb) of bombs or missiles, including Harpoon and Sea Eagle anti-shipping missiles, and Martel anti-radar missiles |

# Blériot-SPAD S.51-4

André Herbemont, the Blériot-SPAD chief designer, gleaned his knowledge of single-seat fighter design during World War I and applied it to a succession of post-war fighter aircraft. The S.51 was built to a French Aéronautique Specification of 1924 that called for a replacement for the Nieuport-Delage 29 C.1 then in service. The first of four prototypes flew in June 1924, and followed Herbemont's familiar unequal-span biplane with a swept back upper wing and straight lower formula, with faired interplane struts, wooden monocoque fuselage and Gnome-Rhône Jupiter engine. Fifty production examples of the S.51-2 prototype were supplied to Poland. The other prototypes were the S.51-3 with variable pitch propeller, and the S.51-4 of 1928 with a supercharged Jupiter engine. Twelve of the latter were built, one of which went to Turkey (pictured above).

| Country of origin: | France |
|---|---|
| Type: | single-seat fighter biplane |
| Powerplant: | one 600hp (447kW) Gnome-Rhône Jupiter radial piston engine |
| Performance: | maximum speed 231km/h (143mph); service ceiling 9000m (29,530ft); endurance 2hrs |
| Weights: | empty equipped 838kg (1843lb); maximum take-off weight 1311kg (2890lb) |
| Dimensions: | span 9.47m (31ft); length 6.45m (21ft 2in); height 3.1m (10ft 2in); wing area 23.95 sq m (258 sq ft) |
| Armament: | two fixed forward-firing .303in Vickers machine guns |

# Blériot-SPAD S.510

The S.510 was the last biplane fighter to serve with the French Air Force. Its origins lay in the S.91 designed by Blériot-SPAD to meet a 1926 requirement for a lightweight (or 'Jockey') fighter. The S.510 was clearly a linear descendant of the S.91, but had a number of more modern features including nicely faired and spatted main units of the divided type for the fixed tailskid landing gear. The S.510 had a tortuous design history and proved inferior to the rival Dewoitine D.510 monoplane, but the French air ministry was persuaded to order 60 examples of the obsolescent S.510 in parallel with the D.510. The S.510C.1 entered service early in 1936, and was still in limited service on the outbreak of World War II, seeing limited operational use in France before being relegated to second-line service in North Africa. The aircraft pictured was operated by ERC 4/561 of the Armée de l'Air, based at Havre-Octeville in October 1939.

| | |
|---|---|
| Country of origin: | France |
| Type: | (S.510C.1) single-seat fighter |
| Powerplant: | one 690hp (515kW) Hispano-Suiza 12Xbrs 12-cylinder Vee engine |
| Performance:: | maximum speed 372km/h (231mph); climb to 4000m (13,125ft) in 4 minutes 31 seconds; service ceiling 10,500m (34,450ft); range 875km (544 miles) |
| Weights: | empty 1250kg (2756lb); maximum take-off 1830kg (4034lb) |
| Dimensions: | span 8.84m (29ft); length 7.46m (24ft 5.75in); height 3.72m (12ft 2.5in) |
| Armament: | two 7.5mm fixed forward-firing machine guns in the upper part of the forward fuselage and two 7.5mm fixed forward-firing machine guns in gondola fairings below the lower wing, or four 7.5mm fixed forward-firing machine guns in gondola fairings under the lower wing |

# Bloch MB. 200

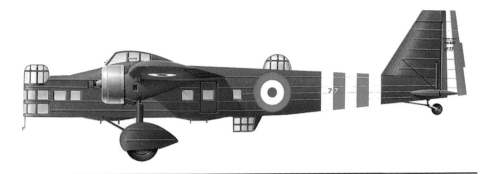

Designed to replace the obsolete Liorè-et-Olivier LeO 20 in the night bomber role, the
Bloch MB.200 was typical of the highly angular French warplanes of the late 1920s and
early 1930s and first flew in MB.200.01 prototype form in June 1933. An initial 30
MB.200B.4 bombers were ordered in December of the same year, and the type entered
service in 1934. Eventual French production by six companies – Bloch, Breguet, Hanriot,
Loire, Potez and SNCASO – was 208 aircraft, and another 124 aircraft were built under
licence in Czechoslovakia by the Aero and Avia companies. The type was obsolete by 1939,
and most French aircraft were soon relegated to the training role. Many continued in
service after France's defeat. A number of the aircraft were expropriated by the Germans
for their own use and transfer to allies. Pictured is one of the aircraft operated by Section
de Remorquage d'Orange in May 1940.

| | |
|---|---|
| Country of origin: | France |
| Type: | (MB.200B.4) four-seat medium bomber |
| Powerplant: | two 870hp (649kW) Gnome-Rhône 14Kirs/Kjrs Mistral-Major 14-cylinder two-row radial engines |
| Performance: | maximum speed 283km/h (176mph); climb to 4000m (13,125ft) in 13 minutes; service ceiling 8000m (26,245ft); range 1000km (621 miles) |
| Weights: | empty 4300kg (9840lb); maximum take-off 7480kg (16,490lb) |
| Dimensions: | span 22.45m (73ft 7.88in); length 15.80m (51ft 10in); height 3.92m (12ft 10in) |
| Armament: | one 7.5mm trainable forward-firing machine gun in the nose turret, one 7.5mm trainable machine gun in the dorsal turret and one 7.5mm trainable rearward-firing machine gun in the ventral gondola, plus an external bomb load of 1200kg (2646lb) |

# Bloch MB.151 and MB.152

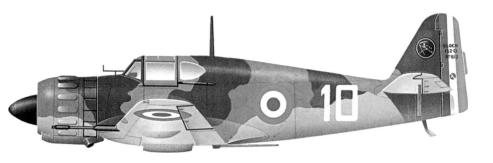

As first completed in MB.150.01 prototype form, this fighter refused even to take-off, but after revision to MB.151.01 standard with a larger wing finally flew in August 1938. The type was ordered into production as the MB.151C.1; the first 25 of the 140 aircraft had the 920hp (686kW) Gnome-Rhône 14N-11 engine, later production aircraft had the improved 14N-25 engine. Performance and handling were indifferent, and the type was generally used as a fighter lead-in trainer. In parallel there emerged 481 production examples of the MB.152C.1 with an uprated engine and a different armament fit. The type saw limited service in the defence of France in May and June 1940, and remained in service with the Vichy regime after France's defeat. Germany took over a number of the aircraft as trainers, and later passed 20 MB.151 and MB.152 fighters to Romania. Pictured is an MB. 152 of the 1st Escadrille, Groupe de Chasse I/1, based at Chantilly-les-Aigles in May 1940.

| Country of origin: | France |
| --- | --- |
| Type: | (MB.152C.1) single-seat fighter |
| Powerplant: | one 1080hp (805kW) Gnome-Rhône 14N-25 or 1060hp (790kW) Gnome-Rhône 14N-49 14-cylinder two-row radial engine |
| Performance: | maximum speed 509km/h (316mph); climb to 4000m (13,125ft) in 6 minutes 55 seconds; service ceiling 10,000m (32,810ft); range 540km (335 miles) |
| Weights: | empty 4758lb (2158kg); maximum take-off 6173lb (2800kg) |
| Dimensions: | span 10.54m (34ft 7in); length 9.10m (29ft 10.5in); height 3.03m (9ft 11.25in) |
| Armament: | four 7.5mm fixed forward-firing machine guns, or two 20mm fixed forward-firing cannon and two 7.5mm fixed forward-firing machine guns, in each case in the leading edges of the wing |

# Bloch MB.174

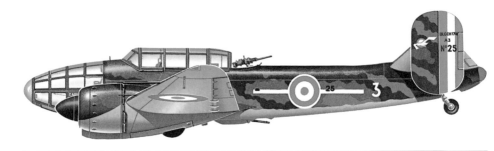

The origins of the Bloch MB.174 can be traced to a time late in 1936, when Bloch began to plan the MB.170 multi-role warplane that could be operated in the A.3 three-seat army co-operation or AB.2 two-seat attack bomber roles. The MB.170 first flew in February 1938, and the type was eventually ordered as the MB.174, primarily for reconnaissance and target-marking operations but with light bombing as a secondary role. The MB.174A.3 retained the flying surfaces, landing gear and powerplant of the MB.170B.3 in combination with a redesigned fuselage. The cockpit was moved farther to the rear and the nose received a fair measure of glazing. Only 56 of this model were completed and played a modest part in the defensive campaign that preceded France's capitulation in June 1940. Pictured is one of the aircraft operated by Groupe de Reconnaissance II/33 during the Battle of France. Some were later used by the Vichy Air Force.

| | |
|---|---|
| Country of origin: | France |
| Type: | (MB.174A.3) three-seat light reconnaissance bomber |
| Powerplant: | two 1140hp (850kW) Gnome-Rhône 14N-48/49 14-cylinder two-row radial engines |
| Performance: | maximum speed 530km/h (329mph); climb to 8000 m (26,250ft) in 11 minutes 0 seconds; service ceiling 11,000m (36,090ft); range 1285km (798 miles) with an 400kg (882lb) bomb load |
| Weights: | empty 5600kg (12,346lb); maximum take-off 7160kg (15,784lb) |
| Dimensions: | span 17.90m (58ft 8.75in); length 12.25m (40ft 2.25in); height 3.55m (11ft 7.75in) |
| Armament: | two 7.5mm fixed forward-firing machine guns in the leading edges of the wing, two 7.5mm trainable rearward-firing machine guns in the dorsal position and three 7.5mm rearward-firing machine guns in the ventral position, plus an internal bomb load of 400kg (882lb) |

# Bloch MB.155

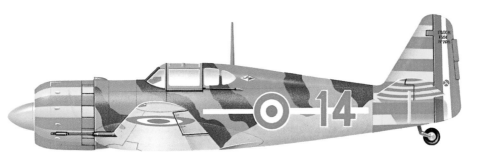

With the MB.155.01 prototype conversion from MB.152C.1 standard, the MB.150 series finally began to come of age as a genuinely effective fighter. The main change in the MB.155 was the installation of the engine inherited from the MB.152. The prototype first flew in 1940, and there followed for the Vichy French Air Force a total of 33 production aircraft with the designation MB.155C.1. These differed from the prototype is having their cockpit repositioned farther to the rear, which permitted the introduction of a new fuel tank for an enlarged overall capacity and the addition of more armour protection. After the German occupation of Vichy France in November 1942, several of the aircraft were seized for subsequent German use as fighter trainers. The colourful, even lurid paint scheme applied to this aircraft indicates that it was the personal mount of Groupe de Chasse II/8. This Vichy French Air Force unit was based at Marignane in July 1940.

| Country of origin: | France |
|---|---|
| Type: | (MB.155C.1) single-seat fighter |
| Powerplant: | one 1060 hp (790kW) Gnome-Rhòne 14N-49 14-cylinder two-row radial engine |
| Performance: | maximum speed 520km/h (323mph); climb to 4000m (13,125ft) in 6 minutes; service ceiling 10,000m (32,810ft); range 1050km (652 miles) |
| Weights: | empty 2158kg (4757lb); normal take-off 2748kg (6058lb); maximum take-off 2850kg (6283lb) |
| Dimensions: | span 10.54m (34ft 7in); length 9.05m (29ft 8.33in); height 3.03m (9ft 11.25in) |
| Armament: | two 20mm fixed forward-firing cannon and two or four 7.5mm fixed forward-firing machine guns, or six 7.5mm fixed forward-firing machine guns in the leading edges of the wing |

# Blohm und Voss Bv 138

The Bv 138 was projected and built in prototype form as the Ha 138, with three Junkers Jumo 205D Diesel engines, before undergoing a virtually total redesign in 1938, the year in which the Hamburger Flugzeugbau was absorbed fully into Blohm und Voss. The first of six Bv 138A-0 pre-production flying boats made its maiden flight in February 1939. These machines were followed by 25 Bv 138A-1 production examples with three 600hp (447kW) Jumo 205C-4 engines, and the type saw its first operational service in April 1940. Six and 14 Bv 138B-0 and B-1 machines introduced a strengthened structure and greater power respectively, while the definitive Bv 138C-1 (about 227 aircraft built) had more strengthening and better defensive armament. The designation Bv 138MS was used for minesweeper conversions. Pictured here is a BV 138C-1 of 2/KüF/Gr. 406, based in northern Norway in March 1942.

| Country of origin: | Germany |
| --- | --- |
| Type: | (Bv 138C-1) five-seat maritime reconnaissance flying boat |
| Powerplant: | three 1000hp (746kW) Junkers Jumo 205D 12-cylinder vertically opposed Diesel engines |
| Performance: | maximum speed 285km/h (177mph); climb to 3000m (9845ft) in 22 minutes 48 seconds; ceiling 5000m (16,405ft); range 4300km (2672 miles) |
| Weights: | empty 11,770kg (25,948lb); maximum take-off 17,650kg (38,912lb) |
| Dimensions: | span 26.94m (88ft 4.75in); length 19.85m (65ft 1.5in); height 5.90m (19ft 4.25in) |
| Armament: | one 20mm trainable forward-firing cannon in the bow turret, one 20mm trainable rearward-firing cannon in the rear-hull turret, one 13mm trainable rearward-firing machine gun behind the central engine nacelle, and one 7.92mm trainable lateral-firing machine gun in starboard hull position, plus a bomb load of 300kg (661lb) |

# Blohm und Voss Bv 141

Designed as a tactical reconnaissance aeroplane to the same requirement as the Focke-Wulf Fw 189, the Bv 141 had a highly unusual asymmetric layout with the fully glazed crew nacelle offset to starboard of the centreline and a boom (carrying the engine at its front and a tail unit at its rear) offset to port. The first of three prototypes flew in February 1938, and there followed five Bv 141A-0 pre-production aircraft. The type had poor performance as a result of its use of the 865hp (645kW) BMW 132N engine, so the next five aircraft were redesigned Bv 141B-0 machines with an uprated powerplant as well as a strengthened structure and a revised tail unit. These aircraft were used for operational trials over the UK and the USSR from the autumn of 1941, but there were development delays and the programme was ended in 1943. Depicted is one of the pre-production aircraft (BV 141A-04), as evaluated by the Luftwaffe at the Erprobungstelle factory in late 1939.

| | |
|---|---|
| Country of origin: | Germany |
| Type: | (Bv 141B-0) three-seat tactical reconnaissance and observation aeroplane with limited close support capability |
| Powerplant: | one 1560hp (1163kW) BMW 801A 14-cylinder two-row radial engine |
| Performance: | maximum speed 438km/h (272mph); initial climb rate not available; service ceiling 10,000m (32,810ft); range 1900km (1181 miles) |
| Weights: | empty 4700kg (10,362lb); maximum take-off 6100kg (13,448lb) |
| Dimensions: | span 17.46m (57ft 3.5in); length 13.95m (45ft 9.25in); height 3.60m (11ft 9.75in) |
| Armament: | two 7.92mm fixed forward-firing machine guns in the front of the crew nacelle, one 7.92mm trainable rearward-firing machine gun in the dorsal position, and one 7.92mm trainable rearward-firing machine gun in the rotating tailcone position, plus an external bomb load of 200kg (441lb) |

# Blohm und Voss Bv 222 Wiking

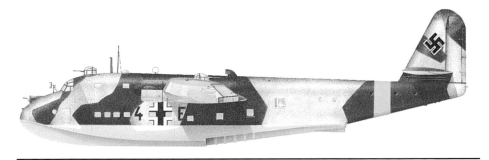

The Wiking (Viking) started life as a 1937 project for a 24-passenger flying boat airliner to operate between Berlin and New York. The type was then revised as a long-range maritime reconnaissance type and was the largest flying boat to enter operational service in World War II. There were eight prototypes, the first of them flying in September 1940, the Bv 222B was the unrealised civil model, and the military version was planned as the Bv 222C, of which only four Bv 222C-0 pre-production examples were completed. The prototypes entered transport service in mid-1941, mainly in the Mediterranean, and from 1943 were revised for the reconnaissance role and supplemented by the four pre-production 'boats. The 'boats then served over the Atlantic, Baltic and Arctic regions. Only four 'boats survived to the end of the war. One of these was flown to RAF Calshot for evaluation, and later equipped No 201 Squadron.

| Country of origin: | Germany |
|---|---|
| Type: | (Bv 222C) transport and maritime reconnaissance flying boat |
| Powerplant: | six 1000hp (746kW) Junkers Jumo 207C 12-cylinder vertically opposed Diesel engines |
| Performance: | maximum speed 390km/h (242mph); initial climb rate 144m (473ft) per minute; ceiling 7300m (23,950ft); range 6100 km (3790 miles) |
| Weights: | empty 30,650kg (67,572lb); maximum take-off 49,000kg (108,025lb) |
| Dimensions: | span 46m (150ft 11in); length 37m (121ft 4.75in); height 10.90m (35ft 9in) |
| Armament: | one 20mm trainable cannon in the dorsal turret, one 20mm trainable cannon in each of the two power-operated wing turrets, one 13mm trainable forward-firing machine gun in the bow position, and one 13mm trainable lateral-firing machine gun in each of the four lateral hull positions |

# Boeing B-17C Flying Fortress

The Model 299 was designed to meet a 1934 requirement for a multi-engined medium bomber and envisaged primarily for the coast-defence role. The aircraft first flew as a private-venture prototype with provision for a 4800lb (2177kg) bomb load and was later evaluated as the XB-17. Orders were then placed for 14 YB-17 and YB-17A service test aircraft that were later accepted as B-17 and B-17A aircraft, and paved the way for the 39 B-17B aircraft with a modified nose, 38 B-17B aircraft with greater power and defensive armament, and 42 B-17D aircraft with an additional crew member. Some 20 B-17Cs were transferred to the UK as Fortress Mk I machines; most of the B-17D bombers were stationed in the Far East, where about half were destroyed by Japan's pre-emptive attacks of December 7, 1941. Note the ventral bathtub and flush waist positions on the B-17C illustrated here. The B-17C was the fastest of all versions, with a maximum speed of 515km/h (320 mph).

| | |
|---|---|
| **Country of origin:** | USA |
| **Type:** | (B-17C) nine-seat medium bomber |
| **Powerplant:** | four 1200hp (895kW) Wright R-1820-65 nine-cylinder single-row radial engines |
| **Performance:** | maximum speed 515km/h (320 mph); climb to 3050m (10,000ft) in 7 minutes 30 seconds; service ceiling 11,280m (37,000ft); range 5471km (3400 miles) |
| **Weights:** | empty 13,880kg (30,600lb); maximum take-off 22,521kg (49,650lb) |
| **Dimensions:** | span 31.62m (103ft 9in); length 20.70m (67ft 11in); height 4.70m (15ft 5in) |
| **Armament:** | two 0.3in forward-firing machine guns in cheek positions, three 0.5in machine guns in dorsal positions, two 0.5in machine guns in the ventral position, and one 0.5in machine gun in each of the two waist positions, plus an internal bomb load of 4761kg (10,496lb) |

# Boeing B-17F Flying Fortress

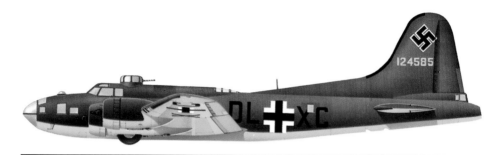

The B-17D paved the way for the first large-scale production model of the Flying Fortress, the B-17E. Some 512 were delivered and featured a wholly redesigned and enlarged tail unit for improved stability at high altitude, and a completely revised defensive scheme including a twin-gun tail position and power-operated twin-gun dorsal and ventral turrets. The B-17E entered service in 1942, and was soon supplemented by the B-17F. This was the definitive model, as indicated by a production total of 3,405 aircraft from three manufacturers. The B-17F introduced a frameless Plexiglas nose transparency, structural strengthening for higher-weight operations, and further refinement of the defensive armament. Small numbers of B-17E and B-17F bombers were operated by the British with the designations Fortress Mk IIA and Fortress Mk II respectively. A number were captured intact by the Germans and evaluated in Luftwaffe markings.

| | |
|---|---|
| Country of origin: | USA |
| Type: | (B-17F) 10-seat medium bomber |
| Powerplant: | four 1200hp (895kW) Wright R-1820-97 nine-cylinder single-row radial engines |
| Performance: | maximum speed 523km/h (325mph); climb to 6095m (20,000ft ) in 25 minutes 42 seconds; ceiling 11,430m (37,500ft); range 7113km (4420miles) |
| Weights: | empty 16,206kg (35,728lb); maximum take-off 32,6591kg (72,000lb) |
| Dimensions: | span 31.63m (103ft 9.38in); length 22.78m (74ft 9in); height 5.85m (19ft 2.5in) |
| Armament: | two 0.3in trainable forward-firing machine guns in cheek positions, three 0.5in trainable machine guns in dorsal positions, two 0.5in trainable machine guns in the ventral position, and one 0.5in trainable lateral-firing machine gun in each of the two waist positions, plus an internal bomb load of 4761kg (10,496lb) |

# Boeing B-17G Flying Fortress

The B-17G Flying Fortress resulted directly from the experience of the US bomber crews in 1943, which revealed that the B-17F lacked adequate defence against head-on fighter attack. The primary change in the B-17G was therefore the introduction of a power-operated chin turret armed with two 0.5in machine guns and controlled remotely from the glazed nose position. This proved to be a more practical unit as it lost the one or two manually operated 0.5in machine guns that had been fitted in the B-17F. Deliveries began in September 1943. A number of other operational improvements were steadily incorporated during the production of 8680 aircraft from three manufacturers in the period up to April 1945. The B-17G was the cornerstone of the US Army Air Forces' bomber effort in Europe during 1944 and 1945. The aircraft pictured is the famed B-17G *A Bit o'Lace* of the 711th BS, 447th BG, based at Rattlesden.

| Country of origin: | USA |
| --- | --- |
| Type: | (B-17G) 10-seat heavy bomber |
| Powerplant: | four 1200hp (895kW) Wright R-1820-97 nine-cylinder radial engines |
| Performance: | maximum speed 486km/h (302mph); climb to 6095m (20,000ft) in 37 minutes; service ceiling 10,850m (35,600ft); range 2897km (1800 miles) |
| Weights: | empty 20,212kg (44,560lb); maximum take-off 32,659kg (72,000lb) |
| Dimensions: | span 31.63m (103ft 9.4in); length 22.78m (74ft 9 in); height 5.82m (19ft 1in) |
| Armament: | two 0.5in machine guns in chin turret, one 0.5in machine gun in each cheek position, two 0.5in trainable machine guns in dorsal turret, one 0.5in machine gun in roof position, two 0.5in machine guns in ventral turret, one 0.5in machine gun in each waist position, two 0.5in machine guns in tail, plus a bomb load of 7983kg (17,600lb) |

# Boeing B-29 Superfortress

The B-29 is generally remembered as the warplane which, on 6 and 9 August 1945, dropped atomic weapons that destroyed the cities of Hiroshima and Nagasaki, persuading the Japanese to surrender. Yet by this time the B-29 had been at the forefront of a campaign to neutralise the war-making potential of Japan by burning her cities, destroying her communications network and crippling her industries. First entering service from the summer of 1944, the Superfortress was an extremely clean bomber with turbocharged engines. The baseline B-29, of which 2458 were completed, was complemented by the B-29A of which 1119 were manufactured with greater span and a four- rather than two-gun forward dorsal barbette, and the B-29B of which 310 were delivered with reduced defensive armament but a greater bomb load and higher speed. The aircraft pictured was allocated to the 500th Bomb Group of the 73rd Bomb Wing.

| | |
|---|---|
| **Country of origin:** | USA |
| **Type:** | (B-29) nine-seat long-range heavy bomber |
| **Powerplant:** | four 2200hp (1640kW) Wright R-3350-23 18-cylinder two-row radial engines |
| **Performance:** | maximum speed 576km/h (358mph); climb to 6095m (20,000ft) in 38 minutes; service ceiling 9710m (31,850ft); range 9382km (5830 miles) |
| **Weights:** | empty 31,816kg (70,140lb); normal take-off 47,628kg (105,000lb); maximum take-off 56,246kg (124,000lb) |
| **Dimensions:** | span 43.05m (141ft 2.75in); length 30.18m (99ft); height 9.02m (29ft 7in) |
| **Armament:** | one 20mm trainable rearward-firing cannon and two 0.5in trainable rearward-firing machine guns in the tail position, and two 0.5in trainable machine guns in each of two dorsal and two ventral barbettes, plus an internal bomb load of 9072kg (20,000lb) |

# Boeing RB-47H Stratojet

**B**oeing began studies of jet bombers in 1943, but it was the discovery of the research that had been done into swept wings in Germany that spurred the Model 450. The design had passed through several stages, from the straight winged Model 424, through the swept wing Model 448 with fuselage mounted turbojets, until the final design was dubiously bought by the USAAF in October 1945. The bomber was at the peak of its career in the mid 1950s when it was probably the most important military aircraft in the West. Peak strength in SAC was reached in 1957, when about 1800 of all models were in service. Many hundreds were converted for a variety of specialist roles. Thirty-two were RB-47H models, completed in production for electronic reconnaissance missions, with the bomb bay converted to accommodate equipment and three Electronic Warfare officers.

| | |
|---|---|
| Country of origin: | USA |
| Type: | strategic reconnaissance aircraft |
| Powerplant: | six 3,266kg (7200lb) General Electric J47-GE-25 turbojets |
| Performance: | maximum speed at 4970m (16,300ft) 975km/h (606mph); service ceiling 12,345m (40,500ft); range 6437km (4,000 miles) |
| Weights: | empty 36,630kg (80,756lb); maximum take-off 89,893kg (198,180lb) |
| Dimensions: | wingspan 35.36m (116ft); length 33.48m (109ft 10in); height 8.51m (27ft 11in); wing area 132.66sq m (1428 sq ft) |
| Armament: | two remotely controlled 20mm cannon in tail |

# Boeing B-52D Stratofortress

The B-52 has been in continuous service with Strategic Air Command in one form or another since 1955, with service life for the current generation of B-52H aircraft only scheduled to end in 2038. Development of this remarkable warhorse, which started life as a turboprop-powered project, began in 1945. The first prototype flew on October 2, 1951, and deliveries of 98 A, B, and C models began in June 1955. Boeing extensively revised the fore -control system for the tail-mounted armament of four 0.5in machine guns for the B-52D (Model 464-201-7). The company built 101 B-52Ds at its Seattle plant, before production was moved to Wichita where another 69 were completed. Deliveries of this version began in 1956. The aircraft had been designed to carry stand-off nuclear weapons but in 1964 a rebuilding program began to allow it to carry 105 'iron bombs'. The B-52D saw service over North Vietnam.

| | |
|---|---|
| Country of origin: | USA |
| Type: | long-range strategic bomber |
| Powerplant: | eight 4536kg (10,000lb) Pratt & Whitney J57 turbojets |
| Performance: | maximum speed at 7315m (24,000ft) 1014km/h (630mph): service ceiling 13,720m-16,765m (45,000ft-55,000ft); standard range with maximum load 9978km (6,200 miles) |
| Weights: | empty 77,200-87,100kg (171,000-193,000lb); loaded 204,120kg (450,000lb) |
| Dimensions: | wingspan 56.4m (185ft); length 48m (157ft 7in); height 14.75m (48ft 3in); wing area 371.60sq m (4,000sq ft) |
| Armament: | remotely controlled tail mounting with four 0.5in machine guns; normal internal bomb capacity 12,247kg (27,000lb) including all SAC special weapons; modified to take up to 31,750kg (70,000lb) of conventional bombs on internal and external pylons |

# Boeing B-52G Stratofortress

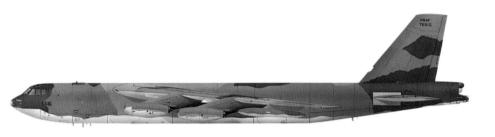

The B-52G introduced a host of significant improvements, including a wet wing that housed far more fuel, more powerful Pratt & Whitney J57-43W turbojets (as on the E and F models), a shortened fin of increased chord, and a remote controlled rear turret. The aircraft also benefited from the upgraded and much improved navigation and bombing systems introduced on the previous two variants. It was also fitted with Quail countermeasures vehicles and could carry a pair of North American AGM-28 Hound Dog missiles. First flown in October 1958, this model was delivered to SAC from the following February. A total of 193 B-52G models were built, the last in 1960. Some 173 of these were later converted to carry 12 Boeing AGM-86B Air Launched Cruise Missiles in addition to the eight AGM-69 SRAMS or other weapons carried in the internal bay.

| | |
|---|---|
| **Country of origin:** | USA |
| **Type:** | long-range strategic bomber |
| **Powerplant:** | eight 6238kg (13,750lb) Pratt & Whitney J57-P-43W turbojets |
| **Performance:** | maximum speed at 7315m (24,000ft) 1014km/h (630mph): service ceiling 16,765m (55,000ft); standard range with maximum load 13,680km (8500 miles) |
| **Weights:** | empty 77,200-87,100kg (171,000-193,000lb); loaded 221,500kg (448,000lb) |
| **Dimensions:** | wingspan 56.4m (185ft); length 48m (157ft 7in); height 12.4m (40ft 8in); wing area 371.60sq m (4000sq ft) |
| **Armament:** | remotely controlled tail mounting with four 0.5in machine guns; normal internal bomb capacity 12,247kg (27,000lb) including all SAC special weapons; external pylons for two AGM-28B Hound Dog missiles |

# Boeing KC-135E Stratotanker

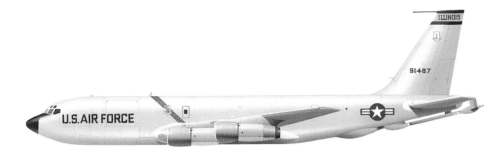

The family of Boeing jet transports all stemmed from a privately-funded prototype, designated the Model 367-80, which first flew in July 1954. After evaluation the US Air Force decided to buy 29 developed versions to serve in the dual roles of tanker for Strategic Air Command, and logistic transport for Military Airlift Command. The first KC-135A left the assembly line at Renton, Washington in July 1956, with initial deliveries to the 93rd Air Refuelling Squadron the following June. Production of the aircraft totalled 724; when production ended in January 1965 it was decided to keep these aircraft operational until the next century, and a major overhaul programme was started in the mid-1970s. At the heart of this programme lay the task of reskinning the lower wing surfaces; by 1985 more than 500 aircraft had undergone this treatment.

| | |
|---|---|
| Country of origin: | USA |
| Type: | inflight-refuelling tanker/cargo/transport aircraft |
| Powerplant: | four 8165kg (18,000lb) Pratt & Whitney TF33-P-5 turbofans |
| Performance: | cruising speed at 40,000ft 853km/h (530mph); range 4627km (2875 miles) |
| Weights: | maximum take-off 146,284kg (322,500lb); maximum fuel load 92,210kg (203,288lb) |
| Dimensions: | wingspan 39.88m (130ft 10in); length 41.53m (136ft 3in); height 12.7m (41ft 8in); wing area 226.03sq m (2,433sq ft) |

# Boeing RC-135V

**B**oeing's Model 717 (the military designation for the 707) has served in countless different roles, including reconnaissance, airborne early warning, electronic surveillance, VIP transport and avionics testing. Although derived from the 707, the RC-135V bears little physical relation to the civil aircraft. The R designation denotes a reconnaissance aircraft in USAF parlance; the RC-135V was the tenth of 12 variants, which have been tasked with electronic surveillance since the mid-1960s. The eight RC-135Vs were converted from RC-135C and one RC-135U aircraft. As well as the cheek antennae fairings and sidewards-looking airborne radar (SLAR) from these models, the modified aircraft were fitted with a distinctive thimble nose and a vast array of underfuselage blade aerials. These aircraft serve alongside RC-135Ws with the 55th Strategic Reconnaissance Wing.

| | |
|---|---|
| **Country of origin:** | USA |
| **Type:** | electronic reconnaissance aircraft |
| **Powerplant:** | four 8156kg (18,000lb) Pratt & Whitney TF33-P-9 turbojets |
| **Performance:** | maximum speed at 7620m (25,000ft) 991km/h (616mph); service ceiling 12,375m (40,600ft) range 4305km (2675 miles) |
| **Weights:** | empty 46,403kg (102,300lb) maximum take-off 124,965g (275,500lb) |
| **Dimensions:** | wingspan 39.88m (130ft 10in); length 41.53m (136ft 3in); height 12.7m (41ft 8in); wing area 226.03sq m (2,433sq ft) |

# Boulton Paul P.75 Overstrand

The Boulton & Paul P.75 Overstrand prototype was developed on the production line from the airframe of the eighth production P.29 Sidestrand, a twin-engined medium bomber designed to meet an Air Ministry specification of 1924. The first three conversions were designated Sidestrand Mk V, but the name Overstrand was adopted in March 1934. The aircraft shared the general configuration of its predecessor, but had a number of innovative features. Principal among them was the power-operated nose turret, one of the first to be fitted to a production aircraft, an enclosed cockpit, three-axis autopilot, and the luxury of a heating system that supplied hot air to all crew positions. The 27 Overstrands were the last aircraft built at Boulton Paul's (as the company became in 1933) Norwich factory, which moved to Wolverhampton during the production cycle. Bicester-based No 101 Squadron received its first aircraft in January 1935, operating the aircraft until late 1938.

| Country of origin: | United Kingdom |
| --- | --- |
| Type: | five-seat medium bomber |
| Powerplant: | two 580hp (433kW) Bristol Pegasus IIM.3 radial piston engines |
| Performance: | maximum speed 246km/h (153mph); service ceiling 6860m (22,500ft); range 877km (545 miles) |
| Weights: | empty 3600kg (7936lb); maximum take-off weight 5443kg (12,000lb) |
| Dimensions: | span 21.95m (72ft); length 14.02m (46ft); height 4.72m (15ft 6in); wing area 91.04 sq m (980 sq ft) |
| Armament: | one .303in Lewis gun in nose turret; one .303in Lewis gun in each of the two dorsal ventral positions; internal bay with provision for up to 726kg (1600lb) of bombs |

# Boulton Paul Defiant

In the 1930s there developed an enthusiasm for the turret fighter in which fixed forward-firing armament was replaced by a multi-gun turret. The two main attractions of such a fighter were a reduction in pilot workload and the turreted armament's significantly greater field of fire. The British response to this idea was the Defiant, which entered service in December 1939. On entering combat in May 1940 the type was initially successful as a result of its novelty, but German pilots soon learned to use the greater agility of their lighter fighters to engage the Defiant head-on or from below, where the guns could not be trained. The Defiant was subsequently utilised as a night-fighter and finally for target-towing duties. Production was 723 Mk I and NF.Mk I machines, 210 Mk II and NF.Mk II aircraft with the 1260hp (939.5kW) Merlin XX engine, and 140 TT.Mk I machines ordered as Mk II fighters.

| | |
|---|---|
| Country of origin: | United Kingdom |
| Type: | (Defiant Mk I) two-seat fighter |
| Powerplant: | one 1030hp (768kW) Rolls-Royce Merlin III 12-cylinder Vee engine |
| Performance: | maximum speed 489km/h (304mph); climb to 4800m (15,750ft) in 8 minutes 30 seconds; service ceiling 9250m (30,350ft); range 748km (465 miles) |
| Weights: | empty 2757kg (6078lb); maximum take-off 3788kg (8350lb) |
| Dimensions: | span 11.99m (39ft 4in); length 10.77m (35ft 4in); height 4.39m (14ft 5in) |
| Armament: | four 0.303in trainable machine guns in the dorsal turret |

# Breda Ba 88 Lince

First flown in October 1936, the Lince (lynx) proved fiercer in name than deed. Great things were expected of the type, which set a number of records during development. However, the addition of military equipment added weight and drag resulting in wholly inadequate performance and degraded handling, despite the adoption of an uprated powerplant and two rather than one vertical tail surfaces. The first 88 aircraft were completed between May and October 1939. In the first phase of the North African campaign the aircraft proved tactically useless, and the survivors were soon being used as decoys for attacking British warplanes. By this time 155 aircraft had been made, but most of the new aircraft were scrapped. The designation Ba 88M was used for three aircraft converted in 1943 as dive-bombers with a lengthened wing, downrated powerplant and revised armament. Pictured is a Ba 88 of the 7th Gruppo, 5th Stormo da Combattimento, based in Libya in 1940.

| | |
|---|---|
| Country of origin: | Italy |
| Type: | two-seat ground-attack warplane |
| Powerplant: | two 1000hp (746kW) Piaggio P.XI RC.40 14-cylinder two-row radial piston engines |
| Performance: | maximum speed 490km/h (304mph); climb to 3000m (9845ft) in 7 minutes 30 seconds; service ceiling 8000m (26,245ft); range 1640km (1020 miles) |
| Weights: | empty 4650kg (10,252lb); maximum take-off 6750kg (14,881lb) |
| Dimensions: | span 15.60m (51ft 2in); length 10.79m (35ft 5in); height 3.10m (10ft 2.75in) |
| Armament: | three 12.7mm fixed forward-firing machine guns and one 7.7mm trainable rearward-firing machine gun, plus an internal bomb load of 1000kg (2205lb) |

# Breguet Bre.14 A.2

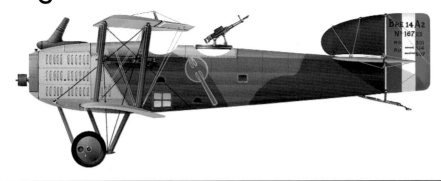

Louis Breguet established his aircraft manufacturing company at Douai in 1909, but was forced to relocate to Villacoublay in 1914 in front of the rapid German advance. In the summer of 1916 his Chief Engineer Louis Vullierme began the design of Breguet's most successful wartime product, the Bre. 14. The prototype of this two-seat reconnaissance/light bomber aircraft made its first flight barely five months later, and the first Bre.14 A2 production aircraft entered service with the Aéronautique Militaire the following spring. The Bre.14 quickly established a reputation for toughness and reliability, and by the end of the year orders for some 2650 aircraft had been placed with the five licensees. The B.2 bomber, with trailing edge flaps, was the next version, followed by the Bre.14S ambulance. Military and civil versions of this outstanding aircraft were in production until 1926. Pictured is a Breguet Bre. 14 A.2 of the 15e Escadrille, 5e Groupe, French Air Force, in 1921.

| Country of origin: | France |
|---|---|
| Type: | two-seat reconnaissance/light bomber biplane |
| Powerplant: | one 300hp (224kW) Renault 12Fe inline piston engine |
| Performance: | maximum speed 184km/h (114mph); service ceiling 6000m (19,690ft); endurance 3hrs |
| Weights: | empty 1030kg (2271lb); maximum take-off weight 1565kg (3450lb) |
| Dimensions: | span 14.36m (47ft 1in); length 8.87m (29ft 1in); height 3.3m (10ft 10in); wing area 47.50 sq m (530 sq ft) |
| Armament: | one fixed forward-firing .303 machine gun; twin .303in Lewis machine guns on ring mounting in rear cockpit; underwing racks with provision for up 40kg (88lb) of bombs |

# Breguet Bre.19

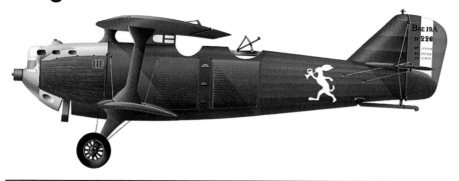

Almost certainly built in larger numbers (perhaps 1500 aircraft including 400 licence-built machines) than any other warplane type in the period between the world wars, the Bre.19 was designed to succeed the Bre.14 that had performed so magnificently in World War I. The prototype made its maiden flight in November 1921, and production versions included the Bre.19A.2 observation and reconnaissance model with engines in the power range between 400 and 860hp (298 and 693kW), the Bre.19B.2 light bomber with provision for an external bomb load, and the Bre.19GR reconnaissance model. Many were sold to foreign clients for evaluation or operational service. Variants built in smaller numbers included the Bre.19bis, ter, T, Tbis, 19.1, 19.2, 19.7, 19.8 and 19.9. The type was still in first-line service with Greece when it was invaded by Italy during October 1940. Pictured is one of the 50 Bre.19.7s ordered by Turkey in 1933.

| Country of origin: | France |
|---|---|
| Type: | (Bre.19A.2) two-seat army cooperation and reconnaissance aircraft |
| Powerplant: | one 513hp (382.5kW) Renault 12Kb 12-cylinder Vee engine |
| Performance: | maximum speed 235km/h (146mph); climb to 5000m (16,405ft) in 29 minutes 50 seconds; service ceiling 6900m (22,640ft); range 1200km  (746 miles) |
| Weights: | empty 1722kg (3796lb); maximum take-off 3110kg (6856lb) |
| Dimensions: | span 14.83m (48ft 7.75in); length 9.51m (31ft 2.5in); height 3.69m (12ft 1.25in) |
| Armament: | one 7.7mm or 7.5mm fixed forward-firing machine gun in the star board side of the forward fuselage, one or two 7.7mm or 7.5mm rearward-firing machine guns in the rear cockpit, and provision for one 7.7mm or 7.5mm trainable machine gun in the ventral position, plus a bomb load of 1764lb (800kg) |

# Breguet Bre.521 Bizerte

After buying a single example of the Short S.8 Calcutta flying boat from the UK and building four more under licence with the designation S.8/2, Breguet developed its own version as the Bre.521 Bizerte. This first flew in prototype form during September 1933, and was followed by three pre-production 'boats and then 27 'boats to the full production standard with an uprated powerplant and other improvements. The Bre.521Hy.8 entered service late in 1935, and at the start of World War II the French had 20 'boats in service with four squadrons of the French naval air service. After the defeat of France the surviving 'boats were entrusted to two Vichy French units, and when in November 1942 the Germans occupied Vichy France they seized eight Bizertes for continued use in the air/sea rescue role. One is seen here in the colours of 1.Seentostaffel of the Luftwaffe, based at Brest-Hourtin in north west France in winter of 1943-44.

| | |
|---|---|
| **Country of origin:** | France |
| **Type:** | (Bre.521Hy.8) eight-seat maritime reconnaissance and bomber flying boat |
| **Powerplant:** | three 900hp (671kW) Gnome-Rhòne 14Kirs-1 Mistral-Major 14-cylinder two-row radial engines |
| **Performance:** | maximum speed 243km/h (151mph); climb to 2000m (6560ft) in 8 minutes 46 seconds; service ceiling 6000m (19,685ft); range 3000 km (1864 miles) |
| **Weights:** | empty 9470kg (20,878lb); maximum take-off 16,600kg (36,597lb) |
| **Dimensions:** | span 35.15m (115ft 4in); length 20.48m (67ft 2.25in); height 7.48m (24ft 6.5in) |
| **Armament:** | five 7.5mm trainable machine guns mounted singly in the tail position, two port and starboard forward positions, and two port and starboard waist positions, plus external bomb load of 300kg (661lb) |

# Breguet Bre.693

The Bre.690 resulted from a 1934 requirement for a three-seat heavy fighter, but after the selection of the Potez 630 was revised as the Bre.691 two-seat attack warplane, and was ordered only in 1937, first flying in this form in March 1938 and paving the way for 78 Bre.691AB.2 production aircraft with two Hispano-Suiza 14 radial engines. Although thought was given to the creation of a Bre.692 with Gnome-Rhône 14N radial engines, the next model was the Bre.693 evolution of the Bre.691 with Gnome-Rhône 14M radial piston engines and, in later aircraft, one obliquely downward- and rearward-firing 7.5mm machine gun in the rear of each engine nacelle. The first Bre.693AB.2 flew in March 1940, and 254 such aircraft were delivered, later aircraft serving with the Vichy French air force after the fall of France in June 1940. In November 1942 the aircraft were confiscated by the Germans and transferred to the Regia Aeronautica for use as trainers.

| | |
|---|---|
| Country of origin: | France |
| Type: | two-seat light attack bomber |
| Powerplant: | two 700hp (522kW) Gnome-Rhône 14M-6/7 Mars 14-cylinder two-row radial engines |
| Performance: | maximum speed 475km/h (295mph); climb to 4000m (13,125ft) in 7 minutes 12 seconds; ceiling 8500m (27,885ft); range 1350km (839 miles) |
| Weights: | empty 3010kg (6636lb); maximum take-off 5500kg (12,125lb) |
| Dimensions: | span 15.36m (50ft 5in); length 9.67m (31ft 8.75in); height 3.19m (10ft 5.75in) |
| Armament: | one 20mm fixed forward-firing cannon and two 7.5mm fixed forward-firing machine guns, one 7.5mm fixed obliquely rearward-firing machine gun, two 7.5mm fixed obliquely downward/rearward-firing machine guns and one 7.5mm trainable rearward-firing machine gun, plus an internal bomb load of 400kg (882lb) |

# Breguet Bre.695

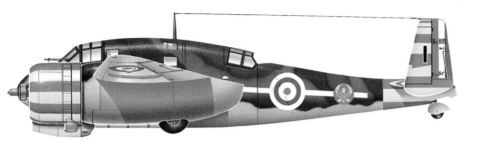

**W**orried about the strategic danger to the country as a result of its limited aero engine manufacturing capability, France decided in 1939 to adopt a policy of ensuring that every major warplane type in French service would be capable of accepting an imported American or British engine. This led to the Bre.695.01 that was the Bre.690.01 prototype revised with two Pratt & Whitney R-1830-SB4G Twin Wasp radial engines, which were of lighter weight and greater power than the French engines they replaced but also of larger diameter. The Bre.695.01 first flew in March 1940, and while flight trials confirmed the overall viability of the revised powerplant, they also revealed a number of problems. Even so, large-scale orders for the Bre.695AB.2 were planned, but only 50 had been completed before France's defeat in June 1940. Pictured is a Breguet 695 AB.2 of the 1e Escadrille, GBA I/151 of the Armée de l'Air de l'Armistice, based at Lézignan-Corbières in June 1942.

| | |
|---|---|
| Country of origin: | France |
| Type: | two-seat light attack bomber |
| Powerplant: | two 825hp (640.5kW) Pratt & Whitney R-1830-SB4G Twin Wasp 14-cylinder two-row radial engines |
| Performance: | maximum speed 560km/h (348mph); service ceiling 9000m (29,530ft); range 1500km (932 miles) |
| Weights: | maximum take-off 5400kg (11,905lb) |
| Dimensions: | span 15.36m (50ft 5in); length 9.67m (31ft 8.75in); height 3.19m (10ft 5.75in) |
| Armament: | one 20mm fixed forward-firing cannon and two 7.5mm fixed forward-firing machine guns, one 7.5mm fixed obliquely rearward-firing machine gun, two 7.5mm fixed obliquely downward/rearward-firing machine guns and one 7.5mm trainable rearward-firing machine gun, plus an internal bomb load of 400kg (882lb) |

# Brewster F2A and Buffalo

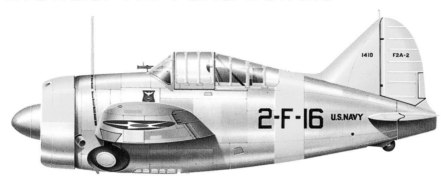

Ordered as the US Navy's first monoplane fighter, the F2A first flew in XF2A-1 prototype form in January 1938 and paved the way for 11 F2A-1 production aircraft that entered service in July 1939 with the 940hp (701kW) R-1820-34 engine, then 43 and 108 examples of the F2A-2 and F2A-3, the former with an uprated engine and the latter with more armour and a longer nose. The F2A was generally unsuccessful in American service, the type was also ordered in B-239 (44 for Finland, which was the sole country to operate the type with major success), B-339B (40 for Belgium of which 38 were delivered to the UK as Buffalo Mk Is), B-339D (72 for the Netherlands East Indies), B-339E (170 for the UK as Buffalo Mk Is), and B-439 (20 for the Netherlands East Indies but all impressed by the US Army that later delivered 17 to Australia) form. Pictured here is a Brewster F2A-2 of VF-2 'The Flying Chiefs', US Navy, aboard USS *Lexington* in March 1941.

| | |
|---|---|
| Country of origin: | USA |
| Type: | (F2A-3) single-seat carrierborne and land-based fighter/fighter-bomber |
| Powerplant: | one 1200hp (895kW) Wright R-1820-40 Cyclone nine-cylinder single-row radial engine |
| Performance: | maximum speed 517km/h (321mph); initial climb rate 698m (2290ft) per minute; service ceiling 10,120m (33,200ft); range 2704km (1680 miles) |
| Weights: | empty 2146kg (4732lb); normal take-off 2867kg (6321lb); maximum take-off 3247kg (7159lb) |
| Dimensions: | span 10.67m (35ft); length 8.03m (26ft 4in); height 3.68m (12ft 1in) |
| Armament: | two 0.5in fixed forward-firing machine guns in upper part of the forward fuselage; two 0.5in fixed forward-firing machine guns in the leading edges of the wing, plus an bomb load of 105kg (232lb) |

# Bristol Type 22 F.2B

Frank Barnwell designed the Type 9 R.2A as a two-seat reconnaissance aircraft, but by August 1916 this had been re-engined and redesignated as the Type 12 F.2A, to denote its new fighter role. The first production F.2As were delivered in February 1917 and, although their early operational tactical employment as a gun platform was naive and resulted in heavy casualties, pilots soon adopted single-seat fighter tactics and the aircraft went on to become one of the most successful and prolific British fighters of World War I. The F.2B was the main production variant and incorporated modified upper longerons for improved pilot visibility, enlarged fuel tank and a variety of engines. Production total was 5308 aircraft, with licensed manufacture by eight subcontractors. Post-war, the aircraft was operated by Australia, Belgium, Canada, the Irish Free State, Greece, Mexico, New Zealand, Norway, Peru, and Spain, and remained in RAF service until 1932.

| | |
|---|---|
| **Country of origin:** | United Kingdom |
| **Type:** | two-seat fighter/army cooperation aircraft |
| **Powerplant:** | one 275hp (205kW) Rolls Royce Falcon III inline piston engine |
| **Performance:** | maximum speed 198km/h (123mph); service ceiling 5485m (18,000ft); endurance 3hrs |
| **Weights:** | empty 975kg (2150lb); maximum take-off weight 1474kg (3250lb) |
| **Dimensions:** | span 11.96m (39ft 3in); length 7.87m (25ft 10in); height 2.97m (9ft 9in); wing area 37.62 sq m (405 sq ft) |
| **Armament:** | one fixed forward-firing .303in Vickers machine gun, plus one or two .303 Lewis guns on flexible mount in rear cockpit; underwing racks with provision for up to 12 9kg (28lb) of bombs |

# Bristol Type 26 Pullman

First flown in August 1918, the Bristol Type 24 Braemar triplane bomber never saw service in its intended role and was scrapped in 1920. The second prototype, which flew in February 1919, was designated the Type 25 Braemar II and shared the same basic configuration, although the inadequate original powerplant of four 230hp (172kW) Armstrong Siddeley Puma engines was replaced by four Liberty engines. The Armistice ended the Air Ministry's requirement for long-range bomber aircraft and the third prototype Braemar was completed as the Type 26 Pullman 14-seat passenger transport. This was exhibited and well-received at the International Air Show at Olympia in 1920, whilst engaged in a programme of testing at the British test facility at Martlesham Heath, but was dismantled without ever entering production.

| | |
|---|---|
| Country of origin: | United Kingdom |
| Type: | triplane heavy bomber |
| Powerplant: | four 400hp (298kW) Liberty 12 inline piston engines |
| Performance: | maximum speed 196km/h (122mph); absolute ceiling 5180m (17,000ft) |
| Weights: | empty 5084kg (11,208lb); maximum take-off weight 7490kg (16,512lb) |
| Dimensions: | span 24.89m (81ft 8in); length 15.7m (51ft 6in); height 6.3m (20ft 8in); wing area 176.97 sq m (1905 sq ft) |

# Bristol Type 105A Bulldog Mk IIA

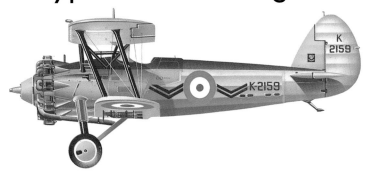

In September 1926 the British Air Ministry issued a requirement for a new single-seat day/night fighter aircraft powered by a radial air-cooled engine and armed with two .303 Vickers machine guns, to equip the RAF. No fewer than nine submissions were received, most of them powered by Bristol's Jupiter radial engine. The field was narrowed down to the Bristol Type 105 and the Hawker Hawfinch, designed by Sidney Camm, and after a stiff competition the Bristol design was selected for development. The prototype Bulldog Mk I flew for the first time in May 1927, and after the fuselage had been lengthened entered production as the Bulldog Mk II. The first aircraft was delivered to No 3 Squadron, RAF, in June 1929, powered by a 440hp (328kW) Bristol Jupiter engine. Pictured is the main production variant, Mk IIA (213 aircraft built), with larger fin, wider track main gear, bigger tyres, and an improved oil system.

| Country of origin: | United Kingdom |
| --- | --- |
| Type: | single-seat biplane fighter |
| Powerplant: | one 490hp (365kW) Bristol Jupiter VIIF radial piston engine |
| Performance: | maximum speed 280km/h (174mph); service ceiling 8940m (29,300ft); range 482km (300 miles) |
| Weights: | empty 1008kg (2222lb); maximum take-off weight 1583kg (3490lb) |
| Dimensions: | span 10.3m (33ft 10in); length 7.7m (25ft 2in); height 2.7m (8ft 9in); wing area 28.47 sq m (307 sq ft) |
| Armament: | two fixed forward-firing .303in Vickers machine guns; underwing racks with provision for up to four 9kg (20lb) bombs |

# Bristol Bombay

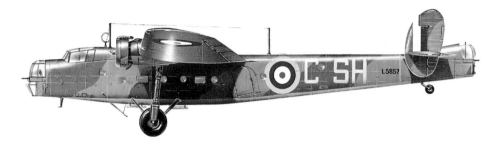

As first flown in June 1935, the Bombay was a comparatively simple high-wing monoplane with fixed tailwheel landing gear, and resulted from a 1931 requirement for dual-role transport and bomber optimised for service in Africa, the Middle East and India. Thus the new type had to be able to carry 24 troops or an equivalent weight of freight (including items as large as an aero engine), be fitted with defensive armament, and possess the capability for service as a bomber with an externally carried bomb load. Orders were placed for 50 production aircraft, and these entered service in March 1939, by which time they were technically obsolete. Even so, the aircraft performed valuable service in the North African and Mediterranean theatres as transports and were also used at times as bombers. The survivors were retired mid-way through World War II. Shown here in the colours of No 216 Squadron, RAF, based in Egypt in 1940–1, is a Bombay Mk 1.

| | |
|---|---|
| **Country of origin:** | United Kingdom |
| **Type:** | (Bombay Mk I) three/six-seat transport and bomber |
| **Powerplant:** | two 1010hp (753kW) Bristol Pegasus XXII nine-cylinder radial engines |
| **Performance:** | maximum speed 309km/h (192mph); climb to 4570m (15,000ft) in 20 minutes; service ceiling 7620m (25,000ft); range 2230 miles (3589km) |
| **Weights:** | empty 6260kg (13,800lb); maximum take-off 9072kg (20,000lb) |
| **Dimensions:** | span 29.18m (95ft 9in); length 21.11m (69ft 3in); height 5.94m (19ft 6in) |
| **Armament:** | one 0.303in trainable forward-firing machine gun in nose turret and one 0.303in trainable rearward-firing machine gun in tail turret; option of one 0.303in trainable machine gun in each of two beam positions, plus a bomb load of 907kg (2000lb) |

# Bristol Blenheim Mk I

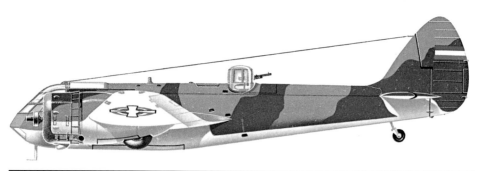

Developed as a militarised version of the Type 142 high-speed light transport, the Type 142M prototype paved the way for the Blenheim Mk I light bomber that entered service in 1939. The Royal Air Force hoped this aircraft would provide a measure of operational capability as well as helping to create a pool of skilled aircrews pending the development of high-performance types. The Blenheim saw extensive service but never was truly effective; the first variant was the Blenheim Mk I of which 1365 were produced by three British manufacturers, 45 and 16 generally similar aircraft being built in Finland and Yugoslavia respectively. In addition a small number were presented to Romania as a diplomatic bribe in 1939, with the result that the Blenheim fought both for and against the Allies during World War II. A number of British aircraft were converted to Blenheim Mk IF night-fighter standard with a ventral pack of four 0.303in machine guns and radar.

| | |
|---|---|
| Country of origin: | United Kingdom |
| Type: | (Blenheim Mk I) three-seat light bomber |
| Powerplant: | two 840hp (627kW) Bristol Mercury VIII nine-cylinder single-row radial engines |
| Performance: | maximum speed 459km/h (285mph); climb to 4570m (15,000ft) in 9 minutes 58 seconds; service ceiling 8315m (27,280ft); range 1810km (1125 miles) |
| Weight: | empty 4013kg (8839lb); maximum take-off 5947kg (13,100lb) |
| Dimensions: | span 17.17m (56ft 4in); length 12.12m (39ft 9in); height 3.00m (9ft 10in) |
| Armament: | one 0.303in fixed forward-firing machine gun in the leading edge of the port wing, and one 0.303in trainable machine gun in the dorsal turret, plus an internal bomb load of 454kg (1000lb) |

# Bristol Blenheim Mk IV

The Blenheim Mk IV was designed to overcome the operational deficiencies of the Blenheim Mk I, and differed in its uprated powerplant and significantly increased fuel capacity. Another revsion was the forward fuselage, which was lengthened by some 0.91 m (3ft) to include a navigator's station under a glazed upper surface with a downward-scalloped port side. The Blenheim Mk IV entered production early in 1939, and by the outbreak of war the RAF had 13 squadrons of Mk IVs. British production by three companies (Bristol, Avro and Rootes) totalled 3285. Finland also produced 10 aircraft for its own use, and 676 aircraft were produced in Canada with the name Bolingbroke. The Blenheim Mk IV bomber equipped 25, 19 and one squadrons in the UK, Middle East and Far East respectively, and numbers of the aircraft were later converted to Blenheim Mk IVF night-fighter standard with a ventral gun pack and radar.

| Country of origin: | United Kingdom |
|---|---|
| Type: | (Blenheim Mk IV) three-seat light bomber |
| Powerplant: | two 995hp (742kW) Bristol Mercury XV nine-cylinder single-row radial engines |
| Performance: | maximum speed 428km/h (266mph); initial climb rate 457m (1500ft) per minute; service ceiling 6705m (22,000ft); range 2350km (1460 miles) with a 454kg (1000lb) bomb load |
| Weights: | empty 4456kg (9823lb); maximum take-off 6804kg (15,000lb) |
| Dimensions: | span 17.17m (56ft 4in); length 12.98m (42ft 7in); height 3.90m (12ft 9.5in) |
| Armament: | One 0.303in fixed forward-firing machine gun in the leading edge of the port wing, two 0.303in trainable machine guns in the dorsal turret, and two 0.303in trainable rearward-firing machine guns in undernose blister position, plus internal bomb load of 454kg (1000lb) |

# Bristol Beaufighter Mk VI

The Beaufighter was a derivative of the Beaufort torpedo bomber and was first flown in July 1939 as a heavy fighter with a smaller fuselage and an uprated powerplant. of two 1400hp (1044kW) Bristol Hercules III or 1500hp (1118kW) Hercules XI radial engines. Some 553 Mk IF radar-equipped night-fighters and 397 Mk IC coastal fighters were fitted with Hercules engines and were later complemented by 597 Mk IIF night-fighters with 1280hp (954kW) Rolls-Royce Merlin XX Vee engines. The type came into its own during 1942 in its Mk VI form. There were three subvariants, namely the Beaufighter Mk VIC torpedo fighter (693 aircraft), the Beaufighter Mk VIF night-fighter (879 aircraft) and the Beaufighter Mk VI Interim Torpedo Fighter (60 aircraft) with underwing provision for eight 60lb (27kg) rockets, providing a heavier punch against ships and surfaced submarines. This aircraft is a Mk VIF, serving with the 416th Night Fighter Squadron, USAAF.

| Country of origin: | United Kingdom |
|---|---|
| Type: | (Beaufighter Mk VIF) two-seat night-fighter |
| Powerplant: | two 1635hp (1219kW) Bristol Hercules VI 14-cylinder two-row radial engines |
| Performance: | maximum speed 536km/h (333mph); initial climb rate not available; service ceiling not available; range 2478km (1540 miles) |
| Weights: | empty 6622kg (14,600lb);maximum take-off 9798kg (21,600lb) |
| Dimensions: | span 17.63m (57ft 10in); length 12.70m (41ft 8in); height 4.82m (15ft 10in) |
| Armament: | four 20mm fixed forward-firing cannon in the underside of the forward fuselage, and six 0.303in fixed forward-firing machine guns in the leading edges of the wing (two to port and four to starboard) |

# Bristol Beaufighter Mks X and XI

The Beaufighter TF.Mk X was an improved version of the Beaufighter Mk VIC with Hercules XVII engines optimised for the low- rather than medium-altitude as required for anti-shipping operations. An AI.Mk VIII radar was fitted in a 'thimble' nose for use in tracking surface vessels, a dorsal gun provided defensive fire, and provision was made for underwing bomb and rocket loads as alternatives to the underfuselage torpedo. The combination of a large dorsal fin and enlarged elevators improved control at high weights. Production of the Beaufighter TF.Mk X, which was the most important British anti-ship attack weapon from 1944 in Europe and the Far East, totalled 2205 aircraft, and another 163 machines were completed to the Beaufighter Mk XIC standard that differed from the Beaufighter TF.Mk X only in possessing no torpedo capability. The aircraft pictured is a TF. Mk X of No 455 Squadron, RAF.

| | |
|---|---|
| **Country of origin:** | United Kingdom |
| **Type:** | (Beaufighter TF.Mk X) two/three-seat anti-ship attack fighter |
| **Powerplant:** | two 1770hp (1320kW) Bristol Hercules XVII 14-cylinder two-row radial engines |
| **Performance:** | maximum speed 512km/h (318mph); climb to 1525m (5000ft) in 3 minutes 30 seconds; service ceiling 4570m (15,000ft); range 2913km (1810 miles) |
| **Weights:** | empty 7076kg (15,600lb); maximum take-off 11,431kg (25,200lb) |
| **Dimensions:** | span 17.63m (57ft 10in); length 12.70m (41ft 8in); height 4.83m (15ft 10in) |
| **Armament:** | four 20mm fixed forward-firing cannon in the underside of the forward fuselage, and one 0.303in trainable rearward-firing machine gun in the dorsal position, plus an external torpedo, bomb and rocket load of 1111kg (2450lb) |

# Bristol Beaufighter Mk 21

The Royal Australian Air Force evinced an interest in the Beaufighter from an early stage. Reliable twin-engined powerplant, heavy firepower and good overall performance (especially in range) were attractive to a force facing the possibility of Japanese attack on the north coast of Australia, a region that was both inhospitable and lacking in a network of closely spaced airfields. As a result the Department of Aircraft Production commenced building the Beaufighter TF.Mk X as the Beaufighter TF.Mk 21 with two Hercules XVIII engines rated for optimum performance at medium altitude. Other changes included removal of the torpedo shackles, the radar and the dorsal fin fillet, modification of the wing for four 0.5in machine guns, and addition of a bulge in the nose for a Sperry autopilot that was in fact seldom fitted. The first of 364 such aircraft flew in May 1944. The aircraft pictured wears the colours of No 22 Squadron, RAAF.

| | |
|---|---|
| Country of origin: | Australia (from a British design) |
| Type: | (Beaufighter Mk 21) two/three-seat multi-role heavy fighter |
| Powerplant: | two 1770hp (1320kW) Bristol Hercules XVIII 14-cylinder two-row radial engines |
| Performance: | maximum speed 512km/h (318mph); climb to 1525m (5000ft) in 3 minutes 30 seconds; service ceiling 4570m (15,000ft); range 2913km (1810 miles ) |
| Weights: | empty 7076kg (15,600lb); maximum take-off 11,431kg (25,200lb) |
| Dimensions: | Span 17.63m (57ft 10in); length 12.70m (41ft 8in); height 4.83m (15ft 10in) |
| Armament: | four 20mm fixed forward-firing cannon in forward fuselage, four 0.5in fixed forward-firing machine guns in the leading edges of the    wing, and one 0.303in rearward-firing machine gun in the dorsal position, plus an external bomb and rocket load of 2450lb (1111kg) |

# CAMS 55

A development of the CAMS 53 transport flying boat with features of the unsuccessful CAMS 51 and CAMS 54GR reconnaissance types, the CAMS 55 first flew in prototype form in 1928. Successful trials of the five prototypes paved the way for service from 1930 of an eventual 107 production 'boats. The survivors were still in limited service at the start of World War II but were scrapped after France's June 1940 defeat. The main variants were the baseline CAMS 55.1 with two 600hp (522kW) Hispano-Suiza 12Lbr Vee engines; these 43 'boats were followed by 29 examples of the CAMS 55.2 with 480hp (358kW) Gnome-Rhône 9Akx Jupiter radial engines, 28 examples of the CAMS 55.10 upgraded version of the CAMS 55.2, and four examples of the long-range CAMS 55.10 Col. for colonial service. Pictured is a CAMS 55/2 of Escadrille 4S1, Aéronavale (French Naval Air Force), based in North Africa during the 1930s.

| | |
|---|---|
| Country of origin: | France |
| Type: | (CAMS 55.10Hy.5) five-seat maritime reconnaissance flying boat |
| Powerplant: | two 530hp (395kW) Gnome-Rhône 9Kbr Mistral nine-cylinder single-row radial engines |
| Performance: | maximum speed 215km/h (134mph); climb to 2500m (8200ft) in 28 minutes; service ceiling 3400m (11,155ft); range 1300 km (808 miles) |
| Weights: | empty 4640kg (10,231lb); maximum take-off 6530kg (14,396lb) |
| Dimensions: | span 20.39m (66ft 11in); length 15m (49ft 2.5in); height 5.41m (17ft 9in) |
| Armament: | two 7.7mm trainable forward-firing machine guns in the bow position, and two 7.7mm trainable rearward-firing machine guns in the dorsal position, plus an external bomb load of 150kg (330lb) |

# CANT Z.501 Gabbiano

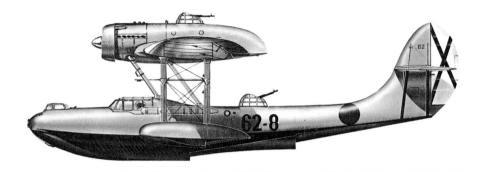

The first Gabbiano (Seagull) made its maiden flight in 1934, and gave notice of its capabilities by establishing a world seaplane distance record of 3080 miles (4955 km) between Trieste and Berbera in British Somaliland. Production for the Italian air force started in 1936, and some 202 'boats of this type were in service when Italy entered World War II in June 1940. Operational experience in the maritime reconnaissance role soon revealed that the Z.501 lacked the performance and defensive firepower for successful operation against fighter opposition, resulting in the type's relegation to the air/sea rescue and coastal patrol tasks. Even so production continued to the middle of 1943 and resulted in the overall delivery of 444 'boats including small numbers delivered to Romania and Nationalist Spain. Pictured is one of the aircraft operated by 2 Escuadrilla, Grupo 62, Agrupacion Espanola (Spanish nationalist air force) based in Majorca in 1939.

| | |
|---|---|
| Country of origin: | Italy |
| Type: | (Z.501) five-seat maritime reconnaissance and bomber flying boat |
| Powerplant: | one 900hp (671kW) Isotta-Fraschini Asso XI R2C.15 12-cylinder Vee engine |
| Performance: | maximum speed 275km/h (171mph); climb to 4000m (13,125ft) in 16 minutes; service ceiling 7000m (22,965ft); range 2400km (1491miles) |
| Weights: | empty 3840kg (8466lb); maximum take-off 7050kg (15,542lb) |
| Dimensions: | span 22.50m (73ft 9.75in); length 14.30m (46ft 11in); height 4.40m (14ft 6in) |
| Armament: | one 7.7mm trainable forward-firing machine gun in the bow position, one 7.7mm trainable machine gun in the nacelle turret, and one 7.7mm trainable rearward-firing machine gun in the dorsal turret, plus an external bomb load of 640kg (1411lb) |

# CANT Z.506 Airone

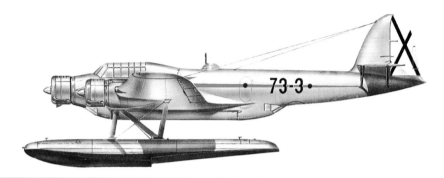

The Z.506 was derived from the Z.505 prototype that was planned as a mailplane to connect Italy with its East Africa colonies, which lacked major airfields. The aircraft was subsequently placed in production as a 15-passenger civil transport (20 aircraft) before production switched to the Z.506B Airone ('Heron') military derivative that entered service in 1938. Production of the Z.506B totalled some 324 aircraft, of which 95 were in service at the time of Italy's entry into World War II. The type was initially operated in the bomber role, but then revised with stronger defensive armament and reassigned to the maritime reconnaissance, convoy escort, and anti-submarine roles. A number of aircraft were also converted to the Z.506S standard for the air/sea rescue task, and a number of the aircraft were retained in service up to 1959. Illustrated here is a Z.506B wearing the colours of Grupo 73, Agrupacion Espanola, based at Majorca in 1939

| Country of origin: | Italy |
|---|---|
| Type: | (Z.506B) five-seat maritime reconnaissance and bomber floatplane |
| Powerplant: | three 750hp (559kW) Alfa Romeo 126 RC.34 nine-cylinder single-row radial engines |
| Performance: | maximum speed 350km/h (217mph); climb to 4000m (13,125ft) in 20 minutes; service ceiling 8000m (26,245ft); range 1705 miles (2745 km) |
| Weights: | empty 8300kg (18,298lb); maximum take-off 12,705kg (28,008lb) |
| Dimensions: | span 26.50m (86ft 11.33in); length 19.24mn (63ft 1.7in); height 7.45m (24ft 5.5in) |
| Armament: | one 12.7mm trainable machine gun in the dorsal turret, one 7.7mm trainable rearward-firing machine gun in the rear of the ventral gon dola, and one 7.7mm trainable lateral-firing machine gun in each of the two lateral positions, plus an internal bomb load of 1200kg (2646lb) |

# CANT Z.1007 Alcione

**F**irst flown in prototype form during March 1937, the Z.1007 Alcione ('Kingfisher')
entered service late in 1938 and became one of Italy's most important medium
bombers. Production of the Z.1007 totalled only about 35 aircraft with 840hp (626kW)
Piaggio Asso XI radial engines and a defensive armament of four 7.7mm machine guns. This
initial variant was followed by 526 examples of the Z.1007bis and Z.1007ter. The former
introduced a larger airframe, an uprated powerplant with engines in revised nacelles, and
different armament as well as two types of tail unit (single vertical surface in first three
batches and twin surfaces in the last six batches). The latter had the uprated powerplant of
three 1175hp (876kW) Piaggio P.XIX radial engines but a reduced 1000kg (2205lb) bomb
load. This aircraft has the markings of the Aviazione Nazionale Republicana, the air force
formed from the remnants of the Regia Aeronautica in late 1943.

| | |
|---|---|
| Country of origin: | Italy |
| Type: | (Z.1007bis) five-seat medium bomber |
| Powerplant: | three 1000hp (746kW) Piaggio P.XI R2C.40 14-cylinder two-row radial engines |
| Performance: | maximum speed 466km/h (290mph); climb to 4000m (13,125ft) in 10 minutes 30 seconds; service ceiling 8200m (26,900ft); range 1750km (1087 miles) with a 1200kg (2646lb) bomb load |
| Weights: | empty 9396kg (20,715lb); maximum take-off 13,621kg (30,029lb) |
| Dimensions: | span 24.80m (81ft 4.33in); length 18.35mn (60ft 2.5in); height 5.22m (17ft 5in) |
| Armament: | one 12.7mm trainable machine gun in the dorsal turret, one 12.7mm trainable rearward-firing machine gun in the ventral step position, and one 7.7mm lateral-firing machine gun in each of the two beam positions, plus an internal bomb load of 1200kg (2646lb) |

# CASA C-101EB-01 Aviojet (E.25 Mirlo)

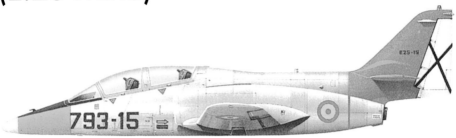

The C-101 was developed by the Spanish CASA company (Construcciones Aeronauticas SA) from the mid-1970s as a replacement for Hispano HA.200 jet trainer in service with the Spanish Air Force (EdA). Assistance in the design was provided by Northrop and MBB, and many of the parts were sourced from foreign contractors, including the Dowty-built landing gear, Martin-Baker ejector seats, Garrett-AiResearch turbofan and Sperry flight control system. The first flight was made in June 1977. Production deliveries of the 92 aircraft supplied to the EdA began in 1980. From 1990 CASA upgraded the weapons system on the C-101 in the hope of encouraging export orders. These were forthcoming from Honduras (4 C-101BB), Chile (for a licence-built version designated T-36 and the upgraded C-101CC, which are designated A-36) and Jordan, who operate the C-101CC aircraft.

| Country of origin: | Spain |
|---|---|
| Type: | two-seat advanced flying/weapons trainer |
| Powerplant: | one 1588kg (3500lb) Garrett AiResearch TFE731-2-2J turbofan |
| Performance: | maximum speed at 6095m (20,000ft) 806km/h (501mph); service ceiling 12,800m (42,000ft); endurance 7 hours |
| Weights: | empty 3470kg (7650lb); maximum take-off 4850kg (10,692lb) |
| Dimensions: | wingspan 10.6m (34ft 9.25in); length 12.5m (41ft); height 4.25m (13ft 11.25in); wing area 20sq m (215.3sq ft) |
| Armament: | one 30mm DEFA cannon; six external hardpoints with provision for up to 2000kg (4410lb) of stores, including rocket pods, missiles, bombs and drop tanks |

# Canadair Sabre Mk 4

Italy was one of nearly 20 countries which operated the North-American designed Sabre. Fiat licence-built 221 of the F-86K version for the Aeronautica Militare Italia. This aircraft, however, is a Sabre Mk 4 (F-86E), one of 430 built by the Canadair company with funds provided by the Mutual Defense Assistance Program to re-equip RAF fighter squadrons. The aircraft were later fitted with extended leading edges and passed on to Italy, who took 180, Yugoslavia, Greece and Turkey. Unlike the Canadair-built Sabres Mk 5 and Mk 6, which were powered by a licence-built Orenda turbojet, the Mk 4 aircraft had the original General Electric engine. In all other respects the Mk 4 was the same as the F-86E, including the 'all-flying tail'. Note the prancing horse insignia on the tail, reminiscent of the badge used on a certain marque of Italian car!

| | |
|---|---|
| Country of origin: | USA/Canada |
| Type: | single-seat fighter-bomber |
| Powerplant: | one 2358kg (5200lb) General Electric J47-GE-13 turbojet |
| Performance: | maximum speed at sea level 1091km/h (678mph); service ceiling 15,240m (50,000ft); range 1344km (835 miles) |
| Weights: | empty 5045kg (11,125lb); maximum loaded 9350kg (20,611lb) |
| Dimensions: | wingspan 11.30m (37ft 1in); length 11.43m (37ft 6in); height 4.47m (14ft 8.75in); wing area 27.76sq m (288sq ft) |
| Armament: | six 0.5in Colt-Browning M-3 with 267 rpg, underwing hardpoints for two tanks or two stores of 454kg (1000lb), plus eight rockets |

# Canadair CL-41G-5 Tebuan (CL-41 Tutor)

The Tutor has been the standard jet trainer of the Canadian Armed forces for over 30 years. In service the aircraft is known by the designation CT-114. The aircraft represented a significant step for the Canadian aerospace industry, as it was the first aircraft designed and built solely in that country. Early development was privately funded by the company because of a lack of interest from the Canadian government. Two prototypes were built powered by the built Pratt & Whitney JT12-A5 turbojet. Production examples were fitted with the indigenously built version of the General Electric CJ610, made in Canada as the J85-CAN-40. Production orders totalled some 190 aircraft, with 20 extensively modified CL-41G-5 Tebuan aircraft for Malaysia. The majority of the Canadian aircraft are based with No. 2 Flying Training Scholl at Moose Jaw in Saskatchewan.

| | |
|---|---|
| Country of origin: | Canada |
| Type: | two-seat jet trainer |
| Powerplant: | one 1338kg (2950lb) Orenda (General Electric) J85-CAN-40 turbojet |
| Performance: | maximum speed 797km/h (495mph); service ceiling 13,100m (43,000ft); standard range 1000km (621 miles) |
| Weights: | empty 2220kg (4895lb); maximum take-off 3532kg (7787lb) |
| Dimensions: | wingspan 11.13m (36ft 6in); length 9.75m (32ft); height 2.76m (9ft 1in); wing area 20.44sq m (220sq ft) |
| Armament: | six external hardpoints with provision for up to 1814kg (4000lb) of stores |

# Canadair CF-5 Freedom Fighter

When the Canadian government selected the Northrop F-5 for its air force, Canadair Ltd in Montreal was chosen to built the aircraft under licence in two versions, the CF-5A single-seat version and the CF-5D tandem seat aircraft. Canadair were able to incorporate a number of significant improvements to the design; the most important upgrade being uprated engines than the original US model. The potential range of the aircraft was also improved by fitting an inflight refuelling probe. Canadair have successfully exported the aircraft to a number of countries, including the Netherlands. In 1987 Bristol Aerospace received a contract to update 56 CF-5A/Ds for further use as lead-in trainers by the Canadian Air Force. This programme extended airframe life by 4000 hours and, with other improvements, should have allowed the aircraft to remain in service for some time. However all the remaining RCAF aircraft were retired in 1995.

| | |
|---|---|
| **Country of origin:** | USA and Canada |
| **Type:** | fighter and light attack aircraft |
| **Powerplant:** | two 1950kg (4300lb) Orenda (General Electric) J85-CAN-15 turbojets |
| **Performance:** | maximum speed at 10,970m (36,000ft) 1575km/h (978mph); service ceiling 15,500m (50,580ft); combat radius at maximum load 314km (195 miles) |
| **Weights:** | empty 3700kg (8157lb); maximum take-off 9249kg (20,390lb) |
| **Dimensions:** | wingspan 7.87m (25ft 10in); length 14.38m (47ft 2in); height 4.01m (13ft 2in); wing area 15.79sq m (170sq ft) |
| **Armament:** | two 20mm M39 cannon, underwing hardpoints with provision for two AIM-9 Sidewinder AAMs, gun and rocket pods, and bombs |

# Caproni Ca.1

The Societa di Aviazione Ing Caproni in Italy and Igor Sikorsky in Russia showed remarkable foresight in producing the first heavy bombers. Caproni flew the Ca.30 bomber in 1913, at a time when the British had no explicit military aircraft and little compulsion to use them. The Ca.30 had a short central nacelle with three 80hp (60kW) Gnome rotary engines, one driving a pusher screw, the others geared to tractor propellers on the tail booms. The later Ca.31 first flew in late 1914 with three 100hp (75kW) Fiat A.10 engines mounted on the front of the tail booms; it was put into production as the Ca.1. Some 162 aircraft were produced before production switched to the Ca.2, with the central engine replaced by a 150hp (112kW) Isotta-Fraschini V.4B, and the main production variant, the Ca.3, with three Isotta-Fraschini V.4Bs. The latter gave rise to a post-war development, the 36M. Pictured is a Ca.1 of the Aéronautique Militaire, on the Plateau de Malzéville during 1916.

| | |
|---|---|
| **Country of origin:** | Italy |
| **Type:** | four-seat heavy day bomber |
| **Powerplant:** | three 100hp (75kW) Fiat A.10 6-cylinder piston engines |
| **Performance:** | maximum speed 116km/h (72mph); range 550km (340 miles) |
| **Weights:** | empty 2500kg (5512lb); maximum take-off weight 3302kg (7280lb) |
| **Dimensions:** | span 22.2m (72ft 10in); length 10.9m (35ft 9in); height 3.7m (12ft 2in) |
| **Armament:** | one or two 7.7mm Revelli machine guns on flexible mount in front cockpit; plus a maximum bomb load of 850kg (1874lb) |

# Caproni Ca.3

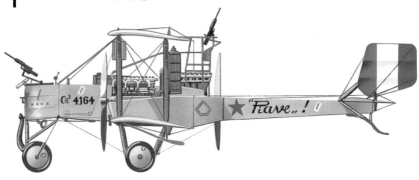

After entering service with the Corpo Aeronautica, the Ca.2 carried out the first Italian bombing raids of the war on 25 August 1915, and soon established a proud tradition of arduous missions on the Austro–Hungarian front over difficult mountainous terrain for what were essentially extremely flimsy aircraft. They were followed into service in 1917 by the Ca.3. This aircraft had more powerful engines and greater bomb-load, and was undoubtedly the most successful Allied bomber of the war. Some 83 Ca.3s were built under licence in France by Robert Esnault-Pelterie, and equipped two units of the Aéronautique Militaire. At the beginning of 1918 the Ca.5 was introduced, although this designation in fact encompassed three different aircraft – the Ca.44, Ca.45, and Ca.46. Pictured is a Ca.3 of Squadriglia VII, Gruppo XI of the Corpo Aeronautica.

| | |
|---|---|
| Country of origin: | Italy |
| Type: | four-seat heavy day bomber |
| Powerplant: | 150hp (112kW) Isotta-Fraschini V.4B inline piston engines |
| Performance: | maximum speed 140km/h (87mph); service ceiling 4100m (13,450ft); range 450km (280 miles) |
| Weights: | empty 2300kg (5071lb); maximum take-off weight 3312kg (7302lb) |
| Dimensions: | span 22.2m (72ft 10in); length 10.9m (35ft 9in); height 3.7m (12ft 2in) |
| Armament: | two or four 7.7mm Revelli machine guns on flexible mounts in cockpit positions; plus a maximum bomb load of 450kg (992lb) |

# Caproni Ca 101

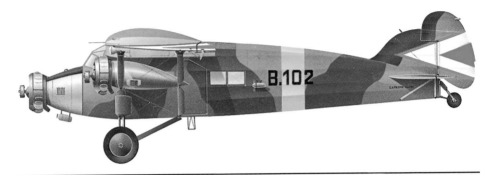

In 1927 Caproni introduced the Ca 101 transport as an enlarged tri-motor development of the Ca 97 transport that was produced with one, two and three engines. The type was soon ordered by the Italian air force as a bomber with three 370hp (276kW) Piaggio P.VII radial engines. The Ca 101 did not remain in Italian metropolitan service for long, and after their relegation from this primary role the aircraft were revised for dual-role bomber and transport service in Italy's East African colony of Eritrea with less powerful but more reliable and economical Alfa Romeo Dux or D.2 radial engines. Some 20 aircraft were sold to Hungary, which operated them on the Eastern Front against the USSR, phasing the aircraft out of service only at the start of 1943. Pictured is a Ca 101 of the C./III Bombázó Osztály, Magyar Királyi Légierö (Royal Hungarian air force), based at Papa in Hungary, early in 1941.

| | |
|---|---|
| Country of origin: | Italy |
| Type: | (Ca.101) three-seat light reconnaissance bomber |
| Powerplant: | three 240hp (179kW) Alfa Romeo D.2 nine-cylinder single-row radial engines |
| Performance: | maximum speed 165km/h (103mph); climb to 5000m (16,405ft) in 40 minutes 30 seconds; ceiling 6100m (20,015ft); range 2000km (1243 miles) |
| Weights: | empty 3275kg (7221lb); maximum take-off 4975kg (10,968lb) |
| Dimensions: | span 19.68m (64ft 6.75in); length 14.37m(47ft 1.75in); height (3.89m) 12ft 9.25in |
| Armament: | one 7.7mm trainable machine gun in the dorsal position, one or two 7.7mm trainable rearward-firing machine guns in the ventral position, and on some aircraft one 7.7mm trainable lateral-firing machine guns in each of the one or two beam positions, plus an internal and external bomb load 500kg (1102lb) |

# Caproni Ca 133

An improved version of the Ca 101 dual-role bomber and transport, the Ca 133 introduced a number of drag-lowering features, namely neat long-chord cowlings (housing three uprated engines), together with faired legs and spatted wheels for the main landing gear units, an improved tail unit and split flaps on the wing trailing edges. The Italian Air Force soon realised that despite its improvements the type was suitable only for colonial use in North and East Africa. Ca 133 production totalled 419 aircraft, and conversions included 21 Ca 133S air ambulances and 329 Ca 133T pure transports with reduced defensive armament. The Ca 133 during heavy losses at the hands of British fighters after Italy's entry into World War II in June 1940. A small batch of Ca 133 aircraft was also exported to Austria in the mid-1930s. Pictured is one of the aircraft operated by Bomberstaffel 1B, Fliegerregiment Nr 2 of the Austrian air force, based at Zeltwig in 1937.

| Country of origin: | Italy |
| --- | --- |
| Type: | (Ca 133) three-seat bomber and transport |
| Powerplant: | three 460hp (343kW) Piaggio Stella P.VII C.16 seven-cylinder single-row radial engines |
| Performance: | maximum speed 265km/h (165mph); service ceiling 5500m (18,045ft); range 1350km (838 miles) |
| Weights: | empty 4190kg (9237lb); maximum take-off 6700kg (14,771lb) |
| Dimensions: | span 21.24m (68ft 8in); length 15.36m (50ft 4.75in); height 4.00m (13ft 1in) |
| Armament: | one 7.7mm trainable machine gun in the dorsal position, two 7.7mm trainable rearward-firing machine guns in the ventral position, and one 7.7mm trainable lateral-firing machine gun in the door on the port side of the fuselage, plus an external bomb load of 1200kg (2646lb) |

# Caproni Bergamaschi Ca 135

Intended as a fast medium bomber of modern concept, the Ca 135 proved a major disappointment to the Italians. The prototype first flew in April 1935, and the Italian Air Force ordered 14 Ca 135 tipo Spagna aircraft for operational evaluation in the Spanish Civil War. In the event deliveries were made too late for this to happen. Some 32 generally similar Ca 135 tipo Peru bombers were delivered to the Peruvian Air Force. After evaluation of two Ca 135 tipo Spagna aircraft revised with two 1000hp (746kW) Fiat A.80 RC.41 radial engines, which proved unreliable, the main production model was the Ca 135/P.XI with Piaggio radial engines. About 100 of these aircraft were completed for delivery to the Hungarian Air Force, which relegated the survivors from the operational to the training role in the second half of 1942. One of these aircraft is depicted here, wearing recognition markings indicative of service in southern Russia.

| | |
|---|---|
| Country of origin: | Italy |
| Type: | (Ca 135/P.XI) four-seat medium bomber |
| Powerplant: | two 1000hp (746kW) Piaggio P.XI RC.40 14-cylinder two-row radial engines |
| Performance: | maximum speed 440km/h (273mph); climb to 5000m (16,405ft) in 17 minutes 24 seconds; service ceiling 6500m (21,325ft); range 1200km (746 miles) with a 1600kg (3527lb) bomb load |
| Weights: | empty 6050kg (13,340lb); maximum take-off 9550kg (21,050lb) |
| Dimensions: | span 18.80m (61ft 8in); length 14.40m (47ft 2.75in); height 3.40m (11ft 1.75in) |
| Armament: | one 12.7mm trainable forward-firing machine gun in the nose turret, one 12.7mm trainable machine gun in the dorsal turret, and one 12.7mm trainable machine gun in the ventral turret, plus an internal bomb load of 1600kg (3527lb) |

# Caproni Bergamasca Ca 310 Libeccio

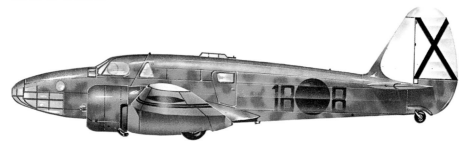

A close relative of the Ca 308 Borea civil transport and Ca 309 Ghibli multi-role colonial warplane (with fixed undercarriage), the Ca 310 Libeccio (south-west wind) was the first of a major series of attack, bomber, reconnaissance, torpedo and trainer aircraft with retractable landing gear. The Ca 310 first flew in prototype form during April 1937 and entered limited Italian service in 1938, when 16 aircraft were sent to Spain for operational trials. Caproni was more successful in the export market, soon capturing orders from Hungary, Norway, Peru and Yugoslavia. Not all the aircraft were delivered after the customers found that performance was well below that promised, and 33 aircraft returned by Hungary were taken onto Italian Air Force strength as temporary replacements for the unsatisfactory Breda Ba 65. Pictured is a Ca 103M of the 8a Escuadrilla, Grupo num 18, Agrupacion Espanola in Spain during late 1938.

| | |
|---|---|
| Country of origin: | Italy |
| Type: | (Ca 310) three-seat light reconnaissance bomber |
| Powerplant: | two 470hp (350.5kW) Piaggio P.VII C.35 seven-cylinder single-row radial engines |
| Performance: | maximum speed 365km/h (227mph); climb to 4000m (13,125ft) in 12 minutes 23 seconds; service ceiling 7000m (22,965ft); range 1200km (746 miles) |
| Weights: | empty 3040kg (6702lb); maximum take-off 4650kg (10,251lb) |
| Dimensions: | span 16.20m (53ft 1.75in); length 12.20m (40ft 0.33in); height 3.52m (11ft 6.5in) |
| Armament: | two 7.7mm fixed forward-firing machine guns in the leading edges of the wing and one 7.7mm trainable machine gun in the dorsal turret, plus an internal bomb load of 400kg (882lb) |

# Caudron R.11

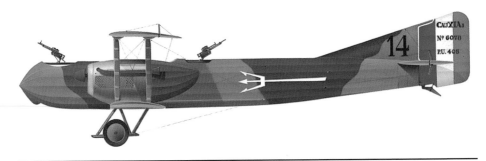

The Caudron brothers, René and Gaston, began design and manufacture of aircraft in 1909 and during the war built a very successful series of artillery observation aircraft under designation G.3. Former Aviation Militaire pilot Paul Delville took over the job of chief designer when Gaston was killed testing the R.4 twin-engine reconnaissance/bomber aircraft. Delville improved on the R.4 design with the R.5 and R.10 prototypes, but it was the R.11 that proved most successful. This owed much to the R.4 having a full length fuselage, single fin and rudder, unequal-span wings and twin tractor engines, but the R.11 differed by having a more streamlined nose, no nose wheel, and engines mounted in nacelles. Production began in 1917, though the first aircraft were not delivered until February 1918. The R.11 was not used for reconnaissance, but as an escort fighter for bomber formations. Pictured is an R.11 of Escadrille C.46, Aviation Militaire, flown by the bombers of the 13e Escadre in 1918.

| | |
|---|---|
| Country of origin: | France |
| Type: | three-seat escort fighter |
| Powerplant: | two 215hp (160kW) Hispano-Suiza 8Bba inline piston engines |
| Performance: | maximum speed 183km/h (114mph); service ceiling 5950m (19,520ft); endurance 3hrs |
| Weights: | empty 1422kg (3135lb); maximum take-off weight 2167kg (4777lb) |
| Dimensions: | span 17.92m (58ft 9in); length 11.22m (36ft 9in); height 2.8m (9ft 2in); wing area 54.25 sq m (584 sq ft) |
| Armament: | two .303in Lewis machine guns on flexible mount in front cockpit; two .303in Lewis machine guns on flexible mount in rear cockpit; one .303in Lewis machine gun on fixed mount in the front cockpit firing downwards and to the rear |

# Caudron C.714 Cyclone

An interesting but ultimately unsuccessful attempt to create a cheap and quickly built light interceptor out of a highly successful series of wooden racing aircraft, the C.714 began military life as the C.710.01 prototype that first flew in July 1936 with the 450hp (335.5kW) Renault 12R-01 engine and an armament of two 20mm cannon. This was turned into the C.713.01 prototype by the introduction of retractable main landing gear units and the revision of the vertical tail surface. The C.713 was in turn developed into the C.714.01 prototype with a strengthened structure and a revised wing, and this was followed by the C.714C.1 production model, of which 92 (including six for Finland) were completed for limited service from early in 1940. After France's fall nine of the aircraft were used as fighter trainers by Vichy France and by Germany respectively. Pictured is a C.714 of the Groupe de Chasse Polonaise, based at Lyon-Bron in May 1940.

| | |
|---|---|
| Country of origin: | France |
| Type: | (C.714C.1) single-seat lightweight interceptor fighter |
| Powerplant: | one 500hp (373kW) Renault 12R-03 12-cylinder inverted-Vee engine |
| Performance: | maximum speed 460km/h (286mph); climb to 4000m (13,125ft) in 9 minutes 40 seconds; service ceiling 9100m (29,855ft); range 900km (559 miles) |
| Weights: | empty 1395kg (3076lb ); maximum take-off 1880kg (4045lb) |
| Dimensions: | span 8.97m (29ft 5.13in); length 8.63m (28ft 3.88in); height 2.87m (9ft 5in) |
| Armament: | four 7.5mm fixed forward-firing machine guns in two flush-fitting trays under the wing |

# Cessna A-37B Dragonfly

The 318E is a development of the Cessna Model T-37, one of the jet aircraft used during the 1950s and 1960s for pilot training in the US. In 1962 two T-37s were evaluated by the USAFs Special Warfare Centre for possible use in the counter-insurgency role. The aircraft were subsequently modified to accept engines that produced more than double the power of the original Continental J69-T-25s, permitting an increase in the possible weapons load. The war in South East Asia highlighted the need for such an aircraft and Cessna were requested in 1966 to convert 39 T-37s from the production line to a light strike role, equipped with eight underwing hardpoints, wing tip tanks, and powered by the more powerful engines. Delivery began in May 1967. The A-37B had a reinforced structure, increased maximum fuel capacity, and provision for inflight refuelling.

| | |
|---|---|
| **Country of origin:** | USA |
| **Type:** | light attack and reconnaissance aircraft |
| **Powerplant:** | two 1293kg (2850lb) General Electric J85-GE-17A turbojets |
| **Performance:** | maximum speed at 4875m (16,000ft) 816km/h (507mph); service ceiling 12,730m (41,765ft); range with 1860kg (4100lb) load 740km (460 miles) |
| **Weights:** | empty 2817kg (6211lb); maximum take-off 6350kg (14,000lb) |
| **Dimensions:** | wingspan including tip tanks 10.93m(35ft 10.25in); length 8.62m (28ft 3in); height 2.7m (8ft 10.25in); wing area 17.09sq m (183.9sq ft) |
| **Armament:** | one 7.62mm GAU-2 Minigun six-barrell machine gun, eight underwing hardpoints with provision for more than 2268kg (5000lb) of stores, including bombs, rocket and gun pods, napalm tanks, and other equipment |

# Chance Vought V-166 Corsair

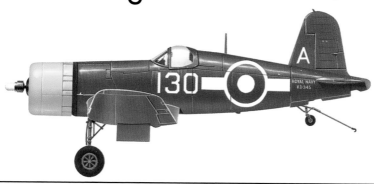

The Corsair was undoubtedly one of the finest aircraft of the war, and was virtually unmatched in the Pacific theatre after its service entry in February 1943. Development of the V-166B began in 1938, with the aim of tailoring the smallest possible airframe to fit the powerful Pratt & Whitney XR-2800 Double Wasp engine. The highly cranked wing was designed to allow clearance for the large diameter propeller, without the need for overlong main gear units. The XF4U-1 prototype first flew in May 1940, but it was not until the following February that the US Navy placed and order for 585 F4U-1 production aircraft. Carrier evaluation proved disappointing, leading to changes in the landing gear and cockpit height to improve forward view. Most aircraft were modified on the production line and were designated F4U-1A. Initial operational service was with the USMC (February 1943), but the aircraft later distinguished itself with both the US Navy and Fleet Air Arm.

| | |
|---|---|
| Country of origin: | USA |
| Type: | (F4U-1A) single-seat shipborne and land-based fighter |
| Powerplant: | one 2,000hp (1491kW) Pratt & Whitney R-2800-8 Double Wasp radial engine |
| Performance: | maximum speed 671km/h (417mph); climb to 951m (3,120ft) in 1 minute; service ceiling 11,245m (36,900ft); range 1633km (1015 miles) |
| Weights: | empty 4074kg (8982lb); maximum take-off 6350kg (14,000lb) |
| Dimensions: | span 12.5m (41ft); length 10.16m (33ft 4in); height 4.9m (16ft 1in) |
| Armament: | six 0.5in fixed forward-firing machine guns in the leading edge of the wing |

# Chance Vought F7U-1 Cutlass

The Cutlass was designed in 1946, when fighter aerodynamics had been thrown into considerable turmoil by wartime German research and emerging jet technology. The design incorporated a 38-degree swept wing carrying wide-span powered elevons, airbrakes, and full- span leading edge slats. Twin vertical tails were mounted at one-third span. These features were remarkably advanced for the time, as was the use of afterburning engines, an automatic stabilisation system, and controls with artificial feedback. Three prototype XF7U-1s were completed, and the first of these flew on September 29, 1949. After only 14 F7U-1s had been completed, the production run was halted and a number of major design revisions were made. Even so, the F7U-2 suffered severe engine difficulties and the final productions version, the F7U-3 and missile-armed -3M, had non-afterburning engines.

| | |
|---|---|
| Country of origin: | USA |
| Type: | carrier-based fighter-bomber |
| Powerplant: | two 1905kg (4200lb) Westinghouse J34-32 turbojets |
| Performance: | maximum speed at sea level 1070km/h (665mph); service ceiling 12,500m (41,000ft); combat radius with maximum fuel  966km (600 miles) |
| Weights: | empty 5385kg (11,870lb); maximum take-off 7640kg (16,840lb) |
| Dimensions: | wingspan 11.78m (38ft 8in); length 12.07m (39ft 7in); height 3m (9ft 10in); wing area 46.08sq m (496sq ft) |
| Armament: | four 20mm M-2 cannon |

# Commonwealth Wirraway

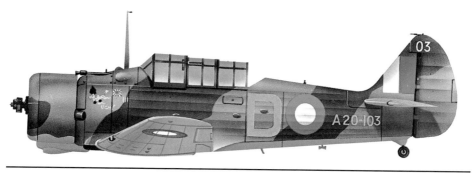

In 1936 the Australian government decided to embark on a programme to create a national aircraft industry that could eventually make Australia independent of imported aircraft, and created the Commonwealth Aircraft Corporation. CAC's first product was the CA-1 Wirraway, which was the Australian version of the North American NA-33, an improved version of the NA-26 advanced trainer produced for the US Army Air Corps as the BC-1. Of the two CA-1 prototypes, the first flew in March 1939 and paved the way for the Wirraway Mk I, of which 755 were built in seven blocks during World War II. The type entered service in June 1939, and as a result of its good performance and armament was pressed into limited operational service during 1942. Pictured is a CA-5 Wirraway, one of 30 completed for the Royal Australian Air Force, and operated by No 4 Squadron in New Guinea during December 1942. The pilot of this aircraft clearly has a kill of some sort to his credit.

| | |
|---|---|
| Country of origin: | Australia |
| Type: | (Wirraway Mk I) two-seat advanced flying and armament trainer |
| Powerplant: | one 600hp (447kW) CAC-built Pratt & Whitney R-1340-S1H1-G Wasp nine-cylinder single-row radial engine |
| Performance: | maximum speed 354km/h (220mph); initial climb rate 594m (1950ft) per minute; service ceiling 7010m (23,000ft); range 1159km (720 miles) |
| Weights: | empty 1811kg (3992lb); maximum take-off 2991kg (6595lb) |
| Dimensions: | span 13.11m (43ft); length 8.48m (27ft 10in); height 2.66m (8ft 8.75in) |
| Armament: | two 0.303in fixed forward-firing machine guns in the upper side of the forward fuselage, and provision for one 0.303in trainable rearward-firing machine gun in the rear of the cockpit, plus an external bomb load of 1000lb (454 kg) |

# Commonwealth Boomerang

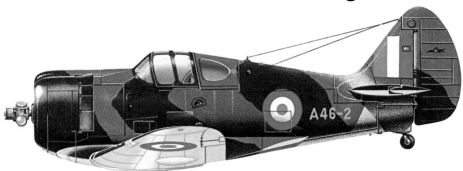

Given the very real possibility that it may become isolated from sources of major equipment items, Australia decided in 1941 to develop an indigenous weapons design and manufacturing capability. The Boomerang was ordered as an emergency fighter that was based on many assemblies and components already in production for the Wirraway trainer, itself a development of the North American NA-33, and a powerful Australian-built US engine. The resulting Boomerang fighter-bomber prototype first flew in May 1942, only 14 weeks after the design had been approved. Production of the basically similar Boomerang Mk I totalled 105 aircraft delivered by June 1943, and there followed 95 Boomerang Mk II warplanes that differed only in minor details. The Boomerang combined adequate performance with good armament, low-level agility and strength. Pictured is a Boomerang Mk 1 of No 2 Operational Training Unit, RAAF, based at Port Pirie in South Australia in late 1942.

| Country of origin: | Australia |
| --- | --- |
| Type: | (Boomerang Mk II) single-seat fighter and fighter-bomber |
| Powerplant: | one 1200hp (895kW) Pratt & Whitney R-1830-S3C4G Twin Wasp 14-cylinder two-row radial engine |
| Performance: | maximum speed 491km/h (305mph); climb to 6095m (20,000ft) in 9 minutes 12 seconds; service ceiling 10,365m (34,000ft); range 2575km (1600 miles) |
| Weights: | empty 2437kg (5373lb); normal take-off 3492kg (7699lb); maximum take-off 3742kg (8249lb) |
| Dimensions: | span 10.97m (36ft); length 7.77m (25ft 6in); height 2.92m (9ft 7in) |
| Armament: | two 20mm fixed forward-firing cannon and four 0.303in fixed forward-firing machine guns in the leading edges of the wing, plus an external bomb load of 227kg (500lb) |

# Consolidated P2Y-2

Captain Dick Richardson designed a monoplane flying-boat in 1927 to specifications laid down by a US Navy requirement. This had a fabric-covered parasol wing and aluminium skinned hull and, after winning a contract, first flew in prototype form (XPY-1) in January 1929. Much to Consolidated's chagrin a production contract for nine aircraft was awarded to the rival Glenn L. Martin company of Baltimore, and these were built under the designation P3M-1 and P3M-2. In May 1931 Consolidated received another US Navy contract for development of an improved XP2Y-1. This had an enclosed cockpit, a small lower wing, and three Wright R-1820E Cyclone radials, and first flew in March 1932. After testing the third engine was removed and in this form the aircraft was produced as the P2Y-1 (23 built). The last production P2Y-1 was fitted with twin R-1820-88 engines in wing fairings, and in 1936 all P2Y-1s in service were converted to this P2Y-2 standard.

| Country of origin: | USA |
| --- | --- |
| Type: | five-seat patrol flying-boat |
| Powerplant: | two 750hp (559kW) Wright R-1820-88 Cyclone radial piston engines |
| Performance: | maximum speed 224km/h (139mph); service ceiling 4905m (16,100ft); range 1899km (1180 miles) |
| Weights: | empty 5792kg (12,769lb); maximum take-off weight 11,460kg (25,266lb) |
| Dimensions: | span 30.48m (100ft); length 18.82m (61ft 9in); height 5.82m (19ft 1in); wing area 140.65 sq m (1514 sq ft) |
| Armament: | one .3in Browning machine gun on flexible mount in bow position; one .3in Browning machine gun on flexible mount in each of the two dorsal hatches; plus a bomb load of 907kg (2000lb) |

# Consolidated PB2Y Coronado

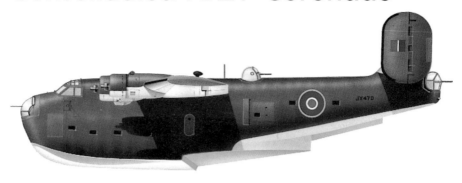

The XPB2Y-1 prototype was ordered by the US Navy in 1936. The Navy had perceived a need for a patrol flying-boat offering increased performance and weapons-carrying capability over the PBY-1 then entering service. The aircraft was delivered to the Navy in early 1938 following a first flight in December 1937, and after assessment against the Sikorsky XPBS-1 was adjudged to be the most suitable of the two for production. A number of problems were highlighted during flight testing, including serious lateral instability, but the delayed procurement enabled Consolidated to rectify these before the US Navy ordered six in March 1939 under the designation PB2Y-2 Coronado for use as service trials aircraft. Deliveries to VP-13 began in December 1940. The main production variant (210 built) was the PBY2-3 Coronado, which had increased armament and self-sealing tanks. Late production aircraft had ASV radar, and various engines were retrofitted.

| Country of origin: | USA |
| --- | --- |
| Type: | nine-seat maritime patrol flying-boat |
| Powerplant: | four 1200hp (895kW) Pratt & Whitney R-1830-88 Twin Wasp, 14-cylinder, two-row radial engines |
| Performance: | maximum speed 359km/h (223mph); service ceiling 6250m (20,500ft); range 3814km (2370 miles) |
| Weights: | empty 18,568kg (40,935lb); maximum take-off weight 30,844kg (68,000lb) |
| Dimensions: | span 35.05m (115ft); length 24.16m (79ft 3in); height 8.38m (27ft 6in); wing area 165.36 sq m (1780 sq ft) |
| Armament: | two 0.5 in machine guns in bow turret; two 0.5 in machine guns in ventral turret; two 0.5 in machine guns in tail turret; one 0.5in trainable lateral-firing machine gun in each of two 'beam' positions; provision for up to 5443kg (12,000lb) of bombs in an internal bay |

# Consolidated PBY-1 to PBY-5 Catalina

The PBY series, now almost universally known as the Catalina after its British designation, was built in larger numbers than all other flying boats combined, and was manufactured over a period of 10 years on no fewer than six production lines. The type was extremely slow, even by the standards of flying boats in World War II, but it was also extremely reliable and possessed very good endurance. The XP3Y-1 prototype made its maiden flight in March 1934, and there followed 60, 50, 66, 33 and 1024 examples respectively of the PBY-1, improved PBY-2, PBY-3 with uprated engines, PBY-4 with further uprated engines, and PBY-5 with still more power and with waist blisters rather than hatches. The type was also built in Canada as the Boeing PB2B (290 machines) and in the USSR (considerably more than 400 aircraft). The PBY-5 pictured here was supplied to the RAAF as part of an order for 18 and assigned to No 11 Squadron. Note the ASV.II radar aerials ahead of the struts.

| Country of origin: | USA |
| --- | --- |
| Type: | (PBY-5) nine-seat maritime reconnaissance and bomber flying boat |
| Powerplant: | two 1200hp (895kW) Pratt & Whitney R-1830-82 Twin Wasp 14-cylinder two-row radial engines |
| Performance: | maximum speed 322km/h(200mph ); maximum rate of climb 302m (990ft) per minute; ceiling 6585m (21,600ft); range 3050km (1895 miles) |
| Weights: | empty 7893kg (17,400lb); maximum take-off 15,145kg (33,389lb) |
| Dimensions: | span 31.70m (104ft); length 19.45m (63ft 10in); height 5.76m (18ft 11in) |
| Armament: | two 0.3in trainable forward-firing machine guns in bow turret, one 0.3in trainable rearward-firing machine gun in ventral tunnel position, and one 0.5in trainable lateral-firing machine gun in each 'blister' beam position, plus an external load of 4500lb (2041kg) |

# Consolidated PBY-5A and PBY-6A Catalina

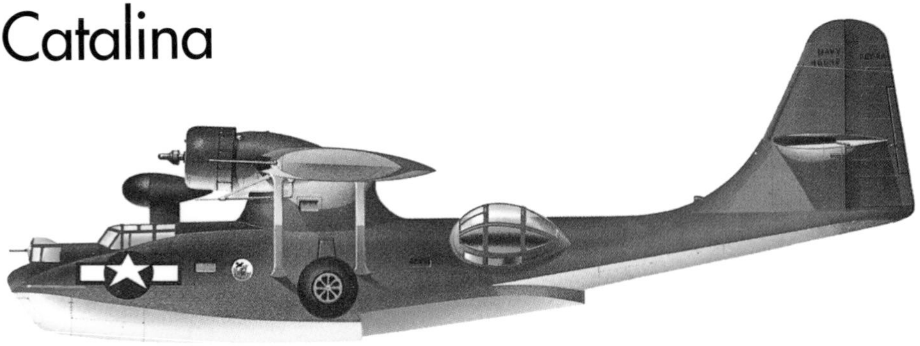

The XPBY-5A prototype first flew in November 1939, improving the versatility of the PBY series by the introduction of retractable tricycle landing gear. This new amphibian flying boat type entered production as the PBY-5A of which 794 were delivered to the US Navy. The Royal Air Force received 225 generally similar PBY-5B 'boats. Further development of the amphibian resulted in the PBY-6A (235 machines) with revised armament and an enlarged tail, and the Naval Aircraft Factory PBN-1 Nomad (156 machines) to a PBY-5A standard improved with a larger tail unit, greater fuel capacity and revised armament. The PBY-5A was also built in Canada as the Canadian Vickers PVB-1A, and numbers of aircraft were transferred to the US Army Air Forces with designations in the OA-10 series. Pictured here is one of the last of all Catalinas, a PBY-6A with US Navy number 46648. Note the pylon-mounted radar and nose turret housing two 0.5in machine guns.

| Country of origin: | USA |
| --- | --- |
| Type: | (PBY-5A) nine-seat maritime reconnaissance and bomber amphibian flying boat |
| Powerplant: | two 1200hp (895kW) Pratt & Whitney R-1830-92 Twin Wasp 14-cylinder two-row radial engines |
| Performance: | maximum speed 288km/h (179mph); climb to 3050m (10,000ft) in 19 minutes 18 seconds; service ceiling 4480m (14,700ft); range 5713 km (3550 miles) |
| Weights: | empty 9485kg (20,910lb); maximum take-off 16,067kg (35,420lb) |
| Dimensions: | span 31.70m (104ft); length 19.45m (63ft 10in); height 5.76m (18ft 11in) |
| Armament: | two 0.3 in trainable forward-firing machine guns in bow turret, one 0.3in trainable rearward-firing machine gun in ventral tunnel position, and one 0.5in trainable lateral-firing machine gun in each 'blister' position, plus an external load of 2041kg (4500lb) |

# Consolidated B-24D Liberator

**P**roduced in a number of variants for a host of operational and training tasks, the Liberator was built in larger numbers (18,431 machines) than any other US warplane of World War II and was delivered in greater quantities than any other bomber in aviation history. First flown in December 1939, the single XB-24 prototype paved the way for seven YB-24 service test aircraft, and then nine B-24A initial production machines with heavier defensive armament. The XB-24 was then upgraded to the XB-24B standard that led to the nine B-24C bombers and then the first major production models, the B-24D (2738 aircraft), generally similar B-24E (791 aircraft) and B-24G (430 aircraft with a power-operated nose turret). The B-24 made its operational debut in June 1942 with the long-range raids from Egypt against Hitler's Romanian oilfields. Pictured here is B-24D-85-CO *Teggie Ann*, the Group Lead Ship of the 47th Bomb Wing, 376th BG, painted in desert pink.

| | |
|---|---|
| Country of origin: | USA |
| Type: | (B-24D) ten-seat long-range heavy bomber |
| Powerplant: | four 1200hp (895kW) Pratt & Whitney R-1830-43 or -65 14-cylinder two-row radial engines |
| Performance: | maximum speed 488km/h (303mph); climb to 6095m (20,000ft) in 22 minutes 0 seconds; service ceiling 9755m (32,000ft); range 4586km (2850 miles) |
| Weights: | empty 14,490kg (32,605lb); maximum take-off 27,216kg (60,000lb) |
| Dimensions: | span 33.53m (110ft); length 20.22m (66ft 4in); height 4.46m (17ft 11in) |
| Armament: | two 0.5in trainable forward-firing machine guns in the nose, two 0.5in trainable machines guns in each of the dorsal, ventral and tail turrets, and one 0.5in trainable lateral-firing machine gun in each of the waist positions, plus an internal bomb load of 3992kg (8800lb) |

# Consolidated B-24J Liberator

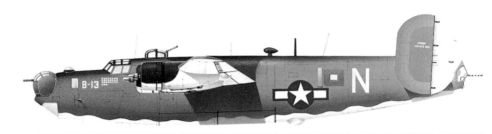

The B-24G, equipped with a nose turret, paved the way for further Liberator development, which included the B-24H (738 built by Consolidated with a Consolidated nose turret, and 2362 made by Douglas and Ford with an Emerson turret), the B-24J that was an improved B-24H with an autopilot and other operational enhancements including a more capable bomb sight (6678 made by Consolidated, Douglas, Ford and North American), the B-24L with two manually operated tail guns rather than a turret (1667 aircraft from Consolidated and Ford), and the B-24M improved version of the B-24J (2593 aircraft from Consolidated and Ford). As with the earlier models, there were also LB-30, C-87 and RY transport, AT-22 trainer, F-7 long-range photo-reconnaissance and PB4Y-1 maritime reconnaissance variants. Seen here in the markings of VP-110, one of the US Navy anti-submarine squadrons, this PB4Y-1 operated from Dunkeswell, Devon.

| | |
|---|---|
| Country of origin: | USA |
| Type: | (B-24J) eight/12-seat long-range heavy bomber |
| Powerplant: | four 1200hp (895kW) Pratt & Whitney R-1830-65 14-cylinder two-row radial engines |
| Performance: | maximum speed 483km/h (300mph); climb to 6095m (20,000ft) in 25 minutes; service ceiling 8535m (28,000ft); range 3380km (2100 miles) |
| Weights: | empty 16,556kg (36,500lb); maximum take-off 29,484kg (65,000lb) |
| Dimensions: | span 33.53m (110ft); length 20.47m (67ft 2in); height 5.49m (18ft) |
| Armament: | two 0.5in trainable machine guns each in the nose, dorsal, ventral and tail turrets, and one 0.5in trainable lateral-firing machine gun in each of the waist positions, plus an internal bomb load of 3992kg (8800lb) |

# Consolidated TBY Sea Wolf

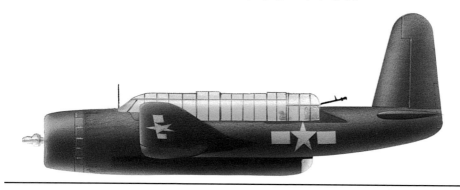

In 1939 the US Navy issued a requirement for a carrierborne torpedo and level bomber to succeed the Douglas TBD Devastator, and the best of 13 design submissions were made by Brewster, Grumman and Vought. The Brewster type was then discarded, the Grumman type matured as the TBF Avenger, and the Vought type was ordered as the XTBU-1 prototype that first flew in December 1941. This offered better performance than the TBF and was ordered into production. Vought was hard pressed to meet current orders and the contract therefore passed to Consolidated, resulting in a change of designation to TBY. An order for 1100 aircraft was placed in September 1943, these gaining the name Sea Wolf. The first aircraft flew in August 1944, but production was slow and the contract was terminated after the delivery of 180 aircraft that were used only for training. Pictured here is a TBY-2 in US Navy markings.

| Country of origin: | USA |
|---|---|
| Type: | (TBY-2) three-seat carrierborne torpedo and level bomber |
| Powerplant: | one 2100hp (1566kW) Wright R-2600-22 Cyclone 14 14-cylinder two-row radial engine |
| Performance: | maximum speed 502km/h (312mph); initial climb rate 539m (1770ft) per minute; service ceiling 8960m (29,400ft); range 1650km (1025 miles) |
| Weights: | empty 5142kg (11,336lb); maximum take-off 8591kg (18,940lb) |
| Dimensions: | span 17.35m (56ft 11in); length 11.94m (39ft 2in); height 4.72m (15ft 6in) |
| Armament: | three 0.5in fixed forward-firing machine guns in leading edges of the wing and in the forward fuselage, one 0.5in trainable rearward-firing machine gun in the dorsal turret, and one 0.3in trainable rearward-firing machine gun in the ventral position, plus a torpedo and bomb load of 726kg (1600lb) |

# Convair F-102 Delta Dagger

In 1948 Convair flew the world's first delta wing aircraft, the XF-92A, which was part of a program intended to lead to a supersonic fighter. This was terminated, but the US Air Force later issued a specification for an extremely advanced all-weather interceptor to carry the Hughes MX-1179 electronic control system. This effectively made the carrier aircraft subordinate to its avionics, a radical concept in the early 1950s. The contract was contested between six airframe manufacturers, and awarded to Convair in September 1961. In the event the Hughes ECS system could not be delivered in time and was rescheduled for the F-106 program. Early flight trials of the F-102 prototype were disappointing, but once the design was right right, 875 were delivered. In the search mode the pilot flew with two control columns; the left hand being used to adjust the sweep angle and range of the radar.

| | |
|---|---|
| Country of origin: | USA |
| Type: | supersonic all-weather single-seat fighter-interceptor |
| Powerplant: | one 7802kg (17,200lb) Pratt & Whitney J57-P-23 turbojet |
| Performance: | maximum speed at 10,970m (36,000ft) 1328km/h (825mph); service ceiling 16,460m (54,000ft); range 2172km (1350 miles) |
| Weights: | empty 8630kg (19,050lb); maximum take-off 14,288kg (31,500lb) |
| Dimensions: | wingspan 11.62m (38ft 1.5in); length 20.84m (68ft 4.5in); height 6.46m (21ft 2.5in); wing area 61.45sq m (661.5sq ft) |
| Armament: | two AIM-26/26A Falcon missiles, or one AIM-26/26A plus two AIM-4A Falcons, or one  AIM-26/26A plus two AIM-4C/Ds, or six AIM-4As, or six AIM-4C/Ds, some aircraft fitted with 12 2.75in folding-fin rockets |

# Convair F-106 Delta Dart

The F-106 was originally designated F-102B to indicate the strong family connection with the earlier Delta Dagger. The aircraft is notable because of the fact that it was designed from the outset as an integral weapon system, in which each of the differing units (airframe, weapons, etc) would integrate as a compatible system. Central to this project was an electronic weapons control system. It had been hoped to realise this objective with the Delta Dagger, but delays in the program meant that the ECS was not ready until late in 1955, an unacceptable time scale to the USAF who planned to bring the F-102 into service that year. The F-106 program was delayed by engine problems, and flight tests proved disappointing. The Hughes designed MA-1 ECS was also not performing well. The aircraft eventually entered service in October 1959 and remained in service, in updated versions, until 1988.

| | |
|---|---|
| Country of origin: | USA |
| Type: | light attack and reconnaissance aircraft |
| Powerplant: | two 1293kg (2850lb) General Electric J85-GE-17A turbojets |
| Performance: | maximum speed at 4875m (16,000ft) 816km/h (507mph); service ceiling 12,730m (41,765ft); range with 1860kg (4100lb) load 740km (460 miles) |
| Weights: | empty 2817kg (6211lb); maximum take-off 6350kg (14,000lb) |
| Dimensions: | wingspan including tip tanks 10.93m (35ft 10.25in); length 8.62m (28ft .4in); height 2.7m (8ft 1.33in); wing area 17.09sq m (183.9sq ft) |
| Armament: | one 7.62mm GAU-2 Minigun six-barrelled machine gun, eight underwing hardpoints with provision for more than 2268kg (5000lb) of stores, including bombs, rocket and gun pods, napalm tanks, and other equipment |

# Convair B-58A Hustler

The B-58 was an historic aircraft on many counts. It was the first supersonic bomber and the first to reach Mach 2. It was the first aircraft constructed mainly from a stainless steel honeycomb sandwich, the first to have a slim body and fat payload pod so that when the load was dropped, the aircraft became slimmer and lighter, the first to have stellar-inertial navigation, and the first weapon system to be procured as a single package from the prime contractor. The technical problems in realising the aircraft were daunting, yet the aircraft was developed with admirable speed and success. The first flight was made on November 11, 1956, and development continued for almost three years. The first production aircraft was delivered in September 1959, and the type entered service with the 43rd Bomber Wing of SAC in March 1960. However with increasing reliance on the ballistic missile submarine fleet for deterrence, the USAF retired the B-58 in 1970.

| Coutry of origin: | USA |
|---|---|
| Type: | three-seat supersonic bomber |
| Powerplant: | four 7076kg (15,600lb) General Electric J79-5B turbojets |
| Performance: | maximum speed 2125km/h (1385mph); service ceiling 19,500m (64,000ft); range on internal fuel 8248km (5125 miles) |
| Weights: | empty 25,200kg (55,560lb); maximum take-off 73,930kg (163,000lb) |
| Dimensions: | wingspan 17.31m (56ft 10in); length 29.5m (96ft 9in); height 9.6m (31ft 5in); wing area 145.32sq m (1542sq ft) |
| Armament: | one 20mm T171 Vulcan rotary cannon in radar-aimed tail barbette, plus nuclear or conventional weapons in disposable underfuselage pod |

# Curtiss JN-4

The famous Curtiss 'Jenny' was one of the most important American aircraft of the inter-war period. The JN-4 has its origins in the Curtiss J, designed in 1914 by B. Douglas Thomas and used in operations against Pancho Villa's Mexican revolutionaries in 1916. The J evolved into the JN-2, and then the JN-3. This last aircraft was built in numbers totalling 100 aircraft for the US Army and the UK. The JN-4 in its original form closely resembled the JN-3, with the same unequal-span two-bay biplane wing and cross-axle main gear, and first appeared in 1916. The British took 105 and 21 went to the US Army, before the improved JN-4A and JN-4B appeared with larger tailplanes. Some 857 of these two types were built. The JN-4 Can (pictured here in the colours of the School of Aerial Fighting in 1918) was one of many civil and military versions. It was developed by Canadian Aeroplanes Ltd, which built 1260 of this aircraft.

| Country of origin: | USA |
| --- | --- |
| Type: | two-seat primary trainer |
| Powerplant: | one 90hp (67kW) Curtiss OX-5 inline piston engine |
| Performance: | maximum speed 121km/h (75mph); service ceiling 1980m (6500ft) |
| Weights: | empty 630kg (1390lb); maximum take-off weight 871kg (1920lb) |
| Dimensions: | span 13.3m (43ft 8in); length 8.33m (27ft 4in); height 3.01m (9ft 10in); wing area 32.7 sq m (352 sq ft) |

# Curtiss Model 33/34 (PW-8)

The inspiration that Curtiss gained from the company's racing activities is clearly visible in the designs of its fighter aircraft. In early 1922 Curtiss began development of a new fighter design, the L-18-1, which clearly owed much to the R-6. By the end of the year this had become the prototype PW-8, which flew in January 1923. It was a two-bay biplane with considerable wing stagger, a streamlined fuselage of metal construction, powered by a Curtiss D-12 engine. Following service trials of three prototypes with the US Army during the spring, an order for 25 production aircraft was received. Deliveries began in June 1924. The second prototype was modified with tapered wings for the 1924 Pulitzer Trophy, and took third place at this competition. This XPW-8B formed the basis for the new Curtiss Hawk P-1.

| | |
|---|---|
| Country of origin: | USA |
| Type: | single-seat fighter biplane |
| Powerplant: | one 440hp (328kW) Curtiss D-12 12-cylinder Vee piston engine |
| Performance: | maximum speed 275km/h (171mph); service ceiling 6205m (20,350ft); range 875km (544 miles) |
| Weights: | empty 991kg (2185lb); maximum take-off weight 1431kg (3155lb) |
| Dimensions: | span 9.75m (32ft); length 7.03m (23ft 1in); height 2.76m (9ft 1in); wing area 25.94 sq m (279 sq ft) |
| Armament: | two fixed forward-firing .3in Browning machine guns |

# Curtiss P-1B

The second XPW-8 prototype was modified at the behest of the US Army Air Corps to feature redesigned wings, and became the XPW-8B. However, during testing, problems associated with wing flutter prompted Curtiss to revert to the single-bay wing of the R-6 for the production P-1 Hawk. Ten were ordered in March 1925, and these differed from the prototype only in having extra centre-section bracing and a modified rudder. Service trials at McCook Field began in mid-August, prior to delivery to the 27th and 94th Pursuit Squadrons at Selfridge Field, Michigan. The initial contract also covered production of five additional aircraft with the 505hp (377kW) Curtiss V-1400 engine, designated P-2. Continuing development of the P-1 resulted in the P-1A, with a lengthened fuselage, modified cowling and Curtiss D-12C engine. Twenty-five were ordered in September 1925, followed by 23 P-1Bs (pictured), and 33 P-1Cs with a V-1150 engine.

| Country of origin: | USA |
|---|---|
| Type: | single-seat pursuit aircraft |
| Powerplant: | one 435hp (324kW) Curtiss V-1150-3 piston engine |
| Performance: | maximum speed 248km/h (154mph); service ceiling 6344m (20,800ft); range 1046km (650 miles) |
| Weights: | empty 970kg (2136lb); all-up weight 1349kg (2973lb) |
| Dimensions: | span 9.6m (31ft 6in); length 7.06m (23ft 2in); height 2.72m (8ft 11in); wing area 23.41 sq m (252 sq ft) |
| Armament: | two fixed forward-firing .3in machine guns |

# Curtiss P-6D Hawk

To produce the prototype XP-6 Hawk, Curtiss took the airframe of a P-1 and installed a Curtiss V-1570 Conqueror engine. This was flown into second place at the 1927 National Air Races at Skopane, Washington. A second (XP-A) conversion had the same Conqueror engine, untapered wings, and drag-reducing wing radiators, and took first place at the then remarkable speed of 201mph (323km/h). The US Army contracted Curtiss for 18 P-6s for evaluation, which had modified cowl and deeper fuselage. Nine had the 'Prestone' cooling system (including the aircraft pictured) and were designated P-6A. One of these was used as trials aircraft for the turbo-charged V-1570C Conqueror engine driving a three-blade screw. In the spring of 1932 all the P-6s were re-engined with this unit, becoming P-6Ds. The XP-6B, which flew from the eastern United States to Alaska, was a P-1C fitted with the same V-1570 engine.

| Country of origin: | USA |
|---|---|
| Type: | single-seat pursuit aircraft |
| Powerplant: | one 700hp (522kW) Curtiss V-1570C Conqueror inline piston engine |
| Performance: | maximum speed 319km/h (198mph); service ceiling 7530m (24,700ft); range 459km (285 miles) |
| Weights: | empty equipped 1224kg (2669lb); maximum take-off weight 1559kg (3436lb) |
| Dimensions: | span 9.6m (31ft 6in); length 7.06m (23ft 2in); height 2.72m (8ft 11in); wing area 23.41 sq m (252 sq ft) |
| Armament: | two fixed forward-firing .3in machine guns |

# Curtiss Model O-39 Falcon

Two variants of the Curtiss V-1150-engined O-1 Falcon were produced. The A-3 was a light bomber version of the O-1E for the US Army with twin .3in machine guns mounted on the lower wing and underwing racks, with provision for 91kg (200lb) of bombs. Production of the A-3 totalled 66 aircraft; six of these were converted as A-3A dual control trainers, followed by 78 A-3Bs which incorporated the improvements applied to the O-1E. The O-11 was the first of the Liberty-engined Falcons, some 66 of which were built from 1927. Several more one-off variants with different powerplants were evolved (XO-11 to X0-18). The final production version for the Army was the O-39, a Curtiss V-1570-engined variant similar to the O-1G, with smaller rudder, spatted wheels, radiator sourced from the P-6E Hawk, and on some, a glazed canopy.

| Country of origin: | USA |
| --- | --- |
| Type: | two-seat observation biplane |
| Powerplant: | one 700hp (522kW) Curtiss V-1570-25 Conqueror inline piston engine |
| Performance: | maximum speed 227km/h (141mph); service ceiling 4665m (15,300ft); range 1014km (630 miles) |
| Weights: | empty equipped 1325kg (2922lb); maximum take-off weight 1972kg (4347lb) |
| Dimensions: | span 11.58m (38ft); length 8.28m (27ft 2in); height 3.2m (10ft 6in); wing area 32.79 sq m (353 sq ft) |
| Armament: | one fixed forward-firing .3in Browning machine gun |

# Curtiss BF2C-1

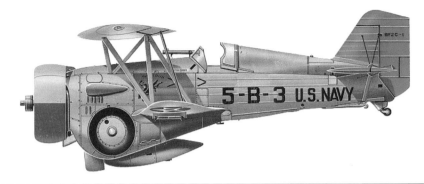

The US Navy attached great importance to dive-bombing and in the 1930s the Curtiss Goshawk family became well known in this role. The BF2C-1 was developed from the Model 35 Hawk II fighter, which was basically a P-6E with a radial engine and partially faired mainwheels. Two of these, designated XF11C-1 and XF11C-2, were purchased by the US Navy, powered by a 700hp (522kW) Curtiss V-1570-23 Conqueror and 600hp (447kW) Wright R-1510 Whirlwind engine respectively. The Navy ordered 28 F11C-2 production aircraft in October 1932, equipped with a special crutch for launching a 227kg (500lb) bomb in a dive. One of the F11C-2 production aircraft was modified with manually retracting landing gear (XFB2C-1), resulting in a US Navy order for 27 BF2C-1s that were delivered from October 1934. However, serious problems with the landing gear were encountered, prompting the swift withdrawal of this type. F11C-2s served until 1938.

| Country of origin: | USA |
| --- | --- |
| Type: | single-seat dive-bomber |
| Powerplant: | one 600hp (448kW) Wright SR-1820F2 Cyclone radial piston engine |
| Performance: | maximum speed 325km/h (202mph); service ceiling 7650m (25,100ft); range 840km (522 miles) |
| Weights: | empty equipped 1378kg (3037lb); maximum take-off weight 1874kg (4132lb) |
| Dimensions: | span 9.6m (31ft 6in); length 6.88m (22ft 7in); height 2.96m (9ft 8in); wing area 24.34 sq m (262 sq ft) |
| Armament: | two fixed forward-firing .3in machine guns; underfuselage crutch for one 227kg (500lb) bomb, or four 51kg (112lb) bombs on underwing racks |

# Curtiss Model 77 (SBC Helldiver)

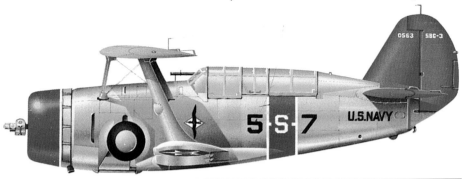

In response to their need for a new-two seat fighter the US Navy ordered a prototype from Curtiss in 1932 of their Model 73, in the form of a two-seat parasol wing monoplane with retractable landing gear. It was later decided to use this aircraft in a scout capacity and later still in the role of scout bomber. Dive-bombing trials highlighted serious structural deficiencies in the design of the wing, and the aircraft was redesigned as the XSBC-2 (Model 77) with a biplane wing and a 700hp (522-kW) Wright R-1510-12 Whirlwind 14 engine. This engine was changed in March 1936 to the Pratt & Whitney R-1535-82 Twin Wasp Junior and the aircraft was redesignated XSBC-3. In August 1936 the aircraft was ordered into production as SBC-3 for the US Navy, and the first of 83 aircraft was delivered to VS-5 in July 17, 1937. These were followed by 174 improved SBC-4s with a more powerful Wright engine, and were still in service with two squadrons in December 1941.

| Country of origin: | USA |
|---|---|
| Type: | two-seat carrier based scout-bomber |
| Powerplant: | (SBC-4) one 900hp (671-kW) Wright R-1820-34 Cyclone 9 radial engine |
| Performance: | maximum speed 377km/h (234 mph) at 4365m (15,200ft); service ceiling 7315m (24,000ft); range with 227kg (500lb) load 652km (405 miles) |
| Weights: | empty 2065kg (4,552lb); maximum take-off 3211kg (7,080lb) |
| Dimensions: | span 10.36m (34ft); length 8.57m (28ft 1 1/2in); height 3.17m (10ft 5in) |
| Armament: | one forward firing 0.3in machine gun; one trainable 0.3 machine gun in rear cockpit, plus bomb load of 227kg (500lb) |

# Curtiss P-36 and Mohawk

Anticipating the US Army's need for such an aeroplane, Curtiss designed and built the Model 75 – the USA's first 'modern' monoplane fighter – as a private venture. The prototype made its maiden flight in May 1935 with a Wright SGR-1670-G5 radial engine that was soon replaced by an uprated Wright R-1820-F Cyclone radial engine. The US Army then ordered three YP-36 aircraft for service trials, and this paved the way for 209 production aircraft in the form of 178 P-36A fighters that entered service from April 1938 and 31 P-36C fighters with two additional 0.3in machine guns in the wing. The type was also exported in Model 75A form to several countries including the UK, where the type was known as the Mohawk, and in downgraded Model 75 (or Hawk 75) form with fixed and spatted main landing gear units. The aircraft shown here wears the standard wartime olive-drab colour scheme of the US Army Air Force and early 1942 type national insignia.

| | |
|---|---|
| Country of origin: | USA |
| Type: | (P-36C) single-seat fighter |
| Powerplant: | one 1200hp (895kW) Pratt & Whitney R-1830-17 14-cylinder two-row radial engine |
| Performance: | maximum speed 500km/h (311mph); climb to 4570m (15,000ft) in 4 minutes 54 seconds; service ceiling 10,270m (33,700ft); range 1320km (820 miles) |
| Weights: | empty 2096kg (4620lb); maximum take-off 2726kg (6010lb) |
| Dimensions: | span 11.37m (37ft 3.5in); length 8.79m (28ft 10in); height 2.82m (9ft 3in ) |
| Armament: | one 0.5in fixed forward-firing machine gun and one 0.3in fixed forward-firing machine gun in the upper part of the forward fuselage, and two 0.3in fixed forward-firing machine guns in the leading edges of the wing |

# Curtiss P-40 and Tomahawk

The R-1830 engine was reliable and powerful by the standards of the 1930s, but when it became clear that it lacked the potential for development into more powerful forms full exploitation of the Model 75 airframe was schemed on the basis of the Allison V-1710 Vee engine. The installation of this engine into a converted P-36A created the Model 81 that first flew in October 1938 as the XP-40 . The first production model was the P-40 of which 199 were delivered with the 1150hp (976kW) V-1710-33 engine for service from May 1940. There followed 131, 193, 22 and 2320 examples of the P-40B, P-40C, P-40D and P-40E as well as 2060 Tomahawk Mk I aircraft for the UK. The P-40 was an adequate fighter by the standards prevailing early in World War II, but really made its mark as a capable fighter-bomber in the close support role. Pictured here is the personal aircraft of Henry Geselbracht, one of the pilots of the 2nd Squadron, American Volunteer Group.

| Country of origin: | USA |
|---|---|
| Type: | (P-40B) single-seat fighter |
| Powerplant: | one 1040hp (775kW) Allison V-1710-33 (C15) 12-cylinder Vee engine |
| Performance: | maximum speed 567km/h (352mph); climb to 4570m (15,000ft) in 5 minutes 6 seconds; service ceiling 9875m (32,400ft); range 1513km (940 miles) |
| Weights: | empty 2536kg (5590lb); maximum take-off 3447kg (7600lb) |
| Dimensions: | span 11.37m (37ft 3.5in); length 9.66 m (31ft 8.5in); height 3.22m (10ft 7in) |
| Armament: | two 0.5in fixed forward-firing machine guns in the upper part of the forward fuselage, and two 0.3in fixed forward-firing machine guns in the leading edges of the wing |

# Curtiss P-40 Warhawk and Kittyhawk

Further development of the Model 81 resulted in the Model 87, which featured the Packard V-1650 (Rolls-Royce Merlin) engine and a lengthened fuselage. The XP-40F prototype conversion (from a standard P-40D airframe) and the three YP-40F service test aircraft paved the way for 1311 P-40F fighter-bombers. The other main variants included the P-40K version of the P-40F with the V-1710-73 engine (1300 short-fuselage aircraft), P-40L with two wing guns removed (700 aircraft), P-40M with the V-1710-81 engine (600 aircraft), P-40N (a lightened version of the P-40L/M —5219 aircraft built), and finally the P-40R re-engined conversions of 300 P-40F/L aircraft. The British also purchased, or received under the Lend-Lease scheme, Kittyhawk Mk II to IV variants of the P-40F, K/M and N. Some 2097 of the American aircraft were shipped to the USSR. Shown here is a Kittyhawk Mk III of No 250 (Sudan) Squadron, RAF, based in southern Italy during late 1943.

| Country of origin: | USA |
| --- | --- |
| Type: | (P-40M) single-seat fighter and fighter-bomber |
| Powerplant: | one 1200hp (895kW) Allison V-1710-81 12-cylinder Vee engine |
| Performance: | maximum speed 552km/h (343mph); climb to 6095m (20,000ft) in 8 minutes 48 seconds; service ceiling 9450m (31,000ft); range 1207km (750 miles) |
| Weights: | empty 2812kg (6200lb); maximum take-off 5171kg (11,400lb) |
| Dimensions: | span 11.37m (37ft 3.5in); length 10.16m (33ft 4in); height 3.23m (10ft 7in) |
| Armament: | six 0.5in fixed forward-firing machine guns in the leading edges of the wing, plus an external bomb load of 680kg (1500lb) |

# Curtiss SB2C Helldiver

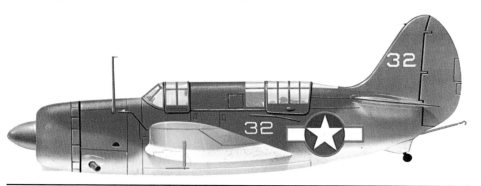

The SB2C Helldiver, schemed as successor to the SBD Dauntless, first flew in XSB2C-1 prototype form in December 1940. The aircraft was never fully effective but, for lack of anything better, was built to the extent of 7200 aircraft including the A-25 land-based version for the US Army as well as the Canadian-built SBF and SBW (300 and 894 respectively) by Canadian Fairchild and Canadian Car & Foundry. The type made its operational debut in November 1943. The main models were the SB2C-1 baseline variant (978 aircraft in two subvariants), SB2C-3 (1112 aircraft) with the 1900hp (1417kW) R-2600-20 engine, SB4C-4 (2045 aircraft in two subvariants) with provision for additional underwing stores, and SB2C-5 (970 aircraft) with increased fuel tankage. Pictured here is an SB2C-1, which by November 1943 was aboard USS *Bunker Hill* with squadron VB-17. The unit was heavily involved in attacks against the Japanese stronghold at Rabaul.

| | |
|---|---|
| Country of origin: | USA |
| Type: | (SB2C-1C) two-seat carrierborne and land-based scout and dive-bomber |
| Powerplant: | one 1700hp (1268kW) Wright R-2600-8 Cyclone 14 14-cylinder two-row radial engine |
| Performance: | maximum speed 452km/h (281mph); climb to 3050m (10,000ft) in 7 minutes 42 seconds; ceiling 7375m (24,200ft); range 2213 km (1375miles) |
| Weights: | empty 4588kg (10,114lb); maximum take-off 7626kg (16,812lb) |
| Dimensions: | span 15.15m (49ft 8.26in); length 11.18m (36ft 8in); height 4.00m (13ft 1.5in) |
| Armament: | two 20mm fixed forward-firing cannon in the leading edges of the wing, and two 0.3in trainable rearward-firing machine guns in the rear of the cockpit, plus an internal and external torpedo, bomb and depth charge load of 1361kg (3000lb) |

# Curtiss-Wright CW-14R Osprey

In 1930 Curtiss and the Travel Air Company merged to form the Curtiss-Wright Aeroplane Company. The first truly commercially successful produce of the partnership was the CW-1 Junior, an ultralight parasol wing sportsplane. The CW-12 Sport Trainer of 1930 was aimed squarely at the trainer market and was developed in three variants, before introduction of the CW-14. This was developed from a Travel Air Company design, the 4000/4 Speedwing. Under Curtiss-Wright production it was known as the Sportsman and, for the military export market, the Osprey. The CW-14 was built in five variants – the CW-A14D was a three-seater (5 built), the CW-B14B Speedwing Deluxe and CE-B14R Special Speedwing Deluxe were 'GT' versions with powerful engines, and the CW-C14B and CW-C14R were armed military aircraft for the export market. Pictured is a CW-C14R Osprey of the Bolivian Cuerpo de Aviaciones in 1935.

| Country of origin: | USA |
| --- | --- |
| Type: | two-seat reconnaissance and light attack biplane |
| Powerplant: | one 300hp (224kW) Wright R-975E Whirlwind nine-cylinder radial piston engine |
| Performance: | maximum speed 241 km/h (150mph); service ceiling 5000m (16,400ft); range386km (250 miles) |
| Weights: | empty 800kg (1764lb); maximum take-off weight 1700kg (3749lb) |
| Dimensions: | span 11.44m (37ft 6in); length 9m (29ft 6in); height 3.4m (11ft 2in) |
| Armament: | one .3in machine-gun on flexible mount in rear cockpit; underwing racks with provision for up to 500kg (1103lb) of stores |

# Dassault M.D. 450 Ouragan

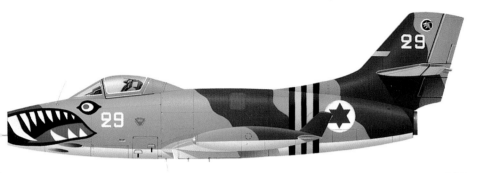

**W**orld War II effectively destroyed the French aircraft industry, and it had to be largely rebuilt from scratch while learning the new technology of jet propulsion. Most companies in the newly nationalised French aviation industry failed to see any of their designs built in any quantity, but the private firm of Dassault produced what is undoubtedly one of the most enduring and successful families of combat aircraft in the world. The whole line of Mirages, Etendards, Mystères, and Rafales stem from the simple, conventional, but highly effective Ouragan (Hurricane) of 1949. Powered by a licence built version of the British Rolls-Royce Nene turbojet, the first unarmed prototype was flown on February 28, 1949. Equipped with a pressurised cockpit and wingtip fuel tanks, the first of 150 production aircraft entered service in 1952.

| | |
|---|---|
| **Country of origin:** | France |
| **Type:** | single-seat fighter/ground attack aircraft |
| **Powerplant:** | one 2300kg (5070lb) Hispano-Suiza Nene 104B turbojet |
| **Performance:** | maximum speed 940km/h (584mph); service ceiling 15,000m (49,210ft); range 1000km (620 miles) |
| **Weights:** | empty 4150kg (9150lb); maximum take-off 7600kg (17,416lb) |
| **Dimensions:** | wingspan over tip tanks 13.2m (43ft 2in); length 10.74m (35ft 3in); height 4.15m (13ft 7in); wing area 23.8sq m (256.18sq ft) |
| **Armament:** | four 20mm Hispano 404 cannon; underwing hardpoints for two 434kg (1000lb) bombs, or 16 105mm rockets, or eight rockets and two 458 litre (101 Imp gal) napalm tanks |

# Dassault Mystère IIC

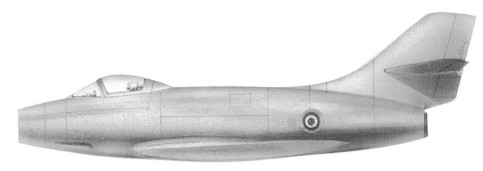

Marcel Dassault's design philosophy was always to progress in easy steps. The first Mystère was merely an M.D 450 Ouragan with 30 degrees of sweep to the wings and tail. This aircraft, designated the Mystère I, first flew in February 1951. Over the course of the following two years, eight further prototypes were built and flown. The original aircraft was powered by the ubiquitous Rolls-Royce Nene, while the remainder were fitted with a licence-built (by Hispano Suiza) version of the Tay. Pre-production aircraft were fitted with the all-French Atar axial engine, the first use of any French gas turbine for military aircraft propulsion. In April 1953 the Armee de l'Air ordered 150 of the fighters; ultimately 180 were built, 156 for France and 24 for Israel (never delivered). Service career was short, but the aircraft is important as the first swept-wing fighter to go into production in Europe.

| | |
|---|---|
| Country of origin: | France |
| Type: | single-seat fighter bomber |
| Powerplant: | one 3000kg (6600lb) SNECMA Atar 101D3 turbojet |
| Performance: | maximum speed 1060km/h (658mph); service ceiling 13,000m (42,650ft); range 1200km (745 miles) |
| Weights: | empty 5250kg (11,514lb); loaded 7450kg (16,442lb) |
| Dimensions: | wingspan 13.1m (42ft 9.75in); length 11.7m (38ft 6.25in); height 4.25m (13ft 11.75in) |
| Armament: | two 30mm Hispano 603 cannon with 150 rounds each |

# Dassault Mystère IVA

Although superficially similar to the II series aircraft, the IVA was in fact a completely new aircraft, with hardly a single structural part being common to both. The wing of the IV was thinner, more sharply swept, and much strengthened. The fuselage and tail were completely new and the pilot enjoyed powered controls. The US Air Force tested the prototype, which first flew as M.D 454-01 on September 28, 1952, and placed an off shore contract for 225 of the production aircraft in April 1953 to equip the Armée de l'Air. The first 50 production aircraft had the Rolls Royce Tay engine, but the remainder each had a Hispano Suiza Verdon 350. Exports orders were won from Israel and India, in addition to the aircraft supplied to the Armée de l'Air. The French aircraft saw action during the Suez conflict in 1956; several variants have been built with radar and with a dual cockpit.

| Country of origin: | France |
| --- | --- |
| Type: | single-seat fighter bomber |
| Powerplant: | one 2850kg (6,280lb) Hispano Suiza Tay 250A turbojet; or 3500kg (7716lb) Hispano Suiza Verdon 350 turbojet |
| Performance: | maximum speed 1120km/h (696mph); service ceiling 13,750m (45,000ft); range 1320km (820 miles) |
| Weights: | empty 5875kg (11,514lb); loaded 9500kg (20,950lb) |
| Dimensions: | wingspan 11.1m (36ft 5.75in); length 12.9m (42ft 2in); height 4.4m (14ft 5in) |
| Armament: | two 30mm DEFA 551cannon with 150 rounds, four underwing hardpoints with provision for up to 907kg (2000lb) of stores, including tanks, rockets, or bombs |

# Dassault Super Mystère B2

The Super Mystère developed from a Rolls-Royce Avon-engined version of the Mystère IV, known as the IVB. The Mystère IVB was a major leap forward, with tapered, milled and che-milled sheets, integral tanks, flush aerials, and a radar gunsight in the new nose.This aircraft proved to be a stepping stone to the bigger, heavier, and more powerful SMB.2, which introduced yet another new wing with 45 degrees of sweep and aerodynamics copied from the North American F-100 Super Sabre. The flattened nose also had more than a passing relationship to the American fighter. Although the first SMB.2 flew with the Rolls Royce Avon RA.7R, production examples were fitted with the Atar 101G. On its fourth flight, SMB.2-01, with Avon, easily exceeded Mach 1 in level flight, to make this the first supersonic aircraft to go into production, or in service.

| Country of origin: | France |
| --- | --- |
| Type: | single-seat fighter bomber |
| Powerplant: | one 4460kg (9833lb) SNECMA Atar 101 G-2/-3 turbojet |
| Performance: | maximum speed at 12,000m (39,370ft) 1195km/h (743mph); service ceiling 17,000m (55,775ft); range 870km (540 miles) |
| Weights: | empty 6932kg (15,282lb); maximum take-off 10,000kg (22,046lb) |
| Dimensions: | wingspan 10.52m (34ft 6in); length 14.13m (46ft 4.25in); height 4.55m (14ft 11in); wing area 35sq m (376.75sq ft) |
| Armament: | two 30mm DEFA 551cannon, internal Matra launcher for 35 SNEB 68mm rockets, two underwing hardpoints with provision for up to 907kg (2000lb) of stores, including tanks, rockets, or bombs |

# Dassault Mirage IIIEA

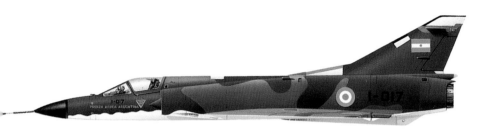

The hugely successful Mirage programme has brought incalculable prestige to the French aviation industry in the past five decades. The early prototype aircraft was conceived to meet an Armée de l'Air light interceptor specification of 1952. Once again Dassault found the powerplant insufficient and produced a larger, heavier, and more powerful aircraft, the Mirage III. On 24 October 1958 pre-production Mirage IIIA-01 became the first West European fighter to attain Mach 2 in level flight. The production version was designated the IIIC, a slightly developed version with either guns or a booster rocket for faster climb. Altogether 244 models were delivered to the Armée de l'Air, South Africa, and Israel. From this model emerged the longer and heavier IIIE for ground attack, with the Atar 9C turbojet and increased internal fuel. This variant first appeared on 20 April 1961.

| | |
|---|---|
| Country of origin: | France |
| Type: | single-seat day visual fighter bomber |
| Powerplant: | one 6200kg (13,668lb) SNECMA Atar 9C turbojet |
| Performance: | maximum speed at sea level 1390km/h (883mph); service ceiling 17,000m (55,755ft); combat radius at low level with 907kg (2000lb) load 1200km (745 miles) |
| Weights: | empty 7050kg (15,540lb); loaded 13,500kg (27,760lb) |
| Dimensions: | wingspan 8.22m (26ft 11.875in); length 16.5m (56ft); height 4.50m (14ft 9in); wing area 35sq m (376.7sq ft) |
| Armament: | two 30mm DEFA 552A cannon with 125 rpg; three external pylons with provision for up to 3000kg (6612lb) of stores, including bombs, rockets, and gun pods |

# Dassault Etendard IVP

The Dassault Etendard was designed to meet a NATO need for a light strike fighter capable of high subsonic speed and operation from unpaved forward strips. NATO specified that the engine should be the 4850lb thrust Bristol Orpheus, and this aircraft took shape as the Etendard VI. However, it became clear at an early stage that this aircraft was woefully underpowered. The enigmatic M. Dassault decided to risk company money on developing a private venture aircraft with the Atar engine. The NATO competition was in fact won by the Fiat G91, but Dassault's private venture Etendard IV attracted the attention of the Aeronavale and went into production in two forms, the IVM strike aircraft and the IVP reconnaissance aircraft. Both aircraft were in service by 1962. The IVM became the standard strike aircraft of the carriers *Foch* and *Clemenceau*, distinguished by a folding refuelling probe.

| | |
|---|---|
| Country of origin: | France |
| Type: | single-seat carrierborne strike/attack and interceptor aircraft |
| Powerplant: | one 4400kg (9700lb) SNECMA Atar 8B turbojet |
| Performance: | maximum speed 1180km/h (683mph) at low level; service ceiling 15,000m (49,215ft); maximum range 1700km (1056 miles) |
| Weights: | empty 5800kg (12,786lb); maximum take-off 12,000kg (26,455lb) |
| Dimensions: | wingspan 9.60m (31ft 6in); length 14.31m (46ft 11.2in); height 3.86m (12ft 8in); wing area 28.4sq m (305.7 q ft) |
| Armament: | two 30mm DEFA cannon with 150 rpg, five external hardpoints with provision for up to 1360 kg (3000lb) of stores, including nuclear weapons |

# Dassault Mirage 5BA

A considerable number of variants have appeared as the Mirage continues its 50-year gestation. The Mirage 5 and 50 were the final development in the III series, and were largely intended for export. Three versions were built under licence in Belgium, as assault, reconnaissance, or trainer aircraft (hence theB designation). Fifteen of the Belgian 5BA aircraft, and five of the 5BD two-seat variants, underwent a major upgrade programme during the early 1990s to allow them to stay in service until 2005. Additions include a Ferranti HUD, laser range finder, updated navigation/attack avionics, fixed canard foreplanes and complete rewiring. The work was undertaken by Belgium's major aerospace company, SABCA. Due to budget cuts, these aircraft were sold to Chile in 1994, who also operate new-build Mirage 50C, Mirage 50DC two-seat trainers and converted French 50F Mirages.

| | |
|---|---|
| **Country of origin:** | France |
| **Type:** | single-seat day visual fighter bomber |
| **Powerplant:** | one 6200kg (13,668lb) SNECMA Atar 9C turbojet |
| **Performance:** | maximum speed 1912km/h (1188mph); service ceiling 17,000m (55,755ft); combat radius at low level with 907kg (2000lb) load 650km (404 miles) |
| **Weights:** | empty 6600kg (14,550lb); maximum take-off 13,700kg (30,203lb) |
| **Dimensions:** | wingspan 8.22m (26ft 11.6in); length 15.55m (51ft); height 4.50m (14ft 9in); wing area 35sq m (376.7 q ft) |
| **Armament:** | two 30mm DEFA 552A cannon with 125 rpg; seven external pylons with provision for up to 4000kg (8818lb) of stores, including bombs, rockets, and gun pods |

# Dassault Mirage 50C

**S**een here in the colours of the Chilean air force, the Mirage 50 retains the same basic airframe as the Mirage III and 5, but is powered by a considerably more powerful version of the SNECMA 9-C turbojet. SNECMA began the programme to develop this engine, designated the 9K-50, in 1966 primarily for the next generation Mirage F.1 and G4 aircraft. Dassault soon realised the potentialities of fitting this engine into the standard delta-winged aircraft. The Mirage 50 was offered by Dassault with any of the considerable number of upgrades under development by the company since 1977, for instance single or dual cockpit, reconnaissance pack, enlarged nose to house radar, and a host of avionics options. Dassault marketed the aircraft quite aggressively, but the only countries to purchase were Chile (16 Mirage 50C) and Venezuela (6 Mirage 50EV and one DV).

| | |
|---|---|
| **Country of origin:** | France |
| **Type:** | single-seat day multi-role fighter bomber |
| **Powerplant:** | one 7200kg (15,873lb) SNECMA Atar 9K-50 turbojet |
| **Performance:** | maximum speed at high altitude 2350km/h (1460mph); service ceiling 18,000m (59,055ft); combat radius at low level with 800kg (1764lb) load 685km (425 miles) |
| **Weights:** | empty 7150kg (15,763lb); maximum take-off 13,700kg (30,203lb) |
| **Dimensions:** | wingspan 8.22m (26ft 11.6in); length 15.55m (51ft); height 4.50m (14ft 9in); wing area 35sq m (376.7sq ft) |
| **Armament:** | two 30mm DEFA 552A cannon with 125 rpg; seven external pylons with provision for R.530 air-to-air missiles, AS.30 or A.30L missiles, rocket launcher pods, and various attack loads including 1000lb bombs |

# Dassault Super Etendard

**D**uring the late 1960s it had been expected that the original Etendard force would be replaced in about 1971 by a specially developed carrier version of the Jaguar. This was rejected by the Aeronavale for political and financial reasons, and Dassault's proposal for an improved Etendard was chosen. The new aircraft has a substantially redesigned structure, a more efficient engine, inertial navigation system, and other upgraded avionics. The first prototype flew on October 3, 1975; deliveries to the Aeronavale began in June 1978. Fourteen Super Etendards were supplied to Argentina from November 1981; the five which had been delivered by the following spring were used to great effect against British shipping during the Falklands (Malvinas) War. Five were also loaned to Iraq. The aircraft in French service are due for replacement by Rafale by 2010, after an upgrade programme was carried out on the force.

| | |
|---|---|
| **Country of origin:** | France |
| **Type:** | single-seat carrierborne strike/attack and interceptor aircraft |
| **Powerplant:** | one 5000kg (11,023lb) SNECMA Atar 8K-50 turbojet |
| **Performance:** | maximum speed 1180km/h (733mph) at low level; service ceiling 13,700m (44,950ft); combat radius 850km (528 miles) on hi-lo-hi mission with one Exocet and two external tanks |
| **Weights:** | empty 6500kg (14,330lb); maximum take-off 12,000kg (26,455lb) |
| **Dimensions:** | wingspan 9.60m (31ft 6in); length 14.31m (46ft 11.2in); height 3.86m (12ft 8in); wing area 28.4sq m (305.7sq ft) |
| **Armament:** | two 30mm DEFA 553 cannon with 125 rpg, five external hardpoints with provision for up to 2100kg (4630lb) of stores, including nuclear weapons, Exocet and (Argentina only) Martin Pescador air-to-surface missiles, Magic air-to-air missiles, bombs and rockets, refuelling and reconnaissance pods |

# Dassault Mirage F1CK

The F1 once again demonstrates the willingness of the Dassault company to risk privately funded ventures. Recognising that the Mirage III family would eventually become redundant, the French government awarded Dassault a development contract for a successor, dubbed the F2. The aircraft was large with a conventional swept wing, breaking away from the classic Mirage form. Dassault privately funded a smaller version of the F2, called F1, sized to be powered by a single Atar engine. The Armée de l'Air subsequently chose to purchase this model. The aircraft marked a huge advance on the tailless delta form of previous models, with lower landing speeds and take-off runs. Other advances were made in the avionics suite and integral tankage for 45 percent more fuel. Manoeuvrability was also substantially improved. Pictured is the F1CK, in service with Kuwait until 1993.

| | |
|---|---|
| Country of origin: | France |
| Type: | single-seat multi-mission fighter attack aircraft |
| Powerplant: | one 7200kg (15,873lb) SNECMA Atar 9K-50 turbojet |
| Performance: | maximum speed at high altitude 2350km/h (1460mph); service ceiling 20,000m (65,615ft); range with maximum load 900km (560 miles) |
| Weights: | empty 7400kg (16,314lb); maximum take-off 15,200kg (33,510lb) |
| Dimensions: | wingspan 8.4m (27ft 6.75in); length 15m (49ft 2.25in); height 4.5m (14ft 9in); wing area 25sq m (269.11sq ft) |
| Armament: | two 30mm 553 DEFA cannon with 135 rpg, five external pylons with provision for up to 6300kg (13,889lb) of stores; Magic air-to-air missiles on wingtip rails, weapons include Matra Super 530 air-to-air missiles, conventional and laser guided bombs, rockets, AS.30L laser-guided air-to-surface missiles, AM.39 Exocet anti-ship missiles, ARMAT anti-radiation missiles, or Durandal, Belouga, or BAP anti-runway weapons |

# Dassault Mirage 2000C

Early research and experience had shown that the delta wing configuration carried some notable disadvantages, not least a lack of low speed manoeuvrability. With the development of fly-by-wire technology during the late 1960s and early 1970s, it was possible for airframe designers to overcome some of these problems, when coupled with advances in aerodynamics. The 2000C was designed by Dassault to be a single-seat interceptor to replace the F.1. The aircraft was adopted by the French government in December 1975 as the primary combat aircraft of the French air force, and was developed initially under contract as an interceptor and air superiority fighter. Deliveries to the Armée de l'Air began in July 1984; early production examples were fitted with the SNECMA M53-5; aircraft built after that date have the more powerful M53-P2.

| Country of origin: | France |
|---|---|
| Type: | single-seat air-superiority and attack fighter |
| Powerplant: | one 9700kg (21,834lb) SNECMA M53-P2 turbofan |
| Performance: | maximum speed at high altitude 2338km/h (1,453mph); service ceiling 18,000m (59,055ft); range with 1000kg (2,205lb) load 1,480km (920 miles) |
| Weights: | empty 7500kg (16,534lb); maximum take-off 17,000kg (37,480lb) |
| Dimensions: | wingspan 9.13m (29ft 11.5in); length 14.36m (47ft 1.25in); height 5.20m (17ft 0.75in); wing area 41sq m (441.3sq ft) |
| Armament: | two DEFA 554 cannon with 125rpg; nine external pylons with provision for up to 6300kg of stores, including R.530 air-to-air missiles, AS.30 or A.30L missiles, rocket launcher pods, and various attack loads including 1000lb bombs. For air defence weapon training the Cubic Corpn AIS \| (airborne instrumentation subsystem) pod, which resembles a Magic missile, may be carried |

# Dassault Rafale M

The Rafale has been designed and built to replace the Armée de l'Air's fleet of Mirage 2000s, F1s and SEPECAT Jaguars, and to form part of the new French nuclear carrier force's air wing. Although both services considered the Eurofighter, they have opted instead for the Rafale, which is smaller and lighter than the multi-national European aircraft. The Dassault company embarked on the project in early 1983, and the first flight took place on 4 July 1986. The airframe is largely constructed of composite materials, with a fly-by-wire control system. Early flight trials were particularly encouraging, with the aircraft achieving Mach 1.8 on only its second flight. Original production orders have been cut since the end of the Cold War. The three versions are the Rafale C single-seat operational aircraft for the Armée de l'Air, the Rafale B two seat multi-role aircraft, and the Rafale M navalised fighter (pictured), the first of which was delivered in 2001.

| Country of origin: | France |
| --- | --- |
| Type: | carrier based multi-role combat aircraft |
| Powerplant: | two 7450kg (16,424lb) SNECMA M88-2 turbofans |
| Performance: | maximum speed at high altitude 2130km/h (1324mph); combat radius air-to-air mission 1853km (1152 miles) |
| Weights: | empty equipped 9800kg (maximum take-off 19,500kg (42,990lb) |
| Dimensions: | wingspan 10.90m (35ft 9.175in); length 15.30m (50ft 2.5in); height 5.34m (17ft 6.25in); wing area 46sq m (495.1sq ft) |
| Armament: | one 30mm DEFA 791B cannon, 14 external hardpoints with provision for up to 6000kg (13,228lb) of stores, including air-to-air missiles, air-to-surface missiles, anti-ship missiles, guided and conventional bombs, rocket launchers, recce, Elint, and jammer pods |

# Dassault/Dornier Alpha Jet A

**R**ealisation that the Jaguar was too advanced and costly to be a standard basic trainer led the Armeé de l'Air to issue a requirement for a new trainer in 1967 (The jaguar was originally conceived in this role). The aircraft was also to be capable in the ground attack role. As it transpired the Luftwaffe had parallel need for such an aircraft, and on July 22, 1969 the two governments agreed to a common specification and agreed to adopt a common type of aircraft produced jointly by the two national industries. Following a design submission by Dassault/Dornier it was announced on July 24, 1970 that the Alpha Jet had been selected for production. Delivery of the first of 176 Alpha Jet A (Appui) light attack aircraft for the Federal German air force began in 1979. The A is distinguished by the pointed nose; that of the trainer is less acute.

| | |
|---|---|
| **Country of origin:** | France and Germany |
| **Type:** | two-seat light strike and reconnaissance aircraft |
| **Powerplant:** | two 1350kg (2976lb) Turbomeca Larzac 04 turbofans |
| **Performance:** | maximum speed 927km/h (576mph); service ceiling 14,000m (45,930ft); comabat range on hi-lo-hi mission 583km (363 miles) |
| **Weights:** | empty 3515kg (7749lb); maximum take-off 8000kg (17,637lb) |
| **Dimensions:** | wingpsan 9.11m (29ft 10.75in); length 13.23m (43ft 5in); height 4.19m (13ft 9in); wing area 17.5sq m (188.37sq ft) |
| **Armament:** | one 27mm IWKA Mauser cannon, five fuselage harpoints with provision for up to 2500kg (5511lb) of stores |

# de Havilland Mosquito Mk IV

One of the most successful warplanes ever built, and rivalled only by the Junkers Ju 88 in terms of versatility, the Mosquito was developed as a private venture to provide the Royal Air Force with a bomber that possessed such oustanding performance that no defensive armament would be required. Built largely of a ply/balsa/ply sandwich material, the Mosquito Mk I prototype first flew in November 1940 and paved the way for a mass of variants. The bombers were the Mk IV (273 aircraft with a 2000lb/907kg bomb load), the Mk VII (25 Canadian-built aircraft), the Mk IX (54 aircraft with an uprated powerplant and, in some machines, the ability to carry a 4000lb/1814kg bomb load), the Mk XVI (1200 aircraft to a Mk IX standard upgraded with a pressurised cockpit), the Mk XX (145 Canadian-built aircraft with American equipment), and Mk 25 (400 Canadian-built aircraft). Pictured here is a Mk IV of No 139 Squadron, RAF, based at Marham in 1942-43.

| Country of origin: | United Kingdom |
|---|---|
| Type: | (Mosquito B.Mk XVI) two-seat light bomber |
| Powerplant: | two 1680hp (1253kW) Rolls-Royce Merlin 72/73 or 76/77 12-cylinder Vee engines |
| Performance: | maximum speed 668km/h (415mph); climb to 4570m (15,000ft) in 7 minutes 30 seconds; service ceiling 11,280m (37,000ft); range 2888km (1795 miles) with a 907kg (2000lb) bomb |
| Weights: | empty 7031kg (15,500lb); maximum take-off 11,766kg (25,917lb) |
| Dimensions: | span 16.51m (54ft 2in); length 13.56m (44ft 6in); height 4.65m (15ft 3in) |
| Armament: | an internal and external bomb load of up to 1814kg (4000 lb) |

# de Havilland Mosquito FB.Mk VI

By far the most important of all the Mosquito variants was the FB.Mk VI, the standard fighter version for the RAF. Some 2,584 of these were built with various armament fits, normally four 0.303in machine guns and four 20mm cannon. The first aircraft flew in June 1942, with single stage engines, the guns of the NF.Mk II, and a short bomb bay for two 250lb bombs and wing racks for two more 250lb bombs. With the series VI aircraft this potential bomb/rocket load was doubled to 2000lb. This made the Mk VI series a hugely effective groud attack aircraft and for the rest of the war the versatile FB.Mk VI ranged across Europe on low-level raids, hitting targets such as the Gestapo HQ in the Hague and V-weapon sites, and in the hands of Coastal Command was used to deadly effect against Axis shipping. Pictured here is one of the 38 FB.Mk VIs exported to Australia and assigned to No 1 Squadron, RAAF.

| | |
|---|---|
| **Country of origin:** | United Kingdom |
| **Type:** | (Mosquito FB.Mk VI ) two-seat long-range fighter bomber |
| **Powerplant:** | two 1480hp (1103.5kW) Rolls-Royce Merlin 21 or 23 12-cylinder Vee engines |
| **Performance:** | maximum speed 595km/h (370mph); climb to 4570m (15,000ft) in 6 minutes 45 seconds; service ceiling 10,515m (34,500ft); range 2744km (1705 miles) |
| **Weights:** | empty 6492kg (14,300lb); maximum take-off 9072kg (20,000lb) |
| **Dimensions:** | span 16.51m (54ft 2in); length 13.08m (42ft 11in); height 5.31m (17ft 5in) |
| **Armament:** | four 20mm fixed forward-firing cannon and four 0.303in fixed forward-firing machine guns in the nose, plus an internal and external bomb, rocket or drop tank load of 907kg (2000lb) |

# De Havilland Vampire FB.Mk 6

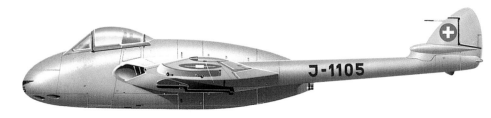

**P**roduction of an improved fighter-bomber version of the Vampire began in 1948 with the FB.Mk 5. This aircraft featured a restressed wing clipped from 12.19m to 11.58m (40ft to 38ft), with wing pylons capable of carrying either two 227kg (500lb) bombs or eight rocket projectiles. The FB.Mk 6 was the result of efforts to improve the performance of the Vampire, with an uprated version of the Goblin turbojet that afforded a marked increase in maximum speed. The FB.Mk 6 was not ordered by the RAF, but attracted much attention from overseas customers. At the time Switzerland was seeking a low-cost replacement for its fleet of Messerschmitt Bf 109s. The low cost and impressive performance of the Vampire persuaded the Swiss government to purchase 75 FB.Mk 6s. A licence was later granted to build the aircraft, and 100 were subsequently completed for the Swiss air force.

| | |
|---|---|
| **Country of origin:** | United Kingdom/Switzerland |
| **Type:** | single-seat fighter-bomber |
| **Powerplant:** | one 1498kg (3300lb) de Havilland Goblin 35 turbojet |
| **Performance:** | maximum speed 883km/h (548mph); service ceiling 13,410m (44,000ft); range with drop tanks 2253km (1400 miles) |
| **Weights:** | empty 3266kg (7200lb); loaded with drop tanks 5600kg (12,290lb) |
| **Dimensions:** | wingspan 11.6m (38ft); length 9.37m (30ft 9in); height 2.69m (8ft 10in); wing area 24.32sq m (262sq ft) |
| **Armament:** | four 20mm Hispano cannon with 150 rounds, wing pylons capable of carrying either two 227kg (500lb) bombs or 60lb rocket projectiles |

# De Havilland Vampire NF.Mk 10

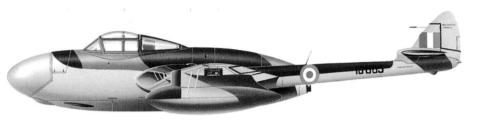

The RAF was remarkably slow to order jet night fighters, and the de Havilland company took the initiative to develop the D.H.113 NF. Mk 10 as a private venture. The aircraft was designed as a two-seater, and development was greatly speeded by the fact that the Vampire nacelle was similar in width to the nose of the Mosquito, so the crew compartment, AI Mk 10 radar and equipment of the NF versions could be transferred with the minimum of changes. Batches were delivered to the Egyptian air force before exports of arms to that country were banned in 1950. The RAF took over the contract and received 95 aircraft, which were first used by No 25 Squadron from West Malling in late 1951. The pilot and observer/radar operator sat close together in ordinary (non-ejecting) seats, which made emergency escape particularly hazardous.

| Country of origin: | United Kingdom |
|---|---|
| Type: | two-seat night fighter |
| Powerplant: | one 1520kg (3350lb) de Havilland Goblin turbojet |
| Performance: | maximum speed 885km/h (549mph); service ceiling 12,200m (40,000ft); range 1255km (780 miles) |
| Weights: | empty 3172kg (6984lb); loaded 5148kg (11,350lb) |
| Dimensions: | wingspan 11.6m (38ft); length 10.55m (34ft 7in); height 2m (6ft 7in); wing area 24.32sq m (262sq ft) |
| Armament: | four 20mm Hispano cannon |

199

# De Havilland Venom FB.Mk 4

The design of the Venom can be traced to the Vampire Mk 8, which the company fitted with a more powerful Ghost engine in place of the Goblin, in the hope of wringing more performance from the same basic design. Other changes included a thinner wing of greater area fitted with a 355 litre (78 Imp gal) tank on each tip with a revised fuel system to match, spring-tab controls and extended boundary-layer deflectors on the fuselage – forward of the inlets. Despite the availability of swept-wing technology de Havilland persisted with conventional aerodynamics, and in one stroke removed any chance the Venom had of competing with its best foreign rivals. From initial deliveries of the FB.Mk 1 in December 1951, de Havilland continued to develop the troubled aircraft. The FB.Mk 4 was a great improvement, with powered controls, more efficient tail surfaces, and an ejector seat.

| | |
|---|---|
| **Country of origin:** | United Kingdom |
| **Type:** | single-seat fighter bomber |
| **Powerplant:** | one 2336kg (5150lb) de Havilland Ghost 105 turbojet |
| **Performance:** | maximum speed 1030km/h (640mph); service ceiling 14,630m (48,000ft); range with drop tanks 1730km (1075 miles) |
| **Weights:** | empty 4174kg (9202lb); maximum loaded 6945kg (15,310lb) |
| **Dimensions:** | wingspan (over tip tanks) 12.7m (41ft 8in); length 9.71m (31ft 10in); height 1.88m (6ft 2in); wing area 25.99sq m (279.75sq ft) |
| **Armament:** | four 20mm Hispano cannon with 150 rounds, two wing pylons capable of carrying either two 454kg (1000lb) bombs or two drop tanks; or eight 27.2kg (60lb) rocket projectiles carried on centre-section launchers |

# De Havilland Sea Vixen FAW Mk 2

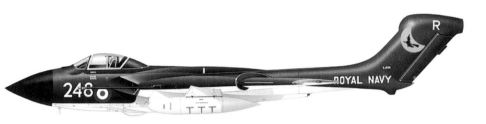

The Sea Vixen, like many of the aircraft operated by the Royal Navy, was originally designed to a Royal Air Force requirement for a land-based all weather interceptor, first issued in 1946. The aircraft lost the competition to the Gloster Javelin. Fortunately for de Havilland the Royal Navy had a similar requirement for a carrier based aircraft, and after successful trials from the deck of HMS *Albion* an initial order was placed in January 1955. The first 92 aircraft to be completed by the de Havilland factory at Christchurch were designated FAW. Mk 1s and featured a hinged and pointed radome, powerfolding wings and hydraulically steerable nosewheel. The later FAW Mk.2 had increased fuel capacity and provision for four Red Top missiles in place of the Firestreaks carried by the Mk 1. Most were brought up to Mk 2 standard by 1964 and remained in service until 1971.

| Country of origin: | United Kingdom |
|---|---|
| Type: | two-seat all-weather strike fighter |
| Powerplant: | two 5094kg (11,230lb) Rolls-Royce Avon 208 turbojets |
| Perfomance: | maximum speed 1110km/h (690mph) at 20,000ft at sea level; climb to 3050m (10,000ft) in 1 min 30 secs; service ceiling 21,790m (48,000ft); range about 600 miles (FAW 1) and 800 miles (FAW 2) |
| Weight: | empty weight about 22,000lb; maximum take-off 18,858kg (41,575lb) |
| Dimensions: | wingspan 15.54m (51ft); length 17.02 m (55ft 7in); height 3.28 m (10ft 9in); wing area 60.20sq m (648sq ft) |
| Armament: | on four inboard wing pylons; four Firestreak air-to-air missiles (FAW 1) or four Red Top air-to-air missiles (FAW 2); on outer pylons 1000 lb bombs, Bullpup air-to-surface missiles or equivalent stores; as built, but not used, provision for 28 folding fin aircraft rockets in two flip-out boxes beneath cockpit floor |

# Dewoitine D.500 series

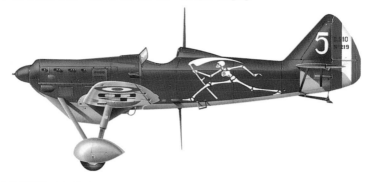

In 1930 the French air ministry issued a requirement for a Nieuport Ni-D.62 replacement, and Dewoitine decided to break away from its previous pattern of parasol-wing monoplane fighters by designing a cantilever low-wing monoplane of all-metal construction. The resulting D.500.01 prototype first flew in June 1932, and there followed for export sales as well as French service 101 D.500C.1 production aircraft with the 690hp (515kW) Hispano-Suiza 12Xbrs engine, 157 D.501C.1 aircraft with the 12Xcrs engine, and finally 120 D.510C.1 aircraft with an uprated engine in a lengthened nose. Together with older D.500 and D.501 aircraft serving with second-line units, 60 D.510 fighters were still operational with the French Air Force in 1939 but were rapidly relegated to training service or redeployed to North Africa. Pictured is a D.510 of the 1st Escadrille, Groupe de Chasse I/8, Armeé de l'Air, based at Marignane in September 1939.

| Country of origin: | France |
| --- | --- |
| Type: | (D.510C.1) single-seat fighter |
| Powerplant: | one 860hp (641kW) Hispano-Suiza 12Ycrs 12-cylinder Vee engine |
| Performance: | maximum speed 375km/h (233mph); climb to 5000m (16,405ft) in 7 minutes 30 seconds; service ceiling 10,200m (33,465ft); range 840km (522 miles) |
| Weights: | empty 1378kg (3038lb); maximum take-off 1823kg (4019lb) |
| Dimensions: | span 11.48m (37ft 8in); length 7.56m (24ft 9.63in); height 2.70m (8ft 10.5in) |
| Armament: | one 20mm fixed forward-firing cannon in the nose and two 7.5mm fixed forward-firing machine guns in the leading edges of the wing |

# Dewoitine D.520

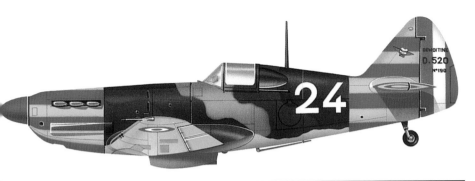

The D.520 resulted from a 1934 requirement for an advanced single-seat fighter to replace types such as the Dewoitine D.510, which had been rendered obsolete by the advent of the first 'modern' fighters such as the Hawker Hurricane. The aircraft was developed via the indifferent D.513 to meet a revised 1936 requirement, and incorporated features such as cantilever low-set flapped wing, enclosed cockpit, landing gear with retractable main units and engine delivering about 1000 hp (746kW) driving a variable-pitch propeller The D.520 prototype first flew in October 1938, and only 36 D.520C.1 fighters had been delivered before the German invasion of May 1940. Further deliveries were made during the German offensive, and the D.520 acquitted itself very well. Production eventually reached 905 aircraft for service mainly with the Vichy French Air Force and were also passed to Germany's allies.

| | |
|---|---|
| Country of origin: | France |
| Type: | (D.520C.1) single-seat fighter |
| Powerplant: | one 930hp (693kW) Hispano-Suiza 12Y-45 12-cylinder Vee engine |
| Performance: | maximum speed 540km/h (336mph); climb to 4000m (13,125ft) in 5 minutes 49 seconds; service ceiling 11,000m (36,090ft); range 1540km (957 miles) |
| Weights: | empty 2125kg (4685lb); maximum take-off 2790kg (6151lb) |
| Dimensions: | span 10.20m (33ft 5.5in); length 8.76m (28ft 8.75in); height 8ft 2.57m (5.25in) |
| Armament: | one 20mm fixed forward-firing cannon in the nose, and four 7.5mm fixed forward-firing machine guns in the leading edges of the wing |

# Dewoitine HD.730

**E**mile Dewoitine established his own company in October 1920 and produced a series of single-seat parasol wing fighter aircraft during the 1920s before the company was absorbed into the nationalised SNCAM concern in 1938. By that time Dewoitine was well advanced with the design of a catapult-launched light observation and scouting aircraft for the French Navy, designated the HD.730. This had twin-float landing gear, twin-fin tailplane and a low cantilever wing mounted on a fuselage providing accommodation for two seated in tandem. Two prototypes were flown with the Renault 6Q-03 engine in early 1940, but trials proved that much more power was required. Development was continued under the Vichy regime and a third prototype was produced with reduced wing span, but by the end of 1945 official interest in the aircraft had faded.

| | |
|---|---|
| Country of origin: | France |
| Type: | two-seat reconnaissance floatplane |
| Powerplant: | one 220hp (164kW) Renault 6Q-03 inline piston engine |
| Performance: | maximum speed 230km/h (143mph); service ceiling 5120m (16,800ft); range 1350km (839 miles) |
| Weights: | empty 1173kg (2586lb); maximum take-off weight 4123kg (1870lb) |
| Dimensions: | span 12.6m (41ft 4in); length 9.75m (32ft); height 3.18m (10ft 5in); wing area 20 sq m (215 sq ft) |
| Armament: | one fixed forward firing 7.5mm Darne machine gun; one 7.5mm Darne machine gun on flexible mount for observer/gunner; underwing racks with provision for up to eight 10kg (22lb) bombs |

# Dorand Ar.1

In 1916 the French Government issued a specification to the aviation industry for a biplane with a tractor engine to replace the Farman F.20. Only Colonel Dorand, Commander of the French Army's Technical Section, showed any interest and submitted an updated version of one of his (unsuccessful) 1914 biplanes, the D.O I. The new aircraft was generally similar to its predecessor, with back-staggered wings, but benefited from a much more powerful engine. Redesignated as the Dorand AR.I this aircraft completed trials in September 1916 and was produced in large numbers for Aviation Militaire for service over the Western and Italian Fronts. The second production version had reduced span wings and a 190hp (142kW) Renault 8Ge engine. The Air Service of the American Expeditionary Force acquired 22 AR.1s and 120 AR.2s respectively.

| | |
|---|---|
| Country of origin: | France |
| Type: | two-seat observation biplane |
| Powerplant: | (AR.1) one 200hp (149kW) Renault 8Gdy inline piston engine |
| Performance: | maximum speed 148km/h (92mph); service ceiling 5500m (18,045ft); endurance 3hrs |
| Weights: | maximum take-off weight 1315kg (2900lb) |
| Dimensions: | span 13.29m (43ft 7in); length 9.14m (30ft); height 3.3m (10ft 10in); wing area 50.17 sq m (540 sq ft) |
| Armament: | one fixed forward-firing .303in Vickers machine gun; plus one or two .303 Lewis guns on flexible mount in rear cockpit |

# Dornier Do JIId Wal

As Head of Design and Construction at Zeppelin-Werke Lindau GmbH in Friedrichshafen, Dr Claudius Dornier made pioneering advances in the development of flying-boats. After the war the works were re-established at Manzell as Dornier Metallbau, but the punitive terms of the Versailles agreement meant no construction could take place at the site. So Dornier established a subsidiary company in Pisa and built the Do J Wal (Whale), the most successful peacetime design that confirmed his status as the greatest flying-boat designer of his generation. It was first flown in 1922 and introduced the classic Dornier flying-boat configuration with a two-step hull incorporating aerodynamic sponsons to give stability on the water, and carrying a strut-braced untapered parasol wing. The Wal was operated by the Spanish and Italian navies in large numbers; pictured is a Dornier-built JIId, serving with I-G 70 Gruppo at Puerto de Pollensa in Majorca during the Spanish Civil War.

| | |
|---|---|
| Country of origin: | Germany |
| Type: | twin-engine patrol flying-boat |
| Powerplant: | two 690hp (515kW) BMW VI inline piston engines |
| Performance: | cruising speed 140km/h (87mph); service ceiling 3500m (11,480ft); range 2200km (1350 miles) |
| Weights: | loaded 5700kg (12,566lb) |
| Dimensions: | span 22.5m (73ft 10in); length 17.25m (56ft 7in); height 5.2m (17ft) |
| Armament: | optional machine gun in nose and dorsal positions |

# Dornier Do 17E

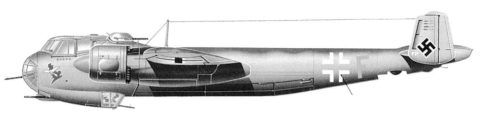

**D**esigned as a fast mailplane for Deutsche Lufthansa and first flown in 1934, the Do 17 was rejected in its planned role after the delivery of three single-finned aircraft and was then developed via 12 prototypes as a high-speed bomber with twin vertical tail surfaces. Entering service in the first months of 1937 and soon receiving the nickname 'The Flying Pencil' as a result of their very slender fuselage, the first two military variants were the Do 17E-1 and Do 17F-1 intended for the high-speed bomber and long-range photo-reconnaissance roles respectively, the latter with additional fuel and the internal bomb bay revised for the carriage of two cameras. The two types offered good performance and adequate all-round capabilities by the standards of the day, but were soon seen as obsolescent. Pictured is one of the Do 17Es operated by KG 40 under the command of Fliegerführer Atlantik from March 1941 onwards.

| Country of origin: | Germany |
| --- | --- |
| Type: | (Do 17E-1) three/four-seat light bomber |
| Powerplant: | two 750hp (559kW) BMW VI 7,3 12-cylinder Vee engines |
| Performance: | maximum speed 355km/h (221mph); service ceiling 5100m (16,730ft); radius 500km (311 miles) with maximum bomb load |
| Weights: | empty 4500kg (9921lb); maximum take-off weight 7040kg (15,520lb) |
| Dimensions: | span 18.00m (59ft 0.67in); length 16.25m (53ft 3.5in); height 4.32m (14ft 2in) |
| Armament: | one 7.92mm trainable forward-firing machine gun in the starboard side of the cockpit, provision for one 7.92mm trainable forward-firing machine gun in the lower nose, one 7.92mm trainable rearward-firing machine gun in the rear of the cockpit, one 7.92mm rearward-firing machine gun; internal bomb load of 750kg (1653lb) |

# Dornier Do 18

The Do 18 was designed as a medium-range maritime reconnaissance type to supersede the Dornier Wal 33 (from 1934 Do 15) and as a mailplane flying boat for service with Deutsche Lufthansa. The first of four prototypes made its maiden flight in March 1935. Only six civil flying boats were completed, the majority of the approximately 148 production 'boats going to the military for service from 1938. The primary military variants were the Do 18D (three subvariants to a total of about 75 machines) with 600hp (447.5kW) Junkers Jumo 205D Diesel engines, the Do 18G improved Do 18D with revised armament and provision for RATO units, and the Do 18H six-seat trainer. Do 18G and Do-18H production was 71 'boats, and many Do 18G machines were converted to Do 18N standard as air/sea rescue flying boats. Pictured here is a Do 18D of 3./Küstenfliegergruppe 406, based at List on the island of Sylt in August 1939.

| Country of origin: | Germany |
| --- | --- |
| Type: | (Do 18G-1) four-seat maritime reconnaissance flying boat |
| Powerplant: | two 880hp (656kW) Junkers Jumo 205D six-cylinder horizontally opposed Diesel engines |
| Performance: | maximum speed 267km/h (166mph); climb to 2000m (6560ft) in 17 minutes 30 seconds; service ceiling 4200m (13,780ft); range 3500 km (2175 miles) |
| Weights: | empty 5980kg (13,183lb); normal take-off 10,000kg (22,046lb); maximum take-off 10,800kg (23,809lb) |
| Dimensions: | span 23.70m (77ft 9.25in); length 19.37m (63ft 7in); height 5.32m (17ft 5.5in) |
| Armament: | one 20mm trainable rearward-firing cannon in the dorsal turret, and one 13mm trainable forward-firing machine gun in the bow position, plus an external bomb load of 100kg (220lb) |

# Dornier Do 24K-1

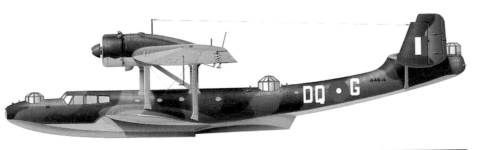

The Dornier Do 24 originated from a requirement issued in 1935 by the Dutch Navy for a flying-boat to replace the Dornier Wals then being used in the Dutch East Indies. The Do 24 was an all-metal monoplane with a hull of typical Dornier design and a strut-braced parasol wing carrying the three engines. The first two prototypes were evaluated for German use powered by Junkers Jumo 205C Diesel engines. The third prototype, which was actually the first to make its maiden flight on 3 July 1937, and the fourth prototypes, were each powered by 875hp (652kW) Wright R-1820-F52 Cyclone radial engines, in order to meet the Netherlands' desire to use the same type of engine as that of the Martin Model 139 bombers used in the East Indies. The prototypes for the Netherlands were successful and were flown to the Indies. In February 1942 the K-1 pictured was flown to Australia and used by the RAAF. Another ten K-1s were completed by the Dornier subsidiary in Switzerland.

| Country of origin: | Germany |
| --- | --- |
| Type: | air-sea-rescue and transport flying-boat |
| Powerplant: | three 875hp (652kW) Wright R-1820-G102 Cyclone radial piston engines |
| Performance: | maximum speed 332km/h (206mph); service ceiling 8050m (26,405ft); range 4700km (2920 miles) |
| Weights: | empty 10,600kg (23,369lb); maximum take-off weight 18,400kg (40,565lb) |
| Dimensions: | span 27m (88ft 7in); length 22.05m (72ft 4in); height 5.75m (18ft 10in); wing area 108 sq m (1163 sq ft) |
| Armament: | one 20mm Hispano-Suiza HS-404 trainable cannon in dorsal turret; one 7.92mm MG 15 trainable forward-firing machine gun in bow turret; one 7.92mm MG 15 trainable rearward-firing machine gun in tail turret |

# Dornier Do 217

The Do 217 was Dornier's response to a 1937 requirement for a long-range warplane optimised for the heavy level and dive bombing roles. The Do 217 was essentially a scaled-up version of the Do 215 version of the Do 17, and first flew in August 1938. The first operational model was the Do 217E of which some 800 aircraft were built in Do 217E-0 to Do 217E-4 subvariants with BMW 801 radial engines. These were followed by 950 examples of the Do 217K night bomber with a revised and unstepped nose, and finally the Do 217M development of the Do 217K with DB 603 inverted-Vee engines. Prototype and pre-production variants were the Do 217C bomber, Do 217P high-altitude reconnaissance, and Do 217R missile launching aircraft. There were also Do 217E and Do 217K subvariants armed with Hs 293 anti-ship missiles and *Fritz-X* guided bombs respectively. Do 217s sank the Italian ship *Roma* as she steamed to the Allies after Italy's surrender.

| | |
|---|---|
| Country of origin: | Germany |
| Type: | (Do 217E-2) four-seat heavy bomber |
| Powerplant: | two 1580hp (1178kW) BMW 801ML 14-cylinder radial engines |
| Performance: | maximum speed 515km/h (320mph); initial climb rate 216m (740ft) per minute; ceiling 9000m (29,530ft); range 2800km (1740 miles) |
| Weights: | empty 10,535kg (23,225lb); maximum take-off 16,465kg (36,299lb) |
| Dimensions: | span 19.00m (62ft 4in); length 18.20m (59ft 8.5in); height 5.03m (16ft 6in) |
| Armament: | one 15mm cannon in lower port side of nose, one 13mm machine gun in dorsal turret, one 13mm machine gun in ventral step position, 7.92mm forward-firing machine gun in nose, one 7.92mm machine gun in each cockpit side window; in the Do 217E-2/R19 subvariant, one remotely-controlled 7.92mm rearward-firing machine gun in the tail cone, plus a bomb load of 4000kg (8818lb) |

# Douglas O-2H

Although unremarkable in design and construction, the Douglas O-2 family gave sterling service and proved suitably flexible to allow a large number of variants to be developed for different roles. The two prototype XO-2s had the Liberty V-1650-1 engine and Packard 1A-1500 engine respectively, but the latter unit proved unreliable and was rejected. A production order for 45 O-2 aircraft for the USAAC, was followed by another 25 O-2s, 18 O-2As equipped for night flying, six O-2B s with dual controls, and 46 O-2Cs with modified radiators and landing gear. The major production versions were the O-2H (96 built) with completely redesigned fuselage, new tailplane, rigid interplane struts and improved landing gear, and the O-2J transport and liaison aircraft with armament deleted. Numerous other variants were built in small numbers with float equipment and different engines, before introduction of the O-25. Pictured is an O-2H of the 91st Observation Squadron, USAAC, in 1928.

| | |
|---|---|
| Country of origin: | USA |
| Type: | two-seat observation biplane |
| Powerplant: | one 420hp (313kW) Liberty V-1650-1 V-12 piston engine |
| Performance: | maximum speed 206km/h (128mph); service ceiling 4960m (16,270ft); range 579km (360 miles) |
| Weights: | empty 1375kg (3032lb); maximum take-off weight 2170kg (4785lb) |
| Dimensions: | span 12.09m (39ft 8in); length 8.76m (28ft 9in); height 3.2m (10ft 6in); wing area 38.18 sq m (411 sq ft) |
| Armament: | one fixed forward-firing .3in machine gun; one .3in machine gun on flexible mount in rear cockpit; underwing racks with provision for up to four 45kg (100lb) bombs |

# Douglas C-47 Skytrain/Dakota

The DC-3 was developed from the DC-2 with greater power and accommodation increased to 21, and first flew in December 1935. Some 445 aircraft were built to civil orders, but the DC-3 remains better known in its military forms as the C-47 Skytrain, R4D and Dakota for the US Army Air Corps, US Navy and Royal Air Force respectively. Production of these and other military variants in the USA totalled some 10,050 aircraft, excluding major production in Japan and the USSR. These aircraft were truly war-winning weapons, providing the Western Allies with an unparalleled transport capability that expanded into paratroop and glider-towing capabilities as World War II progressed. Related developments were the C-48 to C-52 and C-68 impressments, and the C-53 and C-117 personnel transports. Pictured here is a Douglas Dakota III of No 24 Squadron, RAF. The squadron was actually a communications unit, and flew Dakotas to Malta from 1943 onwards.

| | |
|---|---|
| Country of origin: | USA |
| Type: | (C-47) two/three-seat transport with accommodation for 28 troops, or 14 litters plus three attendants or 10,000lb (4536kg) of freight |
| Powerplant: | two 1200hp (895kW) Pratt & Whitney R-1830-92 14-cylinder two-row radial engines |
| Performance: | maximum speed 370km/h (230mph); climb to 3050m (10,000ft) in 9 minutes 36 seconds; service ceiling 7315m (24,000ft); range 2575km (1600 miles) |
| Weights: | empty 8103kg (17,865lb); maximum take-off 14,061kg (31,000lb) |
| Dimensions: | span 28.90m (95ft 0in); length 19.63m (64ft 5.5in); height 5.20m (16ft 11in) |
| Armament: | none |

# Douglas DB-7

Designed by 'Ed' Heinemann under the supervision of 'Jack' Northrop, the Northrop N-7A light attack bomber concept paved the way – after Northrop's take-over by Douglas – for the Model 7B that first flew in October 1938. The type soon drew the attention of a French purchasing mission, which ordered an initial 270 examples of the revised DB-7 bomber with a transparent nose and two 1100hp (820kW) Pratt & Whitney R-1830-SC3G Twin Wasp radial engines. The 100 DB-7A bombers that followed switched to a pair of 1500hp (1118kW) Wright R-2600-A5B radial engines, and the DB-7B differed mainly in its enlarged vertical tail surface. The first DB-7 flew in August 1939, but only a comparatively small number had entered service before France's defeat in June 1940, when the others passed to the UK or were repossessed by the USA. Pictured is a DB-7B-3 serving with Groupe de Bommbardment I/19, Armée de l'Air d'Armistice, in autumn 1940.

| Country of origin: | USA |
| --- | --- |
| Type: | (DB-7B) three-seat light attack bomber |
| Powerplant: | two 1600hp (1193kW) Wright GR-2600-A5B Double Cyclone radial engines |
| Performance: | maximum speed 515km/h (320mph); initial climb rate 609m (2000ft) per minute; ceiling 7470m (24,500ft); range 845km (525 miles) |
| Weights: | empty 5534kg (12,200lb); normal take-off 8959kg (19,750lb); maximum take-off 9789kg (21,580lb) |
| Dimensions: | span 18.69m (61ft 4in); length 14.48m (47ft 6in); height 5.36m (17ft 7in) |
| Armament: | four 0.303in fixed forward-firing machine guns on the sides of the forward fuselage, two 0.303in trainable machine guns in the dorsal position, and one 0.303in trainable machine gun in the ventral position, plus an internal bomb load of 907kg (2000lb) |

# Douglas Boston Mk III

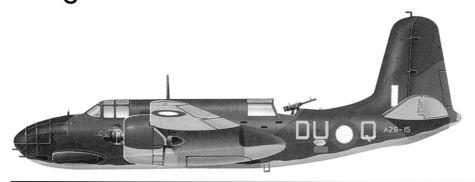

The DB-7 bombers taken over from French contracts (and powered by two R-1830-S3C4G radial engines with two-speed superchargers) were originally to have become Boston Mk II light bombers in British service but in the event were adapted as Havoc Mk I night-fighters. The type entered service in April 1941 with No 85 Squadron. The next light bomber was thus the Boston Mk III, a designation applied to a total of 753 aircraft including 452 DB-7Bs taken over from France. The Boston Mk III had improved self-sealing fuel tanks, additional armour protection, a number of strengthening features to cater for a significantly increased maximum take-off weight, a slightly longer fuselage, and increased fuel capacity. The aircraft were delivered to the UK from the summer of 1941, and entered service in October of the same year. Some aircraft were adapted as Boston Mk III (Intruder) machines with four 20mm cannon in a ventral pack.

| Country of origin: | USA |
|---|---|
| Type: | four-seat light attack bomber |
| Powerplant: | two 1600hp (1193kW) Wright GR-2600-A5B Double Cyclone radial engines |
| Performance: | maximum speed 515km/h (320mph); initial climb rate 609m (2000ft) per minute; service ceiling 7470m (24,500ft); range 1996km (1240 miles) with reduced bomb load |
| Weights: | empty 5534kg (12,200lb); normal take-off 8959kg (19,750lb); maximum take-off 9789kg (21,580lb) |
| Dimensions: | span 18.69m (61ft 4in); length 14.48m (47ft 6in); height 5.36m (17ft 7in) |
| Armament: | four 0.303in fixed forward-firing machine guns on the sides of the forward fuselage, two 0.303in trainable machine guns in the dorsal position, and one 0.303in trainable machine gun in the ventral position, plus an internal bomb load of 907kg (2000lb) |

# Douglas A-20

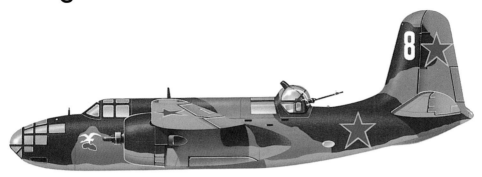

First ordered in June 1939, the A-20 was the American version of the light bomber initially bought by France and the UK as the DB-7 and Boston. The first US orders were for the A-20 and A-20A (63 and 143 aircraft) with supercharged and normally aspirated engines, the former being converted to P-70 night-fighters and the latter entering service in 1941. There followed 999 A-20Bs equivalent to the DB-7A, 948 A-20Cs with British equipment, 17 A-20E conversions from A-20A standard with the powerplant of the A-20B, 2,850 A-20G attack bombers with a 'solid' nose and considerably heavier forward-firing armament, 412 A-20Hs with an uprated powerplant, and 450 and 413 A-20Js and A-20Ks based on the A-20G and A-20H with a frameless transparent nose. The F-3 was a photo-reconnaissance conversion. Pictured here is one of the A-20B aircraft, fitted with a Russian dorsal turret, that served with the Black Sea Fleet Air Force in the spring of 1944.

| Country of origin: | USA |
| --- | --- |
| Type: | (A-20G) three-seat light attack bomber |
| Powerplant: | two 1700hp (1268kW) Wright R-2600-23 14-cylinder two-row radial engines |
| Performance: | maximum speed 546km/h (339mph); climb to 3050m (10,000ft) in 8 minutes 48 seconds; ceiling 7225m (23,700ft); range 3380km (2100 miles) |
| Weights: | empty 7708kg (16,993lb); normal take-off 10,964kg (24,127lb); maximum take-off 12,338kg (27,200lb) |
| Dimensions: | span 18.69m (61ft 4in); length 14.63m (47ft 11.88in); height 5.36m (17ft 7in) |
| Armament: | six 0.5in fixed forward-firing machine guns, two 0.5in trainable machine guns in the dorsal turret, and one 0.5in rearward-firing machine gun in the ventral position; bomb load of 1814kg (4000lb) |

# Douglas SBD Dauntless

The Dauntless was one of World War II's decisive warplanes, particularly in terms of the part it played in the Battle of Midway, and despite the fact that it possessed only indifferent performance and poor manoeuvrability. As a result of these shortcomings the type was phased out of first-line service well before the end of the war despite having only entered service in 1940. The first flight of the XBT-2 (converted Northrop BT-1) prototype was made in April 1938. The main production models were the SBD-1 (57) with the 1000hp (746kW) R-1820-32 engine, SBD-2 (87) with heavier armament and more fuel, SBD-3 (584) with 0.5in rather than 0.3in machine guns, self-sealing fuel tankage and 24- rather than 12-volt electrics, SBD-4 (780) with detail improvements, SBD-5 (3025) with greater power, and SBD-6 (451) with the 1350hp (1007kW) R-1820-66 engine. Illustrated is an SBD-5 Dauntless of Escuadron Aéreo de Pelea 200, Fuerza Aérea Mexicana, in 1946.

| | |
|---|---|
| Country of origin: | USA |
| Type: | (SBD-5) two-seat carrierborne and land-based scout and dive bomber |
| Powerplant: | one 1200hp (895kW) Wright R-1820-60 Cyclone nine-cylinder single-row radial engine |
| Performance: | maximum speed 410km/h (255mph); climb to 3050m (10,000ft) in 8 minutes; service ceiling 7780m (25,530ft); range 2519km (1565 miles) |
| Weights: | empty 2905kg (6404lb); maximum take-off 4853kg (10,700lb) |
| Dimensions: | span 12.66m (41ft 6.38in); length 10.09m (33ft 1.25in); height 4.14m (13ft 7in) |
| Armament: | two 0.5in fixed forward-firing machine guns in the upper part of the forward fuselage, and two 0.3in trainable rearward-firing machine guns in the rear of the cockpit, plus an external bomb load of 1021kg (2250lb) |

# Douglas A-24

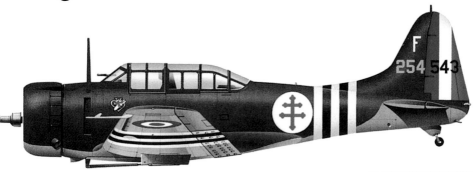

When it began to receive intelligence information about the Germans' successful employment of the Junkers Ju 87 dive-bomber in the early European campaigns, the US Army Air Corps decided to develop a similar capability. After evaluation of borrowed aircraft in 1940 the USAAC opted for the Douglas Dauntless already in service with the US Navy as the SBD. The first model ordered was the A-24 (eventually 178 aircraft) that was essentially similar to the SBD-3A; the first aircraft were delivered between July and October 1942. Combat experience in the South-West Pacific theatre highlighted some fundamental deficiencies, however, and later aircraft were used mainly for training. These later models were the A-24A and A-24B (170 and 615 aircraft to SBD-4A and SBD-5 standards respectively). More than 40 A-24Bs were transferred to France in 1944. This aircraft wears the markings of the Free French air force.

| | |
|---|---|
| **Country of origin:** | USA |
| **Type:** | (A-24) two-seat dive-bomber |
| **Powerplant:** | one 1000hp (746kW) Wright R-1820-52 nine-cylinder single-row radial engine |
| **Performance:** | maximum speed 402km/h (250mph); climb to 3050m (10,000ft) in 7 minutes; service ceiling 7925m (26,000ft); range 2092 km (1300 miles ) |
| **Weights:** | empty 2804kg (6181lb); maximum take-off 4627kg (10,200lb) |
| **Dimensions:** | span 12.66m (41ft 6.38in); length 9.96m (32ft 8in); height 4.14m (13ft 7in) |
| **Armament:** | two 0.5in fixed forward-firing machine guns in the upper part of the forward fuselage, and two 0.3in trainable rearward-firing machine guns in the rear of the cockpit, plus an external bomb load of 544kg (1200lb) |

# Douglas A-26 Invader

Though only produced in small numbers by World War II standards, the A-26 has the distinction of having flown in more conflicts than any other warplane. The type was ordered in XA-26, XA-26A and XA-26B prototype forms, the first as a three-seat attack bomber a potential 2268kg (5000lb) bomb load, the second as a two-seat night-fighter and intruder with radar and cannon in a 'solid' nose, and the third as a three-seat heavy attack fighter with a 75mm cannon in the 'solid' nose. The type first flew in July 1942, and the A-26B (1355 built) entered service in Europe during November 1944, and at the same time became operational in the Pacific. Powered by two 1491kw (2000hp) Pratt & Whitney radial engines that conferred a maximum speed of 571km/h (377 mph) the A-26B was the fastest US bomber of the war. Pictured here is A-26B-15-DT 'Stinky' of the 552nd Bomb Squadron, 386th Bomb Group, US 9th Air Force, based at Beaumont-sur-Oise, France, in April 1945.

| Country of origin: | USA |
|---|---|
| Type: | (A-26B) three-seat light attack and reconnaissance bomber |
| Powerplant: | two 2000hp (1491kW) Pratt & Whitney R-2800-27 or -71 18-cylinder two-row radial engines |
| Performance: | maximum speed 571km/h (355mph); climb to 3050m (10,000ft) in 7 minutes 0 seconds; service ceiling 6735m (22,100ft); range 2092km (1300 miles) with a 1361kg (3000lb) bomb load |
| Weights: | empty 10,147kg (22,370lb); maximum take-off 12,893kg (42,300lb) |
| Dimensions: | span 21.34m (70ft); length 15.42m (50ft 7in); height 5.64m (18ft 6in) |
| Armament: | six 0.5in fixed forward-firing machine guns, two 0.5in trainable machine guns in dorsal barbette, two 0.5in trainable rearward-firing machine guns in optional ventral barbette, and provision for eight 0.5in fixed forward-firing machine guns in four underwing packs, plus a bomb load of 2722kg (6000lb) |

# Douglas A3 Skywarrior

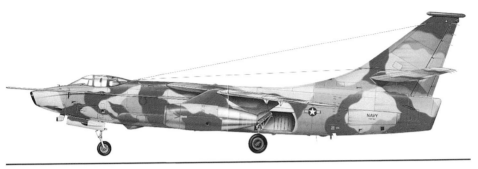

The A3 Skywarrior was realised by a team led by legendary Douglas designer Ed Heinemann at El Segundo. It is notable as the first carrier based strategic nuclear bomber, designed to be operated from the deck of the Forrestal class of carriers that came into service in 1948. Both the outer wings and tail were designed to fold hydraulically and thus minimise the space occupied by the aircraft on deck. An advanced blind-bombing radar was carried in the nose, although delivery from Westinghouse was seriously delayed. The first of the two prototypes flew on October 28, 1952 powered by two Westinghouse engines, but the failure of this program meant that the Pratt & Whitney J57-P-6 powered that production A3D-1. Deliveries began in March 1956 to the US Navy's VH-1 attack squadron. Later variants saw much service in Vietnam as electronic intelligence and electronic countermeasures platforms.

| Country of origin: | USA |
| --- | --- |
| Type: | carrier-based strategic bomber |
| Powerplant: | two 5635kg (12,400lb) Pratt & Whitney turbojets |
| Performance: | maximum speed 982km/h (610mph); service ceiling 13,110m (43,000ft); range with maximum fuel 3220km (2000 miles) |
| Weights: | empty 17,875kg (39,409lb); maximum take-off 37,195kg (82,000lb) |
| Dimensions: | wing span 22.1m (72ft 6in); length 23.3m (76ft 4in); height 7.16m (23ft 6in); wing area 75.43sq m (812sq ft) |
| Armament: | two remotely controlled 20mm cannon in tail turret, plus provision for 5443kg (12,000lb) of conventional or nuclear weapons in internal bomb bay |

# Douglas F4D-1 Skyray

**D**etails of German research into delta wings generated great interest in the US Navy, prompting senior officers to request a design submission from Douglas based on the theories. This was finalised as a variation on a pure delta wing configuration in 1948, and Douglas were awarded a contract to build two prototypes in December of that year. The first aircraft made its maiden flight in January 1951 with an Allison turbojet, although continual engine problems during the development programme led to the selection of a Pratt & Whitney unit for production aircraft. The design was a cantilever mid-wing monoplane controlled by trailing edge elevons serving collectively as elevators or differentially as ailerons. The cockpit was situated well forward of the wing and afforded the pilot excellent all-round visibility.

| | |
|---|---|
| Country of origin: | USA |
| Type: | single-seat carrier-based fighter |
| Powerplant: | one 4626kg (10,200lb) Pratt & Whitney J57-P-8A turbojet |
| Performance: | maximum speed at 10,975m (36,000ft) 1162km/h (695mph); service ceiling above 16,765m (55,000ft); range 1931km (1,200 miles) |
| Weights: | empty 7268kg (16,024lb); maximum take-off 11,340kg (25,000lb) |
| Dimensions: | wingspan 10.21m (33ft 6in); length 13.93m (45ft 8.25in); height 3.96m (13ft); wing area 51.75sq m (557sq ft) |
| Armament: | four 20mm cannon; six underwing hardpoints with provision for up to 1814kg (4000lb) of stores, including AIM-9C Sidewinder air-to-air missiles, bombs, rockets, or drop tanks |

# Douglas B-66 Destroyer

The B-66 Destroyer was produced by Douglas at Long Beach to meet the needs of the US Air Force, whose involvement in the Korean war had highlighted an urgent need for a high performance tactical bomber. Air Force chiefs planned to speed the availability of such an aircraft by procuring a modified version of the A-3D then in service with the US Navy. What began as a minimal modification of the A-3, however, turned into a totally different aircraft. Though it looked similar, hardly a single airframe part or item of equipment was common and the B-66 proved difficult to maintain and expensive. The arrestor gear, folding wing and tail mechanisms, and strengthened gear were all junked, in favour of crew ejector seats, multiple camera installation and precision bombing and navigation radar. Many were built as electronic intelligence and electronic countermeasures aircraft and saw action over South East Asia.

| | |
|---|---|
| Country of origin: | USA |
| Type: | all-day/night reconnaissance and bombing aircraft |
| Powerplant: | two 4627kg (10,200lb) Allison J71-A-11 turbojets |
| Performance: | maximum speed 1015km/h (631mph); service ceiling 11,855m (38,900ft); combat radius 1489km (925 miles) |
| Weights: | empty 19,720kg (43,476lb); maximum take-off 37,648kg (83,000lb) |
| Dimensions: | wing span 22.1m (72ft 6in); length 22.9m (75ft 2in); height 7.19m (23ft 7in); wing area 72.46sq m (780sq ft) |
| Armament: | two remotely controlled 20mm cannon in tail turret, plus provision for 5443kg (12,000lb) of conventional or nuclear weapons in internal bomb bay |

# English Electric P.5 Cork

In 1917 the Admiralty contracted the Phoenix Dynamo Manufacturing Company to construct a new flying-boat around a new monocoque hull designed by Lieutenant Commander Linton Hope and built by Southampton chandler May, Harden and May. Phoenix Dynamo had experience in the field of flying-boat construction with the earlier Porte series, and after delivery of the first hull from Brough completed final assembly of the first aircraft in August 1918, by which time Phoenix had become a part of English Electric. Flight trials began in September, but problems with the dope on the fabric-covered wings forced English Electric to substitute the second set of wings. The second aircraft had an enlarged rudder and a pylon-mounted lower wing. The Armistice relegated the P.5 to a research role, although it emerged in 1925 in slightly different form as the P.5 Kingston.

| | |
|---|---|
| Country of origin: | United Kingdom |
| Type: | reconnaissance flying-boat |
| Powerplant: | two 350hp (261kW) Rolls-Royce Eagle VIII inline piston engines |
| Performance: | maximum speed 169km/h (105mph); service ceiling 4600m (15,100ft); range 1287km (800 miles) |
| Weights: | empty 3373kg (7437lb); maximum take-off weight 3813kg (7437lb) |
| Dimensions: | span 26.06m (85ft 6in); length 14.99m (49ft 2in); height 6.45m (21ft 2in); wing area 118.26 sq m (1273 sq ft) |
| Armament: | one .303in Lewis machine gun on flexible mount in bow cockpit; one .303in Lewis machine gun on flexible mount in each of two waist positions (second prototype had provision for four further .303in Lewis machine guns in two nacelles above the top wing); plus bomb load of 472kg (1040lb) |

# Eurofighter EF-2000 Typhoon

The agreement to develop the Eurofighter was signed in May 1988 between the UK, the former West Germany, and Italy. Spain joined in November of that year. The aircraft was designed ostensibly for the air-to-air role, with secondary air-to-surface capability. With the canard design and fly-by-wire control system the aircraft is supremely manoeuvrable in the air. Other advanced features include extensive use of composite materials for airframe construction and an advanced sensor and avionics suite. Although there have been delays compounded by the crash of a prototype in Spain, the first deliveries have been made and the aircraft will shortly be in RAF and Luftwaffe service, with the Spanish and Italian deliveries coming later. It appears as though the Eurofighter may be an export success – Austria and Greece look likely to buy the aircraft, and other nations have expressed interest.

| | |
|---|---|
| Country of origin: | Germany, Italy, Spain, and United Kingdom |
| Type: | multi-role fighter |
| Powerplant: | two 9185kg (20,250lb) Eurojet EJ200 turbofans |
| Performance: | maximum speed at 11,000m (36,090ft) 2125km/h (1,321mph); combat radius about 463 and 556km |
| Weights: | empty 9750kg (21,495lb); maximum take-off 21,000kg (46,297lb) |
| Dimensions: | wingspan 10.50m (34ft 5.5in); length 14.50m (47ft 4in); height 4.0m (13ft 1.5in); wing area 52.4sq m (564.05sq ft) |
| Armament: | one 27mm Mauser cannon; thirteen fuselage hardpoints for a wide variety of stores including ASRAAM, AMRAAM missile programmes; also air-to-surface missiles, anti-radar missiles, guided and unguided bombs |

# FMA IA 27 Pulquí

The Pulquí (Arrow) was designed by Emile Dewoitine, who had established his own aircraft company in France in 1920. The aircraft achieved two firsts, being not only the first single-seat fighter to be designed in Argentina but also the first turbojet powered aircraft to be built by her fledgling aviation industry. The aircraft followed a conventional low wing cantilever monoplane design, constructed of metal, and powered by the Rolls-Royce Derwent turbojet. The aircraft first flew on August 9, 1947, but flight trials proved disappointing in every aspect. The project was subsequently abandoned. Enlisting the assistance of former Focke-Wulf designer Kurt Tank, the Argentine government sought to rekindle the project with the Pulquí II, but a protracted development period and the withdrawal of Dr Tank meant that it too was abandoned in 1960.

| Country of origin: | Argentina |
| --- | --- |
| Type: | single-seat fighter |
| Powerplant: | one 2268kg (5000lb) Rolls Royce Nene 2 turbojet |
| Performance: | maximum speed at 5000m (16,405ft) 1050km/h (652mph); service ceiling 15,000m (49,210ft); endurance 2 hours 12 minutes |
| Weights: | empty 3600kg (7937lb); maximum take-off 5550kg (12,236lb) |
| Dimensions: | wingspan 10.60m (34ft 9.25in); length 11.68m (38ft 3.75in); height 3.50m (11ft 5.75in); wing area 25.10sq m (270.18sq ft) |
| Armament: | four 20mm cannon |

# FMA IA 63 Pampa

The physical resemblance between the Pampa and the Dassault/Dornier Alpha Jet stems from the close association between Argentinian manufacturer FMA and Dornier on the project. Design work began in 1979 to provide a jet trainer to replace the Morane-Saulnier MS.760 Paris in service with the Argentine air force. Wings and tailplanes for the prototype were based on a unswept version of the Alpha Jet wing. Other features were designed for simplified maintenance and cheap operation, such as the aircraft's single-engined configuration and reduced avionics suite. Rough airstrip operations are possible. The first prototype, which is depicted here with its Paris Air Show registration, flew on 6 October 1984. The first of 100 aircraft ordered for the Argentine air force was delivered to IV Brigada Aérea in April 1988.

| Country of origin: | Argentina |
|---|---|
| Type: | two-seat advanced pilot trainer with combat capability |
| Powerplant: | one 1588kg (3500lb) Garrett TFE731-2-2N turbofan |
| Performance: | maximum speed 750km/h (466mph); service ceiling 12,900m (42,325ft); combat radius on hi-lo-hi mission with 1000kg (2205lb) load 360km (223 miles) |
| Weights: | empty 2821kg (6219lb); maximum take-off 5000kg (11,023lb) |
| Dimensions: | wingspan 9.69m (31ft 9.25in); length (excluding probe) 10.93m (35ft 10.25in); height 4.29m (14ft 1in); wing area 15.63sq m (168.2sq ft) |
| Armament: | provision for a 30mm DEFA cannon and four underwing pylons for up to 1160kg (2557lb) of stores |

# Fairchild Republic OA-10A Thunderbolt II

The Fairchild Republic A-10A grew out of the US Air Force's A-X program, begun in 1967, to produce a highly battleproof, heavily-armed close air support aircraft to replace the A-1 Skyraider. In December 1970 three companies were chosen to build prototypes for evaluation and Fairchild's YA-10A emerged as the winner in January 1973. Six pre-production aircraft were submitted for evaluation, resulting in a production contract for 52 A-10As in December 1974. Some 727 were procured by the USAF. The A-10A is dominated by the huge GAU-8/A cannon, but the range of weaponry that it can carry is truly devastating. This was proved effectively during actions against Iraqi armour the 1991 Gulf War. Since then the aircraft have been redesignated OA-10A to mark their forward air control role. Although the USAF wants to retire the aircraft, the OA-10A keeps proving its worth as a battlefield support tool, latterly in the 2003 war in Iraq.

| | |
|---|---|
| Country of origin: | USA |
| Type: | single-seat close support aircraft |
| Powerplant: | two 4112kg (9065lb) General Electric TF34-GE-100 turbofans |
| Performance: | maximum speed at sea level 706km/h (439mph); combar radius 402km (250 miles) for a 2-hour loiter with 18 Mk82 bombs plus 750 rounds cannon ammunition Weights: empty 11,321kg (24,959lb); maximum take-off 22,680kg (50,000lb) |
| Dimensions: | wingspan 17.53m (57ft 6in); length 16.26m (53ft 4in); height 4.47m (14ft 8in); wing area 47.01sq m (506sq ft) |
| Armament: | one 30mm GAU-8/A rotary cannon with capacity for 1350 rounds of ammunition, eleven hardpointts with provision for up to 7528kg (16,000lb) of disposable stores; weapons include conventional bombs, incendiary bombs, Rockeye cluster bombs, AGM-65 Maverick ir-to-surface missiles, laser and optronically guided bombs and SUU-23 20mm cannon pods |

# Fairey Fox

Fairey produced two types of Fox day bombers in the 1920s, namely the two-seat Fox Mk I with the Curtiss D-12 engine and the three-seat Fox Mk II with the Rolls-Royce Kestrel engine. Two-seat developments of the Fox Mk II, produced mainly by Fairey's Belgian subsidiary, served with the Belgian air force in the first part of World War II. The main variants were the Kestrel-engined Fox Mk II bomber mentioned previously, Fox Mk III reconnaissance fighter, Fox Mk IIIC with an enclosed cockpit and Fox Mk IIIS dual-control trainer. These were followed by the Hispano-Suiza-engined Fox Mk VI reconnaissance fighter, Fox Mk VII single-seat fighter, and Fox Mk VIII improved version of the Mk VI. The type entered service in 1932, was wholly obsolete by the beginning of World War II, and the 50 surviving aircraft suffered heavy losses at German hands. A seaborne reconnaissance version of similar design was the Fairey Seafox.

| | |
|---|---|
| Country of origin: | Belgium (from a British design) |
| Type: | (Fox Mk VIR) two-seat reconnaissance fighter and light bomber |
| Powerplant: | one 860hp (641kW) Hispano-Suiza 12-cylinder Vee engine |
| Performance: | maximum speed 365km/h (227mph); climb to 5000m (16,405ft) in 6 minutes 30 seconds; service ceiling 10,000m (32,810ft); range 600km (373 miles) |
| Weights: | empty 1325kg (2920lb); normal take-off 2245kg (4950lb); maximum take-off 2345kg (5170lb) |
| Dimensions: | span 11.58m (38ft); length 9.17m (30ft 1in); height 3.35m (11ft) |
| Armament: | two 7.62mm fixed forward-firing machine guns in the upper part of the forward fuselage, and one or two 7.62mm trainable rearward-firing machine guns in the rear of the cockpit, plus an external bomb load of 100 kg (220lb) |

# Fairey Swordfish Mk I

The Swordfish has an enduring reputation as one of the finest warplanes of World War II. This reputation resulted from its anachronistic biplane airframe and a combination of ruggedness, reliability, versatility in terms of weapons and equipment, and such completely viceless handling characteristics that it could be flown in most weather conditions from aircraft carriers ranging in size from the largest fleet carriers to the smallest of escort carriers. The type, universally known as the 'Stringbag', resulted from a 1930 requirement for a carrierborne aeroplane to serve in the spotter, reconnaissance and torpedo attack roles. The first of four prototype and pre-production aircraft flew in March 1933. Successful trials led to orders for an eventual 989 aircraft. Fairey built 689 and the remainder were Blackburn-built machines. Service deliveries began in July 1936 and by the beginning of World War II the FAA had 13 operational Swordfish squadrons.

| | |
|---|---|
| **Country of origin:** | United Kingdom |
| **Type:** | (Swordfish Mk I) three-seat carrierborne and land-based torpedo bomber, level bomber and reconnaissance aeroplane |
| **Powerplant:** | one 775hp (578kW) Bristol Pegasus IIIM3 nine-cylinder single-row radial engine |
| **Performance:** | maximum speed 224km/h (139mph); climb to 1525m (5000ft) in 10 minutes 30 seconds; ceiling 3780m (12,400ft); range 1657km (1030 miles) |
| **Weights:** | empty 2359kg (5200lb); maximum take-off 4196kg (9250lb) |
| **Dimensions:** | span 13.87m (45ft 6in); length 11.07m (36ft 4in) with the tail up; height 4.11m (13ft 5.75in) with the tail up |
| **Armament:** | one 0.303in fixed forward-firing machine gun in the starboard side of the forward fuselage, and one 0.303in trainable rearward-firing machine gun in the rear cockpit; external bomb load of 726kg (1600lb) |

# Fairey Swordfish Mk II

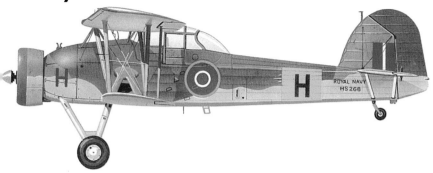

Built by Blackburn to the total of 1080 aircraft, the Swordfish Mk II was a development of the Swordfish Mk I with a strengthened lower wing skinned on its lower surfaces with metal rather than the fabric of the Mk I to permit the carriage and firing of up to eight 3in (76mm) air-to-surface rockets. These could be of two types, differentiated by their warheads. The 60lb (27.2kg) high explosive rocket was notably effective against coastal shipping, while the 25lb (11.3kg) armour-piercing rocket was used mainly against submarines and coastal fortifications. A number of Swordfish Mk II aircraft, which could be operated on floats as alternatives to the standard wheeled landing gear, were converted to Swordfish Mk IV standard with enclosed accommodation for use in Canadian waters. The Swordfish achieved some notable victories during the war, including the first U-boat sinking and the decimation of the Italian fleet at Taranto in November 1940.

| | |
|---|---|
| Country of origin: | United Kingdom |
| Type: | (Swordfish Mk II) three-seat carrierborne and land-based torpedo bomber, level bomber and reconnaissance aeroplane |
| Powerplant: | one 775hp (578kW) Bristol Pegasus IIIM3 or 750hp (559kW) Pegasus XXX nine-cylinder single-row radial engine |
| Performance: | maximum speed 224km/h (139mph); climb to 1525m (5000ft) in 10 minutes 30 seconds; ceiling 3780m (12,400ft); range 1657km (1030 miles) |
| Weights: | empty 2132kg (4700lb); maximum take-off 4196kg (9250lb) |
| Dimensions: | span 13.87m (45ft 6in); length 11.07m (36ft 4in) with the tail up; height 4.11m (13ft 5.75in) with the tail up |
| Armament: | one 0.303in fixed forward-firing machine gun in the starboard side of the forward fuselage, and one 0.303in trainable rearward-firing machine in the rear cockpit, plus an external torpedo, bomb and rocket load of 1600lb (726kg) |

# Fairey Swordfish Mk III

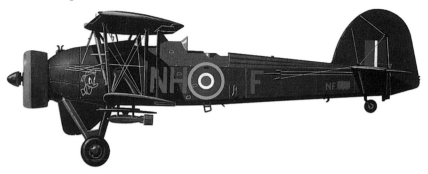

**B**uilt by Blackburn to a total of 320 aircraft, the Swordfish Mk III was a development of the Swordfish Mk II with improved anti-submarine capability bestowed by the addition of ASV.Mk X air-to-surface search radar with its antenna in a large radome between the main landing gear legs. In all other respects the Swordfish Mk III was similar to the Swordfish Mk I and Mk II with the exception of a higher all up weight, and like its Mk II stablemate rendered excellent service while operating from small escort carriers charged with protecting Atlantic and Arctic convoys from German submarine attack. The last of the great torpedo attacks made by these aircraft came in 1942, when an attempt was made to prevent the German battleships *Gneisenau* and *Prinz Eugen* passing through the English Channel. The Fleet Air Arm's last Swordfish unit was No 836 Squadron, which was disbanded in May 1945 just after the surrender of Germany.

| | |
|---|---|
| **Country of origin:** | United Kingdom |
| **Type:** | (Swordfish Mk II) three-seat carrierborne and land-based torpedo bomber, level bomber and reconnaissance aeroplane |
| **Powerplant:** | one 775hp (578kW) Bristol Pegasus IIIM3 or 750hp (559kW) Pegasus XXX nine-cylinder single-row radial engine |
| **Performance:** | maximum speed 224km/h (139mph); climb to 1525m (5000ft) in 10 minutes 30 seconds; ceiling 3780m (12,400ft); range 1657km (1030 miles) |
| **Weights:** | empty 2132kg (4700lb); maximum take-off 4196kg (9250lb) |
| **Dimensions:** | span 13.87m (45ft 6in); length 11.07m (36ft 4in) with the tail up; height 4.11m (13ft 5.75in) with the tail up |
| **Armament:** | one 0.303in fixed forward-firing machine gun in the starboard side of the forward fuselage, and one 0.303in trainable rearward-firing machine in the rear cockpit, plus an external torpedo, bomb and rocket load of 726kg (1600lb) |

# Fairey Albacore

The Albacore was designed to supersede the Fairey Swordfish as the primary torpedo bomber of the Fleet Air Arm. In fact the Albacore was only able to complement the Swordfish in this role; the older aircraft outlived the Albacore by more than one year. Resulting from a 1936 requirement, the Albacore was in effect a modernised and technically somewhat improved development of the Swordfish with enclosed accommodation, a higher-rated engine, hydraulically operated flaps, and a number of aerodynamic revisions designed to reduce drag. The first of two Albacore prototypes made its maiden flight in December 1938, and the first of 798 Albacore Mk I production aircraft entered service in March 1940, initially as a land-based type and only from 1941 on board aircraft carriers. The Albacore spawned no improved models, and was withdrawn from first-line service in 1944. Pictured here is an AlbacoreTB.Mk 1 of No 826 Squadron, Fleet Air Arm.

| | |
|---|---|
| Country of origin: | United Kingdom |
| Type: | (Albacore Mk I) three-seat carrierborne and land-based torpedo bomber and reconnaissance aeroplane |
| Powerplant: | one 1130hp (843kW) Bristol Taurus XII 14-cylinder two-row radial engine |
| Performance: | maximum speed 257km/h (161mph); climb to 1830m (6000ft) in 8 minutes; service ceiling 6310m (20,700ft); range 1497km (930 miles) |
| Weights: | empty 3269kg (7200lb); maximum take-off 5670kg (12,500lb) |
| Dimensions: | span 15.23m (49ft 11.75in); length 12.18m (39ft 11.75in); height 3.81m (12ft 6in) |
| Armament: | one 0.303in fixed forward-firing machine gun in the leading edge of the starboard lower wing, and one or two 0.303in trainable rearward-firing machine guns in the rear cockpit, plus an external torpedo and bomb load of 907kg (2000lb) |

# Fairey Battle

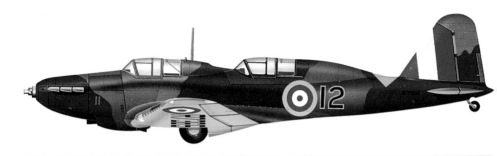

The Battle was an advance over the Hawker light bomber biplanes that it was designed to replace in Royal Air Force service. Nonetheless it was technically and tactically obsolescent by the time it entered service in March 1937, as a result of the rapid pace of aeronautical development during the approach to World War II. This is unsurprising considering the aeroplane was designed to meet a 1932 requirement but did not fly until March 1936. Production of the Battle light bomber totalled 1818 from two British manufacturers for RAF service (subsequently redesignated as the Battle Mks I to V depending on the mark of engine installed) and 18 Belgian-built aircraft for Belgian service. The type was relegated to second-line service in 1940 as the Battle (T) trainer and Battle (TT) target-tug, of which 100 and 266 were built to supplement conversions. Shown here is one of the Battle trainer aircraft in September 1940.

| | |
|---|---|
| Country of origin: | United Kingdom |
| Type: | (Battle Mk II) two/three-seat light day bomber |
| Powerplant: | one 1030hp (768kW) Rolls-Royce Merlin II 12-cylinder Vee engine |
| Performance: | maximum speed 406km/h (252mph); climb to 4570m (15,000ft) in 16 minutes 12 seconds; service ceiling 7925m (26,000ft); range 1931km (1200 miles) with a 644kg (1420lb) bomb load |
| Weights: | empty 3361kg (7410lb); normal take-off 4944kg (10,900lb); maximum take-off 5307kg (11,700lb) |
| Dimensions: | Span 16.45m (54ft); length 12.93m (42ft 5in); height 4.57m (15ft) |
| Armament: | one 0.303in fixed forward-firing machine gun in the leading edge of the starboard wing, and one 0.303in trainable rearward-firing machine gun in the rear cockpit, plus an internal and external bomb load of 680kg (1500lb) |

# Farman F.40

Henry and Maurice Farman began their careers in aviation in the Edwardian era and by the outbreak of World War I were at the forefront of the trailblazing French aeronautical industry. Their F.40 pusher biplane was a joint design and incorporated features of their earlier independent designs. It appeared at the end of 1915 and entered largescale production in early 1916. More than 40 French escadrilles were equipped with the type, popularly known as the 'Horace' Farman, and it was produced in a mind-boggling array of variants, including the F.40P with Le Prieur rockets; F.41 with shorter wings and less streamlined crew nacelle, F.56 with 170hp (127kW) Renault engine, and F.60 with 190hp (142kW) Renault engine. It was also operated by the RNAS and with French units in Macedonia and Serbia. Pictured is an F.40 of the Esquadrilha Expedicionara a Mocambique (a unit of the Portuguese Air Force) based at Mocimboca de Praia, Mozambique, in 1917.

| Country of origin: | France |
| --- | --- |
| Type: | two-seat observation biplane |
| Powerplant: | one 135hp (101kW) Renault 12-cylinder Vee piston engine |
| Performance: | maximum speed 135km/h (84mph); service ceiling 4000m (13,125ft); endurance 2hrs 20mins |
| Weights: | empty 748kg (1649lb); maximum take-off weight 1120kg (2469lb) |
| Dimensions: | span 17.6m (57ft 9in); length 9.25m (30ft 4in); height 3.9m (12ft 9in); wing area 52 sq m (560 sq ft) |
| Armament: | one or two .303 Lewis guns on flexible mount in nose position; light bombs and (F.40P) Le Prieur rockets |

# Farman F.221 and F.222

The F.220.01 bomber prototype was first flown in May 1932, and was then converted as a long-range mailplane. This was followed by the F.221.01 prototype that differed mainly in its redesigned vertical tail surface, fully enclosed nose and ventral gunner's positions, a semi-retractable 'dustbin' in place of the previous hatch position for the ventral gunner, and a considerably uprated powerplant. Next were 10 F.221BN.5 bombers with enhanced defensive armament, and then the F.222BN.5 that was produced in two variants as 11 F.222.1BN.5 machines with retractable main landing gear units and 24 F.222.2BN.5 machines with a lengthened nose and dihedralled outer wing panels. Some 29 aircraft were in service in 1939, and before the fall of France operated in the bomber role before being relegated to transport use up to 1944. Pictured here is an F.222.1 of the 2nd Escadrille, GB I/15, based at Reims-Courcy in May 1940.

| | |
|---|---|
| Country of origin: | France |
| Type: | (F.222.2BN.5) five-seat heavy night bomber |
| Powerplant: | four 970hp (723kW) Gnome-Rhône 14N-11/15 radial engines |
| Performance: | maximum speed 320km/h (199mph); climb to 4000m (13,125ft) in 13 minutes 30 seconds; service ceiling 8000m (26,245ft); range 2000km (1243 miles) with a 2500kg (5511lb) bomb load |
| Weights: | empty 10,500kg (23,148lb); normal take-off 15,200kg (33,510lb); maximum take-off 18,700kg (41,226lb) |
| Dimensions: | span 36.00m (118ft 1.33in); length 21.45m (70ft 4.5in); height 5.19m (17ft 0.33in) |
| Armament: | one 7.5mm trainable forward-firing machine gun in the nose turret, one 7.5mm trainable machine gun in the dorsal turret, and one 7.5mm trainable rearward-firing machine gun in the ventral 'dustbin' position, plus an internal bomb load of 4200kg (9259lb) |

# Farman NC.223

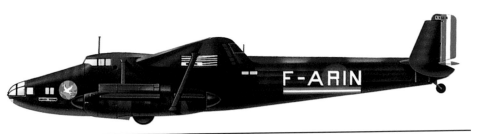

The NC.223 (originally F.223) was a completely new aeroplane that retained a conceptual affinity to its F.222 predecessor, and in overall terms was a blend of ancient and modern. In addition to the obsolete configuration retained from the F.222 bomber, the F.223 was also designed with the rectangular-section fuselage of the F.222. A revised tail unit with two vertical surfaces was added, but in contrast to these drag-producing features an excellent wing of modern stressed-skin concept with braced outer ends was used. The F.223.1.01 was a mailplane prototype and was followed into the air during January 1938 by the NC.223.01 bomber prototype. This was followed by eight or possibly more NC.223.3BN.5 production aircraft that entered service during the Battle of France. The aircraft were then converted as transports. Shown here is *Jules Verne*, one of the NC.223.4 aircraft operated as a long-range bomber by the French Air Force in the opening months of the war.

| Country of origin: | France |
| --- | --- |
| Type: | (NC.223.3BN.5) five-seat heavy night bomber |
| Powerplant: | four 920hp (686kW) Hispano-Suiza 12Y-29 12-cylinder Vee engines |
| Performance: | maximum speed 400km/h (249mph); climb to 4000m (13,125ft) in 10 minutes; absolute ceiling 8000m (26,245ft); range 2400km (1491 miles ) |
| Weights: | empty 10,550kg (23,258lb); maximum take-off 19,200kg (42,329lb) |
| Dimensions: | span 33.58m (110ft 2in); length 22.00m (72ft 2in); height 5.08m (16ft 8in) |
| Armament: | one 20mm trainable cannon in the dorsal turret, one 20mm trainable rearward-firing cannon in the ventral turret, and one 7.5mm trainable forward-firing machine gun in the nose position, plus an internal bomb load of 4200kg (9259lb) |

# Felixstowe F.5

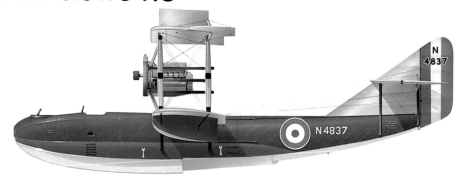

C ommander John C. Porte of the RNAS joined the Curtiss company in 1913 and designed the early 'H' series flying-boats for the company. He returned to Britain for war service and was appointed commander of the RN Air Station at Felixstowe, where he operated H.4 series boats over the North Sea. Porte's attempts to improve upon the hull of this design resulted in the F.2A, the standard RNAS flying-boat of the war. About 100 were built by S. E. Saunders of Cowes, and ten by Aircraft Manufacturing Co of Hendon. The long-span F.3 carried a much heavier bomb load, while the completely redesigned F.5 was the standard RAF flying-boat from 1918 until it was replaced by the Supermarine Southampton in August 1925. In 1918 the US Navy adopted a variant powered by the Liberty engine which was built by Curtiss (60 aircraft), Canadian Aeroplanes of Toronto (30) and the US Naval Aircraft Factory (138).

| Country of origin: | United Kingdom |
| --- | --- |
| Type: | reconnaissance flying-boat |
| Powerplant: | two 350hp (261kW) Rolls-Royce Eagle VIII 12-cylinder Vee piston engines |
| Performance: | maximum speed 142km/h (88mph); service ceiling 2075m (6800ft); endurance 7hrs |
| Weights: | empty 4128kg (9100lb); maximum take-off weight 5752kg (12,682lb) |
| Dimensions: | span 31.6m (103ft 8in); length 15.01m (49ft 3in); height 5.72m (18ft 9in); wing area 130.9 sq m (1409 sq ft) |
| Armament: | one .303in Lewis machine gun on flexible mount in nose position; one .303in Lewis machine gun on flexible mount in each of three midships positions; underwing racks with provision for four 104kg (230lb) bombs |

# Fiat CR.1

The Italian Fiat company established an aircraft manufacturing subsidiary during World War I, and in 1918 it engaged the services of designer Celestino Rosatelli. The first Rosatelli design was the BR single-engine bomber biplane, followed in 1923 by the CR single-seat fighter. The two prototypes were built and tested in 1923 and after proving its superiority to the SIAI S.52, the aircraft was selected for largescale production for the newly formed Regia Aeronautica. Production aircraft were designated CR.1 and the first deliveries of an eventual 240 aircraft began in 1925. During the 1930s many Italian CR.1s were modified to take the 44hp (328kW) Isotta Fraschini Asso Caccia engine, and these served until 1937. The aircraft was exported to Latvia (9 machines) and was tested with different engines as the CR.2, CR.10 and CR.5.

| | |
|---|---|
| **Country of origin:** | Italy |
| **Type:** | single-seat fighter biplane |
| **Powerplant:** | one 300hp (224kW) Hispano-Suiza 42 8-cylinder radial engine |
| **Performance:** | maximum speed 272km/h (169mph); service ceiling 7450m (24,440ft); endurance 2hrs 35mins |
| **Weights:** | empty equipped 839kg (1850lb); maximum take-off weight 1154kg (2544lb) |
| **Dimensions:** | span 8.95m (29ft 4in); length 6.16m (20ft 2in); height 2.4m (7ft 10in); wing area 23 sq m (248 sq ft) |
| **Armament:** | two fixed forward-firing .303in Vickers machine guns |

# Fiat CR.20

The CR.1 was the first in a line of classic Rosatelli- designed single-seat Fiat fighter biplanes, and reached its climax in the 1930s. The CR.20 of 1926 was an unequal-span biplane of steel tube and fabric construction, and in prototype form was powered by the Fiat AR.20 engine. The first flight was made in June 1926 and in the autumn of the same year it took centre stage at the influential Paris Salon de l'Aéronautique. Production for the Regia Aeronautica began in 1927, and the CR.20 swiftly became its standard fighter aircraft. The CR.20 took part in the Italian conquest of Libya and Abyssinia as a ground attack aircraft. By the late 1930s the type had been relegated to training units. Forty-six examples of a twin-float seaplane variant was built by Macchi and CMASA as the CR.20 Idro. Pictured is a CR.20 of the Magyar Királyi Légierö (Royal Hungarian Air Force) in 1936.

| Country of origin: | Italy |
|---|---|
| Type: | single-seat fighter biplane |
| Powerplant: | one 410hp (306kW0 Fiat A.20 12-cylinder Vee piston engine |
| Performance: | maximum speed 260km/h (161mph); service ceiling 8500m (27,885ft); endurance 2hrs 30mins |
| Weights: | empty 970kg (2138lb); maximum take-off weight 1390kg (3064lb) |
| Dimensions: | span 9.8m (32ft 1in); length 6.71m (22ft); height 2.79m (9ft 1in); wing area 25.5 sq m (274 sq ft) |
| Armament: | two fixed forward-firing .303in Vickers machine guns |

# Fiat CR.20bis

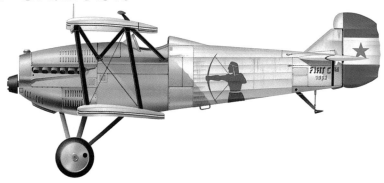

In service, the fragile cross-axle rubber-sprung landing gear of the CR.20 proved to be something of an achilles heel and Fiat set about improving the arrangement. The CR.20bis of 1930 had oleo-pneumatic shock absorbers and wheel brakes and was built in numbers totalling 232 aircraft. The CR.20bis AQ had a Fiat A.20 AQ engine for improved high-altitude performance, while the CR.20 Asso had an Issota Fraschini powerplant in a special cowling and larger horizontal stabilizer. Numbers were bought by Austria, Hungary, Lithuania, Paraguay, Poland and the Soviet Union. After the *Anschluss* with Austria in 1938 a number of aircraft were repainted in Luftwaffe colours and briefly saw service as trainers .Pictured here is a CR.20bis of the Escuadron de Caza 'Los Indios' ('The Indians' Fighter Squadron), Fuerza Aereas del Ejercito Nacional Paraguayo (Paraguayan National Army Air Force) in the 1930s.

| Country of origin: | Italy |
| --- | --- |
| Type: | single-seat fighter biplane |
| Powerplant: | one 410hp (306kW) Fiat A.20 12-cylinder Vee piston engine |
| Performance: | maximum speed 260km/h (161mph); service ceiling 8500m (27,885ft); endurance 2hrs 30mins |
| Weights: | empty 970kg (2138lb); maximum take-off weight 1390kg (3064lb) |
| Dimensions: | span 9.8m (32ft 1in); length 6.71m (22ft); height 2.79m (9ft 1in); wing area 25.5 sq m (274 sq ft) |
| Armament: | two fixed forward-firing .303in Vickers machine guns |

# Fiat CR.32quater

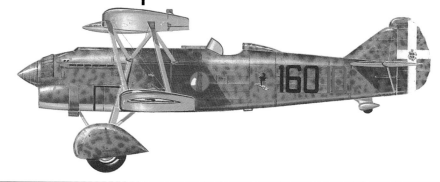

The CR.32 was the most important biplane fighter of the 1930s, certainly in terms of the number built (1712) and arguably because of its influence on the Spanish Civil War. The CR.32 stemmed from the CR.30, designed by Chief Engineer Rosatelli in 1931 as a single-seat fighter and bearing many of his hallmarks, such as W-form interplane bracing. Fitted with a Fiat A.30 Vee-12 engine, the CR.30 offered a considerable leap in performance over the CR.1 and was ordered for the Regia Aeronautica. Rosatelli was not content to rest in his laurels and refined the Cr.30 to produce the CR.32, which was built in larger numbers and formed the backbone of the Regia Aeronautica fighter force in 1935–40. The CR.32 was used extensively in Spain, and its performance in this theatre lulled the Italian Air Ministry into the false belief that the fighter biplane was a viable weapon of war. In June 1940, 324 were still in front-line service, despite being hopelessly outclassed by the new monoplanes.

| | |
|---|---|
| **Country of origin:** | Italy |
| **Type:** | single-seat fighter biplane |
| **Powerplant:** | one 600hp (447kW) Fiat A.30 RA bis 12-cylinder Vee piston engine |
| **Performance:** | maximum speed 375km/h (233mph); service ceiling 8800m (28,870ft); range 680km (422 miles) |
| **Weights:** | empty 1325kg (2921lb); maximum take-off weight 1850kg (4079lb) |
| **Dimensions:** | span 9.5m (31ft 2in); length 7.45m (24ft 5in); height 2.63m (8ft 7in); wing area 22.10 sq m (238 sq ft) |
| **Armament:** | two fixed forward-firing .303in Breda-SAFAT machine guns |

# Fiat CR.42 Falco

**B**y the mid-1930s most of Celestino Rosatelli's contemporaries had switched their attentions to designing stressed-skin monoplanes, but the Fiat Chief Engineer persisted with the open-cockpit, fabric-covered CR family and developed the CR.41 (a variant of the CR.32 with 900hp (671kW) Gnome-Rhône radial engine and modified tail surfaces). From this stemmed the CR.42. Although this was a robust, clean and attractive aircraft, it was obsolete by the time of its first flight in 1936. Despite this fact, the CR.42 found a ready market and went into largescale production for the Regia Aeronautica and for Belgium, Hungary and Sweden. Pictured is one of the Cr.42s that served in North Africa with 97a Squadriglia. The unit was based at Benina in Libya during 1940. Until the Hawker Hurricane arrived the Falco was the best fighter available to either side, but as it became further outdated it was used in a ground-attack role.

| Country of origin: | Italy |
|---|---|
| Type: | (CR.42) single-seat fighter |
| Powerplant: | one 840hp (626kW) Fiat A.74 R1C.38 14-cylinder, two-row radial engine |
| Performance: | maximum speed 472km/h (293mph); climb to 6000m (16,405ft) in 7mins 30secs; service ceiling 9835m (32,265ft); range 670km (416 miles) |
| Weights: | empty 1975kg (4354lb); maximum take-off 2415kg (5324lb) |
| Dimensions: | span 10.96m (35ft 11.5in); length 7.79m (25ft 6.75in); height 2.96m (9ft 8in) |
| Armament: | two 12.7mm Breda-SAFAT fixed forward-firing machine guns in upper part of forward fuselage |

# Fiat CR.42bis Falco

A group of 50 CR.42bis aircraft were stationed in Belgium from October 1940 to January 1941 under the command of Luftflotte II, but these suffered such horrendous losses at the hands of RAF pilots that they were redeployed to North Africa, and when the situation became untenable there, the survivors were flown to Italy in readiness for the invasion of June 1943. During the autumn and early winter Allied forces advanced steadily forward to the Gothic line supported by a vast air armada. With their own stocks running low, the Germans took a leaf out of the Russians' book and pressed any available aircraft into service for night nuisance attacks. This CR.42bis Falco was requisitioned and served with 2.Staffel of Nachtschlachtgruppe (9 NSGr.9), formed at Casella Torino in February 1944 under the command of Luftflotte II. Note the cut-down spats.

| Country of origin: | Italy |
| --- | --- |
| Type: | (CR.42) single-seat fighter |
| Powerplant: | one 840hp (626kW) Fiat A.74 R1C.38 14-cylinder, two-row radial engine |
| Performance: | maximum speed 472km/h (293mph); climb to 6000m (16,405ft) in 7mins 30 seconds; service ceiling 9835m (32,265ft); range 670km (416 miles) |
| Weights: | empty 1975kg (4354lb); maximum take-off weight 2415kg (5324lb) |
| Dimensions: | span 10.96m (35ft 11in); length 7.79m (25ft 7in); height 2.96m (9ft 8in) |
| Armament: | two 12.7mm Breda-SAFAT fixed forward-firing machine guns in upper part of forward fuselage |

# Fiat BR.20 Cicogna

The BR.20 Cicogna ('Stork') was the first 'modern' medium bomber produced in Italy during the period leading up to World War II, and first flew in prototype form during February 1936 for service from the autumn of the same year. Delivery of 320 aircraft, including 85 for Japan and one for Venezuela, was followed by production of 264 improved BR.20M bombers. This model featured improved nose contours, revised armament and increased armour protection. The final variant was the BR.20bis (15 aircraft) with two 1250hp (932kW) Fiat A.82 RC.42S radial engines, a redesigned nose, two 7.7mm machine guns in waist positions, and a power-operated dorsal turret. More than 160 Cicogna bombers were available when Italy entered World War II, and all but a handful were lost in extensive operations before Italy's September 1943 armistice with the Allies. Pictured here is a BR.20M of the 4th Squdriglia, 11th Gruppo, 13th Stormo, based in Belgium during late 1940.

| | |
|---|---|
| Country of origin: | Italy |
| Type: | (BR.20M) five-seat medium bomber |
| Powerplant: | two 1030hp (768kW) Fiat A.80 RC.41 14-cylinder two-row radial engines |
| Performance: | maximum speed 430km/h (267mph); climb to 5000m (16,405ft) in 17 minutes 56 seconds; service ceiling 7200m (23,620ft); range 1240km (770.5 miles) with a 1000kg (2205lb) bomb load |
| Weights: | empty 6740kg (14,859lb); maximum take-off 10,340kg (22,795lb) |
| Dimensions: | span 21.56m (70ft 8.8in); length 16.17m (53ft 0.5in); height 4.30m (14ft 1.25in) |
| Armament: | one 7.7mm trainable forward-firing machine gun in the nose turret, two 7.7mm or one 12.7mm trainable rearward-firing machine guns in the dorsal turret, and one 7.7mm trainable machine gun in the ventral hatch position, plus an internal bomb load of 1600kg (3527lb) |

# Fieseler Fi 156 Storch

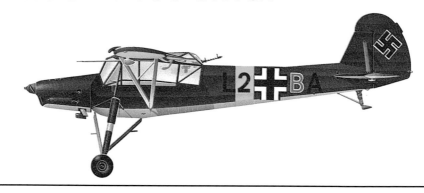

One of the most remarkable aircraft produced by the German aero industry during the Nazi regime, the Storch ('Stork') remains a vivid example of Gerhard Fieseler's interest in STOL aircraft with powerful high-lift devices. This is borne out by some remarkable statistics: the Storch could take-off in 65m (71 yards), land in 20m (22 yards) and virtually hover in a 25mph (40km/h) wind without any loss of control. Resulting from a 1935 requirement for an army co-operation, casualty evacuation and liaison aeroplane, the Fi 156 first flew in the spring of 1936 and entered service in 1937. Production totalled about 2900 aircraft, and the main variants were the initial, unarmed Fi 156A model, Fi-156C armed model in four main subvariants, and Fi 156D air ambulance model in two subvariants. Pictured here is an Fi 156C Storch of the *Kurierstaffel Oberkommando de Luftwaffe*, operating on the Don section of the Eastern Front in August 1942.

| | |
|---|---|
| Country of origin: | Germany |
| Type: | (Fi 156C-2) three-seat army co-operation, battlefield reconnaissance, liaison and casualty evacuation aeroplane |
| Powerplant: | one 240hp (179kW) Argus As 10C-3 eight-cylinder inverted-Vee engine |
| Performance: | maximum speed 175km/h (109mph); climb to 1000 m (3280ft) in 3 minutes 24 seconds; service ceiling 5200m (17,060ft); range 1015km (631 miles) |
| Weights: | empty 940kg (2072lb); maximum take-off 1320kg (2910lb) |
| Dimensions: | span 14.25m (46ft 9in); length 9.90m (32ft 5.75in); height 3.05m (10ft) |
| Armament: | one 7.92mm trainable rearward-firing machine gun in the rear of the cockpit |

# Fieseler Fi 167

In 1936 the German navy laid down its first aircraft carrier, which was launched in 1938 but never completed. Shortly after the keel of the new ship had been laid, the German air ministry issued to selected companies a requirement for a multi-role carrierborne warplane with excellent STOL capability, a folding biplane wing cellule, and the strength to make dive-bombing attacks at high speeds. Only Arado and Fieseler responded, and the two Fi 167 prototypes revealed good handling (including the ability to land at very low speeds), performance and payload. Fieseler received an order for 12 Fi 167A-0 pre-production aircraft with jettisonable main landing gear units but the abandonment of the carrier programme made the Fi 167 superfluous and nine aircraft were passed to Romania for coastal operations over the Black Sea. Shown here is an Fi 167A-0 of *Erprobungsstaffel 167*, based in the Netherlands during 1940–42.

| | |
|---|---|
| **Country of origin:** | Germany |
| **Type:** | Fi 167A-0) two-seat torpedo bomber and reconnaissance aeroplane |
| **Powerplant:** | one 1100hp (820kW) Daimler-Benz DB 601B 12-cylinder inverted-Vee engine |
| **Performance:** | maximum speed 325km/h (202mph); climb to 1000m (3280ft) in 2 minutes 42 seconds; service ceiling 8200m (26,905ft); range 1500km (932 miles) |
| **Weights:** | empty 2800kg (6173lb); maximum take-off 4850kg (10,692lb) |
| **Dimensions:** | span 13.50m (44ft 3.5in); length 11.40m (37ft 4.75in); height 4.80m (15ft 9in) |
| **Armament:** | one 7.92mm fixed forward-firing machine gun in the starboard upper side of the forward fuselage, and one 7.92mm trainable rearward-firing machine gun in the rear cockpit, plus an external torpedo and bomb load of 1000kg (2205lb) |

# Focke-Wulf Fw 187 Falke

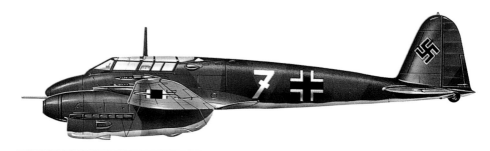

Early in 1936 Kurt Tank began work on the design of a twin-engined heavy fighter which, he estimated, would attain a maximum speed of 560km/h (348mph) with two 960hp (716kW) Daimler-Benz DB 600 engines. Work later began on two initial prototypes, and the first of these made its maiden flight in the summer of 1937 with two 680hp (507kW) Junkers Jumo 210Da engines. There followed four more prototypes armed with two 7.92mm machine guns and a pair of 20mm cannon, a lengthened cockpit canopy, revised engine nacelles and, in the sixth machine, two DB 600A engines. The final order was for three Fw 187A-0 pre-production aircraft with heavier armament, and these were used by a unit protecting the Focke-Wulf factory in summer 1940 before undergoing fruitless trials with 13. (Zerstörer) Staffel of JG 77 in Norway. The aircraft pictured was part of the unit tasked with defending the Focke-Wulfe factory.

| | |
|---|---|
| Country of origin: | Germany |
| Type: | (Fw 187A-0) two-seat heavy fighter |
| Powerplant: | two 700hp (522kW) Junkers Jumo 210Ga 12-cylinder inverted-Vee engines |
| Performance: | maximum speed 529km/h (329mph); climb to 6000m (19,685ft) in 5 minutes 48 seconds; service ceiling 10,000m (32,810ft) |
| Weights: | empty 3700kg (8157lb); maximum take-off 5000kg (11,023lb) |
| Dimensions: | span 15.30 m (50ft 2.25in); length 11.10m (36ft 5in); height 3.85m (12ft 7.5in) |
| Armament: | two 20mm fixed forward-firing cannon and four 7.92mm fixed forward-firing machine guns in the nose |

# Focke-Wulf Fw 189 Eule

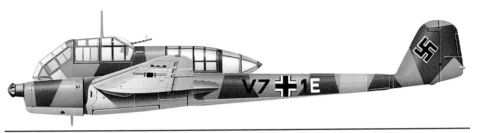

Given the fact that the Luftwaffe was designed primarily as a tactical air force for the support of the army, it is an unusual reflection on the service's overall thinking that during World War II it used only two main types of short-range reconnaissance aircraft, one of them Focke-Wulf Fw 189 Eule ('Owl') twin-boom monoplane with the crew in an extensively glazed central nacelle. This first flew in July 1938 and entered service late in 1940. Production totalled 848 excluding 16 prototype and pre-production aircraft. The main model was the Fw 189A in subvariants such as the baseline Fw 189A-1, Fw 189A-2 with twin rather than single defensive machine guns, Fw 189A-3 dual-control trainer, and Fw 189A-4 tactical support model with ventral armour and 20mm cannon rather than machine guns in the wing roots. Pictured here is an Fw 189A-2 of 1.(H) Staffel, Aufklärungsgruppe 32, based on the Eastern Front in 1943.

| | |
|---|---|
| **Country of origin:** | Germany |
| **Type:** | (Fw 189A-2) three-seat short-range tactical reconnaissance aeroplane with limited close-support and night fighter capabilities |
| **Powerplant:** | two 465hp (347kW) Argus As 410A-1 12-cylinder engines |
| **Performance:** | maximum speed 350km/h (217mph); climb to 4000m (13,125ft) in 8 minutes 18 seconds; service ceiling 7300m (23,950ft); range 670km (416 miles) |
| **Weights:** | empty 3245kg (7154lb); maximum take-off 4170kg (9193lb) |
| **Dimensions:** | span 18.40m (60ft 4.5in); length 12.03m (39ft 5.5in); height 3.10m (10ft 2in) |
| **Armament:** | two 7.92mm fixed forward-firing machine guns in wing roots, one 7.92mm two-barrel machine gun in dorsal position, and one 7.92mm two-barrel machine gun in the tailcone turret, plus a bomb load of 200kg (441lb) |

# Focke-Wulf Fw 190A-1 to A-4

The Fw 190 was the only German fighter to enter service and large-scale production during the course of the war, and despite being designed for a radial engine was developed to a definitive standard as the Fw 190D with a Vee engine. The first Fw 190 prototype flew in June 1939 and, after intensive development concentrated on the alternative BMW 139 or BMW 801 engines and a shorter- or longer-span wing, the Fw 190A entered production with the BMW 801 and larger wing. The 40 Fw 190A-0 pre-production aircraft were followed by 100 Fw 190A-1 fighters, and the type entered service in the autumn of 1941. There followed 426 longer-span Fw 190A-2 fighters with heavier armament, 509 Fw 190A-3 fighter-bombers with revised armament, and 894 Fw 190A-4 fighter-bombers with a methanol/water power boost system. Pictured here is a Fw 190A-4/U3 of the Gefechtsverband Druschel (II/SchG-1), during the battle for Kursk in July 1943.

| | |
|---|---|
| **Country of origin:** | Germany |
| **Type:** | (Fw 190A-3) single-seat fighter-bomber |
| **Powerplant:** | one 1700hp (1267.5kW) BMW 801D-2 14-cylinder two-row radial engine |
| **Performance:** | maximum speed 605km/h (382mph); initial climb rate 863m (2830ft) per minute; service ceiling 10,600m (34,775ft); range 800km (497 miles) |
| **Weights:** | empty 2900kg (6393lb); maximum take-off 3980kg (8770lb) |
| **Dimensions:** | span 10.50m (34ft 5.5in); length 8.80m (28ft 10.5in); height 3.95m (12ft 11.5in) |
| **Armament:** | four 20mm fixed forward-firing cannon in the leading edges of the wing, and two 7.92mm fixed forward-firing machine guns in the upper part of the forward fuselage |

# Focke-Wulf Fw 190F

Though schemed as a fighter, the Fw 190 was so adaptable that it was readily developed as the Fw 190F series for the dedicated ground-attack role, in which it was preceded by the long-range Fw 190G interim model. Entering service at the end of 1942, the Fw 190F-1 (about 30 aircraft) was the production-line version of the Fw 190A-5/U3 fighter based on the Fw 190A-4 with strengthened landing gear, more armour protection, and a combination of one ETC 501 bomb rack under the fuselage and four ETC 50 bomb racks under the wings. There followed 271 Fw 190F-2s with an improved canopy, about 250 Fw 190F-3s with a revised wing structure, 385 Fw 190F-7s based on the Fw 190A-7, and an unknown number of Fw 190F-9s with the 2270hp (1692.5kW) BMW 801TS/TH turbocharged engine. There were also numerous subvariants. Shown here is 'Blue Eight', and Fw 190F-8 of Schlachtgeschwader 4 during Unternehmen 'Bodenplatte' of January 1st, 1945.

| Country of origin: | Germany |
| --- | --- |
| Type: | (Fw 190F-3) single-seat ground-attack and close-support fighter |
| Powerplant: | one 1700hp (1267.5kW) BMW 801D-2 14-cylinder two-row radial engine |
| Performance: | maximum speed 635km/h (395mph); initial climb rate 642m (2106ft) per minute; service ceiling 10,600m (34,780ft); range 750km (466 miles) |
| Weights: | empty 3325kg (7328lb); maximum take-off 4925kg (10,858lb) |
| Dimensions: | span 10.5m (34ft 5.5in); length 8.95m (29ft 4.25in); height 3.95m (12ft 11.5in) |
| Armament: | two 20mm fixed forward-firing cannon in the wing roots and two 13mm fixed forward-firing machine guns in the upper part of the forward fuselage, plus an external bomb load of 1200kg (2646lb) |

# Focke-Wulf Fw 200 Condor

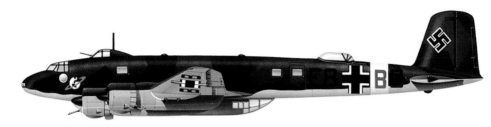

The Condor is best remembered as the long-range reconnaissance aeroplane that
searched for Allied convoys in the North Atlantic during World War II and then either
attacked them directly with bombs/missiles or vectored-in packs of German U-boats. The
type was designed as a transatlantic airliner, however, and first flew in this form during July
1937. The first of 259 Fw 200C military aircraft entered service in September 1939. A few of
these aircraft were used as VIP transports, but the majority of the machines were long-range
reconnaissance bombers in seven subvariants, some of which spawned their own
subvariants with different armament fits, radar fits and provision for missile carriage and
guidance, as well as stripped-down forms for special transport tasks. Pictured here is F8-BB,
one of the first few 200C-1 Condors with a ventral gondola and full maritime and bombing
equipment. It was assigned to Stab I/KG 40 and took part in the invasion of Norway.

| | |
|---|---|
| **Country of origin:** | Germany |
| **Type:** | (Fw 200C-3/U4) six-seat maritime reconnaissance bomber |
| **Powerplant:** | four 1200hp (895kW) BMW-Bramo 323R-2 Fafnir nine-cylinder single-row radial engines |
| **Performance:** | maximum speed 360km/h (224mph); service ceiling 6000m (19,685ft); range 4440km (2759 miles) |
| **Weights:** | empty 12,950kg (28,549lb); maximum take-off 22,700kg (50,044lb) |
| **Dimensions:** | span 32.84m (107ft 8in); length 23.46m (76ft 11.5in); height 6.30m (20ft 8in) |
| **Armament:** | one 20mm trainable cannon in forward ventral gondola position, one 13mm trainable machine gun in rear dorsal position, one 13mm trainable machine gun in each beam position, one 7.92mm machine gun in rear ventral position, and one 7.92mm machine gun in forward dorsal turret, plus a bomb load of 2100kg (4630lb) |

# Fokker E.III

Fok.E.III 417/15

Anthony Fokker designed and built his first aircraft in 1912. The Fokker Spin was a tandem-seat monoplane, with considerable dihedral but no lateral control. It was rejected by the British, who considered it 'badly built', although this probably stemmed from the general dislike of monoplanes among British officialdom rather than any scientific examination. Fokker thereupon offered his services to Germany, which built his M.5 monoplane in large numbers. In April 1915 Roland Garros' aircraft, with his self-designed bullet deflector gear, fell into German hands, prompting them to develop a more effective interrupter gear. This was fitted to a short-span M.5k scout to produce the E.I, and from April until the end of December 1915 the Fokker monoplane was the scourge of Allied pilots on the Western Front. The E.III (pictured) was the definitive model, with some 300 aircraft produced, and was the chosen mount of the German aces Böelcke and Immelmann.

| Country of origin: | Germany |
|---|---|
| Type: | single-seat fighting scout |
| Powerplant: | one 100hp (75hp) Oberusel U.I 9-cylinder rotary engine |
| Performance: | maximum speed 134km/h (83mph); service ceiling 3500m (11,500ft); endurance 2hrs 45mins |
| Weights: | empty 500kg (1100lb); loaded 635kg (1400lb) |
| Dimensions: | span 9.52m (31ft 3in); length 7.3m (23ft 11in); height 3.12m (9ft 6in); wing area sq m (sq ft) |
| Armament: | one fixed forward-firing 7.92mm LMG 08/15 machine gun |

# Fokker Dr.I

Fok DR₁ 152/17

When the Sopwith Triplane first appeared over the Western Front in late 1916 its performance far outshone any of the current German scouts, and the authorities immediately issued a request for triplane fighters. No fewer than 14 submissions were received, although they were all beaten to the mark by the Fokker Flugzeugwerke Dr.I (Dreidecker), because Fokker had seen the aircraft in action in April 1917 and did not have to wait for the captured example in July. Rheinhold Platz, his chief engineer, was no advocate of the triplane layout but nevertheless quickly produced the V.3 prototype. This had stubby, unbraced wings, the only struts being those carrying the top wing. Flight trials revealed some unpleasant handling characteristics and the aircraft was extensively modified before a production order for 350 aircraft was granted.

| | |
|---|---|
| Country of origin: | Germany |
| Type: | single-seat fighting scout |
| Powerplant: | one 110hp (82kW) Oberusel Ur.II 9-cylinder rotary piston engine |
| Performance: | maximum speed 185km/h (115mph); service ceiling 6100m (20,015ft); endurance 1hr 30mins |
| Weights: | empty 406kg (894lb); maximum take-off weight 586kg (1291lb) |
| Dimensions: | span 7.19m (23ft 7in); length 5.77m (18ft 11in); height 2.95m (9ft 8in); wing area 18.66 sq m (201 sq ft) |
| Armament: | two fixed forward-firing 7.92mm LMG 08/15 machine guns |

# Fokker Dr.I

**F**okker Dr.I 425/17 was the final mount of Manfred, Baron von Richtofen (the Red Baron), the top-scoring German ace of World War I with 81 kills, and probably the most famous fighter pilot of all time. In fact, Richtofen scored the majority of his kills in other aircraft such as the Albatros D.III. By the time the rotary-engined Dr.I was introduced into service in October 1917, although undoubtedly a supremely manoeuvrable fighter it was being outclassed by a new generation of fighting scouts and offered only mediocre performance due to the high drag of its triplane wing structure. Its construction was relatively simple, and when coupled with a skilled pilot it had the measure of many more powerful machines in a dogfight. However, speed and range were poor by 1917 standards, and Fokker expressed some surprise that the Dreidecker received such accolades.

| Country of origin: | Germany |
|---|---|
| Type: | single-seat fighting scout |
| Powerplant: | one 110hp (82kW) Oberusel Ur.II 9-cylinder rotary piston engine |
| Performance: | maximum speed 185km/h (115mph); service ceiling 6100m (20,015ft); endurance 1hr 30mins |
| Weights: | empty 406kg (894lb); maximum take-off weight 586kg (1291lb) |
| Dimensions: | span 7.19m (23ft 7in); length 5.77m (18ft 11in); height 2.95m (9ft 8in); wing area 18.66 sq m (201 sq ft) |
| Armament: | two fixed forward-firing 7.92mm LMG 08/15 machine guns |

# Fokker D.VII

The early 'D' series scouts (D.I to D.VI) were unremarkable aircraft produced by Fokker between August 1915 and late 1917, with undistinguished service careers and unsparkling performance. They were eclipsed by the D.VII designed in late 1917 by a team led by Fokker's Chief Engineer Rheinhold Platz, in time for the German standard fighter competition of January 1918. The D.VII proved vastly superior to any of the other submissions and after modification with a longer fuselage and fixed fin it was put into production. The first unit to receive the type was Manfred von Richtofen's unit JG I, which was commanded by Hermann Göring after the death of the Red Baron in April 1918. Approximately one thousand of this extremely capable aircraft had been completed by the time of the Armistice. Pictured above is a D.VII of Jasta 13, based on the Western Front in 1918.

| | |
|---|---|
| Country of origin: | Germany |
| Type: | single-seat fighting scout |
| Powerplant: | one 185hp (138kW) B.M.W III 6-cylinder inline piston engine |
| Performance: | maximum speed 200km/h (124mph); service ceiling 7000m (22,965ft); endurance 1hr 30mins |
| Weights: | empty 735kg (1620lb); maximum take-off weight 880kg (1940lb) |
| Dimensions: | span 8.9m (29ft 2in); length 6.95m (22ft 9in); height 2.75m (9ft); wing area 20.5 sq m (221 sq ft) |
| Armament: | two fixed forward-firing 7.92mm LMG 08/15 machine guns |

# Fokker C.I

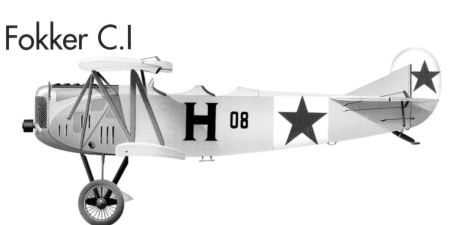

The C.I was in effect an enlarged version of the earlier D.VII. The prototype was tested as the V 38 at Schwerin in 1918 and was placed in to production immediately, but none had been completed by the time of the Armistice. Fokker smuggled the uncompleted C.I airframes out of Germany under the eyes of the French and into the Netherlands, where production continued. In total some 250 aircraft were produced, with engines of between 185 and 260hp. The Dutch military was the largest customer, taking 62 C.Is for use in the reconnaissance role. The USSR purchased 42, many of which were fitted with skis and Denmark bought two and built three others. The C.Ia of 1929 was a version for the Dutch army air corps with 200hp (149kW) Armstrong Siddeley Lynx radial engine and redesigned tail, the C.I-W was an experimental floatplane, the C.II a three-seat passenger carrying aircraft with enclosed passenger cockpit and the C.III was an advanced trainer sold to Spain.

| Country of origin: | Germany |
|---|---|
| Type: | two-seat reconaissance aircraft |
| Powerplant: | one 185hp (138kW) B.M.W IIIa 6-cylinder inline piston engine |
| Performance: | maximum speed 175km/h (109mph); service ceiling 4000m (13,125ft); range 620km (385 miles) |
| Weights: | empty equipped 855kg (1,885lb); maximum take-off weight 1255kg (2,767lb) |
| Dimensions: | span 10.5m (34ft 5 1/2in); length 7.23m (23ft 8 1/4in); height 2.87m (9ft 5in); wing area 26.25sq m (282.56sq ft) |
| Armament: | one fixed forward firing .303in machine gun, one .303in machine gun on ring mount over rear cockpit, underwing racks with provision for four 12.5kg (27.5lb) bombs |

# Fokker C.V

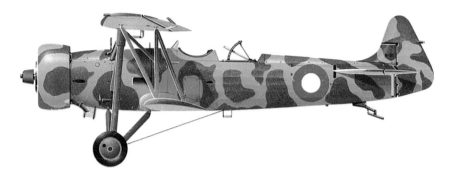

In 1923 Fokker flew the prototype of its C.IV reconnaissance biplane, and in May 1924 followed with the first flight of the C.V that was a development with a slimmer fuselage. The C.V was one the most successful general-purpose aircraft of the 1920s and 1930s, and numbers were still in service with smaller air forces in the first part of World War II. Production exceeded 750 aircraft built in the Netherlands and under licence with a number of air- and water-cooled engine types and wing cellules of different span and area. The two most important models were sesquiplanes with tapered rather than constant-chord wing panels, and were the C.V-D used mainly in the escort fighter and reconnaissance roles, and the C.V-E with an enlarged wing cellule for greater lifting power and therefore used mainly for the bombing role. Pictured is a Fokker C.V of the 3. Eskadrille of Danish army aviation during the mid-1930s.

| Country of origin: | Netherlands |
| --- | --- |
| Type: | (C.V-D) two-seat reconnaissance and artillery-spotting aeroplane with secondary light bombing and escort capabilities |
| Powerplant: | one 450hp (335.5kW) Hispano-Suiza 12 12-cylinder Vee engine |
| Performance: | maximum speed 225km/h (140mph); initial climb rate not available; service ceiling 5500m (18,045ft); range 770km (478 miles) |
| Weights: | empty 1250kg (2756lb); normal take-off 1850kg (4078lb); maximum take-off 1915kg (4222lb) |
| Dimensions: | span 12.50m (41ft 0.25in); length 9.50m (31ft 2in); height 3.50m (11ft 5.75in) |
| Armament: | one or two 7.92mm fixed forward-firing machine guns in forward fuselage, one or two 7.92mm trainable rearward-firing machine guns in the rear cockpit, and provision for one 7.92mm rearward-firing machine gun in the ventral position; bomb load of 200kg (441lb) |

# Fokker C.X

In 1933 Fokker decided that the time was ripe for the development of a successor to its C.V two-seat warplane, and the resulting C.X was first flown in 1934 as a development of the C.V-E, and thus a trim biplane with fixed landing gear and its predecessor's mixed metal and wood construction. Production totalled 71 aircraft, the later aircraft with an enclosed cockpit, and comprised 32 aircraft for the Netherlands and Dutch East Indies with the 650hp (485kW) Rolls-Royce Kestrel V Vee engine, and 39 aircraft (including 35 built under licence) for Finland with a radial engine. Some 10 aircraft were still in Dutch service in 1940 and were destroyed, but the Finnish aircraft served with modest success throughout the Finnish involvement in World War II and the last was written off only in 1958. Shown here is a Fokker C.X of TLeLV 12, Suomen Ilmavoimat (Finnish Air Force) based at Suur-Merijoki in the winter of 1939–40.

| | |
|---|---|
| Country of origin: | Netherlands |
| Type: | (C.X) two-seat tactical reconnaissance and army co-operation warplane |
| Powerplant: | one 890hp (663.5kW) Tammerfors-built Bristol Pegasus XII or XXI nine-cylinder single-row radial engine |
| Performance: | maximum speed 335km/h (208mph); climb to 3000m (9845ft) in 6 minutes ; service ceiling 8100m (26,575ft); range 900km (559 miles) |
| Weights: | empty 1550kg (3417lb); maximum take-off 2900kg(6393lb ) |
| Dimensions: | span 12.00m (39ft 4.5in); length 9.20m (30ft 2.25in); height 3.30m (10ft 10in ) |
| Armament: | one 7.62mm fixed forward-firing machine gun in the upper part of the forward fuselage, and one 7.62mm trainable rearward-firing machine gun in the rear cockpit, plus an external bomb load of 500kg (1102lb) |

# Fokker D.XXI

**D**esigned to meet a requirement of the Netherlands East Indies Army Air Service, the D.XXI was a moderately advanced fighter in Fokker's traditional mixed metal and wood construction with fixed landing gear but advanced features such as a cantilever low-set wing, an enclosed cockpit and trailing-edge flaps. The D.XXI-1 prototype flew in March 1936, and the type was ordered for Dutch rather than Dutch East Indies service (35 aircraft), with Denmark and Finland taking two and seven aircraft, the former then building another 10 aircraft and the latter 85 (50 with the 825hp/615kW Pratt & Whitney R-1535-SB4 engine) to complement five assembled for spares. most of the Dutch aircraft were destroyed in the German invasion of May 1940, but the Finnish aircraft were moderately successful and the last were not retired until 1948. Shown here is a Fokker D.XXI of TLeLV 12, Suomen Ilmavoimat (Finnish Air Force) in June 1941.

| | |
|---|---|
| **Country of origin:** | Netherlands |
| **Type:** | (D.XXI-2) single-seat fighter |
| **Powerplant:** | one 830hp (619kW) Bristol Mercury VIII nine-cylinder single-row radial engine |
| **Performance:** | maximum speed 460km/h (286mph); climb to 6000m (19,685ft) in 7 minutes 30 seconds; service ceiling 11,000m (36,090ft); range 930km (578 miles ) |
| **Weights:** | empty 1450kg (3197lb); maximum take-off 2050kg (4519lb) |
| **Dimensions:** | span 11.00 m (36ft 1in); length 8.20m (26ft 10.75in); height 2.95m (9ft 8in) |
| **Armament:** | two 7.92mm fixed forward-firing machine guns in the upper part of the forward fuselage, and two 7.92mm fixed forward-firing machine guns in the leading edges of the wing |

# Fokker G.I

During the mid-1930s there was considerable interest in the concept of the twin-engined heavy fighter that would offer, in the opinion of many analysts, speed and climb performance comparable with that of single-engined fighters, together with longer range, heavier firepower and all the reliability advantages of a twin-engined powerplant. Among the countries that essayed such a type was the Netherlands with the G.I that first flew in two-seat prototype form during March 1937. About 36 of the two/three-seat G.IA initial production model followed, and orders were placed by six countries for the G.IB export model. Three of these were pressed into Dutch service in May 1940, when virtually all the aircraft were destroyed, and about 20 more were later completed for German use as trainers. Shown here is one of the G.IB aircraft that was thrown into battle against the German invaders by the Luchtvaartafdeling (Dutch Air Force) in May 1940.

| Country of origin: | Netherlands |
|---|---|
| Type: | (G.IA) two/three-seat heavy fighter and close-support warplane |
| Powerplant: | two 830hp (619kW) Bristol Mercury VIII nine-cylinder single-row radial engines |
| Performance: | maximum speed 475km/h (295mph); climb to 6000m (19,685ft) in 8 minutes 54 seconds; service ceiling 9300m (30,510ft); range 1500km (932 miles) |
| Weights: | empty 3330kg (7341lb); maximum take-off 5000kg (11,023lb) |
| Dimensions: | span 17.16m (56ft 3.6in); length 10.87m (35ft 7.9in); height 3.80m (12ft 5.6in) |
| Armament: | eight 7.92mm fixed forward-firing machine guns in the nose, and one 7.92mm trainable rearward-firing machine gun in the nacelle tailcone position, plus an external bomb load of 400kg (882lb) |

# Fokker T.VIII-Wg

Fokker's T-series floatplanes were specifically designed for service in the East Indies, the major Dutch colonial possession of the interwar period. The T.IV was one of Fokker's most ungainly designs, but was a tough, seaworthy combat aircraft which operated with some distinction against the Japanese invaders. The T.VIII-W was built in three versions: the T.VIII-Wg was of mixed wood-and-metal construction; the T-VIII-Wm was all metal; and the T.VIII-Wc was a scaled-up version in wood-and-metal with more powerful engines. Five were in service by June 1939, when the Fokker factory was overrun. A total of 36 were built, 25 of which were requisitioned by the Luftwaffe (including five T.VIII-Wc aircraft on order for Finland). Eight survivors were flown to England on 14 May 1940, and were operated by their crews as No 320 (Dutch) Squadron of RAF Coastal Command until they ran out of spares in late 1940.

| | |
|---|---|
| Country of origin: | Netherlands |
| Type: | three-seat torpedo-bomber/reconnaissance floatplane |
| Powerplant: | two 450hp (336kW) Wright Whirlwind R-975-E3 9-cylinder radial engines |
| Performance: | maximum speed 285km/h (177mph); service ceiling 6800m (22,310ft); range 2750km (1709 miles) |
| Weights: | empty 3100kg (6834lb); maximum take-off weight 5000kg (11,023lb) |
| Dimensions: | span 18m (59ft); length 13m (42ft 8in); height 5m (16ft 5in); wing area 44 sq m (474 sq ft) |
| Armament: | one fixed forward-firing .31in machine gun; one .31in machine gun on flexible mount in rear cockpit; plus up to 605kg (1334lb) of stores carried externally |

# Fuji T-1A

Once the Japanese aircraft industry had been cleared to begin production again in 1953, the government awarded a number of substantial contract to Fuji with the aim of producing indigenous jet powered aircraft to replace American supplied piston engined T-6 Texans. The company had already constructed a small turbojet engine to power just such an aircraft, but the first T1F1 was powered by an imported Bristol Siddeley Orpheus engine. The design leant heavily on the North American F-86 Sabre. Designated T-1A by the JASDF, the Orpheus powered aircraft began to enter service in 1961 and by July of the following year 40 had been delivered. The company also produced a T1-B version, powered, or rather underpowered, by the Japan Jet Engine Co. J3-3. This engine delivered only two-thirds of the thrust of the Bristol engine.

| | |
|---|---|
| **Country of origin:** | Japan |
| **Type:** | two-seat intermediate jet trainer |
| **Powerplant:** | one 1814kg (4000lb) Rolls-Royce (Bristol Siddeley) Orpheus Mk 805 turbojet |
| **Performance:** | maximum speed 925km/h (575mph) at high altitude; service ceiling 14,400m (47,250ft); range 1860km (1156 miles) at high altitude with drop tanks |
| **Weights:** | empty 2420kg (5335lb); maximum take-off 5000kg (11,023lb) |
| **Dimensions:** | wingpsan 10.49m (34ft 5in); length 12.12m (39ft 9.2in); height 4.08m (13ft 4.6in); wing area 22.22sq m (239.2sq ft) |
| **Armament:** | optional 0.5in Browning M53-2 gun in nose; two underwing pylons with provision for up to 680kg (1500lb) of stores, including bombs, Sidewinder air-to-air missiles, or gun pods; usually only tanks carried |

# General Dynamics F-111

The variable geometry F-111 suffered a difficult gestation, earning it the unwelcome nickname, Aardvark. Developed to meet a bold Department of Defense edict that a common type of fighter should be developed to meet all future tactical needs of the US armed forces, the F-111 seemed at the outset both a success and a great failure. Public disagreements over who should get the contract were further clouded by problems in the development of almost every one of the aircraft's systems. Eventually the first of 117 aircraft, designated F-111As, were delivered into service in 1967. Its most famous moment was the bombing of Libya in 1986. A carrierborne long-range interceptor variant of the F-111 for the US Navy foundered after only nine had been built. The Royal Australian Air Force bought the F-111C with increased span and stronger undercarriage but this was the only export success for the aircraft. The F-111 is no longer in service.

| Country of origin: | USA |
|---|---|
| Type: | two-seat multi-purpose attack aircraft |
| Powerplant: | two 11,385kg (25,100lb) Pratt & Whitney TF-30-P100 |
| Performance: | maximum speed at optimum altitude 2655km/h (1650mph); service ceiling above 17,985m (59,000ft); range with internal fuel 4707km (2925 miles) |
| Weights: | empty 21,398kg (47,175lb); maximum take-off 45,359kg (100,000lb) |
| Dimensions: | wingspan unswept 19.20m (63ft); swept 9.74m (32ft 11.5in); length 22.40m (73ft 6in); height 5.22m (17ft 1.5in); wing area 48.77sq m (525sq ft) unswept |
| Armament: | one 20mm multi-barrelled M61A-1 cannon and one 340kg (750lb) B43 bomb, or two B43 bombs in internal bay, eight underwing hardpoints with provision for 14,290kg (31,000lb) of stores, inner four pivot to keep stores in alignment as wings sweep |

# General Dynamics F-16A

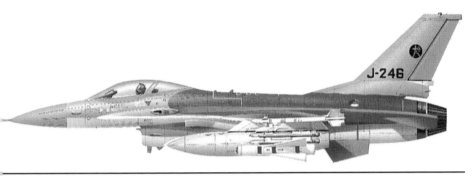

The F-16 is undoubtedly one of the most important fighter aircraft of this century. It started fairly inauspiciously as a technology demonstrator to see to what degree it would be possible to build a useful fighter that was significantly smaller and cheaper than the F-15 Eagle. The US Air Force termed this the Lightweight Fighter programme and it was not initially intended to lead to a production aircraft. Contracts for two prototypes each of the General Dynamics 401 and Northrop P.530 were awarded in April 1972. Interest in the concept from a number of America's NATO allies led to a total revision of the LWF program; it was subsequently announced that the US Air Force would buy 650 of the successful Air Combat Fighter design. In December 1974 the General Dynamics design was announced as the winner. The first production F-16A was flown on 7 August 1978. Approximately 4500 F-16s have been built, the latest examples being the Block 60.

| | |
|---|---|
| Country of origin: | USA |
| Type: | single-seat air combat and ground attack fighter |
| Powerplant: | either one 10,800kg (23,770lb) Pratt & Whitney F100-PW-200 or one 13,150kg (28,984lb) General Electric F110-GE-100 turbofan |
| Performance: | maximum speed 2142km/h (1320mph); service ceiling above 15,240m (50,000ft); operational radius 925km (525 miles) |
| Weights: | empty 7070kg (15,586lb); maximum take-off 16,057kg (35,400lb) |
| Dimensions: | wingspan 9.45m (31ft); length 15.09m (49ft 6in); height 5.09m (16ft 8in); wing area 27.87sq m (300sq ft) |
| Armament: | one General Electric M61A1 20mm multi-barrelled cannon, wingtip missile stations; seven external hardpoints with provision for up to 9276kg (20,450lb) of stores, including air-to-air missiles, air-to-surface missiles, ECM pods, reconnaissance or rocket pods, conventional or laser guided bombs, or fuel tanks |

# General Dynamics F-16B

The F-16B is a two-seat trainer version of General Dynamics' highly successful Fighting Falcon, and shares a physically similar airframe. The second cockpit occupies the area taken up by a fuel tank in the single-seat F-16A. Two of the eight pre-production aircraft were ordered as two-seaters, with the first one flying in August 1977. The USAF has ordered approximately 204 of the two-seat version, and most foreign customers have opted to purchase both types in conjunction. The USAF fleet of F-16A/Bs have undergone a mid-life Multi-national Staged Improvement Program to ensure their effectiveness as combat aircraft into the next century. A further two-seat variant designated the F-16D has been produced, which incorporates the avionics and systems improvements that have been retrofitted to the MSIP F-16A/B aircraft. The F-16 will remain in service with many nations for years to come, and it is still being aggressively marketed.

| | |
|---|---|
| Country of origin: | USA |
| Type: | single-seat air combat and ground attack fighter |
| Powerplant: | either one 10,800kg (23,770lb) Pratt & Whitney F100-PW-200 or one 13,150kg (28,984lb) General Electric F110-GE-100 turbofan |
| Performance: | maximum speed 2142km/h (1320mph); service ceiling above 15,240m (50,000ft); operational radius 925km (525 miles) |
| Weights: | empty 7070kg (15,586lb); maximum take-off 16,057kg (35,400lb) |
| Dimensions: | wingspan 9.45m (31ft); length 15.09m (49ft 6in); height 5.09m (16ft 8in); wing area 27.87sq m (300sq ft) |
| Armament: | one General Electric M61A1 20mm multi-barrelled cannon, wingtip missile stations; seven external hardpoints with provision for up to 9276kg (20,450lb) of stores, including air-to-air missiles (AIM-9 Sidewinder and AIM-120 AMRAAM), air-to-surface missiles, ECM pods, reconnaissance or rocket pods, conventional or laser guided bombs, or fuel tanks |

# Gloster Grebe Mk II

After learning his craft at Nieuport during World War I, Harry Folland took his talents to the Gloucester (later Gloster) Aircraft Company and from his drawing board emerged a long line of very successful biplane fighters. The family began with the Gloster Grouse of 1923, used exclusively for research, which was the airframe of the Gloster Sparrowhawk II company demonstrator married to a new biplane wing designed by Folland. This was followed by the Grebe, which together with the Armstrong Whitworth Siskin and Hawker Woodcock was the first new fighter to be selected for the RAF in the interwar years. The prototype completed a highly successful series of flight trials in 1923 and was subsequently redesignated Grebe Mk I. Production aircraft received some minor modifications and were designated Grebe Mk IIs, of which 129 were supplied to the RAF.

| Country of origin: | United Kingdom |
|---|---|
| Type: | single-seat biplane fighter |
| Powerplant: | one 400hp (298kW) Armstrong Siddeley Jaguar IV 14-cylinder radial piston engine |
| Performance: | maximum speed 243km/h (151mph); service ceiling 7010m (23,000ft); endurance 2hrs 45mins |
| Weights: | empty 780kg (1720lb); maximum take-off weight 1189kg (2622lb) |
| Dimensions: | span 8.94m (29ft 4in); length 6.17m (20ft 3in); height 2.82m (9ft 3in); wing area 23.6 sq m (254 sq ft) |
| Armament: | two fixed forward-firing .303in Vickers machine guns |

# Gloster Gamecock Mk I

The Gloster Gamecock was a development of the Mk III Grebe, and was built to Air Ministry Specification 27/23. It differed from the Grebe primarily by way of its Bristol Jupiter engine, which replaced the unreliable Armstrong Siddeley Jaguar. Other changes included improved ailerons, refined fuselage contours and internally mounted machine guns. It was first flown in February 1925, and 100 were acquired by the RAF, remaining in service until 1931. Although its wood-and-fabric construction was unremarkable, the Gamecock was a tough and reliable aircraft, able to survive almost anything thrown at it. The Gamecock Mk II (three aircraft were built) had a revised centre wing section. Gloster (as the company became known in 1926) supplied three Gamecock Mk IIs to Finland, which license-built another 15 under the name Kukko. Pictured is a Gamecock Mk I of No 32 Squadron, based at RAF Kenley.

| | |
|---|---|
| Country of origin: | United Kingdom |
| Type: | single-seat biplane fighter |
| Powerplant: | one 425hp (317kW) Bristol Jupiter VI 9-cylinder radial engine |
| Performance: | maximum speed 249km/h (155mph); service ceiling 6705m (22,000ft); endurance 2hrs |
| Weights: | empty 875kg (1930lb); maximum take-off weight 1299kg (2863lb) |
| Dimensions: | span 9.08m (29ft 9in); length 5.99m (19ft 8in); height 2.95m (9ft 8in); wing area 24.53 sq m (264 sq ft) |
| Armament: | two fixed forward-firing .303in Vickers Mk I machine guns |

# Gloster Gauntlet Mk I

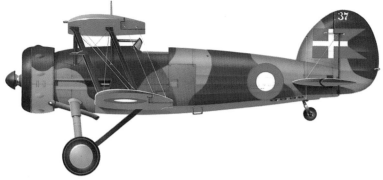

The Gauntlet was one of the most prolific RAF fighters of the 1930s, and in 1937 equipped no fewer than 14 squadrons. It had a rather convoluted development process due to the unsuccessful Goldfinch design, which was an all-metal version of the Gamecock built to an Air Ministry order and evaluated in prototype form but never ordered. Gloster then offered the aircraft as a single-seat fighter under Specification F.9/26 but again failed to win a production contract. The company had almost completed a new aircraft to meet F.9/26 when the Air Ministry issued a new Specification F.20/27 for a high-altitude single-seat fighter. Gloster's submission was the S.S.18 prototype, which was developed over a four-year period to its production form as the Gauntlet Mk I, which had a 640hp (477kW) Bristol Mercury VIS2 engine. The first aircraft of an order for 24 was delivered to the RAF in May 1935, by which time Gloster was under the control of Hawker.

| Country of origin: | United Kingdom |
| --- | --- |
| Type: | single-seat fighter biplane |
| Powerplant: | one 640hp (477kW) Bristol Mercury VIS2 9-cylinder radial engine |
| Performance: | maximum speed 370km/h (230mph); service ceiling 10,120m (33,500ft); range 740km (460 miles) |
| Weights: | empty 1256kg (2770lb); maximum take-off weight 1801kg (3970lb) |
| Dimensions: | span 9.99m (32ft 9in); length 8.05m (26ft 5in); height 3.12m (10ft 3in); wing area 29.26 sq m (315 sq ft) |
| Armament: | two fixed forward-firing .303in Vickers Mk I machine guns |

# Gloster Gauntlet Mk II

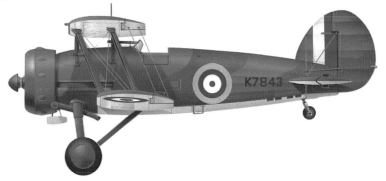

The major production version of the Gauntlet was the Mk II, which embodied many Hawker construction techniques in the fuselage following the rationalisation of techniques within the newly formed Hawker Siddeley Group. Two orders for a total of 204 aircraft were completed, the last of them delivered in 1937. The last batches had a Fairey Reed three-blade metal propeller in place of the two-blade Watts of laminated wood. The Gauntlet was the last open-cockpit fighter to be produced for the RAF and served until June 1940 in the Middle East. Seventeen Gauntlets were produced under licence in Denmark. Ex-RAF Gauntlets were supplied to the Royal Australian Air Force (6), Finland (25), Rhodesia (3) and South Africa (6). Pictured is a Mk II of No 3 Squadron, Royal Australian Air Force, based at Helwan in Egypt in November 1940.

| | |
|---|---|
| Country of origin: | United Kingdom |
| Type: | single-seat fighter biplane |
| Powerplant: | one 640hp (477kW) Bristol Mercury VIS2 9-cylinder radial engine |
| Performance: | maximum speed 370km/h (230mph); service ceiling 10,120m (33,500ft); range 740km (460 miles) |
| Weights: | empty 1256kg (2770lb); maximum take-off weight 1801kg (3970lb) |
| Dimensions: | span 9.99m (32ft 9in); length 8.05m (26ft 5in); height 3.12m (10ft 3in); wing area 29.26 sq m (315 sq ft) |
| Armament: | two fixed forward-firing .303in Vickers Mk I machine guns |

# Gloster Gladiator

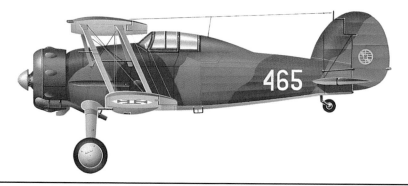

The last and finest biplane British fighter, the Gladiator was a conceptual development of the Gauntlet with improved features such as an enclosed cockpit, trailing-edge flaps and cantilever main landing gear legs. The prototype flew in September 1934, and the first of 378 Gladiator Mk I fighters entered service in 1937 pending the large-scale advent of more advanced monoplane fighters. The Gladiator Mk I was supplemented by the Gladiator Mk II, of which 311 were delivered with the Mercury VIIIA or VIIIAS engine. Some 38 of the aircraft were converted to Interim Sea Gladiator standard, paving the way for the carrierborne Sea Gladiator of which 60 were completed. The Gladiator saw first-line service in the northern European and Mediterranean theatres to 1940 and the middle of 1941, and numbers of the aircraft were also exported. Pictured here is a Gladiator Mk II of the Arma de Aeronautica (Portugese Air Force) in 1940.

| Country of origin: | United Kingdom |
|---|---|
| Type: | (Gladiator Mk I) single-seat fighter |
| Powerplant: | one 830hp (619kW) Bristol Mercury IX nine-cylinder single-row radial engine |
| Performance: | maximum speed 407km/h (253mph); climb to 4570m (15,000ft) in 5 minutes 40 seconds; service ceiling 9995m (32,800ft); range 689km (428 miles) |
| Weights: | empty 1633kg (3600lb); maximum take-off 2083kg (4592lb) |
| Dimensions: | span 9.83m (32ft 3in); length 8.36m (27ft 5in); height 3.22m (10ft 7in) |
| Armament: | two 0.303in fixed forward-firing machine guns in the sides of the forward fuselage, and two 0.303in fixed forward-firing machine guns in the leading edges of the lower wing |

# Gloster Meteor F.Mk 8

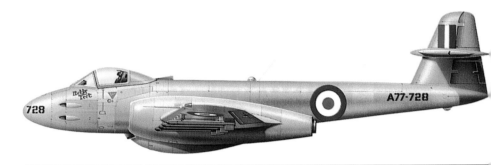

The Gloster Meteor was designed by George Carter to Air Ministry Specification F.9/40. It was the first Allied jet combat design, and the only one to see service during World War II. Trials were carried out with various basic engine types, the Rolls-Royce W.2B, the de Havilland developed Halford H.1, and the Metrovick F.2 among them. The first 20 production aircraft were powered by modified W.2B/23C Welland turbojets. The Meteor entered service with No. 616 Squadron on July 12, 1944, and saw action against V-1 flying bombs. The F.Mk 8 was the most prolific variant, with a lengthened fuselage, redesigned tail, and additional 432-litre (95 Imp gal) fuel tank, and a bubble canopy. Later F.Mk 8s also had bigger engine inlets. The aircraft also boasted a gyro-stabilised gunsight and one the first Martin Baker ejection seats. The first of 1183 F.Mk 8s was flown on 12 October 1948.

| Country of origin: | United Kingdom |
|---|---|
| Type: | single-seat fighter |
| Powerplant: | two 1,587kg (3,600lb) Rolls Royce Derwent 8 turbojets |
| Performance: | maximum speed at 10,000m (33,000ft) 962km/h (598mph); service ceiling 13,106m (43,000ft); range 1580km (980 miles) |
| Weights: | empty 4820kg (10,626lb); loaded 8664kg (19,100lb) |
| Dimensions: | wingspan 11.32m (37ft 2in); length 13.58m (44ft 7in); height 3.96m (13ft) |
| Armament: | four 20mm Hispano cannon, foreign F.8s often modified to carry two iron bombs, eight rockets, or other offensive stores |

# Gotha G.V

A longside the airships and 'R' series from the Zeppelin works, the series of 'G' (*Grossflugzeug*, large aeroplane) designs from Gothaer Wagonfabrik played a major role in German strategic bombing in World War I. The G.I stemmed from a prototype built under the direction of Oskar Ursinus, a German Army major. Gotha built a small number under licence for tactical bombing over the Western and Eastern Fronts. The G.II was designed by with the fuselage mounted on the lower rather than upper wing, and with nosewheels to prevent nosing over. The G.II had a direct-drive Mercedes D.IVa, and a few had a tunnel extending to a rear gunners cockpit that covered the previous defensive 'blind spot'. This was standard fitment on the G.IV, the major production version, which first flew in December 1916 and was followed by a limited number of G.V and G.Va aircraft, used for a short time before night-bombing was abandoned by the German Air Service in April 1918.

| Country of origin: | Germany |
| --- | --- |
| Type: | three-seat long-range biplane bomber |
| Powerplant: | two 260hp (194kW) Mercedes D.IVa 6-cylinder inline piston engines |
| Performance: | maximum speed 140km/h (87mph); service ceiling 6500m (21,325ft); range 500km (500 km) |
| Weights: | empty 2740kg (6041lb); maximum take-off weight 3975kg (8763lb) |
| Dimensions: | span 23.7m (77ft 9in); length 11.86m (38ft 11in); height 4.3m (14ft 1in); wing area 89.5 sq m (963 sq ft) |
| Armament: | two 7.92mm Parabellum machine guns on flexible mount in nose position; two 7.92mm Parabellum machine guns on flexible mount in dorsal position; plus maximum bomb load of 500kg (1102lb) |

# Gotha Go 244

The Go 242 was the German Air Force's standard transport glider in the second half of
World War II, deliveries totalling 1526 Go 242A and Go 242B gliders with skid and
wheeled landing gear respectively. The success of the latter paved the way for the Go 244
that was in essence a powered version of the glider and evaluated with low-powered
German or captured Soviet and French engines. The last were preferred, and deliveries
totalled 174 aircraft including 133 Go 242B conversions. These were completed in forms
corresponding to the five Go 242B production versions, and were the Go 244B-1 freighter
with torsion-bar shock absorption, Go 244B-2 freighter with wider-track main units and
oleo shock absorption, Go 244B-3 and B-4 paratroop transport versions of the Go 244B-1
and B-2, and Go 244B-5 with dual controls and balanced rudders. Shown here is a Gotha
Go 244B-1 of an unidentified Luftwaffe transport unit.

| Country of origin: | Germany |
| --- | --- |
| Type: | (Go 244B-2) two-seat transport with accommodation for 23 troops or freight |
| Powerplant: | two 700hp (522kW) Gnome-Rhòne 14M-4/5 14-cylinder two-row radial engines |
| Performance: | maximum speed 290km/h (180mph); climb to 5000m (16,405ft) in 18 minutes 30 seconds; ceiling 7650m (25,100ft); range 740km (460 miles) |
| Weights: | empty 5225kg (11,517lb); maximum take-off 7800kg (17,196lb) |
| Dimensions: | span 24.50m (80ft 4.5in); length 15.80m (51ft 10.25in); height 4.60m (15ft 1in) |
| Armament: | one 7.92mm machine gun in cockpit roof position, one 7.92mm machine gun in tail of central nacelle, one 7.92mm machine gun in each side of central nacelle, and provision for the troops to fire up to four 7.92mm machine guns from hold windows |

# Grumman F3F

This G-11 design was evolved by Grumman as a slightly enlarged version of the G-8 (F2F) fighter with changes to correct the earlier warplane's lack of directional stability and tendency to spin. The US Navy ordered a single XF3F-1 prototype, and this made its maiden flight in March 1935 with the Pratt & Whitney R-1535-72 Twin Wasp Junior engine. Two other prototypes followed before the US Navy contracted for 54 examples of the F3F-1 production version that differed from the third XF3F-1 only in a slight increase in fuselage length. The aircraft were delivered between January and September 1936, and were initially flown by three squadrons, namely VF-5B and VF-6B (later VF-4 and VF-3) on the aircraft carriers USS *Ranger* and USS *Saratoga*, and VF-4M (later VMF-2) of the US Marine Corps shore-based at San Diego. These aircraft were the forerunners of the famous 'Cat' series of fleet fighters that formed the basis of US Navy air strength during the Pacific campaign.

| Country of origin: | USA |
| --- | --- |
| Type: | (F3F-1) single-seat carrierborne and land-based fighter and fighter-bomber |
| Powerplant: | one 700hp (522kW) Pratt & Whitney R-1535-84 Twin Wasp Junior 14-cylinder two-row radial engine |
| Performance: | maximum speed 372km/h (231mph ); initial climb rate 579m (1900ft) per minute; service ceiling 8685m (28,500ft); range 1609km (1000 miles) |
| Weights: | empty 1339kg (2952lb); maximum take-off 1997kg (4403lb) |
| Dimensions: | span 9.75m (32ft); length 7.09m (23ft 3.1in); height 2.77m (9ft 1in) |
| Armament: | one 0.5in fixed forward-firing machine gun and one 0.3in fixed forward-firing machine gun in the upper part of the forward fuselage, plus an external bomb load of 105kg (232lb) |

# Grumman F4F Wildcat

The F4F was the US Navy's most important fighter at the time of the USA's entry into World War II in December 1941 after the Japanese attack on Pearl Harbor, and it remained in production right through the war. The aircraft was originally schemed as the XF4F-1 biplane, before being revised as the XF4F-2 monoplane that first flew in September 1937. This was followed by the XF4F-3 that paved the way for the 284 F4F-3 initial production aircraft with the R-1830-76 engine. Later variants were the F4F-3A with the R-1830-90 engine (95 aircraft), F4F-4 with manually folding wing tips (1144 aircraft) and unarmed photo-reconnaissance F4F-7 (21 aircraft). General Motors also built 1140 FM-1 (F4F-4) aircraft and 4467 FM-2 aircraft with the R-1830-56 engine and a taller fin. The 1082 F4Fs were delivered to the UK, where the type was initially known as the Martlet and then as the Wildcat in variants up to the Mk VI.

| | |
|---|---|
| Country of origin: | USA |
| Type: | (F4F-4 and Wildcat Mk II) single-seat carrierborne fighter and fighter-bomber |
| Powerplant: | one 1200hp (895kW) Pratt & Whitney R-1830-86 Twin Wasp 14-cylinder two-row radial engine |
| Performance: | maximum speed 512km/h (318mph); initial climb rate 594m (1950ft ) per minute; service ceiling 10,365m (34,000ft); range 2012km (1250 miles) |
| Weights: | empty 2612kg (5758lb); maximum take-off 3607kg (7952lb ) |
| Dimensions: | span 11.58m (38ft 0in); length 8.76m (28ft 9in); height 2.81m (9ft 2.5in) |
| Armament: | six 0.5in fixed forward-firing machine guns in the leading edges of the wing, plus an external bomb load of 91kg (200lb) |

# Grumman TBF Avenger

Making a disastrous combat debut in the Battle of Midway (June 1942), the TBF rapidly matured as the classic torpedo bomber of World War II. The first of two XTBF-1 prototypes made the type's maiden flight in August 1941. Grumman then built only the TBF-1 model, whose total of 2289 aircraft completed by March 1945 included subvariants such as the baseline TBF-1, winterised TBF-1J Avenger, TBF-1P photo-reconnaissance type, TBF-1B (402 aircraft) delivered to the UK, TBF-1C (764 aircraft) with two 0.5in machine guns in the leading edges of the wing, TBF-1CP photo-reconnaissance type, TBF-1D for the anti-submarine role with radar and underwing rockets, TBF-1E with podded air-to-surface radar, and TBF-1L with a retractable searchlight for night illumination of surfaced submarines. The Royal Navy's wartime Avengers were mostly TBF-1Bs (404 received). In Fleet Air Arm service they were designated Tarpon Mk I and then Avenger Mk I in January 1944.

| | |
|---|---|
| Country of origin: | USA |
| Type: | (TBF-1C) three-seat carrierborne and land-based torpedo bomber |
| Powerplant: | one 1700hp (1268kW) Wright R-2600-8 Cyclone 14 14-cylinder two-row radial engine |
| Performance: | maximum speed 414km/h (257mph); climb to 3050m (10,000ft) in 13 minutes; service ceiling 6525m (21,400ft); range 4321km (2685 miles) |
| Weights: | empty 4788kg (10,555lb); maximum take-off 7876kg (17,364lb) |
| Dimensions: | span 16.51m (54ft 2in); length 12.42m (40ft 9in); height 4.19m (13ft 9in) |
| Armament: | two 0.5in fixed forward-firing machine guns in the leading edges of the wing, one 0.5in Browning trainable rearward-firing machine gun in the dorsal turret, and one 0.3in rearward-firing machine gun in ventral position, plus torpedo, bomb and rocket load of 1134kg (2500lb) |

# Grumman F6F-3 Hellcat

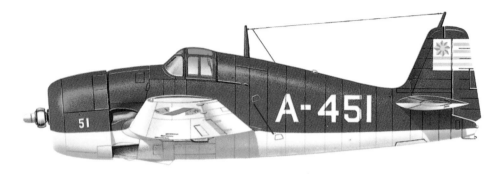

The most successful fighter of the Pacific campaign, shooting down 5156 Japanese aircraft for the loss of only 270 of its own number in air-to-air combat; the F6F was designed from the spring of 1941 as an F4F successor. The F6F was in effect an enlarged and better streamlined F4F with a considerably more potent engine, and the XF6F-3 first prototype flew in June 1942. The F6F-3 initial production model (4402 aircraft including 205 F6F-3N night-fighters and 18 radar-equipped F6F-3E night intruders) entered combat in August 1943, and soon revealed a superb balance of high performance, hard-hitting firepower, great strength and adequate agility. Some 252 of the standard fighters were transferred under Lend-Lease to the UK for service with the Fleet Air Arm with the designation Gannet Mk I soon changed to Hellcat Mk I. Pictured here is one of F6F-5 Hellcats supplied to the Aviacion Navale Uruguaya.

| | |
|---|---|
| **Country of origin:** | USA |
| **Type:** | (F6F-3): single-seat carrierborne fighter and fighter-bomber |
| **Powerplant:** | one 2000hp (1491kW) Pratt & Whitney R-2800-10 or -10W Double Wasp 18-cylinder two-row radial engine |
| **Performance:** | maximum speed 603km/h (375mph); initial climb rate 1067m (3500ft) per minute; service ceiling 11705m (38,400ft); range 2559km (1590 miles) |
| **Weights:** | empty 4128kg (9101lb); maximum take-off 7025kg (15,487lb) |
| **Dimensions:** | span 13.06m (42ft 10in); length 10.24m (33ft 7in); height 3.99m (13ft 1in ) |
| **Armament:** | six 0.5in fixed forward-firing machine guns in the leading edges of the wing, plus an external bomb load of 454kg (1000lb) |

# Grumman A-6 Intruder

Selected from 11 competing designs in December 1957, the Intruder was specifically planned for first pass blind attack on point surface targets at night or in any weather conditions. The aircraft was designed to be subsonic and is powered by two straight turbojets. In the original design the efflux was routed through tilting jetpips to enhance STOL capabilities. Despite its considerable gross weight the Intruder has excellent slow flying qualities with full span slats and flaps. The crew are afforded a good all round view by the broad canopy. The navigator controls one of the most sophisticated avionics suites on any current aircraft. The Intruder first came into service with the US Navy in February 1963; during the Vietnam War the A-6A was tasked with round-the-clock precision bombing missions that no other aircraft was capable of undertaking until the introduction of the F-111. The A-6 is no longer in service.

| | |
|---|---|
| Country of origin: | USA |
| Type: | two-seat carrierborne and landbased all-weather strike aircraft |
| Powerplant: | two 4218kg (9300lb) Pratt & Whitney J52-P-8A turbojets |
| Performance: | maximum speed at sea level 1043km/h (648mph); service ceiling 14,480m (47,500ft); range with full weapon load 1627km (1011 miles) |
| Weights: | empty 12,132kg (26,746lb); maximum take-off 26,581kg (58,600lb) for carrier launch or 27,397kg (60,400lb) for field take-off |
| Dimensions: | wingspan 16.15m (53ft); length 16.69; height 4.93m (16ft 2in); wing area 49.13sq m (528.9sq ft) |
| Armament: | five external hardpoints with provision for up to 8165kg (18,000lb) of stores, including nuclear weapons, conventional and guided bombs, air-to-surface missiles, and drop tanks |

# Grumman EA-6 Prowler

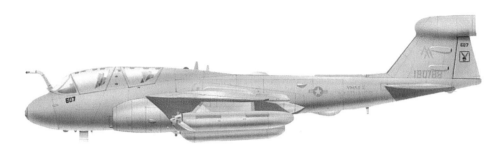

The US Navy rarely undertakes a strike mission without the protection offered by the EA-6 electronic countermeasures (ECM) aircraft. This was developed from the successful A-6 Intruder family, although it is substantially different in almost every respect. The large cockpit provides seating for the pilot and three electronic warfare officers, who control the most sophisticated and advanced ECM equipment ever fitted to a tactical aircraft. At the heart of this system is the ALQ-99 tactical jamming system, which is capable of dealing with multiple hostile electronic signals across a broad range of frequencies. The aircraft first entered service in 1972 with VAQ-132. Despite its proven capabilities, the Prowler was only produced in small numbers. In the mid-1990s the US Navy updated many aircraft to ADVCAP (Advanced Capability Standard). Since the retirement of the EF-111 Raven, it is the only US tactical ECM aircraft in service.

| Country of origin: | USA |
|---|---|
| Type: | electronic countermeasures platform |
| Powerplant: | two 5080kg (11,200lb) Pratt & Whitney J52-P-408 turbojets |
| Performance: | maximum speed at sea level 982km/h (610mph); service ceiling 11,580m (38,000ft); combat range with full external fuel 1769km (1099 miles) |
| Weights: | empty 14,588kg (32,162lb); maximum take-off 29,484kg (65,000lb) |
| Dimensions: | wingspan 16.15m (53ft); length 18.24m (59ft 10in); height 4.95m (16ft 3in); wing area 49.13sq m (528.9sq ft) |
| Armament: | none on early models, retrofitted with external hardpoints for four or six AGM-88 HARM air-to-surface anti-radar missiles |

# Grumman F-14A Tomcat

The F-14 was developed largely because of the failure of the F-111B fleet fighter programme, yet has not enjoyed a trouble free service life itself. Continuing problems with the engines have led to escalating maintenance costs (one of the reasons for the development of the cheaper F-18) and a relatively high accident rate. Despite these problems the Tomcat is widely regarded as the finest interceptor flying anywhere in the world. Development of the F-14A was hampered by the loss of the first prototype in December 1970. The aircraft entered service less than two years later with VF-125, before embarking for the first operational tour with VF-1 and VF-2 on USS *Enterprise* in September 1974. The F-14 succeeded the F-4 as the premier fleet defence fighter. A total of 478 F-14As were supplied to the US Navy. Eighty aircraft were exported to Iran from 1976, but these are all now unserviceable.

| Country of origin: | USA |
|---|---|
| Type: | two-seat carrierborne fleet defence fighter |
| Powerplant: | two 9480kg (20,900lb) Pratt & Whitney TF30-P-412A turbofans |
| Performance: | maximum speed at high altitude 2517km/h (1564mph); service ceiling 17,070m (56,000ft); range about 3220km (2000 miles) |
| Weights: | empty 18,191kg (40,104lb); maximum take-off 33,724kg (74,349lb) |
| Dimensions: | wingspan 19.55m (64ft 1.5in) unswept; 11.65m (38ft 2.5in) swept; length 19.10m (62ft 8in); height 4.88m (16ft); wing area 52.49sq m (565sq ft) |
| Armament: | one 20mm M61A1 Vulcan rotary cannon with 675 rounds; external pylons for a combination of AIM-7 Sparrow medium range air-to-air missiles, AIM-9 medium range air-to-air missiles, and AIM-54 Phoenix long range air-to-air missiles |

# Grumman F-14D Tomcat

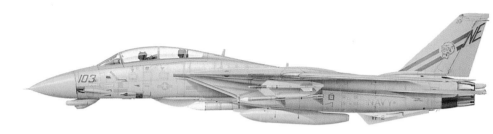

In 1973 the US Navy was forced to curtail development of the first F-14B project, powered by twin 12,741kg (28,090lb) Pratt & Whitney F401-P400 turbofans. The result of the cancellation was that all production F-14As were fitted with the TF30, which had only ever been designed as an interim engine. In 1984 it was decided to develop an interim improved version of the F-14 with General Electric F110-GE-400, designated the F-14A (Plus). Thirty-two aircraft were converted and later designated F-14B. The F-14D project suffered a seemingly endless round of cancellations and reinstatements prior to the funding of 37 new-build aircraft and 18 rebuilds from F-14As. The F-14D benefits from an improved version of the powerful APG-70 radar, the APG-71, redesign of the cockpit instrumentation, improved defensive suite and tactical jamming system. They are currently being replaced in service by the F/A-18 Super Hornet.

| Country of origin: | USA |
| --- | --- |
| Type: | two-seat carrierborne fleet defence fighter |
| Powerplant: | two 12,247kg (27,000lb) General Electric F110-GE-400 turbofans |
| Performance: | maximum speed at high altitude 1988km/h (1241mph); service ceiling 16,150m (53,000ft); range about 1994km (1239 miles) with full weapon load |
| Weights: | empty 18,951kg (41,780lb); maximum take-off 33,724kg (74,349lb) |
| Dimensions: | wingspan 19.55m (64ft 1.5in) unswept; 11.65m (38ft 2.5in) swept; length 19.10m (62ft 8in); height 4.88m (16ft); wing area 52.49sq m (565sq ft) |
| Armament: | one 20mm M61A1 Vulcan rotary cannon with 675 rounds; external pylons for a combination of AIM-7 Sparrow medium range air-to-air missiles, AIM-9 medium range air-to-air missiles, and AIM-54A/B/C Phoenix long range air-to-air missiles |

# Grumman (General Dynamics) EF-111A Raven

During the Vietnam conflict the biggest threat to US aircraft proved to be ground-based radar-guided missiles, supplied by the USSR to North Vietnamese forces. This highlighted the need for effective ECM aircraft to provide jamming coverage for attacking forces, and in 1974 the USAF awarded study contracts to Grumman and General Dynamics for the development of a suitable conversion of the F-111A strike aircraft. Grumman's proposal was accepted, and the aircraft they produced entered service after protracted development of the electronics system in 1981. The most recognisable feature of the EF-111 was the fin-tip pod that houses the jamming system's receiver and antenna. Located in the weapons bay was the proven ALQ-99 tactical jamming system, and this was supplemented by ECM dispenser, radar countermeasures receiver, self-protection and terminal threat warning systems. The EF-111 is no longer in USAF service.

| Country of origin: | USA |
|---|---|
| Type: | two-seat ECM tactical jamming aircraft |
| Powerplant: | two 8391kg (18,500lb) Pratt & Whitney TF-30-P3 turbofans |
| Performance: | maximum speed at optimum altitude 2272km/h (1,412mph); service ceiling above 13,715m (45,000ft); range with internal fuel 1495km (929 miles) |
| Weights: | empty 25,072kg (55,275lb); maximum take-off 40,346kg (88,948lb) |
| Dimensions: | wingspan unswept 19.20m (63ft); swept 9.74m (32ft 11.5in); length 23.16m (76ft); height 6.10m (20ft); wing area 48.77sq m (525sq ft) unswept |

# Halberstadt D.IV

Wartime products of Halberstädter Flugzeugwerke were unremarkable in design and construction, but made a significant contribution to the strength of the Central Powers. The 'C' family of reconnaissance machines began with the C.I, which first flew in May 1916, and ended with the C.V of 1918. The CL light two-seat escorts were effectively employed for ground strafing and close support during the fighting at Somme and Cambrai in autumn 1917. The D.I, like the C.I, was developed from the B.II two-seat reconnaissance aircraft and appeared in late 1915 as a single-seat scout. Although it appeared frail, it had effective structural strengthening in comparison with the earlier two-seater and was ordered into production in March 1916 as the D.II after being re-engined with the Mercedes D.II; 132 aircraft were produced. Turkey received small numbers of the D.III with bigger ailerons and revised wing mounting, and the D.IV (pictured) with a 150hp (112kW) Benz Bz.III and twin machine guns.

| Country of origin: | Germany |
| --- | --- |
| Type: | (D.II) single-seat biplane fighter |
| Powerplant: | one 120hp (89kW) Mercedes D.II inline piston engine |
| Performance: | maximum speed 150km/h (93mph); service ceiling 5000m (16,400ft); range 250km (155 miles) |
| Weights: | empty 520kg (1146lb); maximum take-off weight 730kg (1610lb) |
| Dimensions: | span 8.8m (29ft 10in); length 7.3m (23ft 11in); height 2.67m (8ft 9in); wing area 23.6 sq m (254 sq ft) |
| Armament: | one fixed forward-firing 7.92mm LMG 08/15 machine gun |

# Handley Page 0/10

A s well as its more famous bombing role, the Handley Page 0/400 also served as a navigation trainer during World War I with units based at Andover and Stonehenge. After the war these units expanded their field of operations to prepare crews for the planned imperial air-mail service. During 1919 Handley Page began to modify some surplus aircraft that it bought back from the government with seated accommodation for 12 to 16 passengers as the 0/10. Some 25 of these were operated from the company facility at Cricklewood for joy-riding and on routes linking London to Paris, Brussels and Amsterdam. G-EATN was one of the last HP-built 0/400s, and was converted after the war to 0/10 standard with accommodation for 12 passengers for service with Handley Page Air Transport, which employed it on the Croydon–Paris route. It was also used to test the Aveline Stabilizer, an early two-axis automatic pilot.

| Country of origin: | United Kingdom |
| --- | --- |
| Type: | 12-seat passenger transport biplane |
| Powerplant: | two 360hp (268kW) Rolls Royce Eagle VIII Vee-12 piston engines |
| Performance: | maximum speed 122km/h (76mph); service ceiling 2590m (8500ft); range 724km (450 miles) |
| Weights: | empty 3629kg (8000lb); maximum takeoff weight 6350kg (14,000lb) |
| Dimensions: | span 30.48m (100ft); length 19.16m (62ft 10in); height 6.7m (22ft); wing area 153.1 sq m (1648 sq ft) |

# Handley Page 0/400

In 1916 George Volkert modified the 0/100 into the 0/400 by moving the fuel tanks from the nacelles into the fuselage and fitting Rolls Royce Eagle VIII engines. The other minor modification was the introduction of a compressed air engine starting system. Some 554 0/400s were built by British contractors with any one of four different engines fitted, namely the 284hp (212kW) Eagle IV, 360hp (268kW) Eagle VIII, 275hp (205kW) Sunbeam Maori or 350hp (261kW) Liberty 12. In the summer of 1918 the 0/400 was the backbone of the newly formed Independent Bombing Force. Large formations of up to 40 aircraft mounted night-attacks on German industrial areas and communications centres, ranging as far as Mannheim. By the end of the conflict 0/400s were carrying 748kg (1650lb) bombs and also made a contribution to the campaign in Palestine. Shown above is an aircraft from No. 207 Sqn at Ligescourt, France, in 1918.

| | |
|---|---|
| Country of origin: | United Kingdom |
| Type: | three-seat heavy bomber biplane |
| Powerplant: | two 360hp (268kW) Rolls Royce Eagle VIII Vee-12 piston engines |
| Performance: | maximum speed 122km/h (76mph); service ceiling 2590m (8500ft); range with bomb load 724km (450 miles) |
| Weights: | empty 3629kg (8000lb); loaded 6350kg (14,000lb) |
| Dimensions: | span 30.48m (100ft); length 19.16m (62ft 10in); height 6.7m (22ft); wing area 153.1sq m (1648 sq ft) |
| Armament: | twin .303in Lewis guns on flexible mount in nose cockpit; one .303in Lewis gun on flexible mount in dorsal position; one .303in Lewis gun on flexible mount in ventral position; internal bomb bay with provision for eight 113kg (250lb) or 16 51kg (112lb) bombs |

# Handley Page H.P.35 Clive

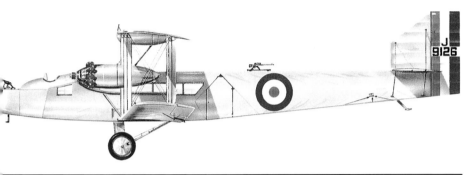

I n the interwar years the RAF placed a great deal of faith and much of its resources into developing a strategic bombing force. Air Ministry Specification 31/22 prompted the development by Handley Page of a night-bomber version of the recently introduced W.8 passenger transport, which entered RAF service in 1925 as the Handley Page (H.P.24) Hyderabad. An improved version was developed to Specification 13/29 as the H.P.33, which differed primarily by way of its Bristol Jupiter VIII radial engines. Two prototypes were followed by six production Hinaidi Mk Is and 33 H.P.36 Hinaidi Mk IIs with an all-metal fuselage structure. The second prototype, with an all-wood structure, was later redesignated Clive Mk I and served as a transport aircraft with accommodation for 23 troops. Two further production aircraft were built as the Clive Mk II, with an all-metal basic structure. During the early 1930s these served at Lahore, India, with the RAF Heavy Transport Flight.

| Country of origin: | United Kingdom |
|---|---|
| Type: | heavy transport aircraft |
| Powerplant: | two 440hp (328kW) Bristol Jupiter VIII radial engines |
| Performance: | maximum speed 196km/h (122mph); service ceiling 4420m (14,500ft); range 1368km (850 miles) |
| Weights: | empty 3647kg (8040lb); maximum take-off weight 6577kg (14,500lb) |
| Dimensions: | span 22.86m (75ft); length 18.03m (59ft 2in); height 5.18m (17ft); wing area 136.66 sq m (1471 sq ft) |

# Handley Page H.P.50 Heyford Mk IA

When it first appeared in 1930 the ungainly appearance of the H.P.50 was roundly derided, yet this aircraft formed the backbone of Britain's so-called strategic bombing fleet in the 1930s and soldiered on until more capable types were introduced. Its clumsy appearance was compounded by its unusual configuration, with shoulder-mounted biplane wing. Handley Page designers reasoned that incorporating a bomb bay into this lower wing would reduce the time required for rearming. Power was provided by two Rolls Royce Kestrels in nacelles mounted beneath the upper wing, and defensive armament took the form of three fuselage-mounted machine guns, one in a retractable dustbin turret. The RAF took delivery of 124 H.P.50s as Heyford Mks I, II and IIIs, which differed mainly in installed powerplant. Eleven squadrons were equipped with the type; by 1939 they had all re-equipped with Vickers Wellingtons, and the Heyford was relegated to training.

| | |
|---|---|
| Country of origin: | United Kingdom |
| Type: | heavy night-bomber |
| Powerplant: | two 575hp (429kW) Rolls Royce Kestrel IIIS 12-cylinder Vee-piston engine |
| Performance: | maximum speed 229km/h (142mph); service ceiling 6400m (21,000ft); range with 726kg (1600lb) bomb load 1481kg (920 miles) |
| Weights: | empty 4173kg (9200lb); maximum take-off weight 7666kg (16,900lb) |
| Dimensions: | span 22.86m (75ft); length 17.68m (58ft); height 5.33m (17ft 6in); wing area 136.56 sq m (1470 sq ft) |
| Armament: | one .303in Lewis machine gun on flexible mount in nose position; one .303in Lewis machine gun on flexible mount in dorsal position; one .303in Lewis machine gun on flexible mount in ventral turret; internal bay with provision for up to 1588kg (3500lb) of bombs |

# Handley Page Hampden

One of the most important medium bombers available to the British at the start of World War II, the Hampden was in many ways a good warplane but was hampered by its narrow fuselage, which prevented crew members from taking over the task of another should he be injured. The Hampden prototype first flew in June 1937, and deliveries of the Hampden Mk I started in September 1938. Deliveries of this model amounted to 1,430 aircraft from two British and one Canadian manufacturers, the last contributing 160 machines. Further capability came from the availability for training purposes of 100 Hereford aircraft that differed only in its powerplant of two 1000hp (746kW) Napier Dagger engines. Nine Herefords were converted to Hampden standard, and from 1942 some 141 surviving Hampden bombers were adapted as Hampden TB.Mk I torpedo bombers for the anti-shipping role. Pictured is a TB.Mk 1 of an Operational Training Unit in Scotland during 1942.

| | |
|---|---|
| Country of origin: | United Kingdom |
| Type: | (Hampden Mk I) four-seat medium bomber |
| Powerplant: | two 1000hp (746kW) Bristol Pegasus XVIII nine-cylinder single-row radial engines |
| Performance: | maximum speed 426km/h (255mph); climb to 4570m (15,000ft) in 18 minutes 54 seconds; service ceiling 6920m (22,700ft ); range 3034km (1885 miles) with a 907kg (2000lb) bomb load |
| Weights: | empty 5343kg (11,780lb); maximum take-off 10,206kg (22,500lb) |
| Dimensions: | span 21.08 m (69ft 2in); length 16.33m (53ft 7in); height 4.55m (14ft 11in) |
| Armament: | one 0.303in fixed forward-firing machine gun in port side of the forward fuselage, one 0.303in forward-firing machine gun in nose position,two 0.303in machine guns in dorsal position, two 0.303in machine guns in ventral position; bomb load of 1814kg (4000lb) |

# Handley Page Halifax

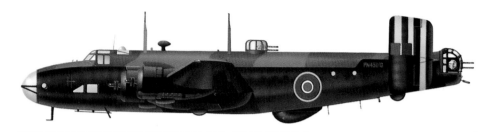

The Halifax was the main, but ultimately less glamorous partner to the Lancaster in the RAF heavy bomber force during the second half of World War II. It proved to be a highly versatile warplane and also undertook maritime reconnaissance, transport and airborne forces roles. The two prototypes, of which the first flew in October 1939, were followed by the Halifax Mk I (84 aircraft in three series) that entered service in November 1940 with 1280hp (954kW) Rolls-Royce Merlin X Vee engines, and the Halifax Mk II (1977 aircraft in three sub-series) with 1390hp (1036kW) Merlin XX or XXII engines. The Halifax Mk III saw a switch to Bristol Hercules radial engines; 2091 aircraft were made by five manufacturers. The Halifax Mk V, of which 904 were completed by two manufacturers in three sub-series, was an improved Mk II and was delivered in both bomber and maritime reconnaissance forms. The aircraft pictured has the markings of a Pathfinder unit.

| | |
|---|---|
| Country of origin: | United Kingdom |
| Type: | (Halifax Mk III) seven-seat heavy bomber |
| Powerplant: | four 1615hp (1204kW) Bristol Hercules VI or XVI 14-cylinder two-row radial engines |
| Performance: | maximum speed 454km/h (282mph); climb to 6095m (20,000ft) in 37 minutes 30 seconds; service ceiling 7315m (24,000ft); range 3194km (1985 miles) with a 3175kg (7000lb) bomb load |
| Weights: | empty 19,278kg (42,500lb); maximum take-off 29,484kg (65,000lb) |
| Dimensions: | span 30.07m (98ft 8in) or in later aircraft 31.59 m (103ft 8in); length 21.74m (71ft 4in); height 6.12m (20ft 1in) |
| Armament: | one 0.303in trainable forward-firing machine gun in the nose position, four 0.303in trainable machine guns in the dorsal turret, and four 0.303in trainable machine guns in the tail turret, plus an internal bomb load of 6577kg (14,500lb) |

# Handley-Page Victor K.Mk 2

The Victor was the third and last of the V-bombers to go into service with RAF Bomber Command in 1955–58. The design of the aircraft, with the distinctive crescent-shaped wing for maximum cruising speed represented a superb technical achievement. Development time was long and by the time the Victor had entered service it could be intercepted by fighters or shot down by missiles. The number ordered was correspondingly small and the cost was high. Survivors of the 50 B.Mk 1 and B.Mk 1H Victors built were converted by Handley Page to K.Mk 1 two-point and K.Mk 1H three-point tanker standard between 1965 and 1967. Thirty-four improved Victor B.Mk 2s, with increased power and redesigned airframe were supplied to the RAF, but their vulnerability led to the conversion of 27 aircraft to K.Mk 2 tanker standard in 1973–74.

| Country of origin: | United Kingdom |
| --- | --- |
| Type: | four-seat air-refuelling tanker |
| Powerplant: | four 9344kg (20,600lb) Rolls-Royce Conway Mk 201 turbofans |
| Performance: | maximum speed at 12,190m (40,000ft) 1030km/h (640mph); maximum cruising height 18,290m (60,000ft); range with internal fuel 7,400km (4,600 miles) |
| Weights: | empty 41,277kg (91,000lb); maximum take-off 105,687kg (233,000lb) |
| Dimensions: | wingspan 36.58m (120ft); length 35.05m (114ft 11in); height 9.2m (30ft 1.5in); wing area 223.52sq m (2,406sq ft) |

# Hansa-Brandenburg C.I

Ernst Heinkel cut his teeth as an aircraft designer whilst in the employment of the Hansa und Brandenburgische Flugzeugwerke Gmbh, which entered aircraft manufacture at the outbreak of World War I. As the chief designer for the company, Heinkel was responsible for the most important family of German floatplanes of the war. He also designed landplanes, a notable example being one of his earliest and most successful designs the C.I two-seat armed reconnaissance aircraft. After entry into service in 1916 this was built in some numbers for the Austrian forces. The aircraft was a conventional two-bay biplane of wood-and-fabric construction, with a tractor engine mounted in the nose of the fuselage that had a combined open cockpit for the pilot and observer/gunner. Production aircraft were seen with powerplants in the 160hp (119kW) to 230hp (172kW) range, and later examples had a single fixed forward-firing machine gun and light bomb racks on the lower wings.

| Country of origin: | Germany |
|---|---|
| Type: | (Hiero engine) two-seat armed reconnaissance aircraft |
| Powerplant: | one 200hp (149kW) Hiero inline piston engine |
| Performance: | maximum speed 158km/h (98mph); service ceiling 6000m (19,685ft); endurance 3hrs |
| Weights: | empty 820kg (1808lb); maximum take-off weight 1320kg (2910lb) |
| Dimensions: | span 12.25m (40ft 2in); length 8.45m (27ft 9in); height 3.33m (10ft 11in) |
| Armament: | one 8mm Schwarzlöse machine gun on pivoted mount in rear of cockpit |

# Hansa-Brandenburg W.12

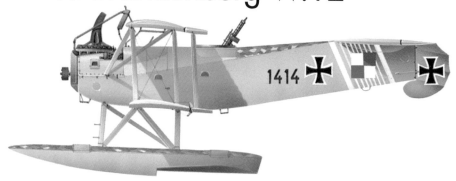

Ernst Heinkel's first floatplane design for Hansa-Brandenburg was the KDW (*Kampf Doppeldecker, Wasser* – or fighting biplane, water), a small single-seater developed from the D.1 landplane, for coastal patrol work on the Baltic, North Sea and Mediterranean shores. The KDW first flew in the summer of 1916, and production of 58 aircraft followed with Benz III, Maybach Mb III or Mercedes engines. The W.12 design was an attempt to rectify the inherent weakness of the KDW – its vulnerability to attack from the rear – and had a rear cockpit to accommodate an observer gunner. Constructed of wood and fabric, the W.12 had an unusual tail unit that provided an uninterrupted field of fire for the rear gun, and a wing that was sufficiently robust for Heinkel to dispense with bracing wires. The prototype flew in early 1917 and was followed by 146 production aircraft, one of which shot down the British airship C.27.

| Country of origin: | Germany |
|---|---|
| Type: | two-seat fighter seaplane |
| Powerplant: | one 160hp (119kW) Mercedes D.III 6-cylinder inline piston engine |
| Performance: | maximum speed 160km/h (99mph); service ceiling 5000m (16,405ft); endurance 3hrs 30mins |
| Weights: | empty 997kg (2198lb); maximum take-off weight 1454kg (3206lb) |
| Dimensions: | span 11.2m (36ft 9in); length 9.6m (31ft 6in); height 3.3m (10ft 10in); wing area 35.3 sq m (380 sq ft) |
| Armament: | one or two fixed forward-firing 7.92mm LMG 08/15 machine guns; one 7.92mm Parabellum machine gun on flexible mount in rear cockpit |

# Hansa-Brandenburg W.33 (A.22)

The monoplane W.29 resulted from the need to improve the performance of Germany's fighter seaplanes, and was a classic design that set the pattern for the later Ernst Heinkel designs. Essentially a W.12 with a monoplane wing, the 78 aircraft that had been delivered by the Armistice did well in combat from April 1918. The majority had Benz Bz.III engines, but a few late-production examples had the more powerful 185hp (138kW) Benz Bz.IIIa. The W.33 was a scaled-up version that was produced in the summer and autumn of 1918. Wartime production totalled 26. After the war the W.33 was used by Denmark and was built by state factory IVL near Helsinki as the A.22 until the late 1920s. Pictured is a ski-equipped A.22 of No 1 Detached Maritime Flying School, Finnish Air Force, based at Viipuri. The skis were used for winter operations from ice.

| | |
|---|---|
| Country of origin: | Germany |
| Type: | two-seat fighter seaplane |
| Powerplant: | one 245hp (183kW) Maybach Mb.IV inline piston engine |
| Performance: | maximum speed 175km/h (109mph); service ceiling 5000m (16,404ft); endurance 5hrs |
| Weights: | empty 1500kg (3300lb); maximum take-off weight 2045kg (4510lb) |
| Dimensions: | span 15.85m (52ft); length 11.1m (36ft 4in); height 3.39m (11ft 1in); |
| Armament: | one or two fixed forward-firing 7.92mm Spandau machine guns; one 7.92mm Spandau machine gun on pivoted mount in rear cockpit |

# Hawker Horsley Mk II

**P**ictured here in the colours of No 33 (Bomber) Squadron, based at Netheravon and Eastchurch in the early 1930s, the Hawker Horsley was a two-seat medium day-bomber developed by the company to Air Ministry Specification 26/23, which called for a replacement for the Airco D.H.9. Hawker began the construction of the prototype in 1924, this having unequal-span slightly swept biplane wings, a conventionally braced tail unit, tailskid landing gear and power provided by a Rolls Royce Condor III inline piston engine. The prototype first flew in 1925, and was followed by an initial production aircraft of the Horsley Mk I aircraft. Early examples of the Horsley Mk II were of mixed wood-and fabric-construction, while the later aircraft had an all-metal basic structure. Total production for the RAF was 123 aircraft.

| | |
|---|---|
| Country of origin: | United Kingdom |
| Type: | two-seat day-bomber |
| Powerplant: | one 665hp (496kW) Rolls-Royce Condor IIIA 12-cylinder Vee-piston engine |
| Performance: | maximum speed 201km/h (125mph); service ceiling 4265m (14,000ft); endurance 10hrs |
| Weights: | empty 2159kg (4760lb); maximum take-off weight 3538kg (7800lb) |
| Dimensions: | span 17.21m (56ft 6in); length 11.84m (38ft 10in); height 4.17m (13ft 8in); wing area 64.38 sq m (693 sq ft) |
| Armament: | one fixed-forward firing .303in Vickers Mk II machine gun; one .303in Lewis machine gun on pivoted mount in rear cockpit; external racks with provision for 680kg (1500lb) of bombs or one 46cm (18in) torpedo |

# Hawker Tomtit Mk I

In 1927 the Air Ministry announced that it was seeking to replace the Avro 504. Designing an aircraft to replace the long-serving and much-loved 504 was not an enviable undertaking, but one that Sidney Camm set about with relish. The single-bay equal-span stagger-wing biplane that he produced was first flown in November 1928 as the Hawker Tomtit. The aircraft structure was of wood and fabric with the instructor and pupil accommodated in tandem cockpits in the fuselage. Over the rear cockpit was fitted a blind flying hood, to supplement the Reid and Sigrist instrumentation for blind-flying instruction. Three months after the first flight the first batch was ordered for the RAF for entry into service in 1930. Production total was 31 aircraft, including two for the Canadian Department of National Defence and four for the New Zealand Permanent Air Force. After a very brief RAF career, the Tomtit was replaced by the Avro Tudor.

| | |
|---|---|
| **Country of origin:** | United Kingdom |
| **Type:** | two-seat military trainer |
| **Powerplant:** | one 150hp (112kW) Armstrong Siddeley Mongoose IIIC 5-cylinder radial piston engine |
| **Performance:** | maximum speed 200km/h (124mph); service ceiling 5945m (19,500ft) |
| **Weights:** | empty 499kg (1100lb); maximum take-off weight 794kg (1750lb) |
| **Dimensions:** | span 8.71m (28ft 7in); length 7.21m (23ft 8in); height 2.54m (8ft 4in); wing area 22.09 sq m (238 sq ft) |

# Hawker Hart

A classic warplane that emerged in the late 1920s and resulted in more aircraft of the basic and derived series than any other British aeroplane of the period between the two world wars, the Hart was the result of a 1926 requirement for a fast day bomber to replace the Airco (de Havilland) D.H.9A and Fairey Fawn. The design was based on the concept of maximum aerodynamic efficiency, and the prototype made its maiden flight in June 1928. There followed 450 Hart Bomber, nine Hart Communications and 507 Hart Trainer aircraft for British service, as well as a number of export machines. These included ten dual control trainers that were built for the Royal Australian Air Force, which designated them Demon Mk II. The Hart was withdrawn from first-line service in the UK during 1938 but was still significant as a trainer after this time. A small number of the aircraft were operational in the Middle East and East Africa up to 1943.

| | |
|---|---|
| Country of origin: | United Kingdom |
| Type: | (Hart Bomber) two-seat light day bomber |
| Powerplant: | one 525hp (391kW) Rolls-Royce Kestrel IB or XDR 12-cylinder Vee engine |
| Performance: | maximum speed 296km/h (184mph); climb to 3050m (10,000ft) in 8 minutes; service ceiling 6510m (21,350ft); range 756km (470 miles) |
| Weights: | empty 1148kg (2530lb ); maximum take-off 2066kg (4554lb) |
| Performance: | span 11.35m (37ft 3in); length 8.94m (29ft 4in); height 3.17m (10ft 5in) |
| Armament: | one 0.303in fixed forward-firing machine gun in the port side of the forward fuselage, and one 0.303in trainable rearward-firing machine gun in the rear cockpit, plus an external bomb load of 263kg (580lb) |

# Hawker Demon Mk I

The performance of the Hawker Hart caused great consternation among the Air Staff, hastening the development by Hawker of a two-seat fighter version to Specification 15/30 as an interim measure before the Hawker Fury became available. Six aircraft were built with two front guns and Rolls Royce Kestrel IIS engines, and were delivered for use by No 23 (Fighter Squadron) at Kenley in July 1931. These were followed by 237 Hawker Demons, which differed from the Hart by having a revised rear cockpit to improve the field of fire for the gun; radio communications equipment; and in some later models a tailwheel. Hawker also built 54 Demons for the RAAF, and 20 dual-control Demon Mk II trainers for the RAF and RAAF, which received 10 apiece. In late 1934 a Demon was flown with a Frazer-Nash power-operated gun turret, and many aircraft were subsequently modified and known as the Turret Demon.

| Country of origin | United Kingdom |
|---|---|
| Type: | two-seat fighter biplane |
| Powerplant: | one 584hp (392kW) Rolls Royce Kestrel IIS 12-cylinder Vee piston engine |
| Performance: | maximum speed 303km/h (188mph); service ceiling 6500m (21,320ft); range 756km (470 miles) |
| Weights: | empty 1148kg (2530lb); maximum take-off weight 2066kg (4554lb) |
| Dimensions: | span 11.35m (37ft 3in); length 8.94m (29ft 4in); height 3.17m (10ft 5in); wing area 32.33 sq m (348 sq ft) |
| Armament: | two fixed forward-firing .303in Vickers Mk II machine guns; one .303in Lewis Mk machine gun on pivoted mount in rear cockpit |

# Hawker Fury Mk I/II

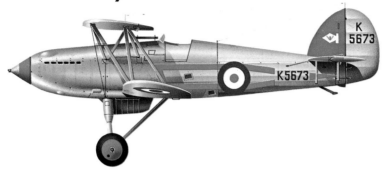

The Fury Mk I entered service in 1931 as the first British fighter capable of more than 200mph (322km/h). As a private venture Hawker then produced the Intermediate Fury and the High-Speed Fury for the evaluation of improved features. These two aircraft paved the way to the Fury Mk II that was a Fury Mk I development with spatted wheels and the uprated Kestrel VI engine whose 20 per cent greater power provided eight per cent and 34 per cent increases in speed and climb rate respectively. The Fury Mk II was accepted as an interim type, and 98 aircraft were completed for service from early 1937 with five RAF squadrons. After they were retired in 1939, most of the aircraft were stored. The previous year 24 had been shipped to South Africa, where they equipped three squadrons that were deployed to East Africa in 1940–41 for possible operations against the Italians. Pictured is a Fury Mk I of No I(F) Squadron, based at Tangmere in 1936-37.

| | |
|---|---|
| Country of origin: | United Kingdom |
| Type: | (Fury Mk II) single-seat fighter |
| Powerplant: | one 640hp (477kW) Rolls-Royce Kestrel VI 12-cylinder Vee engine |
| Performance: | maximum speed 359km/h (223mph); climb to 3050m (10,000ft) in 3 minutes 50 seconds; service ceiling 8990m (29,500ft); range 434.5km (270 miles) |
| Weights: | empty 1240kg (2734lb); maximum take-off 1637kg (3609lb) |
| Dimensions: | span 9.14m (30ft); length 8.15m (26ft 9in); height 3.10m (10ft 2in) |
| Armament: | two 0.303in fixed forward-firing machine guns in the upper part of the forward fuselage |

# Hawker Audax

One of the great proliferation of Hart variants, the Hawker Audax was developed to Air Ministry Specification 7/31, which called for an army cooperation aircraft to replace the venerable Armstrong Whitworth Atlas of only three years vintage, primarily for service in the Middle East and on the North West Frontier of India. The prototype Audax was created by modifying the airframe of an early Hart (K1438) with a message pick-up hook, and first flew in December 1931. In this form the Audax was ordered into production and first entered service in February 1932 with No 4 Squadron. A distinguishing feature was the long exhaust pipe which extended to the fuselage mid-point. Production for the RAF totalled 624 of three main versions, most of them with the Kestrel X engine. The Audax (Export) was sold to Canada, Egypt, Iraq and Persia, the example shown here being the first of 24 Bristol Pegasus IIM2-engined aircraft delivered to Iraq in 1935.

| Country of origin: | United Kingdom |
|---|---|
| Type: | two-seat army cooperation aircraft |
| Powerplant: | one 580hp (433kW) Bristol Pegasus II.M2 radial piston engine |
| Performance: | maximum speed 274km/h (170mph); service ceiling 6555m (21,500ft); endurance 3hrs 30mins |
| Weights: | empty 1333kg (2938lb); maximum take-off weight 1989kg (4386lb) |
| Dimensions: | span 11.35m (37ft 3in); length 9.02m (29ft 7in); height 3.17m (10ft 5in); wing area 32.33 sq m (348 sq ft) |
| Armament: | one fixed forward-firing .303in Vickers Mk II machine gun; one .303in Lewis machine gun on pivoted mount in rear cockpit; underwing racks with provision for four 9kg (20lb) or two 51kg (112lb) stores |

# Hawker Nimrod

The needs of naval aviation were poorly served by the Admiralty in the interwar years and even as late as 1932 the best fighter available to Fleet Air Arm (FAA) fighter squadrons, the Fairey Flycatcher, had a top speed of only 214km/h (133mph). Some RAF wags opined that a sprightly fly might give the aircraft a run for its money! A specification detailing the requirements for a replacement was issued in 1926 but none of the submissions, including Hawker's Hoopoe, was deemed to be acceptable. Undeterred, Hawker built the Norn, which later became the Nimrod. The first production Nimrod Mk Is entered service in 1933 with Nos 801, 802, and 803 Squadrons, FAA, followed in September 1934 by 27 Nimrod Mk IIs with arrestor gear, more powerful engines, and tail surfaces of increased area. One aircraft was supplied to Japan and one to Portugal, and two went to Denmark.

| Country of origin: | United Kingdom |
| --- | --- |
| Type: | single-seat carrier-based fighter |
| Powerplant: | one 608hp (453kW) Rolls-Royce VFP 12-cylinder Vee piston engine |
| Performance: | maximum speed 311km/h (193mph); service ceiling 8535m (28,000ft); endurance 1hr 40mins |
| Weights: | empty 1413kg (3115lb); maximum take-off weight 1841kg (4059lb) |
| Dimensions: | span 10.23m (33ft 7in); length 8.09m (26ft 6in); height 3m (9ft 10in); wing area 27.96 sq m (301 sq ft) |
| Armament: | two fixed forward-firing .303in machine guns; plus provision for four 20lb bombs on underwing racks |

# Hawker Hind

Air Ministry Specification G.7/34 called for a light bomber that could serve as an interim replacement for the Hawker Hart until more modern types such as the Bristol Blenheim and Fairey Battle began to enter service. Sidney Camm proposed an updated version of the Hart, powered by a 640hp (477kW) Kestrel V engine. Other distinguishing features were a cut-down rear cockpit, which afforded a better field of fire for the observer, and a tailwheel in place of the skid. The prototype Hind was flown in September 1934 and was followed by 527 production aircraft which served in no less than 47 RAF bomber squadrons between 1935 and 1939. The Hind also served with the air forces of Afghanistan, Eire, India, Kenya, Latvia, New Zealand and Persia. Many RAF Hinds were converted for training by removing the armament, including the example pictured, which served with No 1 Flying Training School in the early war years.

| | |
|---|---|
| Country of origin: | United Kingdom |
| Type: | two-seat light day-bomber |
| Powerplant: | one 640hp (477kW) Rolls-Royce Kestrel V 12-cylinder Vee piston engine |
| Performance: | maximum speed 298km/h (184mph); service ceiling 8045m (26,400ft); range 692km (430 miles) |
| Weights: | empty 1475kg (3251lb); maximum take-off weight 2403kg (5298lb) |
| Dimensions: | span 11.35m (37ft 3in); length 9.02m (29ft 7in); height 3.23m (10ft 7in); wing area 32.33 sq m (348 sq ft) |
| Armament: | one fixed-forward firing .303in Vickers Mk II machine gun; one .303in Lewis machine gun on pivoted mount in rear cockpit; underwing racks with provision for up to 227kg (500lb) of bombs |

# Hawker Hurricane Mk I

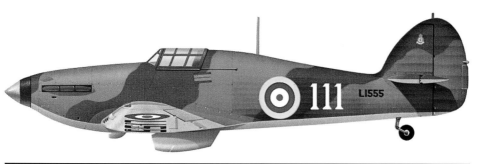

Although the Spitfire has come to be remembered as the fighter that 'won' the Battle of Britain, it was in fact the sturdy and stable Hurricane that served in larger numbers and destroyed more German aircraft than the rest of the defences combined. The Hurricane was the first monoplane fighter to enter British service in the 1930s. Sidney Camm's design was not as advanced technically as the Spitfire and it had an unstressed covering largely of fabric. The prototype first flew in November 1935, and the Hurricane Mk I entered service late in 1937 with a two-blade fixed-pitch propeller that later gave way to a three-blade constant-speed unit. Equipping 19 squadrons on the outbreak of World War II, the type flew with some 29 squadrons in August 1940, and production totalled about 3650 aircraft including 40, 489 and 150 examples of the Canadian-built Mks I, X and XI. Nearly 200 of the RAF Hurricanes were lost in the spring of 1940.

| | |
|---|---|
| **Country of origin:** | United Kingdom |
| **Type:** | (Hurricane Mk I) single-seat fighter |
| **Powerplant:** | one 1030hp (768kW) Rolls-Royce Merlin III 12-cylinder Vee engine |
| **Performance:** | maximum speed 521km/h (324mph); climb to 5670m (15,000ft) in 6 minutes 18 seconds; service ceiling 10,120m (33,200ft); range 716km (445 miles) |
| **Weights:** | empty 2308kg (5085lb); maximum take-off 3024kg (6661lb) |
| **Dimensions:** | span 12.19m (40ft); length 9.55m (31ft 4in); height 4.07m (13ft 4.5in) |
| **Armament:** | eight 0.303in fixed forward-firing machine guns in the leading edges of the wing |

# Hawker Hurricane Mk II

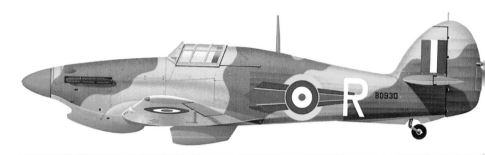

In 1939 Hawker turned to the creation of an improved Hurricane Mk II with an uprated powerplant, heavier armament and enhancements such as metal-skinned wings, three-blade propeller and better protection. These features were also incorporated on later Mk I aircraft. Mk II production reached more than 7500 aircraft for service from September 1940 in variants such as the Mk IIA with eight 0.303in machine guns, the Mk IIB with 12 0.303in machine guns, the Mk IIC with four 20mm cannon and 454kg (1000lb) of external stores, and the anti-tank Mk IID produced in small numbers. The Mk II thus marked the Hurricane's transition to the fighter-bomber role, and many of the aircraft were tropicalised for North African and Far Eastern service with a special chin air filter to prevent sand being ingested into the carburettor. Canadian production added Mk IIB and Mk IIC equivalents as 248 Mk XII and 150 Mk XIIA aircraft.

| Country of origin: | United Kingdom |
| --- | --- |
| Type: | (Hurricane Mk IID) single-seat anti-tank warplane |
| Powerplant: | one 1460hp (1088.5kW) Rolls-Royce Merlin XX 12-cylinder Vee engine |
| Performance: | maximum speed 518km/h (322mph); climb to 6095m (20,000ft) in 12 minutes 24 seconds; service ceiling of 9785m (32,100ft); range 1448km (900 miles) |
| Weights: | empty 2586kg (5700lb); normal take-off 3493kg (7700lb); maximum take-off 3674kg (8100lb) |
| Dimensions: | span 12.19m (40ft 0in); length 9.81m (32ft 2.25in); height 3.98m (13ft 1in ) |
| Armament: | two 40mm fixed forward-firing cannon under the wing, and two 0.303in fixed forward-firing machine guns in the leading edges of the wing |

# Hawker Hurricane Mk IV

**M**aking its debut in 1943 with the designation Hurricane Mk IIE that was used for the first 270 of the 794 aircraft, the Hurricane Mk IV was the final British production model and was basically the Hurricane Mk II with the Merlin 24 or 27 engine, 350lb (159kg) of additional armour protection, and with the so-called Universal Wing that allowed the optimisation of the warplane for a number of ground-attack roles. The wing incorporated two 0.303in machine guns and had undersurface provision for either two 40mm cannon, two bombs of up to 500lb (227kg) in weight, two small bomb carriers, eight 3in (76mm) air-to-surface rocket projectiles each carrying a 60lb (27kg) warhead, or two smoke-laying installations. The Hurricane Mk IV was the last model in British service, the final aircraft being retired in 1946. The aircraft pictured is a Mk IV with heavy underwing anti-tank guns, powerful enough to slow the aircraft significantly in the air when fired.

| | |
|---|---|
| **Country of origin:** | United Kingdom |
| **Type:** | (Hurricane Mk IV) single-seat ground-attack fighter |
| **Powerplant:** | one 1620hp (1208kW) Rolls-Royce Merlin 24 or 27 12-cylinder Vee engine |
| **Performance:** | maximum speed 531km/h (330mph); climb to 6095m (20,000ft) in 9 minutes 18 seconds; service ceiling 9935m (32,600ft); range 1464.5km (910 miles) |
| **Weights:** | empty 2790kg (6150lb); maximum take-off 3833kg (8450lb) |
| **Dimensions:** | span 12.19m (40ft); length 9.81m (32ft 2.25in); height 3.98m (13ft 1in) |
| **Armament:** | two 0.303in fixed forward-firing machine guns in the leading edges of the wings, plus an external bomb or rocket load of 454kg (1000lb) |

# Hawker Typhoon Mk IA

The Typhoon was possibly the Western Allies' finest ground-attack fighter of World War II. In another light it may be regarded as a distinct failure, as it had been planned as a heavily armed interceptor to succeed the Hawker Hurricane and Supermarine Spitfire, the RAF's first-generation monoplane fighters. A cantilever low-wing monoplane of basically all-metal stressed-skin construction with retractable tail wheel landing gear, the Typhoon was finally planned in two forms with the Napier Sabre liquid-cooled H-type engine and the Bristol Centaurus air-cooled radial engine, the latter becoming the Tempest. First flown in prototype form on 24 February 1940, the Typhoon did not fly in Mk IA production form (105 aircraft) until May 1941 and entered service in June of the same year, initially proving a failure as a result of a structural weakness in the tail and wholly indifferent performance at altitude as a result of its thick wing.

| Country of origin: | United Kingdom |
|---|---|
| Type: | (Mk 1a) single-seat interceptor |
| Powerplant: | one 2100hp (1566kW) Napier Sabre I 24-cylinder H-type engine |
| Performance: | maximum speed about 663km/h (412mph); climb to 4570m (15,000ft ) in 5 minutes 50 seconds; service ceiling 10,730m (35,200ft); range 510 miles (821km) with standard fuel |
| Weights: | empty 4445kg (9800lb); normal take-off 5171kg (11,400lb) |
| Dimensions: | span 12.67m (41ft 7in); length 9.73m (31ft 11in); height 4.67m (15ft 4in) |
| Armament: | twelve 0.303in fixed forward-firing machine guns with 500 rounds per gun in the wing |

# Hawker Typhoon Mk IB

The Typhoon Mk IB was the definitive version of the Typhoon. The fixed forward-firing armament was revised to four 20mm cannon with 140 rounds per gun in the wing, the original type of framed canopy with a side door was replaced (from 1943) by a clear-view bubble canopy with a rearward-sliding access section, and the highly unreliable Sabre I engine replaced by the uprated and slightly less troublesome Sabre II generally driving a four- rather than three-blade propeller. These changes coincided with the realisation that the Typhoon would make a superb low-level fighter well able to defeat the fast fighter-bombers with which the German were harassing southern England, and the Typhoon Mk IB could also take the offensive role after being fitted with two underwing hardpoints for bombs or drop tanks. A night-fighter version of the Typhoon designated NF.Mk IB was produced, together with a small number of FR.Mk IB reconnaissance aircraft.

| | |
|---|---|
| **Country of origin:** | United Kingdom |
| **Type:** | single-seat ground-attack and close air support fighter-bomber |
| **Powerplant:** | one 2180hp (1625.5kW) Napier Sabre IIA, or 2200hp (1640kW) Sabre IIB or 2260hp (1685kW) Sabre IIC 24-cylinder H-type engine |
| **Performance:** | maximum speed 663km/h (412mph); climb to 4570m (15,000ft) in 5 minutes 50 seconds; service ceiling 10,730m (35,200ft); range 1577km (980 miles) with drop tanks |
| **Weights:** | empty 4445kg (9800lb); normal take-off 5171kg (11,400lb); maximum take-off 6010kg (13,250lb) |
| **Dimensions:** | Span 12.67m (41ft 7in); length 9.73m (31ft 11in); height 4.67m (15ft 4in) |
| **Armament:** | four 20mm fixed forward-firing cannon in the leading edges of the wing, plus an external bomb load of 907kg (2000lb) |

# Hawker Tempest Mk V

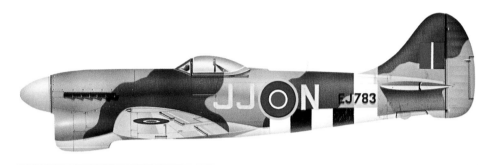

The Tempest was the third Hawker fighter to enjoy operational status in World War II, and while not as well known as the preceding Hurricane and Typhoon, was nonetheless an excellent warplane that proved highly adaptable in terms of its production in variants with air-cooled and liquid-cooled engines. Planned as an advanced fighter to undertake the interceptor role in which the Typhoon had failed, the Tempest was a generally similar aeroplane except for its significantly thinner wing and longer fuselage. It first flew in prototype form during September 1942, retaining the chin radiator of the Typhoon. The type entered service as the Tempest Mk V in April 1944. The Tempest Mk V Series 1 (100 aircraft) had protruding cannon muzzles, but the Tempest Mk V Series 2 (700 aircraft) had cannon muzzles flush with the wing's leading edges. After the war some were converted for use as target tugs and designated Tempest TT.Mk 5.

| | |
|---|---|
| **Country of origin:** | United Kingdom |
| **Type:** | (Tempest Mk V) single-seat fighter and fighter-bomber |
| **Powerplant:** | one 2260hp (1685kW) Napier Sabre IIA, IIB or IIC 24-cylinder H-type engine |
| **Performance:** | maximum speed 700km/h (435mph); climb to 6095m (20,000ft) in 6 minutes 6 seconds; service ceiling 10,975m (36,000ft); range 2092km (1300 miles) |
| **Weights:** | empty 4854kg (10,700lb); normal take-off 5221kg (11,510lb); maximum take-off 6187kg (13,640lb) |
| **Dimensions:** | span 12.50m (41ft); length 10.26m (33ft 8in); height 4.90m (16ft 1in) |
| **Armament:** | four 20mm fixed forward-firing cannon in the leading edges of the wing, plus an external bomb and rocket load of 907kg (2000lb) |

# Hawker Tempest Mk II

As the Tempest Mk V was entering production, Hawker was pressing ahead with the development of improved models, most especially the Tempest Mk II with the altogether different Centaurus radial engine. This first flew in prototype form during June 1943 with the original type of Typhoon tail unit but the newer type of one-piece sliding canopy. Powerplant development proved difficult, and the first of an eventual 472 Tempest Mk II aircraft was completed only in October 1944 after production had been switched from Gloucester to Bristol. Later production was undertaken by Hawker, and the last 300 or so aircraft were completed after World War II to a fighter-bomber rather than fighter standard. The aircraft entered service shortly after the end of World War II. Pictured here is a Tempest Mk II of No 54 Squadron, Royal Air Force, based at Chilbolton in 1946. India and Pakistan took delivery of 89 and 24 similar aircraft during 1947-48.

| | |
|---|---|
| Country of origin: | United Kingdom |
| Type: | (Tempest Mk II) single-seat fighter and fighter-bomber |
| Powerplant: | one 2590hp (1931kW) Bristol Centaurus V 18-cylinder two-row radial engine |
| Performance: | maximum speed 708km/h (440mph); climb to 6095m (20,000ft) in 6 mins 20 seconds; range 1700 miles (2736km) |
| Weights: | empty 4218kg (9300lb); normal take-off 5352kg (11,800lb); maximum take-off 6305kg (13,900lb) |
| Dimensions: | span 12.49m (41ft); length 10.49m (34ft 5in); height 4.42m (14ft 6in) |
| Armament: | four 20mm fixed forward-firing cannon in the leading edges of the wing, plus an external bomb and rocket load of 907kg (2000lb) |

# Hawker Sea Hawk FB.Mk 3

The Sea Hawk was legendary Hawker designer Sir Sidney Camm's first jet fighter. The first flight of the initial prototype took place on September 2, 1947. The Royal Navy ordered 151 of the navalised version fitted with carrier equipment and with the wing span increased by 0.9m (2ft 6 in). Hawker Siddeley built only 35 of these F.1s; all subsequent design and production was handled by Armstrong Whitworth of Coventry. The F.2 featured powered ailerons, and the FB.3 was fitted with underwing racks to permit the carriage of two bombs or mines. The FB. Mk 3 also had a strengthened main wing spar to accommodate the increased weapon load. In total 116 of the FB.Mk 3s were delivered to the Royal Navy. Many were later converted to FB. Mk 5 standard by fitting a more powerful 2449kg (5400lb) Rolls-Royce Nene 103.

| Country of origin: | United Kingdom |
|---|---|
| Type: | single-seat carrier-based fighter-bomber |
| Powerplant: | one 2268kg (5000lb) Rolls-Royce Nene turbojet |
| Performance: | maximum speed at sea level 958km/h (599mph); or 939km/h (587mph) at height; service ceiling 13,560m (44,500ft); standard range 1191km (740 miles) |
| Weights: | empty 9720lb; maximum take-off 7355kg (16,200lb) |
| Dimensions: | wingspan 11.89m (39ft); length 12.09m (39ft 8in); height 2.64m (8ft 8in); wing area 25.83sq m (278sq ft) |
| Armament: | four 20mm Hispano cannon in nose, underwing hardpoints for two 227kg (500lb) bombs |

# Hawker Hunter F.Mk 1

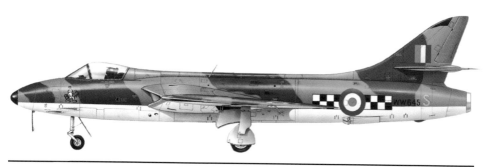

Without question the most successful post-war British fighter aircraft, the Hunter has a grace and elegance that complements its effectiveness as a warplane. It is fondly remembered by a generation of pilots who delighted in its superb handling characteristics. The first production F.Mk 1 entered service in July 1954; the aircraft was produced in dozens of different guises, and enjoyed a service career across the globe that spanned 40 years. The F.Mk 1 was easily supersonic in a shallow dive and packed a devastating punch with four 30mm Aden cannon in a quick-release pack winched up as a unit. One early problem on this otherwise vice-free aircraft was the tendency for the Avon 100 engine to stop when the guns were fired! On September 7, 1953, the one-off Mk 3 raised the world speed record to 727.6mph off the Sussex coast, piloted by Squadron Leader Neville Duke.

| Country of origin: | United Kingdom |
| --- | --- |
| Type: | single-seat fighter |
| Powerplant: | one 2925kg (6500lb) Rolls-Royce Avon 100 turbojet |
| Performance: | maximum speed at sea level 1144km/h (710mph); service ceiling 15,240m (50,000ft); range on internal fuel 689km (490 miles) |
| Weights: | empty 5501kg (12,128lb); loaded 7347kg (16,200lb) |
| Dimensions: | wingspan 10.26m (33ft 8in); length 13.98m (45ft 10.5in); height 4.02m (13ft 2in); wing area 32.42sq m (349sq ft) |
| Armament: | four 30mm Aden cannon; underwing pylons with provision for two 1000lb bombs and 24 3in rockets |

# Hawker Siddeley Gnat T.Mk 1

**B**ritish designer W.E.W. 'Teddy' Petter planned the Gnat to reverse the trend towards larger and more complex combat aircraft, considering a simple lightweight fighter would offer equal performance at a much lower cost. Folland Aircraft proceeded to fund a private venture prototype known as the Midge and eventually gained an order for a development batch of six, the first of which flew in May 1956. India signed a licence agreement in September 1956 and built 213 at Hindustan Aircraft Ltd at Bangalore. With the knowledge that the RAF was seeking to replace its de Havilland Vampire trainer aircraft Folland funded a further private venture to incorporate a dual seat cockpit. A new wing was designed, the fuselage lengthened, and the control surfaces revised. This aircraft entered service as the Gnat T.Mk 1, which served as the RAF's advanced jet trainer.

| | |
|---|---|
| Country of origin: | United Kingdom |
| Type: | two-seat advanced trainer |
| Powerplant: | one 1919kg (4230lb) Bristol Siddeley Orpheus turbojet |
| Performance: | maximum speed at 9450m (31,000ft) 1024km/h (636mph); service ceiling 14,630m (48,000ft); range with two 300 litre (66 Imp gal) tanks 1852km (1151 miles) |
| Weights: | empty 2331kg (5140lb); maximum take-off 3915kg (8630lb) |
| Dimensions: | wingspan 7.32m (24ft); length 9.68m (31ft 9in); height 2.93m (9ft 7.5in); wing area 16.26sq m (175 q ft) |

# Heinkel He 51A-1

W hen Hansa Brandenburg went into liquidation in 1919 Dr Ernst Heinkel joined the Caspar Flugzeugwerke for a year but then took the bold step of setting up his own company, which was registered on 1 December 1922 at Warnemünde on the Baltic coast. The Treaty of Versailles forbade German manufacturers form building military aircraft and so Heinkel, like many other German designers, formed partnerships and subsidiaries in other countries. Heinkel's subsidiary in Sweden provided him with the necessary cover to allow him to carry on developing the 'W' family of seaplanes that had made his name in World War I. As the likelihood of Allied legal action receded, Heinkel dared to build the prototype of an aircraft that blatantly disregarded the Treaty – the He 37 – which first flew in 1928. This was followed by a succession of He 49 prototypes, which formed the basis for the He 51 delivered to the Luftwaffe from July 1934.

| Country of origin: | Germany |
| --- | --- |
| Type: | single-seat fighter biplane |
| Powerplant: | one750hp (559kW) BMW V1 7,3Z 12-cylinder Vee piston engine |
| Performance: | maximum speed 330km/h (205mph); service ceiling 7700m (25,260ft); range 570km (354 miles) |
| Weights: | empty 1460kg (3219lb); maximum take-off weight 1895kg (4178lb) |
| Dimensions: | span 11m (36ft 1in); length 8.4m (27ft 7in); height 3.2m (10ft 6in); wing area 27.2 sq m (293 sq ft) |
| Armament: | two fixed forward-firing 7.92mm MG 17 machine guns |

# Heinkel He 59

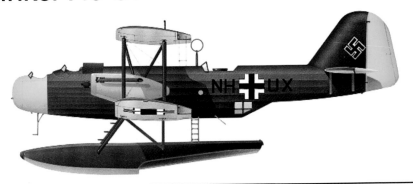

D esigned in 1930, the He 59 resulted from a requirement for a torpedo bomber and
reconnaissance warplane able to operate with equal facility on wheeled landing gear
or twin-float alighting gear. The He 59b landplane prototype was the first to fly, an event
that took place in September 1931, but it was the He 59a floatplane prototype that paved
the way for the He 59B initial production model, of which 142 were delivered in three
variants. Later developments were the He 59C-1 unarmed trainer, He 59C-2 air/sea rescue
model, He 59D-1 combined trainer and ASR model, He 59E-1 torpedo bomber trainer, He
59E-2 reconnaissance trainer, and He 59N navigation trainer produced as He 59D-1
conversions. The trainer models survived slightly longer in service than the operational
models, but all had been retired by 1944. Some aircraft were operated by Legion Condor in
Spain in 1936. Pictured here is a Heinkel He 59 D-1 of the Luftwaffe in 1940.

| | |
|---|---|
| Country of origin: | Germany |
| Type: | (He 59B-2) four-seat coastal reconnaissance and torpedo bomber floatplane with navigational training and air/sea rescue capabilities |
| Powerplant: | two 660hp (492kW) BMW VI 6,0 ZU 12-cylinder Vee engines |
| Performance: | maximum speed 220km/h (137mph); climb to 2000m (6560ft) in 11 minutes 12 seconds; service ceiling 3500m (11,480ft); range 1530km (950 miles) |
| Weights: | empty 5000kg (11,023lb); maximum take-off 9100kg (20,062lb) |
| Dimensions: | span 23.70m (77ft 9in); length 17.40m (57ft 1in); height 7.10m (23ft 3.5in) |
| Armament: | one 7.92mm trainable forward-firing machine gun in the nose position, one 7.92mm trainable rearward-firing machine gun in the dorsal position, and one 7.92mm rearward-firing machine gun in the ventral position, plus torpedo and bomb load of 1000kg (2205lb) |

# Heinkel He 70 Blitz

**D**esigned to meet a 1932 requirement by Deutsche Lufthansa for a high-speed passenger and mail transport, the He 70 first flew in prototype form during December 1932. The programme was then taken over by the German air forces, which saw in the He 70 a type ideal for conversion as an interim communications aeroplane and high-speed bomber. As a result the fourth and fifth prototypes were completed to military standards. This paved the way for the production models, of which 287 were completed. The communications type was the He 70D, but the majority of the aircraft were He 70E bombers and, most importantly, He 70F reconnaissance bombers. The He 70 made its operational debut as a bomber in Spain during August 1936, but by the start of World War II the surviving aircraft had been relegated to communications and training duties. Shown here in the markings of a Luftwaffe Kurierstaffel is an He 70F.

| | |
|---|---|
| **Country of origin:** | Germany |
| **Type:** | (He 70F-2) three-seat reconnaissance bomber generally used in the communications role |
| **Powerplant:** | one 750hp (559kW) BMW VI 7,3 Z 12-cylinder Vee engine |
| **Performance:** | maximum speed 360km/h (223mph); climb to 1000m (3280ft) in 2 minutes 30 seconds; service ceiling 5485m (18,000ft); range 1250km (776 miles) |
| **Weights:** | empty 2530kg (5579lb); maximum take-off 3640kg (7629lb) |
| **Dimensions:** | span 14.79m (48ft 6.75in); length 12.00m (39ft 4.5in); height 3.10m (10ft 2in) |
| **Armament:** | one 7.92mm trainable rearward-firing machine gun in the dorsal position, plus an internal bomb load of 300kg (661lb) |

# Heinkel He 100

**B**itterly disappointed that its He 112 had failed to secure a production order over the rival Messerschmitt Bf 109 as the Luftwaffe's first monoplane fighter, Heinkel started work on the design of a more advanced fighter. The result was the He 100, and the first of its 10 prototypes flew in January 1938. There were considerable technical problems to be overcome with the evaporative cooling system, and it was only in September 1939 that the first of three He 100D-0 pre-production and 12 He 100D-1 production aircraft flew with a larger vertical and horizontal tail surfaces respectively. Shortages of the DB 601 engine meant that there was no German requirement for the type, so six prototypes and the three pre-production aircraft were sold to the USSR and Japan, while the production aircraft were used for defence of the Heinkel factory. The He 100D-1aircraft shown here wears spurious Lufwaffe markings.

| | |
|---|---|
| Country of origin: | Germany |
| Type: | (He 100D-1) single-seat interceptor fighter |
| Powerplant: | one 1175hp (876kW) Daimler-Benz DB 601M 12-cylinder inverted-Vee engine |
| Performance: | maximum speed 670km/h (416mph); climb to 6000m (19,685ft) in 7 minutes 48 seconds; service ceiling 11,000m (36,090ft); range 1010km (627 miles) |
| Weights: | empty 2010kg (4431lb); maximum take-off 2500kg (5511lb) |
| Dimensions: | span 9.40m (30ft 10in); length 8.20m (26ft 10.75in); height 3.60m (11ft 9.75in) |
| Armament: | one 20mm fixed forward-firing cannon in an engine installation, and either two 20mm fixed forward-firing cannon or two 7.92mm fixed forward-firing machine guns in the wing roots |

# Heinkel He 112

The He 112 was the Bf 109's rival for the contract as the German Air Force's first monoplane fighter. The Heinkel was comparatively advanced, and the first of an eventual 12 prototypes flew in the summer of 1935. During the programme a number of powerplant, fuselage, wing and tail unit configurations were investigated. The Luftwaffe then selected the Bf 109, but the German air ministry was sufficiently impressed with the Heinkel fighter to order 43 He 112B-0 pre-production aircraft that operated with a fighter wing during 1938. Seventeen of the aircraft were sent to Spain for operational evaluation, after which the 15 survivors were passed to the Nationalist rebel forces. Of the others Germany sold 13 each to Japan and Romania, the latter later also acquiring 11 of the 13 He 112B-1 production aircraft for service up to 1942. Hungary also acquired a few aircraft. Pictured here is an He 112B-0 on the strength of III/JG 132 during August 1938.

| | |
|---|---|
| Country of origin: | Germany |
| Type: | (He 112B-1) single-seat fighter and fighter-bomber |
| Powerplant: | one 680hp (507kW) Junkers Jumo 210Ea 12-cylinder inverted-Vee engine |
| Performance: | maximum speed 510km/h (317mph); climb to 6000m (19,685ft) in 9 minutes 30 seconds; service ceiling 8500m (27,890ft); range 1100km (683 miles) |
| Weights: | empty 1620kg (3571lb); maximum take-off 2250kg (4960lb) |
| Dimensions: | span 9.10m (29ft 10.25in); length 9.30m (30ft 6in); height 3.85m (12ft 7.5in) |
| Armament: | two fixed forward-firing cannon in the leading edges of the wing and two 7.92mm fixed forward-firing machine guns in the sides of the forward fuselage, plus an external bomb load of 60kg (132lb) |

# Heinkel He 111P

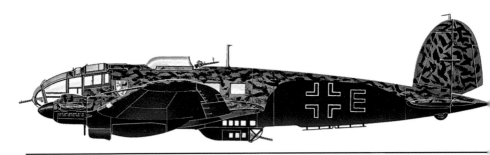

The Heinkel He 111 was Germany's most important medium bomber of World War II, and although ostensibly designed as a civil transport had entered air force service by 1936 as the He 111B bomber with Daimler-Benz DB 601 engines and a conventional forward fuselage with a stepped cockpit. These 300 aircraft were followed by some 190 He 111E bombers with Junkers Jumo 211 engines, and the next significant model, entering service in the spring of 1939, was the He 111P with the asymmetric fully glazed nose typical of all subsequent He 111 models. Built to the extent of some 400 aircraft in bomber and trainer subvariants between the He 111P-1 and He 111P-6, the He 111P was a useful type whose production was curtailed only by the reallocation of DB 601 engine supplies to fighters. Many He 111P-6 aircraft were later adapted as glider tugs. Spanish aircraft manufacturers built 236 He 111Hs under licence during and after the war as the CASA 2.111.

| | |
|---|---|
| Country of origin: | Germany |
| Type: | (He 111P-2) four-seat medium bomber |
| Powerplant: | two 1100hp (820kW) Daimler-Benz DB 601A-1 12-cylinder engines |
| Performance: | maximum speed 398km/h (247mph); climb to 4500m (14,765ft) in 31 minutes 18 seconds; service ceiling 8000m (26,245ft); range 2400km (1491 miles) |
| Weights: | empty 8015kg (17,670lb); maximum take-off 13,500kg (29,762lb) |
| Dimensions: | span 22.60m (74ft 1.75in); length 16.40m (53ft 9.5in); height 3.40m (13ft 1.5in) |
| Armament: | one 7.92mm fixed machine gun in the nose, one 7.92mm machine gun in the nose position, one 7.92mm machine gun in dorsal position, one 7.92mm machine gun in rear of ventral gondola, two 7.92mm machine guns in two beam positions, and provision for one 7.92mm fixed machine gun in the tail cone; bomb load of 2000kg (4409lb) |

# Heinkel He 111H and He 111Z

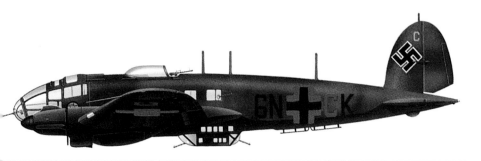

The definitive model of the He 111 series was the He 111H, which was in essence the He 111P with the revised powerplant of two Junkers Jumo 211 engines. The He 111H entered service in 1939, and production totalled about 6150 aircraft in major variants between the He 111H-1 and He 111H-23. These aircraft were characterised by a progressively uprated powerplant, increased fuel capacity, improved defensive as well as offensive armament, additional armour protection, and provision for use in alternative roles such as anti-shipping attack, pathfinding, missile carrying and launching, paratroop delivery and glider towing. The introduction of the huge Messerschmitt Me 321 Gigant glider necessitated the development of the final variant, the He 111Z (Zwilling, or twin), of which small numbers were produced as two He 111H-6 or -16 airframes joined by a new centre section carrying a fifth engine.

| | |
|---|---|
| **Country of origin:** | Germany |
| **Type:** | (He 111H-16): five-seat medium bomber |
| **Powerplant:** | two 1350hp (1007kW) Junkers Jumo 211F-2 12-cylinder engines |
| **Performance:** | maximum speed 405km/h (252mph); climb to 4000m (13,125ft) in 23 minutes 30 seconds; service ceiling 8500m (27,890ft); range 1930km (1199 miles) with maximum bomb load |
| **Weights:** | empty 8680kg (19,136lb); maximum take-off 14,000kg (30,865lb) |
| **Dimensions:** | span 22.60m (74ft 1.75in); length 16.40m (53ft 9.5in); height 3.40m (13ft 1.5in) |
| **Armament:** | one 7.92mm fixed machine gun in the nose, one 7.92mm machine gun in a nose position, one 7.92mm machine gun in dorsal position, one 7.92mm machine gun in rear of ventral gondola, two 7.92mm machine guns in each of two beam positions, and one 7.92mm fixed machine gun in the tail cone, plus a bomb load of 2500kg (5511lb) |

# Heinkel He 115A/B

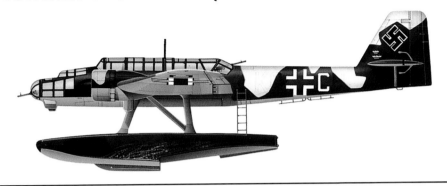

Resulting from a 1935 requirement for an advanced torpedo bomber floatplane that was also to be capable of undertaking a number of other coastal roles such as minelaying and reconnaissance, the He 115 V1 (first of four prototypes) made its maiden flight in August 1937. The He 115 was subsequently ordered into production early in 1938. Some 10 He 115A-0 pre-production aircraft were delivered from the summer of the same year, and paved the way for 137 production machines. The first of these was the baseline He 115A (three subvariants including one for export), and this was followed by the structurally strengthened He 115B. This in turn was operated in two main versions that spawned a number of minor subvariants for the torpedo, bombing, minelaying and reconnaissance roles. Many of these were built under licence by Weser Flugzeugbau. During the course of its career the aircraft served with Germany, Britain and Sweden.

| Country of origin: | Germany |
|---|---|
| Type: | (He 115B-1) three-seat coastal general-purpose and torpedo bomber floatplane |
| Powerplant: | two 960hp (716kW) BMW 132K nine-cylinder single-row radial engines |
| Performance: | maximum speed 295km/h (183mph); service ceiling 5200m (17,600ft); range 2600km (1616 miles) |
| Weights: | empty 6715kg (14,804lb); normal take-off 10,400kg (22,930lb) |
| Dimensions: | span 22.28m (73ft 1in); length 17.30m (56ft 9.25in); height 6.59m (21ft 7.75in) |
| Armament: | one 7.92mm trainable forward-firing machine gun in the nose position, and one 7.92mm trainable rearward-firing machine gun in the dorsal position, plus an internal and external torpedo, bomb and mine load of 920kg (2028lb) |

# Heinkel He 162 Salamander

**P**opularly known as the 'Volksjager' (People's Fighter), the He 162 was designed and produced by the war-torn German aviation industry in only six months. With experienced aircrew, fuel, and materials in desperately short supply this strikes as an incredible achievement. On September 8, 1944 the Riechsluftfahrtsministerium issued a specification calling for a 750km/h (466mph) fighter to be regarded as a piece of consumer goods and to be ready by January 1, 1945. Huge numbers of workers were seconded to the project and a rapid training programme for the Hitler Youth was mounted, using mainly glider aircraft. Heinkel, which had built the world's first turbojet aircraft, the He 178, won the design competition with a tiny wooden machine with an engine perched on top. The first prototype flew on December 6, 1944, and deliveries began in January 1945.

| | |
|---|---|
| Country of origin: | Germany |
| Type: | single-seat jet interceptor |
| Powerplant: | one 800kg (1764lb) BMW 003A-1 turbojet |
| Performance: | maximum speed at 6000m (19,685ft) 840km/h (522mph); service ceiling 12,040m (39,500ft); endurance 57 minutes at 10,970m (35,990ft) |
| Weights: | empty 2050kg (4250lb); maximum take-off 2695kg (5941lb) |
| Dimensions: | wingspan 7.20m (23ft 7.5in); length 9.05m (29ft 8.25in); height 2.55m (8ft 4.25in); wing area 11.20sq m (120.56sq ft) |
| Armament: | two 20mm MG151/20 cannon |

# Heinkel He 177A-1/3 Greif

The Greif (Griffin) was a potentially excellent but ultimately disastrous warplane on which Germany expended enormous and therefore largely wasted resources. The type was schemed as a bomber able to deliver a large bomb load over a considerable range at high speed and high altitude, and in an effort to extract maximum performance from a four-engined powerplant by the minimisation of drag, it was decided that the pair of engines on each wing should be coupled to drive a single propeller. This coupled powerplant was beset by enormous technical problems that were never wholly cured and resulted in numerous inflight fires (the engines had a habit of catching fire without warning). The first of eight He 177 prototypes flew in December 1939, and slow development meant that it was the summer of 1942 before 130 He 177A-1 and 170 He 177A-3 early production aircraft entered service.

| | |
|---|---|
| Country of origin: | Germany |
| Type: | (He 177A-1/R1 Greif) five-crew heavy bomber |
| Powerplant: | two 2700hp (2013kW) Daimler-Benz DB 606 (coupled DB 601) 24-cylinder engines |
| Performance: | maximum speed 510km/h (317mph); service ceiling 7000m (22,965ft); range 1200km (746 miles) with maximum bomb load |
| Weights: | empty 18,040kg (39,771lb); maximum take-off 30,000kg (66,139lb) |
| Dimensions: | span 31.44m (103ft 1.75in); length 20.40m (66ft 11in); height 6.39m (20ft 11.75in) |
| Armament: | one 7.92mm trainable forward-firing machine gun in nose position, one 20mm trainable forward-firing cannon in ventral gondola, two 7.92mm machine guns in ventral gondola, one 13mm machine gun in remotely controlled dorsal barbette, and one 13mm machine gun in tail position, plus a bomb load of 6000kg (13,228lb) |

# Heinkel He 178

**D**eveloped as a private venture in conjunction with the He 176 rocket powered aircraft, the He 178 was powered by Heinkel's HeS 3b turbojet. The aircraft was only ever intended as an experimental test bed, although it made its mark in the history books when on 27 August 1939, Flugkapitan Erich Warsitz lifted off for the first time in a jet-powered aircraft and circled the factory airfield at Rostock-Marienehe. Although officials from the RLM came to inspect the aircraft in October, little official interest was shown and the project was discontinued in favour of the larger He 280. It should be noted though, that the He 178 flew nearly two years before the Gloster E.28/39, despite Britain's early lead in jet technology. Note the fabric-covered tail and high-set wing. The undercarriage retracted into the fuselage just forward of the leading edge.

| Country of origin: | Germany |
| --- | --- |
| Type: | single-seat experimental jet |
| Powerplant: | one 454kg (1000lb) He S 3b turbojet |
| Performance: | n/a |
| Weights: | n/a |
| Dimensions: | n/a |

# Heinkel He 219 Uhu

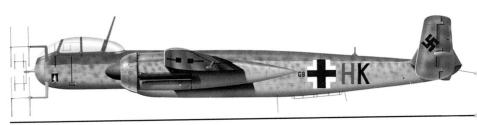

The Uhu ('Owl') was the finest German night-fighter of World War II, but despite its exceptional capabilities was built only in very small numbers as a result of political antipathy to the Heinkel company, which continued to develop and build the type despite orders not to do so. Design of the He 219 began in 1940 as a multi-role warplane, and it was only late in 1941 that the type became a dedicated night-fighter. The first of 10 prototypes flew in November 1942, and by this time there were orders for 300 He 219A initial production aircraft including an initial 130 He 219A-0 pre-production machines. The first production model was the He 219A-2, and more than 150 He 219A aircraft were built in variants up to the He 219A-7 for limited service from the middle of 1943 with various engine and armament fits. On June 11, 1943 Major Werner Streib shot down five Avro Lancasters in a single sortie, and in the first six sorties flown by his unit 20 aircraft were shot down.

| Country of origin: | Germany |
| --- | --- |
| Type: | (He 219A-7/R1) two-seat night-fighter |
| Powerplant: | two 1900hp (1417kW) Daimler-Benz DB 603G 12-cylinder inverted-Vee engines |
| Performance: | maximum speed 670km/h (416mph); initial climb rate 552m (1810ft) per minute; service ceiling 12,700m (41,665ft); range 2000km (1243 miles) |
| Weights: | empty 11,200kg (24,692lb); maximum take-off 15,300kg (33,730lb) |
| Dimensions: | span 18.50m (60ft 8.33in); length 15.54m (50ft 11.75in); height 4.10 m (13ft 5.5in) |
| Armament: | two 30mm fixed forward-firing cannon in the wing roots, two 30mm and two 20mm fixed forward-firing cannon in a ventral tray, and two 30mm obliquely upward/forward-firing in the upper part of the rear fuselage |

# Heinkel He 280

When work on the He 178 was discontinued in the winter of 1939, Heinkel redirected their energies into the twin-engined He 280 project. The aircraft was far more advanced, and designed to be powered by pairs of the more powerful HeS 8 and HeS 30. Development problems with both meant that the first prototype airframe was unpowered, the aircraft being towed to release height by a He 111 for its inaugural test flight on 22 September 1940. By March of the next year the HeS 8 engines were ready for installation, and the aircraft took off under its own power on April 2. With only 500kg (1102lb) of thrust available pilot Fritz Schüfer found that performance was hardly sparkling; by early 1943 this had risen to a little over 600kg. Even with BMW 109-003 engines fitted, the aircraft failed to impress and never entered full-scale production, losing out to the Messerschmitt Me262.

| Country of origin: | Germany |
|---|---|
| Type: | single-seat experimental jet |
| Powerplant: | two 600kg (1323lb) Henkel HeS 8A turbojets |
| Performance: | maximum speed at 6458kg (19,685ft) 800km/h (497mph) |
| Weights: | loaded 4340kg (9550lb) |
| Dimensions: | wingspan 12m (39ft 4in); length 10.4m (34ft 1in) |

# Henschel Hs 123

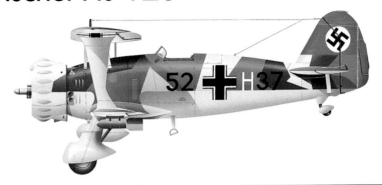

**D**esigned in 1934 and first flown in 1935 for service from 1936, the Hs 123 served in the Spanish Civil War and was technically obsolete by the time World War II started in 1939, but went on to play an important part in Germany's early successes and was still an important anti-partisan weapon in 1945. The Hs 123 was a sturdy single-bay biplane of fabric-covered metal construction with fixed tailwheel landing gear as well as an open cockpit, and although conceived as a dive-bomber was generally operated in the close-support role. Here its great strength, considerable agility and stability as a gun platform offset its limited performance and comparatively light armament. Production of 604 Hs 123A-1 warplanes ended in 1938, but so useful was the type that there were calls in World War II for it to be returned to production. Pictured is an Hs 123A-1 of 7./Stukageschwader 165 'Immelmann' based at Fürstenfeldbruck in October 1937.

| | |
|---|---|
| Country of origin: | Germany |
| Type: | single-seat dive-bomber and close-support warplane |
| Powerplant: | one 730hp (544kW) BMW 132A-3 nine-cylinder radial engine |
| Performance: | maximum speed 290km/h (180mph); climb to 2000m (6560ft) in 4 minutes 24 seconds; service ceiling 4100m (13,450ft); range 480km (298 miles) with a 200kg (441lb) bomb load |
| Weights: | empty 1420kg (3131lb); maximum take-off 2350kg (5181lb) |
| Dimensions: | span 10.50m (34ft 5.33in); length 8.66m (28ft 4.75in); height 3.76m (12ft 4in) |
| Armament: | two 7.92mm fixed forward-firing machine guns in the upper part of the forward fuselage, plus an external bomb load of 450kg (992lb ) |

# Henschel Hs 126

The older of the two types that provided the Germans with the bulk of their battlefield reconnaissance capability in World War II, the Hs 126 was a parasol-wing aeroplane that first flew in early 1935. Three prototypes and 10 Hs 126A-0 pre-production aircraft paved the way for about 800 examples of the two production variants, which entered service during 1938 with the German forces fighting alongside the Nationalist forces in the Spanish Civil War. These models were the Hs 126A-1 with the 880hp (656kW) BMW 132Dc radial engine, and the Hs 126B-1 with a different engine. The Hs 126 served in a front-line role to 1942, and was thereafter relegated to the glider-towing and night harassment roles, the latter with loads of light bombs in regions such as the Baltic and Balkans. Pictured here is one of the Hs 126B-1 aircraft on the strength of 2.(H)/Aufklärungsgruppe 31, operating on the Eastern Front in 1941/42.

| Country of origin: | Germany |
| --- | --- |
| Type: | (Hs 126B-1) two-seat tactical reconnaissance and army co-operation warplane |
| Powerplant: | one 850hp (634kW) BMW-Bramo 323A-1 or Q-1 Fafnir nine-cylinder single-row radial engine |
| Performance: | maximum speed 355km/h (221mph); climb to 4000m (13,125ft) in 7 minutes 12 seconds; service ceiling 8230m (27,000ft); range 720km (447 miles ) |
| Weights: | empty 2032kg (4480lb); maximum take-off 3270kg (7209lb) |
| Dimensions: | span 14.50m (47ft 6.75in); length 10.85m (35ft 7in); height 3.75m (12ft 3.5in) |
| Armament: | one 7.92mm fixed forward-firing machine gun in the starboard upper part of the forward fuselage, and one 7.92mm rearward-firing machine gun in the rear cockpit; external bomb load of 150kg (331lb) |

# Henschel Hs 129

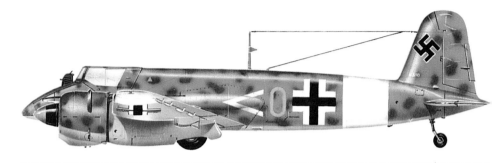

The Hs 129 was designed by Henschel in response to a spring 1937 requirement for a *Schlachtflugzeug* (battle aeroplane) that was to be relatively small but heavily armoured for survivability as it provided close air support for the German ground forces. It emerged as a cantilever low-wing monoplane of all-metal construction and first flew in the spring of 1939 with two 465hp (347kW) Argus As 410 inverted-Vee engines. Development was slow as a result of the aeroplane's poor performance and handling in combination with the pilot's woeful fields of vision, and it was only in April 1942 that the type entered service in its Hs 129B-1 form with an uprated powerplant of captured French radial engines. The aeroplane was still underpowered, and the engines were both unreliable and very vulnerable to battle damage, but the demands of the campaign on the Eastern Front resulted in the delivery of 843 Hs 129B warplanes.

| | |
|---|---|
| **Country of origin:** | Germany |
| **Type:** | (Hs 129B-2) single-seat close-support and anti-tank warplane |
| **Powerplant:** | two 700hp (522kW) Gnome-Rhòne 14M-4/5 14-cylinder two-row radial engines |
| **Performance:** | maximum speed 407km/h (253mph); initial climb rate 486m (1595ft) per minute; service ceiling 9000m (29,530ft); range 560km (348 miles) with an underfuselage pack carrying one 30mm cannon |
| **Weights:** | empty 4020kg (8862lb); maximum take-off 5250kg (11,574lb) |
| **Dimensions:** | span 14.20m (46ft 7in); length 9.75m (31ft 11.75in); height 3.25m (10ft 8in) |
| **Armament:** | two 20mm fixed forward-firing cannon and two 13mm fixed forward-firing machine guns in the upper and lower sides of the fuselage, provision under the fusforward-firing cannon or four 7.92mm forward-firing machine guns; bomb load of 450kg (992lb) |

# Horten Ho IX V2

A s early as the 1920s Reimar and Walter Horten were extolling the merits of tailless aircraft which they believed possessed superior flying characteristics. They began an experimental series in 1931, which culminated in the Ho IX V2 (The prototype Ho X was never completed). Their Ho IX V2 bears more than a passing similarity to the incredible Northrop B2 Spirit, and was the first jet-powered Horten aircraft. Designed as a fighter, the first flight of the unpowered V1 prototype was completed during 1944. A second prototype powered by two 900kg (1984lb) turbojets was built, but after barely two hours of flight tests it was lost after an engine flameout. Production had been planned on a large scale at the Gotha factory. However, only one aircraft had been completed before US forces captured the workshops, and all of the vital research documents.

| Country of origin: | Germany |
| --- | --- |
| Type: | single-seat experimental flying wing jet fighter |
| Powerplant: | two 900kg (1984lb) BMW 003 turbojets |
| Performance: | about 800km/h (500mph) at 6100m (20,000ft) |
| Weights: | about 9080kg (20,000lb) |
| Dimensions: | wingspan 16m (52ft 6in) |
| Armament: | (proposed) four 30mm MK 108 cannon for day fighter; provision for up to 908kg (2000lb) of bombs as fighter-bomber |

# Hunting (Percival) P.84 Jet Provost

In the early 1950s the RAF were continuing to train pilots for fast jet operations on the piston-engined Percival Provost. This situation was less than ideal; Hunting recognised the likelihood of an RAF requirement for a basic jet trainer and developed the Jet Provost as a private venture in response. The prototype retained the wings and tail unit of the piston engined P.56 Provost, mated to a new fuselage housing the turbine engine and landing gear. The T.Mk 1 first flew on 16 June 1953, and subsequently was built in large numbers for the RAF. The Jet Provost remained in service in three basic versions. The last version, the T.Mk 5, introduced a pressurised cabin, lengthened nose to house avionics equipment, and strengthened wings with increased internal fuel capacity. This was the RAF's basic trainer until 1989, when it was replaced by the Shorts Tucano.

| | |
|---|---|
| Country of origin: | United Kingdom |
| Type: | two-seat basic trainer |
| Powerplant: | one 1134kg (2500lb) Bristol Siddeley Viper Mk 202 turbojet |
| Performance: | maximum speed at 7620m (25,000ft) 708km/h (440mph); service ceiling 11,185m (36,700ft); maximum range with tip tanks 1448km (900 miles) |
| Weights: | maximum take-off with tip tanks 4173kg (9200lb) |
| Dimensions: | wingspan 10.77m (35ft 4in); length 10.36m (34ft); height 3.10m (10ft 2in); wing area 19.85 q m (213.7sq ft) |

# IAI Kfir C1

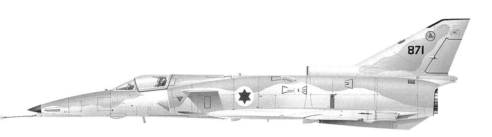

During the 1950s, Israel was forced to rely almost solely on France for procurement of combat aircraft. The original Mirage IIIC actually owes much of its inception to the close ties between Dassault and Israel. During the Six Day War of 5–10 June 1967 this aircraft performed magnificently, yet Dassault was ordered by an irate General de Gaulle that he could not deliver the improved Mirage 5 attack aircraft which had been developed for Israel and already paid for. Israeli Aircraft Industries were thus directed to concentrate their energies on making Israel more self-sufficient in combat aircraft, and to devise an improved version of the Mirage III. The company adapted the airframe to take a General Electric J79 turbojet, under a programme dubbed Black Curtain. Some of these aircraft participated in the 1973 Yom Kippur war.

| Country of origin: | Israel |
| --- | --- |
| Type: | single-seat interceptor |
| Powerplant: | one 8119kg (17,900lb) General Electric J79-J1E turbojet |
| Performance: | maximum speed above 11,000m (36,090ft) 2445km/h (1,520mph); service ceiling 17,680m (58,000ft); combat radius as interceptor 346km (215 miles) |
| Weights: | empty 7285kg (16,090lb); maximum take-off 16,200kg (35,715lb) |
| Dimensions: | wingspan 8.22m (26ft 11.5in); length 15.65m (51ft 4.25in); height 4.55m (14ft 11.25in); wing area 34.80sq m (374.60sq ft) |
| Armament: | one IAI (DEFA) 30mm cannon; nine external hardpoints with provision for up to 5775kg (12,732lb) of stores; for interception duties AIM-9 Sidewinder air-to-air missiles, or indigenously produced AAMs such as the Shafrir or Python |

# Ilyushin Il-2

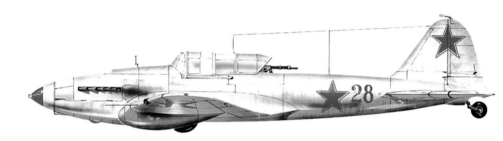

**B**uilt in larger numbers (36,150 aircraft) and at a higher rate than any other warplane in history, the Il-2 was instrumental in the Soviet defeat of Germany by 1945. The type entered service as the single-seat Il-2 three months before the German onslaught of June 1941 and was initially an indifferent warplane with the 1660hp (1238kW) AM-38 engine and an armament of two 20mm cannon and two 7.62mm machine guns as well as bombs and 82mm rockets. The aircraft matured into a formidable ground attack aircraft and was much feared by German forces on the ground. The Il-2 was followed by the Il-2M with the AM-38F engine and 23mm cannon, the Il-2M Tip 3 two-seat version of the Il-2M to allow the provision of rearward defence, and the Il-2M Tip 3M with 37mm rather than 23mm cannon for greater anti-tank capability. Shown here in hastily applied winter camouflage for the Stalingrad counter-offensive in February 1943 is an Il-2m3.

| | |
|---|---|
| **Country of origin:** | USSR |
| **Type:** | (Il-2M Tip 3) two-seat close support and anti-tank warplane |
| **Powerplant:** | one 1770hp (1320kW) Mikulin AM-38F 12-cylinder Vee engine |
| **Performance:** | maximum speed 415km/h (258mph); climb to 5000m (16,405ft ) in 15 minutes; service ceiling 6000m (19,685ft); range 800km (497 miles) |
| **Weights:** | empty 4525kg (9976lb); maximum take-off 6360kg (14,021lb) |
| **Dimensions:** | span 14.60m (47ft 11in); length 12.00m (39ft 4.5in); height 3.40m (11ft 1.75in) |
| **Armament:** | two 23mm fixed forward-firing cannon and two 7.62mm fixed forward-firing machine guns in the leading edges of the wings, and one 12.7mm trainable rearward-firing machine gun in the rear cockpit, plus an internal and external bomb and rocket load of 1000kg (2205lb) |

# Ilyushin Il-4

**D**esigned as the DB-3f and first flown in January 1940 for service from 1941, the Il-4 was a modernised development of the DB-3M optimised for ease of production and field maintenance. The Il-4 remained in production up to 1944 and with a total of 5256 aircraft was among the Soviets' most important medium bombers of World War II. The first aircraft were powered by two 1000hp (746kW) Tumanskii M-88 radial engines, but these were soon replaced by uprated versions of the same engine. Other changes included during the production run included a four- rather than three-man crew, self-sealing fuel tanks, and larger-calibre defensive weapons: the 7.62mm turret gun was replaced by a 12.7mm machine gun and then a 20mm cannon, and the machine gun in the nose was changed to a 20mm cannon. Shown here is an Illyushin Il-4 (DB-3F) of a Red Air Force *bombardirovoishchnaya aviatsionyyl polk* (bomber regiment) in 1944.

| | |
|---|---|
| Country of origin: | USSR |
| Type: | four-seat long-range medium bomber |
| Powerplant: | two 1100hp (820kW) Tumanskii M-88B 14-cylinder two-row radial engine |
| Performance: | maximum speed 420km/h (261mph); climb to 5000m (16,405ft) in 12 minutes; service ceiling 9400m (30,840ft); range 2600km (1616 miles) with a 1000kg (2205lb) bomb load |
| Weights: | empty 5800kg (12,787lb); maximum take-off 10,300kg (22,707lb) |
| Dimensions: | span 21.44m (70ft 4.5in); length 14.80m (48ft 7in); height 4.10m (13ft 5.5in) |
| Armament: | one 7.62mm trainable forward-firing machine gun in nose position, one 7.62mm trainable machine gun in dorsal turret, and one 7.62mm trainable rearward-firing machine gun in ventral hatch position, plus an internal bomb load of 2700kg (5952lb) |

# Ilyushin Il-10

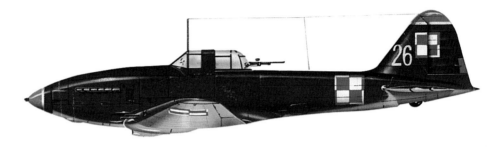

The Il-2 was a remarkably successful warplane, but its proven capabilities did not deter the Soviets from deciding in 1942 to press ahead with the creation of an improved ground-attack and anti-tank type. Various Ilyushin prototypes were evaluated before the decision came down in favour of the Il-10. This aircraft was clearly a linear descendant of the Il-2 but featured improved armour protection, a higher-rated engine, slightly smaller overall dimensions, considerably greater manoeuvrability and much enhanced performance. The Il-10 was ordered into production during August 1944, had fully replaced the Il-2 in production by November 1944, and entered service in February 1945. Some 3500 Il-10s were completed by the end of World War II, and the type remained in production and service until well after this time. The aircraft pictured wears the markings of a Polish air assault regiment in 1951.

| | |
|---|---|
| **Country of origin:** | USSR |
| **Type:** | two-seat close support and anti-tank warplane |
| **Powerplant:** | one 2000hp (1491kW) Mikulin AM-42 12-cylinder Vee engine |
| **Performance:** | maximum speed 551km/h (342mph); climb to 5000m (16,405ft) in 9 minutes 42 seconds; service ceiling 7250m (23,790ft); range 800km (497 miles) |
| **Weights:** | empty 4680kg (10,317lb); maximum take-off 6535kg (14,407lb) |
| **Dimensions:** | span 13.40m (43ft 11.5in); length 11.10m (36ft 5in); height 3.50m (11ft 5.75in) |
| **Armament:** | two 37mm fixed forward-firing cannon and two 7.62mm fixed forward-firing machine guns or four 23mm fixed forward-firing cannon in the leading edges of the wing, and one 20mm trainable rearward-firing cannon in the dorsal turret, plus an internal and external bomb and rocket load of 1000kg (2205lb) |

# Ilyushin Il-28 'Beagle'

First appearing in prototype form as early as 1948, the Il-28 afforded Eastern Bloc armed forces the same degree of flexibility and duration of service as the Canberra did for Britain. The prototype was powered by two Soviet-built turbojets developed directly from the Rolls-Royce Nene, supplied by the British government in a fit of contrition. The unswept wing is set high and well back on the fuselage, to reduce the moment caused by fuel tanks located in the rear fuselage and the aft gunners compartment. The gunner also acts as the radio operator, with the navigator housed in the glazed nose section. After a public fly-past during the 1950 May Day parade, Soviet units began to equip with the Il-28 in some numbers. The aircraft served with all Warsaw Pact light bomber units between 1955–70. A trainer version (Il-28U) was also produced.

| | |
|---|---|
| Country of origin: | USSR |
| Type: | three seat bomber and ground attack/dual control trainer/torpedo carrier |
| Powerplant: | two 2700kg (5952kg) Klimov VK-1 turbojets |
| Performance: | maximum speed 902 km/h (560mph); service ceiling 12,300m (40,355ft); range 2180km (1355 miles); with bomb load 1100km (684 miles) |
| Weights: | empty 12890kg (28,418lb); maximum take-off 21,200kg (46,738lb) |
| Dimensions: | wingspan 21.45sq m (70ft 4.5in); length 17.65m (57ft 10.75in); height 6.70m (21ft 11.8in); wing area 60.80sq m (654.47sq ft) |
| Armament: | two 23mm NR-23 fixed cannon in nose, two 23mm NR-23 trainable cannon in tail turret; internal bomb capacity of up to 1000kg (2205lb), maximum bomb capacity 3000kg (6614lb); torpedo version had provision for two 400mm light torpedoes |

# Ilyushin Il-76MD 'Candid-B'

The Il-76 'Candid' (NATO reporting name) was first seen in the West at the 1971 Paris Air Salon. The design was prepared to meet a basic need in the Soviet Union for a really capable freighter, which, while carrying large indivisible loads, with a high cruising speed and intercontinental range, could operate from relatively poor and partially prepared airstrips. Aeroflot was the first operator, who used it on Siberian routes. The Il-76T 'Candid A' was delivered to the Soviet air force for evaluation in 1974, and featured a rear gun turret. Within two years deliveries of the Il-76M 'Candid-B' began. The Il-76MD pictured features a host of improvements, including an increased fuel capacity which in turn provides an increase in range. The MD is unarmed, has more powerful engines, and can carry a heavier payload. India are among the foreign clients, operating a fleet of 24.

| | |
|---|---|
| Country of origin: | USSR (now CIS) |
| Type: | heavy freight transport |
| Powerplant: | four 12,000kg (26,455lb) Soloviev D-30KP-1 turbofans |
| Performance: | maximum speed at 11,000m (36,090ft) 850km/h (528mph); maximum cruising altitude 12,000m (39,370ft); range with 40,000kg (88,185lb) payload 5000km (3107 miles) |
| Weights: | empty about 75,000kg (165,347lb); maximum take-off 170,000kg (374,786lb) |
| Dimensions: | wingspan 50.50m (165ft 8.2in); length 46.59m (152ft 10.25in); height 14.76m (48ft 5in); wing area 300sq m (3229.28sq ft) |
| Armament: | provision for two 23mm cannon in tail |

# Junkers Ju 52/3m

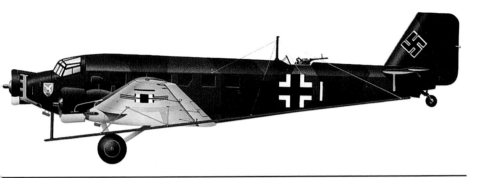

Intended as successor to the highly successful W 33 and W 34 transports, the Ju 52 was planned from the late 1920s as an enlarged version of the same basic design concept, and first flew in prototype form during October 1930 with one 725hp (541kW) BMW VII Vee engine. The Ju 52a to Ju 52d initial production models for the civil market differed only in the type of engine used, but with the Ju 52/3m a three-engined powerplant was introduced for greater payload and performance. The series was built to the extent of some 4850 aircraft, the vast majority of them to meet military orders in variants between the Ju 52/3m ge and the Ju 52/3m g14e. The Ju 52/3m served initially as a bomber as well as transport, but in World War II was a transport and airborne forces aeroplane that saw operational use in every German theatre right up to May 1945. The aircraft pictured is a Ju 52/3mg6e equipped with a large magnetic loop for mine clearance operations.

| | |
|---|---|
| **Country of origin:** | Germany |
| **Type:** | (Ju 52/3m g7e) three-seat transport with accommodation for 18 troops, or 12 litters, or freight |
| **Powerplant:** | three 730hp (544kW) BMW 132T-2 nine-cylinder radial engines |
| **Performance:** | maximum speed 286km/h (178mph); climb to 3000m (9845ft) in 17 minutes 30 seconds; service ceiling 5900m (19,360ft); range 1305km (811 miles) |
| **Weights:** | empty 6500kg (14,328lb); maximum take-off 11,030kg (24,317lb) |
| **Dimensions:** | span 29.20m (95ft 10in); length 18.90m (62ft); height 4.52m (14ft 10in) |
| **Armament:** | one 13mm or 7.92mm trainable rearward-firing machine gun in rear dorsal position, provision for one 7.92mm trainable machine gun in forward dorsal position, and one 7.92mm trainable lateral-firing machine gun in each of the two beam positions |

# Junkers Ju 86

The Junkers Ju 86 was planned as a medium bomber. The first two production variants were the Ju 86D and Ju 86E that entered service in spring 1936 and differed in their powerplants, the latter type having 810hp (655kW) BMW 132 radial engines. Operational service revealed that performance was poor, so the type was then developed as the Ju 86B, Ju 86F and Ju 86Z civil transports, the Ju 86G bomber trainer, and Ju 86K bomber for export . The final versions were the Ju 86P and Ju 86R for the high-altitude role with a pressurised cabin: the Ju 86P bomber had 950hp (708kW) Jumo 207A-1 engines and a span of 84ft 0in (25.60m), while the Ju 86R reconnaissance type had 1000hp (746kW) Jumo 207B-3 engines and a span of 104 ft 11.75in (32.00m) for a ceiling of 47,245ft (14,400m). Production totalled 470 aircraft. Pictured is a Ju-86D-1 medium bomber of 5/Kampfgeschwader 254, based at Eschwege in September 1939.

| Country of origin: | Germany |
| --- | --- |
| Type: | (Ju 86D-1) four-seat medium bomber |
| Powerplant: | two 600hp (447kW) Junkers Jumo 205C-4 vertically opposed Diesel engines |
| Performance: | maximum speed 325km/h (202mph); service ceiling 5900m (19,360ft); range 1140km (708 miles) with maximum bomb load |
| Weights: | empty 5800kg (12,786lb); maximum take-off 8200kg (18,078lb) |
| Dimensions: | span 22.50m (73ft 9.75in); length 17.57m (58ft 7.13in); height 5.06m (16ft 7.25 in) |
| Armament: | one 7.92mm trainable forward-firing machine gun in the nose position, one 7.92mm trainable rearward-firing machine gun in the dorsal position, and one 7.92mm trainable rearward-firing machine gun in the retractable ventral 'dustbin', plus an internal bomb load of 1000kg (2205lb) |

# Junkers Ju 87B-1

With its inverted-gull wing, massive landing gear and screaming dive trumpets, the Ju 87 remains synonymous with German success at the beginning of World War II. The Ju 87 was planned as a *Stuka* (short for *Sturzkampfluzeug*), or dive-bomber) a name that became synonymous with the type, to provide 'flying artillery' to support the armoured forces that would spearhead Germany's Blitzkrieg (lightning war) tactics. The Ju 87 first flew in 1935 with twin vertical tail surfaces and a British engine, but was then developed into the Ju 87A initial production model (200 aircraft) with a single vertical surface and the 680hp (507kW) Junkers Jumo 210 inverted-Vee engine. The Ju 87A entered service in the spring of 1937 and was soon supplanted by the Ju 87B-1 that was the first major model with a considerably uprated powerplant to provide improved performance as well as allow a doubling of the bomb load.

| Country of origin: | Germany |
| --- | --- |
| Type: | two-seat dive-bomber and close support warplane |
| Powerplant: | one 1200hp (895kW) Junkers Jumo 211Da 12-cylinder inverted-Vee engine |
| Performance: | maximum speed 383km/h (238mph); climb to 2000m (6560ft) in 4 minutes 18 seconds; service ceiling 8000m (26,245ft); range 790km (491 miles) |
| Weights: | empty 2710kg (5974lb); maximum take-off 4340kg (9568lb) |
| Dimensions: | span 13.80m (45ft 3.33in); length 11.10m (36ft 5in); height 4.01m (13ft 2in) |
| Armament: | two 7.92mm fixed forward-firing machine guns in the leading edges of the wing and one 7.92mm trainable rearward-firing machine gun in the rear of the cockpit, plus an external bomb load of 500kg (1102lb) |

# Junkers Ju 87D

**B**y the spring of 1940, the new Jumo 211J-1 inverted-Vee piston engine was ready for service, and the Junkers design team set about evolving a development of the Ju 87B to exploit this engine, which offered not only greater power but also the possibility of a considerably cleaner installation. Other changes in the new variant were a complete redesign of the cockpit enclosure to reduce drag, a reduction in the size and complexity of the main landing gear fairings, an increase in the internal fuel capacity, improvement of crew protection through the introduction of more and thicker armour, the doubling of the defensive firepower, and the strengthening of the lower fuselage and attached crutch for the ability to carry one 3968lb (1800kg) bomb. There were seven subvariants of the Ju 87D between the Ju 87D-1 and Ju 87D-8 for a variety of roles ranging form glider-towing (Ju 87D-2) to night ground attack (Ju 87D-7).

| | |
|---|---|
| Country of origin: | Germany |
| Type: | (Ju 87D-1) two-seat dive-bomber and close support warplane |
| Powerplant: | one 1400hp (1044kW) Junkers Jumo 211J-1 12-cylinder inverted-Vee engine |
| Performance: | maximum speed 410km/h (255mph); climb to 5000m (16,405ft) in 19 minutes 48 seconds; service ceiling 7300m (23,950ft); range 1535km (954 miles) |
| Weights: | empty 3900kg (8598lb); maximum take-off 6600kg (14,550lb) |
| Dimensions: | span 13.80m (45ft 3.33in); length 11.50m (37ft 8.75in); height 3.88m (12ft 9.25in) |
| Armament: | two 7.92mm fixed forward-firing machine guns in the leading edges of the wing and one 7.92mm trainable two-barrel rearward-firing machine gun in the rear of the cockpit, plus an external bomb load of 1800kg (3968lb) |

# Junkers Ju 87G

As the increasing ineffectiveness of standard bombs against steadily more heavily armoured tanks became clear to the Luftwaffe in 1942, serious consideration was belatedly given to the adoption of more capable anti-tank armament for the Ju 87, which was now the service's primary anti-tank weapon. The obvious solution was a high-velocity cannon firing a moderately large projectile: the 37mm Flak 18 light anti-aircraft gun was selected, and the revised weapon became the BK 3,7 which, with its magazine and long ejector chute for spent cases, was installed in a pod that could be installed under the wing of the Ju 87 outboard of the main landing gear legs on hardpoints that could otherwise carry bombs. Validated on a Ju 87D-3 conversion, the new armament was introduced on the Ju 87G-1 that entered service in the autumn of 1942. This was the final operational version of the Stuka, with production of all versions totalling 5700.

| Country of origin: | Germany |
|---|---|
| Type: | two-seat anti-tank and close support warplane |
| Powerplant: | one 1400hp (1044kW) Junkers Jumo 211J-1 12-cylinder inverted-Vee engine |
| Performance: | maximum speed 410km/h (255mph); climb to 5000m (16,405ft) in 19 minutes 48 seconds; service ceiling 7300m (23,950ft); range 1535km (954 miles) |
| Weights: | empty 3900kg (8598lb) |
| Dimensions: | span 13.80m (45ft 3.33in); length 11.50m (37ft 8.75in); height 3.88m (12ft 9.25in) |
| Armament: | two 7.92mm fixed forward-firing machine guns in the leading edges of the wing, one 7.92mm trainable two-barrel machine gun in the rear of the cockpit, and two 37mm fixed cannon under the wings, plus provision for an external bomb load as an alternative to the cannon |

# Junkers Ju 88A, D, H, S and T

Rivalling the Mosquito as the most versatile warplane of World War II, and of vital importance to Germany right through this war, the Ju 88 was schemed as a high-speed level and dive bomber and first flew in December 1936 for entry into service during 1939. The most important early model was the Ju 88A, of which some 7000 or more were delivered in variants up to the Ju 88A-17 with steadily uprated engines, enhanced defensive armament and improved offensive capability. The Ju 88D was a long-range reconnaissance development of which some 1450 were delivered. The Ju 88H was another reconnaissance model of which small numbers were completed with 1700hp (1267.5kW) BMW 801 radial engines, and the Ju 88S was a high-speed bomber of which modest numbers were produced with radial or Vee engines. The Ju 88T was a reconnaissance derivative of the Ju 88S. The final total of 15,000 Ju 88s of all models gives an idea of the significance of this aircraft.

| | |
|---|---|
| **Country of origin:** | Germany |
| **Type:** | (Ju 88A-4) four-seat high-speed, level and dive bomber |
| **Powerplant:** | two 1340hp (999kW) Junkers Jumo 211J-1/2 12-cylinder engines |
| **Performance:** | Maximum speed 470km/h (292mph); climb to 5400m (17,715ft) in 23 minutes; service ceiling 26,900ft (8200m); range 2730km (1696 miles) |
| **Weights:** | empty 9860kg (21,737lb); maximum take-off 14,000kg (30,865lb) |
| **Dimensions:** | Span 20.00m (65ft 7.5in); length 14.40m (47ft 2.75in); height 4.85m (15ft 11in) |
| **Armament:** | one 7.92mm fixed or trainable forward-firing machine gun in windscreen, one 13mm or two 7.92mm forward-firing machine guns in nose position, two 7.92mm machine guns in rear of cockpit, and one 13mm or two 7.92mm trainable rearward-firing machine guns in rear of undernose gondola, plus a bomb load of 2500kg (5511lb) |

# Junkers Ju 88G

After its introduction in 1942 the Ju 88C-6 proved effective in its role as the first night-fighter derivative of the Ju 88C heavy fighter development program. However, it was appreciated from an early date that the addition of extra equipment would lead to an inevitable increase in both weight and drag, and result in a degradation of performance. This led to the development and appearance (in spring 1943) of the Ju 88 V58 (Ju 88G VI) prototype of a considerably improved night-fighter model. This prototype was a conversion from Ju 88R standard with the more angular tail unit of the Ju 188. There followed some 2800 or more production aircraft in the Ju 88G-1, G-4, G-6 and G-7 variants, each of the last two in three subvariants with different radar and armament, for service from the summer of 1944. Pictured here is a Ju-88G-7a of IV/NJG 6 during the winter of 1944-45, with the tail painted to represent a Ju 88C for deception purposes.

| | |
|---|---|
| Country of origin: | Germany |
| Type: | (Ju 88G-7b) four-seat night-fighter |
| Powerplant: | two 1725hp (1286kW) Junkers Jumo 213E 12-cylinder inverted-Vee engines |
| Performance: | maximum speed 626km/h (389mph); climb to 9200m (30,185ft) in 26 minutes 24 seconds; service ceiling 10,000m (32,810ft); range 2250km (1398 miles) |
| Weights: | normal take-off 13,110kg (28,902lb); maximum take-off 13,825kg (30,478lb) or 32,352lb (14,765kg) overload |
| Dimensions: | span 20.08m (65ft 10.5in); length 15.55m (51ft 0.25in) or, with tail-warning radar, 16.36m (53ft 8in); height 4.85m (15ft 11in) |
| Armament: | four 20mm fixed forward-firing cannon in the ventral tray, two 20mm fixed obliquely forward/upward-firing cannon in the rear fuselage, and one 13mm machine gun in the rear of the cockpit |

# Junkers Ju 188

O n the outbreak of World War II the design of the Ju 288 as the Ju 88's successor was already well advanced, but by 1941 delays to the Ju 288 programme meant that an interim successor was required. The aircraft selected was the Ju 188, which had emerged from the Ju 88B prototype that had flown in 1940. The Ju 188 entered service in 1942, and production of about 1100 aircraft included the Ju 188A bomber with two 1776hp (1324kW) Junkers Jumo 213A engines, Ju 188D reconnaissance version of the Ju 188A, Ju 188E bomber with radial rather than Vee engines, Ju 188 reconnaissance version of the Ju 188E, Ju 188S high-altitude intruder, and Ju 188T high-altitude reconnaissance aeroplane. Many other variants were trialled or projected for roles that included night-fighting and adverse-weather interception. Pictured here is one of the Ju 188D-2 aircraft on the strength of 1.(F)/124 based at Kirkenes in northern Finland during 1944.

| | |
|---|---|
| Country of origin: | Germany |
| Type: | (Ju 188E-1) four-seat medium bomber |
| Powerplant: | two 1677hp (1250kW) BMW 801D-2 14-cylinder two-row radial engines |
| Performance: | maximum speed 544km/h (338mph); climb to 6000m (19,685ft) in 17 minutes 24 seconds; service ceiling 10,100m (33,135ft); range 2480km (1541 miles) with a 1500kg (3307lb) bomb load |
| Weights: | empty 9410kg (20,745lb); maximum take-off 14,570kg (32,121lb) |
| Dimensions: | span 22.00m (72ft 2in); length 15.06m (49ft 4.9in); height 4.46m (14ft 7.3in) |
| Armament: | one 20mm trainable forward-firing cannon in nose position, one 13mm machine gun in dorsal turret, one 13mm rearward-firing machine gun in rear of cockpit, and one 7.92mm two-barrel machine gun in undernose gondola, plus a bomb load of 3000kg (6614lb) |

# Kawanishi H6K 'Mavis'

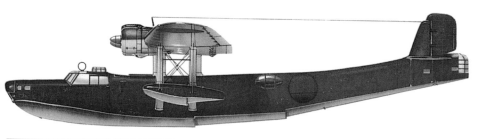

The H6K flying boat resulted from a 1933 requirement and was one of the best warplanes of the Imperial Japanese navy at the start of World War II's Pacific campaign. The type remained in useful service throughout the war as it was supplemented although never really replaced by the superb Kawanishi H8K 'Emily'. The first of four prototypes flew in July 1936, and successful trials led to the H6K2 production model, of which 10 were completed for service from January 1938 with four 1000hp (746kW) Mitsubishi Kinsei 43 radial engines. Further production comprised 127 examples of the H6K4 with revised armament and, in some aircraft, an uprated powerplant, and 36 examples of the H6K5 with greater power. Lesser variants (with numbers) were the H6K2-L transport (16), H6K3 VIP transport (two) and H6K4-L transport (20), many of which remained in service until the end of the war. Pictured is an H6K5 of the Imperial Japanese Navy Air Force.

| | |
|---|---|
| Country of origin: | Japan |
| Type: | (H6K5) nine-seat maritime reconnaissance flying boat |
| Powerplant: | four 1300hp (969kW) Mitsubishi Kinsei 51/53 14-cylinder two-row radial engines |
| Performance: | maximum speed 385km/h (239mph); climb to 5000m(16,405ft) in 13 minutes 23 seconds; service ceiling 9560m (31,365ft); range 6772 km (4208 miles) |
| Weights: | empty 12,380kg (27,117lb); maximum take-off 23,000kg (50,706lb) |
| Dimensions: | span 40.00m (131ft 2.75in); length 25.63m (84ft 0.75in); height 6.27m (20ft 6.75in) |
| Armament: | one 20mm trainable rearward-firing cannon in tail turret, one 7.7mm machine gun in bow turret, one 7.7mm rearward-firing machine gun in dorsal position, and two 7.7mm trainable lateral-firing machine gun in blister positions, plus a torpedo and bomb load of 3527lb (1600kg) |

# Kawanishi N1K-J Shiden 'George'

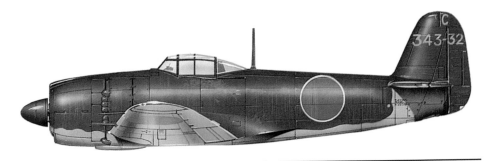

The Shiden (Violet Lightning) resulted from the realisation of the Kawanishi design team in December 1941 that its N1K1 Kyofu floatplane fighter, which had yet to fly, possessed so much potential that a landplane derivative was clearly a possibility. There followed nine prototypes, the first of them flying in December 1942 at the start of a protracted test programme, before the delivery of 1098 N1K1-J production aircraft in three subvariants differentiated by their armaments. These entered service early in 1944, and were later complemented by 415 examples of the two subvariants of the N1K2-J with a redesigned fuselage and tail unit as well as the wing lowered from the mid- to low-set position allowing the use of shorter main landing gear units. The N1K proved an effective fighter although it was troubled by a temperamental engine. Shown here is late-production N1K2-J Kai of the 343rd Kokutai, Imperial Japanese Navy Air Force during 1945.

| | |
|---|---|
| Country of origin: | Japan |
| Type: | (N1K1-J) single-seat fighter and fighter-bomber |
| Powerplant: | one 1990hp (1557kW) Nakajima NK9H Homare 21 18-cylinder two-row radial engine |
| Performance: | maximum speed 581km/h (361mph); climb to 6000m (19,685ft) in 7 minutes 50 seconds; service ceiling 12,500m (41,010ft); range 2544km (1581 miles) |
| Weights: | empty 2897kg (6387lb); maximum take-off 4321kg (9526lb) |
| Dimensions: | span 12.00m (39ft 4.5in); length 8.88m (29ft 1.88in); height 4.06m (13ft 3.85in) |
| Armament: | two 20mm fixed forward-firing cannon in the leading edges of the wing, two 20mm fixed forward-firing cannon in underwing gondolas, and two 7.7mm fixed forward-firing machine guns in the forward fuselage, plus an external bomb load of 120kg (265lb) |

# Kawasaki Ki-45 Toryu 'Nick'

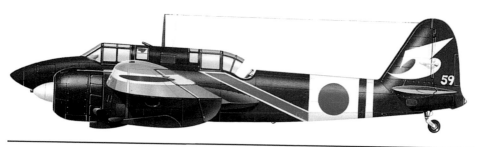

Designed to a 1937 requirement, the Toryu (Dragon Killer) was a twin-engined heavy fighter that became one of the Imperial Japanese Army Air Force's most important warplanes. The first of six prototype and 12 pre-production aircraft flew in January 1939, but considerable development had to be undertaken before the type entered service in autumn 1942 with 1050hp (783kW) Nakajima Ha-25 radial engines as the Ki-45 Kai-a fighter and Ki-45 Kai-b ground-attack/anti-shipping fighter. The Ki-45 Kai-c was a night-fighter development and introduced Mitsubishi engines, while the Ki-45 Kai-d was a ground-attack/anti-shipping model with revised armament including provision to carry 500kg (1102lb) of bombs. Production of the Ki-45 Kai-c reached 477 aircraft, and that of the other three variants 1198 machines. Pictured here is a Ki-45 KAI-c of the 53rd Sentai, Imperial Japanese Army Air Force based at Matsudo in Chiba Prefecture for the defence of the mainland in early 1945.

| Country of origin: | Japan |
|---|---|
| Type: | (Ki-45 Kai-c) two-seat night-fighter |
| Powerplant: | two 1080hp (805kW) Mitsubishi Ha-102 (Army Type 1) 14-cylinder two-row radial engines |
| Performance: | maximum speed 540km/h (336mph); climb to 5000m (16,405ft) in 7 minutes; service ceiling 10,000m (32,810ft); range 2000km (1243 miles) |
| Weights: | empty 4000kg (8818lb); maximum take-off 5500kg (12,125lb) |
| Dimensions: | span 15.02m (49ft 3.25in); length 11.00m (36ft 1in); height 3.70m (12ft 1.75in) |
| Armament: | One 37mm fixed forward-firing cannon in underside of forward fuselage, two 20mm fixed obliquely forward/upward-firing cannon in central fuselage, and one 7.92mm trainable rearward-firing machine gun in rear cockpit, plus a bomb load of 500kg (1102lb) |

# Kawasaki Ki-61 Hien 'Tony'

The Hien (Swallow) was unique among Japanese first-line warplanes of World War II in being powered by an inverted-Vee piston engine. This was a Kawasaki Ha-40 unit, a licence-built version of the German Daimler-Benz DB 601A. The first of 12 prototype and pre-production aircraft flew in December 1941, and revealed excellent performance and good handling. The Ki-61-I entered service in February 1943, and was delivered to the extent of 1380 aircraft in two subvariants differentiated by their armament, before the advent of 1274 Ki-61 Kai fighters with a lengthened fuselage and different armament fits. Further development resulted in the Ki-61-II Kai optimised for high-altitude operations with the Kawasaki Ha-140 engine, and deliveries amounted to 374 aircraft in two subvariants again distinguishable by their different armament fit. Like other Japanese fighters, it was soon eclipsed by its American counterparts.

| | |
|---|---|
| Country of origin: | Japan |
| Type: | (Ki-61-Ib) single-seat fighter |
| Powerplant: | one 1175hp (876kW) Kawasaki Ha-40 (Army Type 2) 12-cylinder inverted-Vee engine |
| Performance: | maximum speed 592km/h (368mph); climb to 5000m (16,405ft) in 5 minutes 31 seconds; service ceiling 11,600m (37,730ft); range 1100km (684 miles) |
| Weights: | empty 2210kg (4872lb); normal take-off 2950kg (6504lb); maximum take-off 3250kg (7165lb) |
| Dimensions: | Span 12.00m (39ft 4.25in); length 8.75m (28ft 8.5in); height 3.70m (12ft 1.75in) |
| Armament: | two 12.7mm fixed forward-firing machine guns in the upper part of the forward fuselage and two 12.7mm fixed forward-firing machine guns in the leading edges of the wing |

# Kawasaki Ki-100

The Ki-61-II Kai was potentially an excellent high-altitude fighter, but was plagued by the unreliability of the Kawasaki Ha-140 Vee engine and a low production rate. By autumn 1944, therefore, Kawasaki were forced to store a number of airframes for lack of the appropriate engines, and in an inspired piece of improvisation combined the Ki-61-II Kai airframe with the Mitsubishi Ha-112-II radial engine. This was wider than the Ha-140, but a remarkably neat installation was devised to combine the radial engine with a narrow fuselage, and the first of three prototype conversions made its maiden flight in February 1945. There followed 272 and 118 new-build aircraft that entered service in two subvariants, including the Ki-100-Ib with an all-round vision canopy, for service from March 1945. The Ki-100 was soon established as the Imperial Japanese Army Air Force's best fighter.

| Country of origin: | Japan |
| --- | --- |
| Type: | (Ki-100-Ia) single-seat fighter and fighter-bomber |
| Powerplant: | one 1500hp (1118kW) Mitsubishi Ha-112-II (Army Type 4) 14-cylinder two-row radial engine |
| Performance: | maximum speed 580km/h (360mph); climb to 5000m (16,405ft) in 6 minutes; service ceiling 11,000m (36,090ft); range 1367 miles (2000km) |
| Weights: | empty 2525kg (5567lb); maximum take-off 3495kg (7705lb) |
| Dimensions: | span 12.00m (39ft 4.5in); length 8.82m (28ft 11.25in); height 3.75 m (12ft 3.63in) |
| Armament: | two 20mm fixed forward-firing cannon in upper part of the forward fuselage, and two 12.7mm fixed forward-firing machine guns in the leading edges of the wing, plus an external bomb load of 500kg (1102lb) |

# Kawasaki C-1

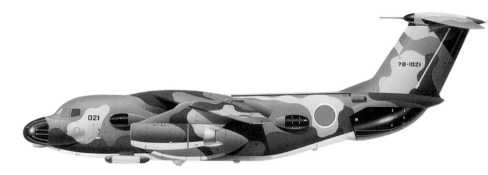

The C-1 was designed specifically to replace the redoubtable Curtiss C-46 Commando transport aircraft in service with the Japanese Air Self Defence Force. The first two prototypes were built during 1968 by Kawasaki Heavy Industries from a design submitted by the Nihon Aeroplane Manufacturing Company. The first flight was made in November 1970; flight testing and evaluation led to a production order for 11 in 1972. The C-1 follows conventional military transport design with a high set wing configuration to maximise cabin volume, podded main landing gear and a rear loading ramp. Limited maximum payload curtailed plans to develop variants, with the exception of the sole C-1Kai ECM trainer pictured. This aircraft differs from standard models by distinctive radomes on the nose and tail, an ALQ-5 ECM system, and antennae beneath the fuselage.

| | |
|---|---|
| Country of origin: | Japan |
| Type: | ECM trainer aircraft |
| Powerplant: | two 6577kg (14,500lb) Mitsubishi (Pratt & Whitney) JT8-M-9 turbofans |
| Performance: | maximum speed at 7620m (25,000ft) 806km/h (501mph); service ceiling 11,580m (38,000ft); range 1300km (808 miles) with 7900kg (17,417lb) payload |
| Weights: | empty 23320kg (51,412lb); maximum take-off 45,000kg (99,208lb) |
| Dimensions: | wingspan 30.60m (100ft 4.75in); length 30.5m (100ft 4in); height 10.0m (32ft 9.3in); wing area 102.50sq m (1297.09sq ft) |

# Latécoére 298

In 1917 Pierre Latécoére established Forges et Ateliers de Construction Latécoére at Toulouse-Montaudron. Drawing on experience gained producing seaplanes in the 1920s, the Laté 298.01 prototype was designed to meet a 1933 requirement, and first flew in May 1936. Successful trials led to the Laté 298 production model. This entered service late 1938 with the French Naval Air Arm, which received 24 and 12 (eventually 27) examples of the Laté 298A and 298B with fixed and folding wings respectively. The Laté 298D was a 298B development with a fixed wing; 95 were ordered. In the event only about 60 machines were built before the German occupation. In 1942 the Germans allowed a resumption of Laté 298 production against a Vichy French requirement for 30 aircraft, but it is unclear how many of these Laté 298F machines (298D aircraft with simplified controls) were completed. Pictured is a 298 of Escadrille T1, Aéronavale, based at Berre, near Marseilles, in late 1939.

| Country of origin: | France |
| --- | --- |
| Type: | (Laté 298D) three-seat coastal reconnaissance and torpedo bomber floatplane |
| Powerplant: | one 880hp (656kW) Hispano-Suiza 12Ycrs-1 12-cylinder Vee engine |
| Performance: | maximum speed 290km/h (180mph); service ceiling 6500m (21,325ft); range 2200 km (1367 miles) |
| Weights: | empty 3062kg (6750lb); maximum take-off weight 4800kg (10,582lb) |
| Dimensions: | span 15.50m (50ft 10in); length 12.56m (41ft 2in); height 5.23m (17ft 1in) |
| Armament: | two 7.5mm fixed forward-firing machine guns; one 7.5mm trainable machine gun in rear of cockpit; plus an external torpedo and bomb load of 670kg (1477lb) |

# Lavochkin LaGG-1 and LaGG-3

The LaGG-1 was one of several new monoplane fighters whose development was ordered by the Soviet authorities in 1939 in an effort to modernise the Soviet air forces at a time of deepening European crisis. Based on a wooden airframe to capitalise on the USSR's abundance of the material, the LaGG-1 was a 'modern' monoplane fighter in its low-wing layout with an enclosed cockpit and retractable main landing gear units. The prototype first flew in March 1940, and trials revealed good speed but poor acceleration, climb rate, range, service ceiling and, most notably, handling. Even so, the type was rushed into production; no fewer than 100 interim LaGG-1 and 6427 slightly improved LaGG-3 fighters being completed by autumn 1941. Suffering enormous losses, the aircraft helped the USSR to survive the German invasion of 1941. The aircraft pictured was operated by a Soviet Air Force unit over the Ukrainian front during 1942.

| | |
|---|---|
| Country of origin: | USSR |
| Type: | (LaGG-3) single-seat fighter and fighter-bomber |
| Powerplant: | one 1260hp (939.5kW) Klimov VK-105PF-1 12-cylinder Vee engine |
| Performance: | maximum speed 575km/h (357mph); climb to 5000m (16,405ft) in 5 minutes 48 seconds; service ceiling 9700m (31,825ft); range 1000km (621 miles) |
| Weights: | empty 2620kg (5776lb); maximum take-off 3190kg (7032lb) |
| Dimensions: | span 9.80m (32ft 1.75in); length 8.81m (28ft 11in); height 2.54m (8ft 4in) |
| Armament: | one 20mm fixed forward-firing cannon in an engine installation and two 7.62mm fixed forward-firing machine guns in the upper part of the forward fuselage, plus an external bomb and rocket load of 200kg (441lb) |

# Lavochkin La-5

The LaGG-3 mentioned previously was an indifferent fighter of wooden construction that was accepted largely because it was easy to build and provided just about adequate capability. The La-5 was a superb fighter, however, which offered truly excellent capabilities through the replacement of the LaGG-3's Klimov M-105 Vee engine by the more potent Shvetsov M-82 radial engine. The change was ordered in August 1941, and the first of several prototypes flew in March 1942. Intensive development led to an early start to the production run, which lasted until late 1994 and amounted to 9920 aircraft in variants such as the La-5 with the 1480hp (1103.5kW) M-82A engine, La-5F with the 1540hp (1148kW) M-82F (later ASh-82F) engine, definitive La-5FN, La-5FN Type 41 with a metal rather than wooden wing, and La-5UTI two-seat conversion trainer of which only a few were completed. Pictured is a Czech La-5FN, based at Malacky during 1945-46.

| Country of origin: | USSR |
|---|---|
| Type: | (La-5FN) single-seat fighter and fighter-bomber |
| Powerplant: | one 1630hp (1215kW) Shvetsov ASh-82FN 14-cylinder two-row radial engine |
| Performance: | maximum speed 648km/h (403mph); climb to 5000m (16,405ft) in 5 minutes; service ceiling 11,000m (36,090ft); range 765km (475 miles) |
| Weights: | empty 2605kg (5743lb); normal take-off 3265kg (7198lb); maximum take-off 3402kg (7500lb) |
| Dimensions: | span 9.80m (32ft 1.75in); length 8.67m (28ft 5.33in); height 2.54m (8ft 4in) |
| Armament: | two 20mm fixed forward-firing cannon in the upper part of the forward fuselage, plus an external bomb and rocket load of 500kg (1102lb) |

# Letov S 328

**E**ntering service in 1934 with the Czechoslovak Air Force, the S 328 was a development from the original S 28 reconnaissance biplane of 1929 via the S 128 and S 228 with steadily more powerful engines, and was designed to a Finnish requirement that in the event yielded no order. The S 328F prototype was followed by 445 examples of the S 328 production model, 13 examples of the S 328N night-fighter model with four fixed and two trainable machine guns, and four examples of the S 328V twin-float seaplane for the target-towing role. The surviving aircraft were seized by Germany after its occupation of Czechoslovakia in March 1939. Most were retained as trainers, but some were passed to allies such as Bulgaria and Slovakia. Slovak insurgents operated a few aircraft against the Germans in autumn 1944. The aircraft pictured was operated by the Slovak Insurgent Air Force from Tri Duby airfield in September 1944.

| | |
|---|---|
| Country of origin: | Czechoslovakia |
| Type: | (S 326) two-seat reconnaissance bomber with secondary ground-attack capability |
| Powerplant: | one 635hp (474kW) Walter-built Bristol Pegasus IIM2 nine-cylinder single-row radial engine |
| Performance: | maximum speed 280km/h (174mph); climb to 5000m (16,405ft) in 17 minutes; service ceiling 7200m (23,620ft); range 795 miles (1280km) |
| Weights: | empty 1680kg (3704lb); maximum take-off 2640kg (5820lb ) |
| Dimensions: | span 13.71m (44ft 11.75in); length 10.36m (33ft 11.75in); height 3.40m (11ft 2in) |
| Armament: | two or four 7.92mm fixed forward-firing machine guns in the leading edges of the upper and lower wings, and one or two 7.92mm machine guns in the rear cockpit, plus a bomb load of 300kg (661lb) |

# Lioré-et-Olivier LeO 20

**D**uring World War I, the company of Fernand Lioré and Henri Olivier constructed Nieuport, Morane-Saulnier and Sopwith designs under licence at Levallois-Perret, and in 1916 produced its first independent design, the LeO 4 reconnaissance biplane. LeO subsequently became the most important manufacturer of large French military aircraft, each of its designs a clear linear descendant of its predecessor. The Leo 12 was a two-seat night-bomber, built to rival the Farman Goliath, with power provided by 400hp (298kW) Lorraine engines. Re-engined with the vastly superior Bristol Jupiter this became the Leo 122, which was built only in prototype form. From this stemmed the LeO 20, the standard French heavy night-bomber between 1928 and 1939. Some 320 of these four-seat aircraft were produced and many others were trialled with various modifications. Despite its antiquated appearance the aircraft remained in production up until the start of the World War II.

| | |
|---|---|
| Country of origin: | France |
| Type: | three/four-seat night-bomber |
| Powerplant: | two 420hp (313kW) Gnome-Rhône 9Ady (license-built Bristol Jupiter) radial piston engines |
| Performance: | maximum speed 198km/h (123mph); service ceiling 5760m (18,900ft); range 1000km (621 miles) |
| Weights: | empty equipped 2725kg (6008lb); maximum take-off weight 5460kg (12,037lb) |
| Dimensions: | span 22.25m (73ft); length 13.81m (45ft 4in); height 4.26m (13ft 12in); wing area 105 sq m (1130 sq ft) |
| Armament: | two 7.7mm  machine guns on pivoted mount in nose ; two 7.7mm machine guns in dorsal position; one 7.7mm machine gun in ventral bin; bomb racks for up to 500kg (1102lb) of bombs |

# Lioré-et-Olivier LeO 451

The finest bomber developed by the French aero industry in the period leading up to World War II, the LeO 451 was an aesthetic masterpiece that helped to confirm in a very striking manner that French designers had finally abandoned the angular, slab-sided machines that had trundled about the skies of France throughout most of the 1930s. Resulting from a November 1934 requirement for an advanced four-seat day bomber, the first of two LeO 45.01 prototypes made its maiden flight in January 1937. These were followed by the LeO 451B.4 production model, which entered service in the autumn of 1939. Production was then rapid, and deliveries totalled about 580 aircraft. The survivors continued in service after the fall of France, some being converted as 12-passenger civil and 17-passenger military transports, with a few remaining in service into the mid-1950s. The example shown here was on the strength of GB1/11 at Oran-La-Sénia (Morocco).

| Country of origin: | France |
| --- | --- |
| Type: | (LeO 451B.4) four-seat medium bomber |
| Powerplant: | two 1140hp (850kW) Gnome-Rhône 14N-48/49 14-cylinder two-row radial engines |
| Performance: | maximum speed 495km/h (307mph); climb to 5000m (16,405ft) in 14 minutes; service ceiling 9000m (29,530ft); range 2300km (1429 miles ) with a 500kg (1102lb) bomb load |
| Weights: | empty 7815kg (17,229lb); normal take-off 11,400kg (25,133lb) |
| Dimensions: | span 22.52m (73ft 10.5in); length 17.17m (56ft 4in); height 5.24m (17ft 2.25in) |
| Armament: | one 7.5mm fixed forward-firing machine gun in the forward fuselage, one 20mm rearward-firing cannon in the dorsal turret, and one 7.5mm machine gun in the ventral turret, plus an external bomb load of 2000kg (4409lb) |

# LN (Loire-Nieuport) .40

First flown in LN.40.01 prototype form in June 1938, the LN.40 was schemed as a carrierborne dive-bomber for the French naval air arm. The first of 23 or more LN.401BP.1 production aircraft (out of an order for 42 machines) were delivered from mid-1939 for service with two shore-based units. The only other model to enter service was the LN.411BP.1, of which 40 were ordered by the French Air Force. The LN.411 was in essence a version of the LN.401 adapted for the solely land-based role by the removal of carrierborne features such as the arrester hook, wing-folding mechanism and flotation bags. Only a very small number was completed before the fall of France. Some 24 more LN.401 and LN.411 aircraft were completed in 1942 for the Vichy French air force through the assembly of existing components. The aircraft pictured here is an LN,401 that formed part of Escadrille AB.2 of the Aéronavale, based at Berck in France in May 1940.

| Country of origin: | France |
| --- | --- |
| Type: | (LN.401BP.1) single-seat carrierborne and land-based dive-bomber |
| Powerplant: | one 690hp (514kW) Hispano-Suiza 12Xcrs 12-cylinder Vee engine |
| Performance: | maximum speed 380km/h (236mph); initial climb rate not available; service ceiling 9500m (31,170ft); range 1200km (746 miles) |
| Weights: | empty 2135kg (4707lb); maximum take-off 2823kg (6224lb) |
| Dimensions: | span 14.00m (45ft 11.25in); length 9.75m (31ft 11.75in); height 3.50m (11ft 5.75in) |
| Armament: | one 20mm fixed forward-firing cannon in an engine installation, and two 7.5mm fixed forward-firing machine guns in the leading edges of the wing, plus an external bomb load of 225kg (496lb) |

# Lockheed Hudson

The Hudson was a development of the Model 14 Super Electra transport to meet a British and commonwealth coastal reconnaissance bomber requirement, and first flew in December 1938. The first of 351 Hudson Mk I aircraft reached the UK by sea in February 1939, and further deliveries of this important type included the Hudson Mk II (20 aircraft) with the same Wright R-1820-G102A engines but different propellers, Hudson Mks III and IIIA (about 428 and 601 aircraft) improved version of the Mk I with 1200hp (895kW) GR-1820-G205A engines, Hudson Mks IV and IVA (130 and 52 aircraft) with 1050hp (918.5kW) Pratt & Whitney R-1830-SC3G Twin Wasp engines, Hudson Mk V (409 aircraft) with 1200hp (895kW) R-1830-S3C4G engines, and Hudson Mk VI (450 A-28A aircraft) delivered under Lend-Lease. The aircraft pictured is a Mk III of No 279 Squadron, RAF, based at Sturgate in 1942, and is carrying an underfuselage load of an airborne lifeboat.

| | |
|---|---|
| Country of origin: | USA |
| Type: | (Hudson Mk I) six-seat coastal reconnaissance bomber |
| Powerplant: | two 1100hp (820kW) Wright GR-1820-G102A Cyclone nine-cylinder single-row radial engines |
| Performance: | maximum speed 357km/h (222mph); climb to 3050m (10,000ft) in 10 minutes; service ceiling 6400m (21,000ft); range 3154km (1960 miles) |
| Weights: | empty 5484kg (12,091lb); maximum take-off 8845kg (19,500lb) |
| Dimensions: | span 19.96m (65ft 6in); length 13.50m (44ft 3.75in); height 3.32m (10ft 10.5in) |
| Armament: | two 0.303in fixed forward-firing machine guns in upper part of forward fuselage, two 0.303in trainable machine guns in dorsal turret, two 0.303in machine guns in beam positions, and one 0.303in machine gun in ventral position; internal bomb load of 612kg (1350lb) |

# Lockheed P-38 Lightning

The P-38A heavy fighter had its empennage carried by two booms supporting the main units of the tricycle landing gear as well as the two engines' turbochargers. The pilot sat in the central nacelle behind heavy nose armament and nosewheel unit. The XP-38 prototype first flew in January 1939, and considerable development paved the way for the P-38D initial operational variant (36 aircraft) that entered service in August 1941. Total production was 9393 aircraft including conversions to F-4 and F-5 reconnaissance standards. The most important fighter variants, featuring steadily more power, were the P-38E (210), P-38F (527), P-38G (1082), P-38H (601), P-38J (2970) and P-38L (3923). There were also night-fighter, trainer and bomber leader conversions, and the type served successfully in every US theatre. The aircraft pictured is a P-38J-5, the most numerous of all the models, with many detail changes during the production run.

| | |
|---|---|
| Country of origin: | USA |
| Type: | (P-38L) single-seat long-range fighter and fighter-bomber |
| Powerplant: | two 1600hp (1193kW) Allison V-1710-111/113 (F30) 12-cylinder Vee engines |
| Performance: | maximum speed 666km/h (414mph); climb to 6095m (20,000ft) in 7 minutes; service ceiling 13,410m (44,000ft); range 4184km (2600 miles) |
| Weights: | empty 5806kg (12,800lb); maximum take-off 9798kg (21,600lb) |
| Dimensions: | span 15.85m (52ft 0in); length 11.53m (37ft 10in); height 3.91m (12ft 10in) |
| Armament: | one 20mm fixed forward-firing cannon and four 0.5in fixed forward-firing machine guns in the nose, plus an external bomb and rocket load of 1814kg (4000lb) |

# Lockheed Ventura

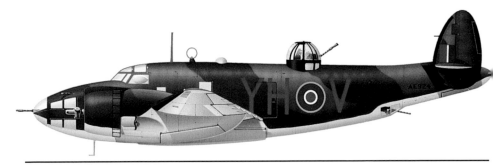

By mid-1939 Lockheed had the Hudson maritime reconnaissance bomber derivative of its Model 14 Super Electra civil transport in production for the UK. The company then started to consider further evolution along the same basic line, using the Model 18 Lodestar with its longer fuselage. Lockheed prepared a preliminary design and it was offered to the British in coastal reconnaissance and light bomber forms as successor to the Hudson and Bristol Blenheim respectively. The British approved of the light bomber idea, but the resulting Ventura Mk I (188 aircraft) that entered service in October 1942 was unsuccessful in the daylight bomber role and therefore retasked to the maritime role. Other orders included 487 Ventura Mk II (235 of them repossessed by the USA), 200 Ventura Mk IIA, and 387 Ventura GR.Mk V machines. The Ventura served with all the Commonwealth nations, the Free French air force and also with the Brazilian Air Force.

| Country of origin: | USA |
|---|---|
| Type: | (Ventura GR.Mk V) five-seat coastal reconnaissance bomber |
| Powerplant: | two 2000hp (1491kW) Pratt & Whitney R-2800-31 Double Wasp 18-cylinder two-row radial engines |
| Performance: | maximum speed 518km/h (322mph); initial climb rate 680m (2230ft) per minute; service ceiling 8015m (26,300ft); range 2671km (1660 miles) |
| Weights: | empty 9161kg (20,197lb); maximum take-off 15,422kg (34,000lb) |
| Dimensions: | span 19.96m (65ft 6in); length 15.77m (51ft 9in); height 3.63m (11ft 11in ) |
| Armament: | two 0.5in machine guns in forward fuselage; (late aircraft without bombardier's window had three 0.5in machine guns in an undernose gun pack), two 0.5in machine guns in dorsal turret, and two 0.303in machine guns in ventral position, plus a bomb load of 2268kg (5000lb) |

# Lockheed P-80A Shooting Star

The P-80A was the first production model of the Shooting Star. The lettered prefix was later changed from 'P' (Pursuit) to 'F' (Fighter) due to changes in the American designation system in 1947. The aircraft pictured 44-85226 'Betsy Jean' is adorned with the vertical coloured stripes of the commander of the 412th Fighter Group. This type of national insignia and the PN buzz-code was used until 1947, when the USAF became an independent service. In June 1947, Colonel Alfred Boyd flew a modified P-80R to a new world speed record of 1003.8 km/h (623.8mph) at Muroc Dry Lake, California. The aircraft was also subject to a great deal of experimentation, with various armament and propulsion packages tried at various points throughout its service life. Many aircraft ended their days as unmanned target drones.

| | |
|---|---|
| Country of origin: | USA |
| Type: | single-seat fighter bomber |
| Powerplant: | one 1746kg (3850lb) Allison J33-GE-11 turbojet |
| Performance: | maximum speed at sea level 966km/h (594mph); service ceiling 14,265m (46,800ft); range 1328km (825 miles) |
| Weights: | empty 3819kg (8420lb); maximum take-off 7646kg (16,856lb) |
| Dimensions: | wingspan 11.81m (38ft 9in); length 10.49m (34ft 5in); height 3.43m (11ft 3in); wing area 22.07sq m (237.6sq ft) |
| Armament: | six 0.5in machine guns, plus two 454kg (1000lb) bombs and eight rockets |

# Lockheed T-33A

F-WEQM

L ongest-serving of all Shooting Star variants was the T-33 trainer conversion, produced by lengthening a standard F-80C airframe by more than a metre to accommodate a second seat beneath a single canopy. The first conversion, designated TF-80C, flew on March 22, 1948. The aircraft was adopted as the standard jet trainer of the US Air Force, and found a ready market overseas. Many were supplied to US allies under the Military Assistance Program. Production by Lockheed continued until August 1959, by which time a total of 5691 had been built. The aircraft has been adapted for many other roles; the QT-33 target drone perhaps the most important of these conversions. A version for service with smaller air forces had armament revision making it suitable for weapons training and counter-insurgency.

| | |
|---|---|
| Country of origin: | USA |
| Type: | two-seat jet trainer |
| Powerplant: | one 2449kg (5400lb) Allison J33-A-35 turbojet |
| Performance: | maximum speed at 7,620m (25,000ft) 879km/h (546mph); service ceiling 14,630m (48,000ft); endurance 3 hours 7 minutes |
| Weights: | empty 3667kg (8084lb); maximum take-off 6551kg (14,442lb) |
| Dimensions: | wingspan 11.85m (38ft 10.5in); length 11.51m (37ft 10in); height 3.56m (11ft 8in); wing area 21.81sq m (234.8sq ft) |
| Armament: | two 0.5mm machine guns; wide variety of ordnance in COIN role |

# Lockheed F-94A Starfire

Retaining many of the features of the F-80 and T-33 aircraft from which it was developed, the tandem-seat Starfire was conceived in 1949 a radar equipped all-weather interceptor. Two prototypes were produced by converting existing T-33 airframes. Changes included the installation of a 2724kg (6000lb) Allison J33-A-33 afterburning turbojet, remodelling the nose to accommodate radar, and revised accommodation for the pilot and radar operator. The first flight took place on July 1, 1949, and production of 110 similar F-94As began the same year. The first deliveries, to the 319th All Weather Fighter Squadron began in June 1950. Two improved variants were produced, the F-94B with a blind landing system and raised tip tanks, and the F-94C, with redesigned wing and fin, longer fuselage, more powerful engine, and 24 Mighty Mouse unguided air-to-air rockets in the nose.

| | |
|---|---|
| Country of origin: | USA |
| Type: | tandem-seat all-weather interceptor |
| Powerplant: | one 2724kg (6000lb) Allison J33-A-33 turbojet |
| Performance: | maximum speed at 30,000ft 933km/h (580mph); service ceiling 14,630m (48,000ft); range 1850km/h (1150 miles) |
| Weights: | empty 5030kg (11,090lb); maximum take-off 7125kg (15,710lb) |
| Dimensions: | wingspan not including tip tanks 11.85m (38ft 10.5in); length 12.2m (40ft 1in); height 3.89m (12ft 8in); wing area 22.13sq m (238sq ft) |
| Armament: | four 0.5in machine guns |

# Lockheed T-1A SeaStar

The final variant in the F-80/T-33/F-94 family was the T2V-1 SeaStar jet trainer, an advanced version of the T-33A two seat trainer aircraft. The navalised version of this aircraft was designated the TV-2, and featured arrestor gear for carrier landings. The T2V-1 (later T1-A) was a further refinement, with humped cockpit, leading and trailing edge flaps, boundary layer control and a 2769kg (6100lb) Allison turbojet. Nearly 700 T2-V aircraft were produced for the US Navy and it served for a considerable time as their standard trainer aircraft. The aircraft pictured served with the US Navy Test Pilot School in Maryland during the 1960s, until replaced by the Northrop T-38 Talon. The red/white colour scheme has been standard for US Navy trainers since the 1950s. Some SeaStars have been converted for use as avionics test beds.

| Country of origin: | USA |
|---|---|
| Type: | two-seat jet trainer |
| Powerplant: | one 2769kg (6100lb) Allison J33-A-35 turbojet |
| Performance: | maximum speed at 7,620m (25,000ft) 879km/h (546mph); service ceiling 14,630m (48,000ft); endurance 3 hours 7 minutes |
| Weights: | empty 3667kg (8084lb); maximum take-off 6551kg (14,442lb) |
| Dimensions: | wingspan 11.85m (38ft 10.5in); length 11.51m (37ft 10in); height 3.56m (11ft 8in); wing area 21.81sq m (234.8sq ft) |

# Lockheed TR-1A

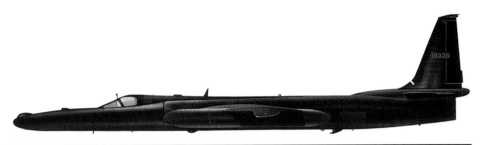

The first U-2s were deployed to Lakenheath, England and Wiesbaden, Germany in 1956. For a long period their true role was shrouded in secrecy. Official reports announced that the glider-like aircraft, the design of which intrigued aviation analysts at the time, were used by the National Advisory Committee for Aeronautics for atmospheric research. In truth they had a far more sinister role – overflying communist territory for clandestine reconnaissance missions. In 1978 the production line was reopened, and the first of 25 TR-1A aircraft followed. The TR-1A is a development of the U-2R; its primary role is that of tactical surveillance. To this end it is equipped with high resolution radar such as the Hughes ASARS-2, which allows the TR-1A to loiter for many hours behind enemy lines searching for enemy tank concentrations and other installations at long oblique ranges.

| | |
|---|---|
| **Country of origin:** | USA |
| **Type:** | single-seat high-altitude reconnaissance aircraft |
| **Powerplant:** | one 7711kg (17,000lb) Pratt & Whitney J75-P-13B turbojet |
| **Performance:** | maximum cruising speed at more than 21,335m (70,000ft); operational ceiling 27,430m (90,000ft); maximum range 10,050km (6250 miles) |
| **Weights:** | empty 7031kg (15,500lb); maximum take-off 18,733kg (41,300lb) |
| **Dimensions:** | wingspan 31.39m (103ft); length 19.13m (62ft 9in); height 4.88m (16ft); wing area 92.9sq m (1000sq ft) |

# Lockheed F-104G Starfighter

The F-104G was a complete redesign of the Starfighter to meet the needs of the Luftwaffe for a tactical nuclear strike and reconnaissance aircraft. This aircraft was developed especially for export to client countries and was first flown in prototype form in June 1960. By comparison with the F-104D the 'F' had a substantially strengthened fuselage, and boasted Nasarr multi-mode radar, inertial navigation system, manoeuvring flaps and other improvements. Ninety-six were supplied to the Luftwaffe who deployed them in a number of different roles. The aircraft pictured carries the MBB Kormoran anti-ship missile and was operated by the Marine Hieger. Some 184 RF-104Gs, which is a tactical reconnaissance version of the Starfighter were constructed. Italy and Germany were among the last major operators of the aircraft.

| | |
|---|---|
| **Country of origin:** | USA |
| **Type:** | single-seat multi-mission strike fighter |
| **Powerplant:** | one 7076kg (15,600lb) General Electric J79-GE-11A turbojet |
| **Performance:** | maximum speed at 15,240m (50,000ft) 1845km/h (1146mph); service ceiling 15,240m (50,000ft); range 1740km (1081 miles) |
| **Weights:** | empty 6348kg (13,995lb); maximum take-off 13,170kg (29,035lb) |
| **Dimensions:** | wingspan (excluding missiles) 6.36m (21ft 9in); length 16.66m (54ft 8in); height 4.09m (13ft 5in); wing area 18.22sq m (196.10sq ft) |
| **Armament:** | one 20mm General Electric M61A1 cannon, provision for AIM-9 Sidewinder on fuselage, under wings or on tips, and/or stores up to a maximum of 1814kg (4000lb) |

# Lockheed SR-71 Blackbird

Even now, over 40 years after entering service, the SR-71 has looks and performance seemingly ahead of its time. Developed by a team led by Kelly Johnson at Lockheed's Skunk Works, the SR-71 was designed as a strategic reconnaissance aircraft to succeed the U-2. Although detailed design work began in 1959, the US Government did not formally acknowledge the existence of the SR-71 until 1964. By this time the aircraft had been evaluated as a possible experimental all-weather interceptor in the Improved Manned Interceptor programme. The three aircraft that had been provisionally ordered for the USAF were designated YF-12A for the duration of the programme, and were later allocated to the joint NASA/USAF AST (Advanced Supersonic Technology) programme. Production of the the SR-71 began in 1963 and deliveries began to the 4200th Strategic Reconnaissance Wing in 1966. The last USAF flight was in 1989, the last NASA flight in 1999.

| Country of origin: | USA |
|---|---|
| Type: | strategic reconnaissance aircraft |
| Powerplant: | two 14,742kg (32,500lb) Pratt & Whitney JT11D-20B bleed-turbojets |
| Performance: | maximum speed at 24,385m (80,000ft) more than 3219km/h (2000mph); ceiling in excess of 24,385m (80,000ft); standard range 4800km (2983 miles) |
| Weights: | empty 27,216kg (60,000lb); maximum take-off 77,111kg (170,000lb) |
| Dimensions: | wingspan 16.94m (55ft 7in); length 32.74m 107ft 5in); height 5.64m (18ft 6in); wing area 167.22sq m (1800sq ft) |

# Lockheed C-141B StarLifter

**D**esigned and developed in the early 1960s to a USAF Military Airlift Command requirement, the StarLifter is still the most numerous of MACs strategic transport aircraft. It had been intended that the C-117 would supplant the older aircraft in service but budget restrictions have led to a reduction in the order. The aircraft entered service in April 1965, and the last aircraft was delivered in February 1968. All 270 surviving C-141As were converted to C-141B standard by stretching the fuselage by 7.11m (23ft 4in) in a programme that began in 1976. The aircraft has seen service in during the Vietnam War, during the US invasion of Grenada, and most recently in the 1991 Gulf War. The aircraft pictured has a 'Europe One' camouflage scheme, although all 77 remaining aircraft have now been repainted with an overall grey scheme. The C-141 is due to be retired by 2006.

| Country of origin: | USA |
|---|---|
| Type: | heavy strategic transport |
| Powerplant: | four 9526kg (21,000lb) Pratt & Whitney TF33-7 turbofans |
| Performance: | maximum speed 912km/h (567mph); range with maximum payload 4723km (2935 miles) |
| Weights: | empty 67,186kg (148,120lb); maximum take-off 155,582kg (343,000lb) |
| Dimensions: | wingspan 48.74m (159ft 11in); length 51.29m (168ft 3.5in); height 11.96m (39ft 3in); wing area 299.88sq m (3,228sq ft) |

# Lockheed S-3A Viking

The development of deep-diving Soviet nuclear submarines highlighted the need within the US Navy for a new generation of hunter-killer ASW aircraft to replace the Grumman S-2. Lockheed was the winner of a contract awarded in 1969, for development of such an aircraft. The first flight was made in January 1972, and service deliveries began in October 1973. The aircraft is a remarkable exercise in packaging, and the cost of the airframe is far outweighed by the equipment it carries. On the original model this included the highly advanced APS-116 radar in the nose, CAINS (carrier aircraft inertial navigation system), comprehensive sonobuoy dispensing and control systems, doppler radar, very extensive radio navaid and altitude systems, radar warning and ECM systems. This aircraft was one delivered to Anti-submarine Squadron 21, aboard USS *John F. Kennedy*.

| | |
|---|---|
| Country of origin: | USA |
| Type: | carrier-based patrol/attack aircraft |
| Powerplant: | two 4207kg (9275lb) General Electric TF34-GE-2 turbofans |
| Performance: | maximum cruising speed 814km/h (506mph); service celing 10,670m (35,000ft); combat range more than 3705km (2303 miles) |
| Weights: | empty 12,088kg (26,650lb); maximum take-off 19,278kg (42,500lb) |
| Dimensions: | wingspan 20.93m (68ft 8in); length 16.26m (53ft 4in); height 6.93m (2ft 9in); wing area 55.55 q m (598sq ft) |
| Armament: | internal weapons bay with provision for up to 907kg (2000lb) of stores, such as four Mk 46 torp does, four Mk 82 bombs, four depth bombs or four mines; two wing pylons can carry single or triple ejectors for bombs, rocket pods, missiles, tanks or other stores |

# Lockheed S-3B Viking

There is no more important part of the US Navy carrier air arm than the S-3A Viking, and as such the aircraft have been substantially upgraded during their service lives to maintain frontline combat capability. All aircraft now wear the low-visibility Tactical Paint Scheme. In 1980 Lockheed was awarded a contract to give the S-3As expanded ASW capability. Known as the Weapon System Improvement Program, this introduced a host of new avionics suites, including the AYS-1 Proteus acoustic signal processor, improved ESM, upgraded Texas Instruments AN/APS 137 (V) 1 radar, a new sonabouy telemetry receiver system, and provision to carry the AGM-64 Harpoon. Two aircraft were initially converted to S-3B standard by Lockheed and fully evaluated by the US Navy. In April 1988 Lockheed were contracted to supply S-3B conversion kits, all of which were delivered by August 1992.

| | |
|---|---|
| Country of origin: | USA |
| Type: | carrier-based patrol/attack aircraft |
| Powerplant: | two 4207kg (9275lb) General Electric TF34-GE-2 turbofans |
| Performance: | maximum cruising speed 814km/h (506mph); service celing 10,670m (35,000ft); combat range more than 3705km (2303 miles) |
| Weights: | empty 12,088kg (26,650lb); maximum take-off 19,278kg (42,500lb) |
| Dimensions: | wingspan 20.93m (68ft 8in); length 16.26m (53ft 4in); height 6.93m (2ft 9in); wing area 55.55 sq m (598 sq ft) |
| Armament: | internal weapons bay with provision for up to 1814kg (4000lb) of stores, such as four Mk 46 torpedoes, four Mk 82 bombs, four depth bombs or four mines; two wing pylons can carry single or triple ejectors for bombs, rocket pods, missiles, tanks or other stores up to a weight of 1361kg (3000lb) |

# Lockheed C-5A Galaxy

For a time during the early 1970s the giant C-5 Galaxy reigned as the world's largest aircraft, although it has now been overtaken by the Antonov An-124 Ruslan 'Condor'. Despite its huge size the Galaxy can operate from rough airstrips. To this end it has a high flotation landing gear with 28 wheels. During the development programme extreme difficulties were encountered with the aerodynamics and structural weight. As the result, the unit cost escalated and eventually production had to be cut to a total of 81, equipping four MAC squadrons. The aircraft can carry complete missile systems and M1 Abrams tanks to potential trouble spots around the globe, and has proved an invaluable asset to the US armed forces in this role. In 1982 the C-5B, was authorised. This included the modifications evolved in the C-5A – uprated engines, extended life wing and better avionics. A new upgrade programme is due to start shortly which will see the C-5 in service until 2040.

| Country of origin: | USA |
| --- | --- |
| Type: | heavy strategic transport |
| Powerplant: | (C5A) four 18,642kg (41,000lb) General Electric TF39-1turbofans |
| Performance: | maximum speed 919km/h (571mph); service ceiling at 272,910kg (615,000lb) 10,360m (34,000ft); range with maximum payload 100,228kg (220,967lb) 6033km (3749 miles) |
| Weights: | empty 147,528kg (325,244lb); maximum take-off 348,810kg (769,000lb) |
| Dimensions: | wingspan 67.88m (222ft 8.5in); length 75.54m (247ft 10in); height 19.85m (65ft 1.5in); wing area 575.98sq m (6,200sq ft) |

# Lockheed K. Mk 1 TriStar

Since March 1986, the Royal Air Force has operated a converted version of the Lockheed Tristar jetliner from Brize Norton in Oxfordshire as its primary tanker aircraft. Six of the 500 series aircraft were acquired from British Airways, and adapted by Marshall of Cambridge for inflight refuelling operations. This involved installing tanks in the cargo holds to give an extra 45,359kg (100,000lb) of fuel, and twin Hose and Drum Units in the rear fuselage. Four of the aircraft retained a commercial type cabin configuration to allow passengers to be carried. These are designated K.Mk 1. The two other aircraft were fitted with a large cargo door on the port side to allow the carriage of freight. These are designated KC.Mk 1. Three more were acquired from Pan-American in 1984/85 and converted to K.Mk 2 tanker/passenger aircraft, with a slightly reduced internal fuel capacity. They saw extensive service during recent operations in Afghanistan and Iraq.

| | |
|---|---|
| **Country of origin:** | UK/US |
| **Type:** | long-range strategic transport and inflight refuelling tanker |
| **Powerplant:** | three 22,680kg (50,000lb) Rolls-Royce RB.211-524B turbofans |
| **Performance:** | maximum cruising speed 964km/h (599mph) at 10,670m (35,000ft); service ceiling 13,105m (43,000ft); range on internal fuel with maximum payload 7783km (4836 miles) |
| **Weights:** | empty 110,163kg (242,684lb); maximum take-off 244,944kg (540,000lb) |
| **Dimensions:** | wingspan 50.09m (164ft 4in); length 50.05m (164ft 2.5in); height 16.87m (55ft 4in); wing area 329.96sq m (3541sq ft) |

# Lockheed F-117 Night Hawk

The F-117 is probably the most important aircraft to enter service in the past two decades, and has redefined our concept of what the flying machine of the 21st century will look like. The development program is shrouded in secrecy, but it is likely that research into stealth technology began in earnest in the wake of a number of successful radar guided missile attacks on US built F-4s during the 1973 Yom Kippur war. Both Lockheed and Northrop submitted proposals for the Experimental Stealth Technology requirement issued by the DOD; Lockheed's proposal was subsequently selected in 1977 and the plane was delivered five years later. In the 1991 Gulf war the Night Hawk really hit the headlines. Exploiting the low radar visibility, pilots were able to penetrate Iraqi airspace undetected and deliver useful quantities of ordnance with pinpoint accuracy.

| | |
|---|---|
| Country of origin: | USA |
| Type: | single-seat stealth attack aircraft |
| Powerplant: | two 4899kg (10,800lb) General Electric F404-GE-F1D2 turbofans |
| Performance: | maximum speed about Mach 1at high altitude: combat radius about 1112km (691 miles) with maximum payload |
| Weights: | empty about 13,608kg (30,000lb); maximum take-off 23,814kg (52,500lb) |
| Dimensions: | wingspan 13.20m (43ft 4in); length 20.08m (65ft 11in); height 3.78m (12ft 5in); wing area about 105.9sq m (1,140sq ft) |
| Armament: | provision for 2268kg (5000lb) of stores on rotary dispenser in weapon bay; including the AGM-88 HARM anti-radiation missile; AGM-65 Maverick ASM, GBU-19 and GBU-27 optronically guided bombs, BLU-109 laser-guided bomb, and B61 free-fall nuclear bomb |

# Lockheed/Boeing F/A-22 Raptor

In April 1991, after a tightly fought competition to find a replacement for the F-15 Eagle, the Pratt & Whitney powered F-22 proposed by the Lockheed/Boeing partnership was declared the winner. The aircraft incorporates all of the most advanced avionics and airframe technology at the disposal of the two companies, such as stealth, a long-range supersonic combat radius, high agility and STOL capability, and an advanced nav/attack system using artificial intelligence to filter data and so reduce the pilot's workload. The definitive airframe design was achieved in March 1992. The YF-22 prototype is shown above. The F/A-22 Raptor as it is now known is beginning to replace the F-15 Eagle as the USAF's premier air combat fighter. The first unit is expected to be operational in 2005, with the USAF expected to buy around 339 aircraft in total. The F/A-22 has the ability to supercruise, which means it can sustain supersonic flight without the use of afterburners.

| | |
|---|---|
| Country of origin: | USA |
| Type: | single-seat supersonic air superiority fighter |
| Powerplant: | two 15,876kg (35,000lb) Pratt & Whitney F119-P-100 turbofans |
| Performance: | maximum speed 2335km/h (1451mph); service ceiling 19,812m (65,000ft); combat radius 1285km (800miles) |
| Weights: | empty 14,061kg (31,000lb); maximum take-off 27,216 kg (60,000lb) |
| Dimensions: | wingspan 13.1m (43ft); length 19.55m (64ft 2in); height 5.39m (17ft 8in); wing area 77.1sq m (830sq ft) |
| Armament: | production aircraft will have cannon armament plus next generation air-to-air missiles in the internal weapons bay |

# Macchi MC.200 Saetta

The Saetta (Lightning) was one of the first generation of Italian low-wing monoplane fighters with advanced features such as retractable main landing gear units, but like many of it's contemporaries was limited in capability by a low-powered engine. Designed from 1936 and first flown in prototype form during December 1937, the MC.200 won the fighter contest held in 1938 and entered service in October 1939. The original type of enclosed cockpit was initially altered to an open and finally a semi-enclosed type ostensibly because Italian pilots preferred this layout! Production totalled 1,150 aircraft, later aircraft having the outer wings of the MC.202 with two 7.7mm machine guns. With the advent of the more capable MC.202, the MC.200 was generally relegated to the escort fighter and fighter-bomber roles (MC.200CB), and the MC.20AS was a tropicalised type for North African service.

| | |
|---|---|
| Country of origin: | Italy |
| Type: | (MC.200CB) single-seat fighter and fighter-bomber |
| Powerplant: | one 870hp (649kW) Fiat A.74 RC.38 14-cylinder two-row radial engine |
| Performance: | maximum speed 503km/h (312mph); climb to 5000m (16,405ft) in 5 minutes 51 seconds; service ceiling 8900m (29,200ft); range 870km (541 miles) |
| Weights: | empty 2019kg (4451lb); normal take-off 2339kg (5597lb) |
| Dimensions: | span 10.58m (34ft 8.5in); length 8.19m (26ft 10.4in); height 3.51m (11ft 5.75in) |
| Armament: | two 12.7mm fixed forward-firing machine guns in the upper part of the forward fuselage, plus an external bomb load of 320kg (705lb) |

# Macchi MC.205V Veltro

After producing the excellent MC.202 Folgore development of the MC.200 with a licence-built version of the Daimler-Benz DB 601A engine, Macchi created the MC.205 as a still further improved version of the same basic concept with a licence-built version of the DB 605 engine. The MC.205 prototype was an MC.202 conversion that first flew in April 1942 with the new engine as well as larger outer wing panels. The new fighter entered production and was built to the extent of 262 MC.205V Veltro (greyhound) aircraft that were committed to combat from July 1943. Later machines had 20mm cannon rather than 7.7mm machine guns in the wings, and most of the aircraft served with Aeronautica Nazionale Repubblicana (the air force of the revised Fascist state) after Italy's September 1943 armistice with the Allies. A high-altitude version completed only in prototype form was the MC.205N Orione.

| Country of origin: | Italy |
| --- | --- |
| Type: | (MC.205V) single-seat fighter and fighter-bomber |
| Powerplant: | one 1475hp (1100kW) Fiat RA.1050 RC.58 Tifone 12-cylinder inverted-Vee engine |
| Performance: | maximum speed 642km/h (399mph); climb to 5000m (16,405ft) in 4 minutes 47 seconds; service ceiling 11,000m (36,090ft); range 1040km (646 miles) |
| Weights: | empty 2581kg (5691lb); normal take-off 3224kg (7108lb); maximum take-off 3408kg (7514lb) |
| Dimensions: | span 10.58m (34ft 8.5in); length 8.85m (29ft 0.5in); height 3.04m (9ft 11.5in) |
| Armament: | two 12.7mm fixed forward-firing machine guns in the upper part of the forward fuselage, and two 20mm forward-firing cannon in the leading edges of the wing, plus bomb load of 320kg (705lb) |

# Martin B-10 and B-12

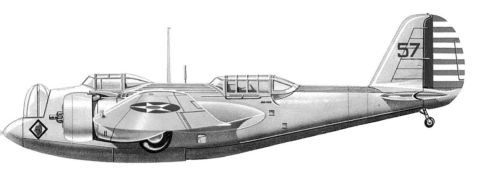

The first American-designed bomber to be flown in combat (albeit by an overseas air force), the B-10 bomber series was obsolete by the beginning of World War II but in its time was a pioneering type. It was the first American bomber of all-metal construction to enter large-scale production, the first American warplane to be fitted with turreted armament, and the US Army Air Corps' first cantilever low-wing monoplane. The USAAC received 151 examples of the B-10 and B-12 bombers, all retired before World War II, but some export aircraft saw combat service. The basic Model 139 was exported to Argentina, China, Thailand and Turkey (35, 9, 26 and 20 machines). The Japanese fought against the Chinese machines as well as the 120 Model 139W and Model 166 aircraft of the Netherlands East Indies in the late 1930s and early 1940s. Shown here is a Martin B-10B of the 28th Bombardment Squadron, US Army Air Corps, based at Luzon in the Phillipines from 1937 to 1941.

| | |
|---|---|
| Country of origin: | USA |
| Type: | (Model 139W) four-seat medium bomber |
| Powerplant: | two 775hp (578kW) Wright R-1820 G-102 Cyclone 9-cylinder single-row radial engines |
| Performance: | maximum speed 322km/h (200mph); initial climb rate 567m (1860ft) per minute; service ceiling 7680m (25,200ft); range 950km (590 miles) with maximum bomb load |
| Weights: | empty 4682kg (10,322lb); maximum take-off 7210kg (15,894lb) |
| Dimensions: | span 21.60 m (70ft 10.5in); length 13.46m (44ft 2in); height 3.53m (11ft 7in) |
| Armament: | one 0.3in trainable forward-firing machine gun in nose turret, one 0.3in trainable rearward-firing machine gun in dorsal position, and one 0.3in trainable rearward-firing machine gun in the ventral position, plus an internal and external bomb load of 1025kg (2260lb) |

# Martin PBM Mariner

The Martin PBM Mariner was of huge importance to the Allied war effort. It was designed in 1936 and proved by the quarter-scale Martin 162A. A full-size prototype was ordered in June 1937 followed by 20 production PBM-1 boats in December. The PBM was a very advanced design, with high wing loading and retractable stabilising floats built into the wing tips. A single XPBM-2 was built with increased fuel capacity and catapult-launching equipment. The most prolific variant was the PBM-3, which had its own subvariants. The PBM-3B (32 built) was supplied to the RAF under the Lend Lease Act as the Mariner Gr Mk I; the -3C (274) introduced greater armour protection and revised armament; the -3D (201) had more powerful engines, self-sealing fuel tanks, turreted armament and greater bomb-carrying capacity; the -3R (50) was a transport version without armament; and the -3s was a long-range anti-submarine version with ASW radar and reduced defensive armament.

| | |
|---|---|
| Country of origin: | USA |
| Type: | nine-seat maritime patrol and anti-submarine flying-boat |
| Powerplant: | two 1900hp (1417kW) Wright R-2600-22 Cyclone radial piston engine |
| Performance: | maximum speed 340km/h (211mph); service ceiling 6035m (19,800ft); range 3605km (2240 miles) |
| Weights: | empty 15,048kg (33,175lb); maximum take-off weight 26,308kg (58,000lb) |
| Dimensions: | span 35.97m (118ft); length 24.33m (79ft 10in); height 8.38m (27ft 6in); wing area 130.80 sq m (1408 sq ft) |
| Armament: | two .5in Browning machine guns in nose turret; two .5in Browning machine guns in dorsal turret; two .5in Browning machine guns in tail turret; one .5in Browning machine gun in two ventral positions; provision for up to 3628kg (8000lb) of bombs or depth charges |

# Martin B-26 Marauder

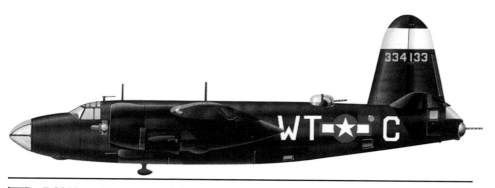

The B-26 Marauder was one of the most important tactical warplanes operated by the USA and its allies in World War II. The type was difficult for an inexperienced pilot to handle as a result of its high wing loading and high landing speed, but once mastered was an excellent warplane that achieved good results at a low loss rate. Entering service in summer 1941, the Marauder was built in a number of variants; the most important were the B-26 (201 machines), B-26A (139 machines with provision for a torpedo), B-26B and identical B-26C (1883 and 1235 machines with uprated engines and, in later aircraft, increased wing span), and B-26F and essentially similar B-26G (300 and 893 machines with increased wing incidence). The British designations for the B-26A, B, C and F/G were Marauder Mk I, IA, II and III respectively. The aircraft pictured is a B-26G-1 of the 456th Bomb Squadron, 323rd Bomb Group, US 9th Air Force, based at Laon-Athies in late 1944.

| Country of origin: | USA |
| --- | --- |
| Type: | (Marauder Mk I) seven-seat medium attack bomber |
| Powerplant: | two 1850hp (1379kW) Pratt & Whitney R-2800-5 18-cylinder two-row radial engines |
| Performance: | maximum speed 507km/h (315mph) at 4570 m (15,000ft); climb to 4570m (15,000ft) in 12 minutes 30 seconds; service ceiling 7620m (25,000ft); range 1609km (1000 miles) |
| Weights: | empty 9696kg (21,375lb); maximum take-off 14,515kg (32,000lb) |
| Dimensions: | span 18.81m (65ft); length 17.07m (56ft); height 6.05m (19ft 10in) |
| Armament: | one 0.5in trainable forward-firing machine gun in the nose position, two 0.5in trainable machine guns in the dorsal turret, and one 0.5in trainable rearward-firing machine gun in the tail position, plus an internal and external bomb load of 4800lb (2177kg) |

# Martin B57-B

The decision by the US Air Force to adopt the English Electric (BAC) Canberra was swiftly followed by the choice of Martin and development of the B-57A as a version built to US standards. The main batch comprised B-57B tandem seaters. First flown in June 1954, this model ran to 202 examples and equipped Tactical Air Command from January 1955. This variant was followed into service by 67 improved B-57Es. The TAC aircraft saw little serious employment until the outbreak of the war in Vietnam, when B-57Bs then serving with the Air National Guard units were recalled fir first-line use as strike bombers. Many were later transferred to the Pakistan Air Force, were they saw service during cross-border conflicts with India. This aircraft wears the colours of No. 7 Squadron, Pakistan Air Force, who operated it in its light bomber and maritime surveillance role.

| Country of origin: | USA |
|---|---|
| Type: | two-seat night intruder bomber |
| Powerplant: | two 3226kg (7,200lb) Wright J65-W5 turbojets |
| Performance: | maximum speed at 12,190m (40,000ft) 937km/h (582 mph); service ceiling 14,630m (48,000ft); range 3701km (2300 miles) |
| Weights: | empty 12,200kg (26,000lb); maximum take-off 24,950kg (55,000lb) |
| Dimensions: | wingspan 19.51m (64ft); length 19.96m (66ft 6in); height 4.75m (15ft 7in); wing area 89.18sq m (960sq ft) |
| Armament: | eight 0.5in machine guns, or four 20mm cannon; 16 underwing rockets and up to 2722kg (6000lb) of bombs in internal bomb bay |

# Martin B-57F

In 1960 Martin entrusted General Dynamics with the task of designing and building a high-altitude version of the B-57, the B-57F, to replace the interim B-57D (all of which were grounded by 1963 due to structural fatigue). Twenty-one of the B-57F models were converted from B and D aircraft, but little of the old is evident. The wing is entirely new, with more than double the area of the original Canberra wing and new fatigue resistant multi-spar structure. Most of the fuselage is new, as is the vertical tail. Four underwing hardpoints for pylons were incorporated, two of which were often occupied by J60 boost engine pods to supplement the turbofans. The nose is packed with electronics, and multi-sensor equipment can be seen all over the fuselage. As well as the US, the aircraft have operated from Japan, Panama, Argentina, Alaska and various Middle Eastern countries.

| Country of origin: | USA |
|---|---|
| Type: | two-seat strategic reconnaissance aircraft |
| Powerplant: | two 8165kg (18,200lb) Pratt & Whitney TF33-11A turbofans and two 1500kg (3300lb) Pratt & Whitney J60-9 single-shaft turbojets |
| Performance: | maximum speed over 800km/h (500mph); service ceiling 22,860m (75,000ft); range 5955km (3700 miles) |
| Weights: | empty 16,330kg (36,000lb); maximum take-off 28,576kg (63,000lb) |
| Dimensions: | wingspan 37.32m (122ft 5in); length 21.03m (69ft); height 5.79m (19ft); wing area 186sq m (2000sq ft) |

# Martinsyde F.4 Buzzard

**H** P. Martin and George Handasyde formed a partnership in 1908 to design and construct aircraft, later renaming the company Martinsyde. Throughout World War I, Martinsyde supplied the RFC with a series of fine scouting aircraft. The F.1 and F.2 were prototypes for the F.3. Designed by George Handasyde and first flown in November 1917, this was an outstanding machine, but was dogged by the continual nagging of the Air Board for engineering changes, and by the scarcity of the specified Rolls Royce Falcon engine. After many modifications and with a 300hp (224kW) Hispano engine installed the aircraft was redesignated F.4, and in service had the official name Buzzard Mk I. The Buzzard was faster than any contemporary British fighter and judged 'superior to any other contemporary single-seat fighter'. Orders were placed for a total of 1700 aircraft from four contractors, and by the Armistice 52 had been delivered. Many were later sold abroad.

| Country of origin: | United Kingdom |
| --- | --- |
| Type: | single-seat fighter |
| Powerplant: | one 300hp (224kW) Hispano-Suiza 8-cylinder Vee piston engine |
| Performance: | maximum speed 233km/h (145mph); service ceiling 7620m (25,000ft); endurance 2hrs 30mins |
| Weights: | empty 776kg (1710lb); maximum take-off weight 1038kg (2289lb) |
| Dimensions: | span 10m (32ft 9in); length 7.77m (25ft 6in); height 3.15m (10ft 4in); wing area 29.73 sq m (320 sq ft) |
| Armament: | two fixed forward-firing .303in Vickers machine guns |

# McDonnell FH-1 Phantom

In 1942 the Bureau of Aeronautics entrusted McDonnell, at that time a relatively new and inexperienced aircraft manufacturer, with the task of designing and building the two prototypes of what would become the US Navy's first carrier-based turbojet-powered single-seat fighter. The resulting prototypes were low-wing monoplanes, with retractable landing gear, with power provided by two turbojets buried in the wing roots. The first flight on January 26, 1945, was made under the power of only one of these engines, as Westinghouse had been unable to deliver the second in sufficient time. Evaluation with the US Navy followed, during which the aircraft became the first US jet to be launched and recovered from an aircraft carrier. An initial contract for 100 FD-1s was placed, although the designation was changed to FH-1 before deliveries began in January 1947.

| Country of origin: | USA |
| --- | --- |
| Type: | carrier-based fighter |
| Powerplant: | two 726kg (1600lb) Westinghouse J30-WE-20 turbojets |
| Performance: | maximum cruising speed 771km/h (479mph); service ceiling 12,525m (41,100ft); combat range 1118km (695 miles) |
| Weights: | empty 3031kg (6683lb); maximum take-off 5459kg (12,035lb) |
| Dimensions: | wingspan 12.42m (40ft 9in); length 11.35m (37ft 3in); height 4.32m (14ft 2in); wing area 24.64sq m (276sq ft) |
| Armament: | four 0.5in machine-guns |

# McDonnell F2H-2 Banshee

The success of the FH-1 Phantom in US Navy and Marine Corps service meant that it was almost inevitable that McDonnell would be asked to submit a design to succeed the Phantom in service. The Banshee design team under G.V Covington kept to a broadly similar configuration to the aircraft's predecessor, with a low mid-set unswept wing, tricycle landing gear. The new aircraft was larger, incorporating folding wings and a lengthened fuselage to accommodate more fuel, and more powerful engines in fattened wing roots. The aircraft was initially designated F-2D, later F2H, and finally F-2. The first F2H-1 aircraft was delivered to the Navy in August 1948, and was followed into service by seven sub-variants. Almost all of the aircraft saw service in Korea, in a wide variety of roles. The F2H-2 was the second production version, with wingtip fuel tanks. Production total was 56.

| Country of origin: | USA |
| --- | --- |
| Type: | carrier-based all-weather fighter |
| Powerplant: | one 1474kg (3,250lb) Westinghouse J34-WE-34 turbojet |
| Performance: | maximum cruising speed 933km/h (580mph); service ceiling 14,205m (46,600ft); combat range 1883km (1170 miles) |
| Weights: | empty 5980kg (13,183lb); maximum take-off 11,437kg (25,214lb) |
| Dimensions: | wingspan 12.73m (41ft 9in); length 14.68m (48ft 2in); height 4.42m (14ft 6in); wing area 27.31sq m (294sq ft) |
| Armament: | four 20-mm cannon; underwing racks with provision for two 227kg (500lb) or four 113kg (250lb) bombs |

# McDonnell F3H-2 Demon

The F3H program was expected to give the US Navy a fighter at least as good as any USAF aircraft, but ultimately proved hugely costly and difficult. Despite the advanced airframe design, serious obstacles were encountered at an early stage. Chief amongst these problems was the failure of the Westinghouse XJ40 engine specifically designed for the aircraft which proved unreliable and unable to deliver sufficient thrust. The problems were compounded by the US Navy, who requested that the aircraft be redesigned as an all-weather night-fighter. The first production F3H-1N aircraft had a substitute J40-WE-22 turbojet, but after 11 accidents, two of them fatal, production was halted. The situation was resolved by installing the Allison J71 turbojet, and the F3H-1 aircraft were either used as ground trainers or retrofitted with the J71. Initial deliveries of the F3H-2 were made to VF-14 in 1956.

| Country of origin: | USA |
|---|---|
| Type: | carrier-based strike fighter |
| Powerplant: | one 6350kg (14,000lb) Allison J71-A-2E turbojet |
| Performance: | maximum cruising speed 1041km/h (647mph); service ceiling 13,000m (42,650ft); combat range 2200km (1370 miles) |
| Weights: | empty 10,039kg (22,133lb); maximum take-off 15,377kg (33,900lb) |
| Dimensions: | wingspan 10.77m (35ft 4in); length 17.96m (58ft 11in); height 4.44m (14ft 7in); wing area 48.22sq m (519sq ft) |
| Armament: | four 20mm cannon; four underwing pylons with provision for up to 2722kg (6000lb) of stores, including bombs and rockets |

# McDonnell F-101A Voodoo

Originally intended a a long-range escort for Strategic Air Command, the early F-101A prototypes proved to have inadequate range for this role and the aircraft was subsequently adopted by Tactical Air Command as an attack aircraft. The first F-101A was flown in September 1954, and service delivery began in early 1957 with the 27th Tactical Fighter Wing at Bergstrom, Texas. At this time they were the heaviest and most powerful single-seat fighter in Air Force service. Fifty F101As were produced, followed by 47 improved 'C' models. The F-101A had only a limited front-line service life and all 'A' and 'C' models were converted to unarmed RF-101G and H reconnaissance aircraft for the Air National Guard. This aircraft wears a typically flamboyant colour scheme, and equipped the 81st Tactical Fighter Wing at Bentwaters and Woodbridge in England.

| | |
|---|---|
| Country of origin: | USA |
| Type: | single-seat day ground attack aircraft |
| Powerplant: | two 6750kg (14,880lb) Pratt & Whitney J57-P-13 turbojets |
| Performance: | maximum speed at 10,675m (35,000ft) 1623km/h (1009mph); service ceiling 16,775m (55,800ft); range 3057km (1900 miles) |
| Weights: | empty 11,336kg (24,970lb); maximum take-off 23,768kg (52,400lb) |
| Dimensions: | wingspan 12.09m (39ft 8in); length 20.54m (67ft 4.75in); height 5.49m (18ft); wing area 34.19sq m (368sq ft) |
| Armament: | four 20mm cannon; one centreline pylon with provsion for one MT tactical nuclear bomb and two wing pylons for two 907kg (2000lb) conventional bombs, or four 310kg (680lb) mines, or other ordnance |

# McDonnell RF-101H Voodoo

Reconnaissance versions of the F-101 Voodoo enjoyed a far longer service life than any other, and are perhaps the most important variants. Two main types were produced, the RF-101A and -C. Both had a lengthened and modified nose housing either four KA-2 and three KA-46 cameras for night photography. Totals of 35 RF-101As and 166 RF-101Cs were built, and were used extensively during the Cuban Missile Crisis and in the Vietnam War. The first RF-101A unit was the 363rd Tactical Reconnaissance Wing at Shaw AFB in South Carolina. The majority of the 47 F-101C interceptor aircraft from which the reconnaissance models were derived were converted to RF-101H standard for use by the Air National Guard. The work was undertaken by Lockheed Aircraft Service Company, who also converted many F-101As to RF-101G standard for the ANG.

| Country of origin: | USA |
| --- | --- |
| Type: | single-seat tactical reconnaissance aircraft |
| Powerplant: | two 6750kg (14,880lb) Pratt & Whitney J57-P-13 turbojets |
| Performance: | maximum speed at 10,675m (35,000ft) 1623km/h (1009mph); service ceiling 16,775m (55,800ft); range 3057km (1900 miles) |
| Weights: | empty 11,503kg (25,335lb); maximum take-off 23,768kg (52,400lb) |
| Dimensions: | wingspan 12.09m (39ft 8in); length 21.13m (69ft 4in); height 5.49m (18ft); wing area 34.19sq m (368sq ft) |

# McDonnell Douglas F-4C Phantom II

The greatest fighter of the post-war era was designed by McDonnell during the 1950s as part of a private venture study to meet anticipated future needs for an aircraft to replace the McDonnell F3H Demon in US Navy service. Although planned as an attack aircraft with four 20mm guns, it was changed into a very advanced gunless all-weather interceptor with missile armament. In this form it entered service as the F-4A (February 1960). In 1961 the F-4B was compared with Air Force fighters then in service and found to outperform all of them, particularly in terms of weapon load and radar performance. As a result it was ordered in modified form as the F-110, later designated the F-4C. This is generally similar to the F-4B but has dual controls, J79-GE-15 engines and a number of systems changes. A total of 635 were built to equip 16 of the 23 Tactical Air Command Wings.

| | |
|---|---|
| **Country of origin:** | USA |
| **Type:** | two seat all-weather fighter/attack aircraft |
| **Powerplant:** | two 7718kg (17,000lb) General Electric J79-GE-15 turbojets |
| **Performance:** | maximum speed at high altitude 2414km/h (1500mph); service ceiling 18,300m (60,000ft); range on internal fuel with no weapon load 2817km (1750 miles) |
| **Weights:** | empty 12,700kg (28,000lb); maximum take-off 26,308kg (58,000lb) |
| **Dimensions:** | span 11.7m (38ft 5in); length 17.76m (58ft 3in); height 4.96m (16ft 3in); wing area 49.24sq m (530sq ft) |
| **Armament:** | four AIM-7 Sparrow recessed under fuselage; two wing pylons for two AIM-7, or four AIM-9 Sidewinder, provision for 20mm M-61 cannon in external centreline pod; four wing pylons for tanks, bombs, or other stores to a maximum weight of 6219kg (13,500lb) |

# McDonnell Douglas RF-4C Phantom II

The importance of tactical reconnaissance was brought home to the USAF during the Korean war, and much emphasis was placed on this aspect of air operations in the following years. The exceptional performance of the Phantom II made it an ideal tool for reconnaissance work, leading to the development of the RF-4B. The aircraft were generally similar to the F-4B, but with lengthened nose to accommodate cameras, sideways-looking radar and infra-red sensors, which replaced the standard avionics equipment. Some 46 were built for the US Marine Corps with deliveries commencing in 1965. Confusingly, the USAF took delivery of 499 RF-4C aircraft (basically an F-4C airframe with the RF-4B equipment fit) from 1964. A reconnaissance version was also offered for export (RF-4E) in 1967 and was subsequently operated by Federal Germany, Greece, Turkey, Iran, Israel and Japan.

| Country of origin: | USA |
|---|---|
| Type: | two-seat tactical reconnaissance aircraft |
| Powerplant: | two 7711kg (17,000lb) General Electric J79-GE-8 turbojets |
| Performance: | maximum speed at 14,630m (48,000ft) 2390km/h (1485mph); service ceiling 18,900m (62,000ft); range 800km (500 miles) |
| Weights: | empty 13,768kg (30,328lb); maximum loaded 24,766kg (54,600lb) |
| Dimensions: | wingspan 11.7m (38ft 5in); length 18m (59ft ); height 4.96m (16ft 3in); wing area 49.24sq m (530sq ft) |

# McDonnell Douglas F-4E Phantom II

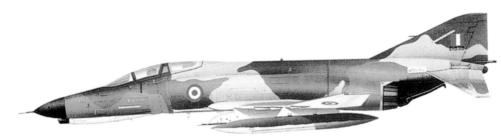

The F-4E represented a significant improvement over the F-4D, and was the most prolific model built, with some 1329 produced for the USAF alone. It had been hoped to fit the APQ-109/CORDS (Coherent On Receive Doppler System) to this model, but in the event CORDS was cancelled and McDonnell Douglas adopted the Westinghouse APQ-120 radar. Another welcome improvement was the inclusion of an integral 20mm multi-barrel Vulcan cannon in a fairing on the centreline. To compensate for the change in the centre of gravity this caused, an additional fuel cell was added to the rear fuselage. Slats on the wing leading edges improved take-off/landing performance. Most significant of the upgrades to the avionics suite was the installation of ASX-1 TISEO (Target Identification System, Electro-Optical, and improved ASG-26 bomb-sight.

| | |
|---|---|
| **Country of origin:** | USA |
| **Type:** | two-seat all-weather fighter/attack aircraft |
| **Powerplant:** | two 8119kg (17,900lb) General Electric J79-GE-17 turbojets |
| **Performance:** | maximum speed at high altitude 2390km/h (1485mph); service ceiling 19,685m (60,000ft); range on internal fuel with no weapon load 2817km (1750 miles) |
| **Weights:** | empty 12,700kg (28,000lb); maximum take-off 26,308kg (58,000lb) |
| **Dimensions:** | span 11.7m (38ft 5in); length 17.76m (58ft 3in); height 4.96m (16ft 3in); wing area 49.24sq m (530sq ft) |
| **Armament:** | one 20mm M61A1 Vulcan cannon and four AIM-7 Sparrow recessed under fuselage or other weapons up to 1370kg (3020lb) on centreline pylon; four wing pylons for two AIM-7, or four AIM-9 Sidewinder, for tanks, bombs, or other stores to a maximum weight of 5888kg (12,980lb) |

# McDonnell Douglas F-4G
# Phantom II

The F-4G was designed and built specifically for the radar suppression role in the wake of significant USAF losses to Soviet supplied SA-2 'Guideline' SAMs over Vietnam. With the combat-proven performance of the Phantom II it was perhaps inevitable that it should be chosen for this role at some stage. By 1972 about 12 F-4C 'Wild Weasels' had been introduced to service. These were equipped with Westinghouse ECM pods and had provision to carry the AGM-45 Shrike anti-radiation missile. The F-4G was the result of a much more extensive modification programme, and were produced by modifying F-4Es when they were returned to MDC for life-extension programmes. The avionics and ECM systems are too extensive to list here but include the APR-38 radar warning, homing and missiles management system and a Texas Instruments computer management system.

| | |
|---|---|
| Country of origin: | USA |
| Type: | two-seat EW/radar-surpression aircraft |
| Powerplant: | two 8119kg (17,900lb) General Electric J79-GE-17 turbojets |
| Performance: | maximum speed at high altitude 2390km/h (1485mph); service ceiling over 18,975m (62,250ft); range on internal fuel with weapon load 958km (595 miles) |
| Weights: | empty 13,300kg (29,321lb); maximum take-off 28,300kg (62,390lb) |
| Dimensions: | span 11.7m (38ft 5in); length 19.20m (63ft); height 5.02m (16ft 5.5in); wing area 49.24sq m (530sq ft) |
| Armament: | two AIM-7 Sparrow recessed under rear fuselage; wing pylons for radar suppression weapons such as AGM-45 Shrike, AGM-65 Maverick, and AGM-88 HARM missiles |

# McDonnell Douglas Phantom FG.Mk 1

The Royal Navy's decision to buy the Phantom was governed by a requirement that the aircraft be equipped with British-built engines. To this end, an Anglicised version of the F-4J was produced, designated the F-4K, that was powered by two Rolls-Royce Spey turbofans. Fitting these engines necessitated widening the fuselage. Twenty-eight aircraft were delivered to the Navy from 1964, with a further 20 for the Royal Air Force. These aircraft are designated FG.Mk 1 in British use. The RAF also received a further 120 F-4M models, which incorporated the British features with those of the F-4C mentioned previously; these aircraft were designated FGR.Mk 2 and also had the option to carry a centreline recce pod for tactical reconnaissance. The last aircraft in Royal Navy service was withdrawn in September 1978; the Phantom continued in RAF service until October 1992, when it was replaced by the Tornado F3.

| | |
|---|---|
| Country of origin: | USA |
| Type: | two-seat all-weather fighter/attack carrier-borne aircraft |
| Powerplant: | two 9305kg (20,515lb) Rolls-Royce Spey 202 turbofans |
| Performance: | maximum speed at high altitude 2230km/h (1386mph); service ceiling over 18,300m (60,000ft); range on internal fuel with no weapon load 2817km (1750 miles) |
| Weights: | empty 12,700kg (28,000lb); maximum take-off 26,308kg (58,000lb) |
| Dimensions: | span 11.7m (38ft 5in); length 17.55m (57ft 7in); height 4.96m (16ft 3in); wing area 49.24sq m (530sq ft) |
| Armament: | four AIM-7 Sparrow recessed under fuselage; two wing pylons for two AIM-7, or four AIM-9 Sidewinder, provision for 20mm M61A1 cannon in external centreline pod; four wing pylons for tanks, bombs, or other stores to a maximum weight of 7257kg (16,000lb) |

# McDonnell Douglas A-4F Skyhawk

During its long service career the Skyhawk has proved to be one of the most versatile combat aircraft ever built, disproving those who argued that the small, lightweight machine would be outclassed by bigger, heavier aircraft. The aircraft pictured is an A-4F, the final attack version for the US Navy, which is distinguished by the dorsal hump carrying additional avionics and the J52-P-8A engine. It bears the markings of Attack Squadron 212, Carrier Air Wing 21, and has the registration of the Air Wing Commander. While equipped with this model VAF-212 deployed four times to the Gulf of Tonkin aboard USS *Hancock*. The aircraft is loaded with a typical mixture external stores, including 500lb Mk 82 bombs, two 300 US gallon drop tanks and two AGM-12 Bullpup-A ASMs. One hundred aircraft were refitted with the 4990kg (11,000lb) J52-P-401.

| Country of origin: | USA |
|---|---|
| Type: | single-seat attack bomber |
| Powerplant: | one 4218kg (9300lb) J52-8A turbojet |
| Performance: | maximum speed 1078km/h (670mph); service ceiling 14,935m (49,000ft); range with 4000lb load 1480km (920 miles) |
| Weights: | empty 4809kg (10,602lb); maximum take-off 12,437kg (27,420lb) |
| Dimensions: | wingspan 8.38m (27ft 6in); length excluding probe 12.22m (40ft 1.5in); height 4.66m (15ft 3in); wing area 24.15 q m (260sq ft) |
| Armament: | two 20mm Mk 12 cannon with 200 rpg; five external hardpoints with provision for 3720kg (8200lb) of stores including AGM-12 Bullpup air-to-surface missiles, AGM-45 Shrike anti-radar missiles, bombs, cluster bombs, dispenser weapons, rocket-launcher pods, cannon pods, drop tanks and ECM pods |

# McDonnell Douglas TA-4J Skyhawk

**F**ew people believed Ed Heinemann, then chief designer at what was Douglas El Segundo when he said he could build a jet attack bomber for the Navy at half of the 30,000lb weight they specified. The first Skyhawk, nicknamed Heinemann's Hot Rod, gained a world record by flying a 500km circuit at over 695mph. The aircraft stayed in production for over 20 years, in a multiplicity of different versions. The TA-4J was a variant built for the US Navy, one of the main operators of the type. The fuselage is lengthened by approximately 2.5ft to accommodate the instructor in a tandem cockpit, reducing the internal fuel capacity. The tactical avionics suite is also reduced, and only one cannon is fitted. A version was also produced for the New Zealand air force, designated the TA-4K and also for the Kuwaiti air force (TA-4KU).

| | |
|---|---|
| Country of origin: | USA |
| Type: | two-seat carrier trainer |
| Powerplant: | one 3856kg (8500lb) J52-P-6 turbojet |
| Performance: | maximum speed 1084km/h (675mph); service ceiling 14,935m (49,000ft); range 1287km (800 miles) |
| Weights: | empty 4809kg (10,602lb); maximum take-off 11,113kg (24,500lb) |
| Dimensions: | wingspan 8.38m (27ft 6in); length excluding probe 12.98m (42ft 7.25in); height 4.66m (15ft 3in); wing area 24.15sq m (260sq ft) |
| Armament: | one 20mm cannon |

# McDonnell Douglas A-4K Skyhawk

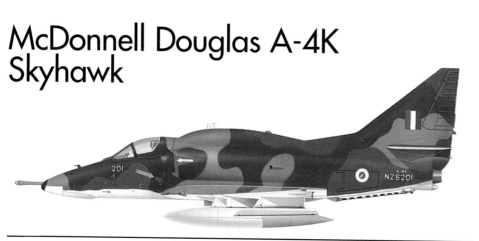

The A-4 was exported to many different countries. The effectiveness of the aircraft during operations in Vietnam encouraged Argentina, Indonesia, Israel, Kuwait, Malaysia, New Zealand and Singapore to buy the aircraft for its armed forces. The Argentine air force used the Skyhawk in combat during the Falklands campaign to good effect. Two versions, designated A-4G and A-K, have been operated by the Royal New Zealand Air Force. The former aircraft were purchased from Australia in 1984, while 10 of the A-4K models were purchased direct from the manufacturer. The A-4K aircraft were fitted with the distinctive dorsal hump housing the considerably uprated avionics suite first introduced on the A-4F. In all other aspects the A-4K is broadly similar to the US A-4F, but is fitted with a braking parachute.

| Country of origin: | USA |
| --- | --- |
| Type: | single-seat attack bomber |
| Powerplant: | one 4218kg (9300lb) J52-8A turbojet |
| Performance: | maximum speed 1078km/h (670mph); service ceiling 14,935m (49,000ft); range with 4000lb load 1480km (920 miles) |
| Weights: | empty 4809kg (10,602lb); maximum take-off 12,437kg (27,420lb) |
| Dimensions: | wingspan 8.38m (27ft 6in); length excluding probe 12.22m (40ft 1.5in); height 4.66m (15ft 3in); wing area 24.15sq m (260sq ft) |
| Armament: | two 20mm Mk 12 cannon with 200 rpg; five external hardpoints with provision for 2268kg (5000lb) of stores including air-to-surface missiles, bombs, cluster bombs, dispenser weapons, rocket-launcher pods, cannon pods, drop tanks and ECM pods |

# McDonnell Douglas F-15A Eagle

To succeed the F-4 Phantom in US service McDonnell Douglas produced the F-15 Eagle. Since its inception, this aircraft has assumed the crown as the world's greatest air superiority fighter, although it has now been superseded by later F-15C and -B variants in US service. The first prototype of the F-15A, a single-seat twin turbofan swept wing aircraft flew in July 1972. The powerful Pratt & Whitney engines and extensive use of titanium in construction (more than twenty percent of the airframe weight of production aircraft) enabled high sustained speeds (Mach 2.5 plus) at high altitude. Impressive flying characteristics became immediately apparent during flight testing, with exceptional time-to-height performance. Deliveries began to the 555th Tactical Fighter Training Wing at Langley AFB, Virginia, in November 1974. Production continued until 1979 with 385 built.

| | |
|---|---|
| Country of origin: | USA |
| Type: | single-seat air superiority fighter with secondary strike/attack role |
| Powerplant: | two 10,885kg (23,810lb) Pratt & Whitney F100-PW-100 turbofans |
| Performance: | maximum speed at high altitude 2655km/h (1650mph); initial climb rate over 15,240m (50,000ft)/min; ceiling 30,500m (100,000ft); range on internal fuel 1930km (1200 miles) |
| Weights: | empty 12,700kg (28,000lb); with maximum load 25,424kg (56,000lb) |
| Dimensions: | wingspan 13.05m (42ft 9.75in); length 19.43in (63ft 9in); height 5.63m (18ft 5in); wing area 56.48sq m (608sq ft) |
| Armament: | one 20mm M61A1 cannon with 960 rounds, external pylons with provision for up to 7620kg (16,800lb) of stores, for example four AIM-7 Sparrow air-to-air missiles and four AIM-9 Sidewinder AAMs; when configured for attack role conventional and guided bombs, rockets, air-to-surface missiles; tanks and/or ECM pods |

# McDonnell Douglas F-15J Eagle

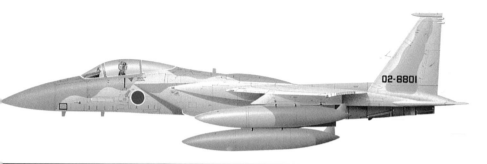

**B**y the late 1970s, the USAF had accepted the increasing tactical necessity for an interceptor that could provide top cover during long range strike missions, but defence budget cuts precluded the immediate development of a new aircraft. Instead, the USAF asked McDonnell to adapt the existing F-15A design to include a host of upgrades. The F-15C progressively replaced the F-15A in service with front line USAF units between 1980–89. The most obvious change to the aircraft is the provision for two low-drag conformal fuel tanks (CFTs) that attach to the engine air inlet trunks without affecting the existing external stores stations. The tanks are fitted with stub pylons to allow an extra 5448kg (12,000lb) of stores. Avionics include APG-70 radar, which trebled the processing speed of the APG 63 it replaced. The aircraft was also built under licence in Japan as the F-15J.

| | |
|---|---|
| **Country of origin:** | USA/Japan |
| **Type:** | single-seat strike/attack aircraft and air superiority fighter |
| **Powerplant:** | two 10,782kg (23,770lb) Pratt & Whitney F100-PW-220 turbofans |
| **Performance:** | maximum speed at high altitude 2655km/h (1,650mph); initial climb rate over 15,240m (50,000ft)/min; ceiling 30,500m (100,000ft); range with conformal fuel tanks 5745km (3570 miles) |
| **Weights:** | empty 12,793kg (23,770lb); maximum take-off 30,844kg (68,000lb) |
| **Dimensions:** | wingspan 13.05m (42ft 9.75in); length 19.43in (63ft 9in); height 5.63m (18ft 5in); wing area 56.48sq m (608sq ft) |
| **Armament:** | one 20mm M61A1 cannon with 960 rounds, external pylons with provision for up to 10,705kg (23,600lb) of stores, typically four AIM-7 Sparrow air-to-air missiles and four AIM-9 Sidewinder AAMs, or eight AIM-120A AMRAAMs; many combinations of conventional and guided bombs, rockets, air-to-surface missiles; tanks and/or ECM pods |

# McDonnell Douglas F-15E Strike Eagle

The Strike Eagle was initially developed as a private venture by MDC, who recognised the potential of the F-15 for performing a far wider range of combat tasks than originally conceived. The F-15E prototype, based on a significantly upgraded F-15B, was first flown in 1982. After evaluation against the General Dynamics F-16XL the USAF decided to proceed with procurement of the McDonnell Douglas aircraft. The Strike Eagle is operated by a crew of two, the pilot and the rear-seat weapons and defensive systems operator. The avionics suite is substantial, and to accommodate it one of the fuselage fuel tanks has been reduced. More powerful engines have been fitted without need for extensive airframe modifications. Strengthened airframe and landing gear allow a higher weapon load. F-15E units were at the forefront of precision bombing during the 1991 Gulf war, and served in the Afghanistan and 2003 Iraq campaigns.

| Country of origin: | USA |
|---|---|
| Type: | twin-seat strike/attack aircraft and air superiority fighter |
| Powerplant: | two 10,885kg (23,810lb) Pratt & Whitney F100-PW-229 turbofans |
| Performance: | maximum speed at high altitude 2655km/h (1650mph); initial climb rate over 15,240m (50,000ft)/min; ceiling 30,500m (100,000ft); range with conformal fuel tanks 5745km (3570 miles) |
| Weights: | empty 14,379kg (31,700lb); maximum take-off 36,741kg (81,000lb) |
| Dimensions: | wingspan 13.05m (42ft 9.75in); length 19.43in (63ft 9in); height 5.63m (18ft 5in); wing area 56.48sq m (608sq ft) |
| Armament: | one 20mm M61A1 cannon with 960 rounds, external pylons with provision for up to 11,100kg (24,500lb) of stores, AIM-7 Sparrow air-to-air missiles, AIM-9 Sidewinder AAMs and AIM-120 AMRAAMs; many combinations of conventional and guided bombs, rockets, air-to-surface missiles; tanks and/or ECM pods |

# McDonnell Douglas F/A-18A Hornet

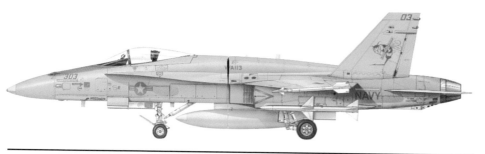

In the early 1970s the US Navy had a requirement for a lightweight, inexpensive carrier-based aircraft that could be adapted for a variety of roles and used in conjunction with the more sophisticated and heavier Grumman F-14 Tomcat and as a replacement for the F-4 Phantom II and Vought A-7 Corsair II aircraft then in service. The USAF had a similar requirement to complement the F-15 Eagle, but opted for the rival F-16 Fighting Falcon. The Hornet was originally derived from the private venture Northrop YF-17. Northrop undertook development work in conjunction with McDonnell Douglas and are also involved in production. Although the aircraft was originally to have been produced in both fighter and attack versions, service aircraft are easily adapted to either role. Deliveries began in May 1980 to the US Navy and were completed in 1987. An enlarged new version, the F/A-18E/F Super Hornet, is replacing the F/A-18C/Ds now in service.

| | |
|---|---|
| Country of origin: | USA |
| Type: | single-seat fighter and strike aircraft |
| Powerplant: | two 7264kg (16,000lb) General Electric F404-GE-400 turbofans |
| Performance: | maximum speed at 12,190m (40,000ft) 1912km/h (1183mph); combat ceiling 15,240m (50,000ft); combat radius 1065km (662 miles) |
| Weights: | empty 10,455kg (23,050lb); maximum take-off 25,401kg (56,000lb) |
| Dimensions: | wingspan 11.43m (37ft 6in); length 17.07m (56ft); height 4.66m (15ft 3.5in); wing area 37.16sq m (400sq ft) |
| Armament: | one 20mm M61A1 Vulcan rotary cannon with 570 rounds; nine external hardpoints with provision for up to 7711kg (17,000kg) of stores, including air-to-air missiles, air-to-surface missiles, anti-ship missiles, free-fall or guided bombs, cluster bombs, dispenser weapons, napalm tanks, rocket launchers, drop tanks and ECM pods |

# McDonnell Douglas CF-18A Hornet

On April 10, 1980, the Canadian Armed Forces minister announced his country's decision to buy 138 single-seat F-18A and 40 tandem seat F-18B aircraft, to replace its ageing CF-104 Starfighters. The order for the single-seat F-18A was progressively cut back to 98, but deliveries of trainer aircraft, designated CF-18B, began in October 1982. Each squadron operates a mixture of the two types, to enhance its multi-role capability. By comparison with the aircraft operated by the US Navy, the CF-18 has different Inertial Landing System, an added spotlight on the port side of the fuselage for ready identification during night formation flying, and provision to carry rocket pods. A comprehensive cold weather survival pack is provided for the pilot/crew. The aircraft pictured carries Sidewinder AAMs on the wingtip rails.

| | |
|---|---|
| Country of origin: | USA |
| Type: | single-seat multi-mission fighter |
| Powerplant: | two 7257kg (16,000lb) General Electric F404-GE-400 turbofans |
| Perfromance: | maximum speed at 12,190m (40,000ft) 1912km/h (1183mph); combat ceiling about 15,240m (50,000ft); combat radius 740km (460 miles) on escort mission or 1065km (662 miles) in attack role |
| Weights: | empty 10,455kg (23,050lb); maximum take-off 25,401kg (56,000lb) |
| Dimensions: | wingspan 11.43m (37ft 6in); length 17.07m (56ft); height 4.66m (15ft 3.5in); wing area 37.16sq m (400sq ft) |
| Armament: | one 20mm M61A1 Vulcan six-barrell rotary cannon with 570 rounds, nine external hardpoints with provision for up to 7711kg (17,000lb) of stores, including AIM-7M and AIM-9L air-to-air missiles, air-to-surface missiles, anti-ship missiles, Mk 82 conventional and guided bombs, Hunting BL755 CBU cluster bombs, LAU-5003 rocket pods containing 19 CRV-7 70mm rockets, tanks and ECM pods |

# McDonnell Douglas CF-17A Globemaster III

A fter a difficult development programme, the Globemaster III now occupies a position as the finest heavy-lift transport aircraft in current service. The early teething problems encountered during development have been ironed out and the aircraft can look forward to a long service life with MAC. The aircraft was designed and developed during the early 1980s to replace the C-141 Starlifter fleet. Cabin volume is similar to the much larger C-5 Galaxy, coupled with the short-field capability of the C-130 Hercules. Service deliveries began in 1994 and confidence in the aircraft's abilities have grown steadily. Although technically a highly complex aircraft, maintenance hours per flying hour are impressively low. All aircraft serve with Air Mobility Command and have seen extensive service during operations in Afghanistan and Iraq. The Royal Air Force has leased four aircraft from 2001 to provide Britain with a strategic airlift capability.

| | |
|---|---|
| Country of origin: | USA |
| Type: | heavy strategic transport |
| Powerplant: | four 18,195kg (41,700lb) Pratt & Whitney F117-P-100 turbofans |
| Performance: | maximum cruising speed at 10,670m (35,000ft) 829km/h (515mph); service ceiling 13,715m (45,000ft); range with 56,245kg (124,000lb) payload 5190km (3225 miles) |
| Weights: | empty 122,016kg (269,000lb); maximum take-off 263,083kg (580,000lb) |
| Dimensions: | wingspan 50.29m (165ft); length 53.04m (174ft); height 16.79m (55ft 1in); wing area 353sq m (3800sq ft) |

# Messerschmitt Bf 109B, Bf 109C and Bf 109D

The Bf 109 is by any standard a classic fighter and, with more than 30,500 examples built before and during World War II, was of vital importance to the German war effort throughout that conflict. The type resulted from the German Air Force's requirement for its first 'modern' monoplane fighter, and the first of 13 prototypes flew in September 1935. The Bf 109B (two variants) entered service in April 1937 with the armament of three 7.92mm machine guns, and was followed by the Bf 109C (two variants) with an armament of four or five machine guns. Both the Bf 109B and Bf 109C saw service in the Spanish Civil War. They were followed by the Bf 109D, which was built to the extent of about 175 aircraft with the 986hp (735kW) Daimler-Benz DB 600Aa engine and an armament of one 20mm cannon and two 7.92mm machine guns. Although some were transferred to night-fighter units most had been relegated to training use by 1939.

| Country of origin: | Germany |
| --- | --- |
| Type: | (Bf 109C-1) single-seat fighter |
| Powerplant: | one 700hp (522kW) Junkers Jumo 210Ga 12-cylinder inverted-Vee engine |
| Performance: | maximum speed 470km/h (292mph); climb 5000m (16,405ft) in 8 minutes 45 seconds; service ceiling 8400m (27,560ft); range 652km (405 miles) |
| Weights: | empty 1597kg (3522lb), maximum take-off 2296kg (5062lb) |
| Dimensions: | span 9.87m (32ft 4.5in); length 8.55m (28ft 0.67in); height 2.40m (7ft 3.75in) |
| Armament: | two 7.92mm fixed forward-firing machine guns in the upper part of the forward fuselage, and two 7.92mm fixed forward-firing machine guns in the leading edges of the wing |

# Messerschmitt Bf 109E-1 to E-4

Germany's standard single-seat fighter at the beginning of World War II, the Bf 109E was instrumental in the Luftwaffe's success over the Polish, Scandinavian and North-West European battlefields between September 1939 and June 1940. It was only when the type was committed at longer range against British fighters in the Battle of Britain that its limitations were first realised. Entering service at the end of 1938 and built to the extent of more than 4000 aircraft, the Bf 109E 'Emil' was in essence the Bf 109D revised with the more powerful DB 601 engine and cannon armament. The main early variants were the Bf 109E-1 with the 1075hp (801.5kW) DB 601A-1 engine, Bf 109E-3 with an uprated engine, improved armour and provision for an engine-mounted 20mm cannon, and Bf 109E-4 with no engine cannon. The *Emil* was regarded by pilots as one of the finest of the Me 109 models, and was at least equal to early Spitfire models.

| Country of origin: | Germany |
| --- | --- |
| Type: | (Bf 109E-4) single-seat fighter |
| Powerplant: | one 1175hp (876kW) Daimler-Benz DB 601Aa 12-cylinder inverted-Vee engine |
| Performance: | maximum speed 560km/h (348mph); climb to 6000m (19,685ft) in 7 minutes 45 seconds; service ceiling 10,500m (34,450ft); range 660km (410 miles) |
| Weights: | empty 2125kg (4685lb); normal take-off 2510kg (5534lb); maximum take-off 2665kg (5875lb) |
| Dimensions: | span 9.87m (32ft 4.5in); length 8.64m (28ft 4.5in); height 2.50m (8ft 2.33in) |
| Armament: | two 20mm fixed forward-firing cannon in the leading edges of the wing, and two 7.92mm fixed forward-firing machine guns in the upper part of the forward fuselage |

# Messerschmitt Bf 109F

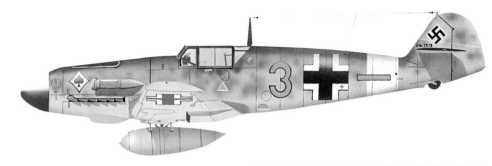

Entering service in spring 1941, the Bf 109F marked the apogee of the Bf 109's development in terms of aerodynamic refinement (improved cowling, rounded wing tips and cantilever tailplane) and handling, although these were achieved only at the expense of armament, which was generally considered too light. It was for this reason that production of the Bf 109F was terminated after the delivery of some 2200 aircraft. The Bf 109F-1 featured two 7.92mm machine guns and a slow-firing 20mm cannon in the engine, the F-2 had a faster-firing 15mm cannon, the F-3 was powered by the 1350hp (1006.5kW) DB 601E engine, the F-4 introduced a fast-firing 20mm cannon and improved protection, the F-5 was a reconnaissance fighter without the cannon, and the F-6 was an unarmed reconnaissance model. The aircraft pictured has the centreline drop tank fitted, a secondary measure to try and wring greater range from the aircraft.

| | |
|---|---|
| Country of origin: | Germany |
| Type: | (Bf 109F-2) single-seat fighter |
| Powerplant: | one 1200hp (895kW) Daimler-Benz DB 601N 12-cylinder inverted-Vee engine |
| Performance: | maximum speed 600km/h (373mph); climb to 5000m (16,405ft) in 5 minutes 12 seconds; service ceiling 11,000m (36,090ft); range 880km (547 miles ) |
| Weights: | empty 2353kg (5188lb); maximum take-off 3066kg (6760lb) |
| Dimensions: | span 9.92m (32ft 6.5in); length 8.94m (29ft 3.88in); height 2.60m (8ft 6.33in) |
| Armament: | one 15mm fixed forward-firing cannon in an engine installation and two 7.92mm fixed forward-firing machine guns in the upper part of the forward fuselage |

# Messerschmitt Bf 109G

**S**till in production (23,500 aircraft) at the end of World War II, the Bf 109G was numerically the most important Bf 109 variant. Few of the pilots who flew it would dispute that improvements in the type's speed and firepower – gained by the introduction of the more powerful DB 605 engine – resulted in poorer overall handling qualities. The Bf 109G was delivered in pressurised (even-numbered) and unpressurised (odd-numbered) subvariants for service from summer 1942. Principal among these were the G-1 and G-2 with the DB 605A engine, one 20mm and two 7.92mm weapons, G-3 and G-4 with different radio, G-5 and G-6 with heavier gun armament and later a wooden tail unit, G-8 reconnaissance fighter, G-10 with the 1850hp (1379.5kW) DB 605D, G-12 tandem seat trainer, G-14 improved G-6, and G-16 improved G-14. Pressurisation was deleted from the 109G-6 and subsequent subvariants onward.

| | |
|---|---|
| **Country of origin:** | Germany |
| **Type:** | (Bf 109G-6) single-seat fighter and fighter-bomber |
| **Powerplant:** | one 1474hp (1100kW) Daimler-Benz DB 605AM 12-cylinder inverted-Vee engine |
| **Performance:** | maximum speed 386mph (621km/h); climb to 5700m (18,700ft) in 6 minutes; service ceiling 11,550m (37,890ft); range 1000km (621 miles ) |
| **Weights:** | empty 2673kg (5893lb); maximum take-off 3400kg (7496lb) |
| **Dimensions:** | span 9.92m (32ft 6.5in); length 8.85m (29ft 0.5in); height 2.50m (8ft 2.5in) |
| **Armament:** | one 20mm or 30mm fixed forward-firing cannon in an engine installation, and two 13mm fixed forward-firing machine guns in the upper part of the forward fuselage, plus an external bomb load of 250kg (551lb) |

# Messerschmitt Bf 110C/D

**A** heavy fighter that first flew in May 1936 and remained in production through World War II for a total of about 6000 aircraft, the Bf 110 entered service as the Bf 110B with two 700hp (522kW) Junkers Jumo 210 engines. Only 45 of Bf 110Bs aircraft were completed before the advent of the Bf 110C with two Daimler-Benz DB 601 engines. About 1300 of the Bf 110C-1 to C-3 fighter variants were built before production switched to the Bf 110C-4 to C-7 models with better protection and provision for the fighter-bomber and reconnaissance roles. The Bf 110D, built in D-1 to D-3 variants, had greater fuel capacity (internal and external) for the long-range fighter, fighter-bomber and shipping escort roles, although some were later adapted as interim night-fighters, the type serving until a time early in 1943 when they were superceded by the purpose-built E series. The Bf 110 proved highly vulnerable during the Battle of Britain against smaller, lighter fighter aircraft.

| | |
|---|---|
| **Country of origin:** | Germany |
| **Type:** | (Bf 110C-4) two/three-seat heavy fighter |
| **Powerplant:** | two 1100hp (820kW) Daimler-Benz DB 601A-1 12-cylinder inverted-Vee engines |
| **Performance:** | maximum speed 560km/h (248mph); climb to 6000m (19,685ft) in 10 minutes 12 seconds; service ceiling 10,000m (32,810ft); range 1095km (680 miles) |
| **Weights:** | empty 5150kg (11,354lb); maximum take-off 6750kg (14,881lb) |
| **Dimensions:** | span 16.20m (53ft 1.8in); length 12.10m (39ft 8.33in); height 4.13m (13ft 6.5in) with the tail up |
| **Armament:** | two 20mm fixed forward-firing cannon and four 7.92mm fixed forward-firing machine guns in the nose, and one 7.92mm trainable rearward-firing machine gun in the rear cockpit |

# Messerschmitt Bf 110E and Bf 110F

From autumn 1940 production of the indifferent Bf 110C/D was scaled down, but in the spring of 1941 two new variants appeared as the Bf 110E and Bf 110F. The Bf 110E was a relatively simple development of the Bf 110D with updated equipment, improved crew protection, a measure of structural strengthening, and racks under the outer wing panels for four 50kg (110lb) bombs as well as the standard pair of 1102lb (500kg) bombs under the fuselage. Bf 110E production stretched through the E-1 to E-3 variants. Appearing slightly later than the Bf 110E and then built in parallel with it, the Bf 110F was introduced to take advantage of the greater power offered by the new DB 601F engine, and there were F-1 to F-3 fighter and fighter-bomber variants before the advent of the F-4 night-fighter with early *Lichtenstein* radar equipment. A total of about 6050 Bf 110 aircraft of all models were built before production ended in March 1945.

| | |
|---|---|
| Country of origin: | Germany |
| Type: | (Bf 110F-2) two-seat heavy fighter |
| Powerplant: | two 1350hp (1007kW) Daimler-Benz DB 601F 12-cylinder inverted-Vee engines |
| Performance: | maximum speed 565km/h (351mph); climb to 6000m (19,685ft) in 9 minutes 12 seconds; service ceiling 10,900 m (35,760ft); range 1200km (746 miles) |
| Weights: | empty 5600kg (12,346lb); maximum take-off 7200kg (15,873lb) |
| Dimensions: | span 16.20m (53ft 1.8in); length 12.10m (39ft 8.33in); height 4.13m (13ft 6.5in) with the tail up |
| Armament: | two 20mm forward-firing cannon and four 7.92mm fixed forward-firing machine guns in the nose, and one 7.92mm trainable rearward-firing machine gun in the rear cockpit |

# Messerschmitt Me 163B Komet 1

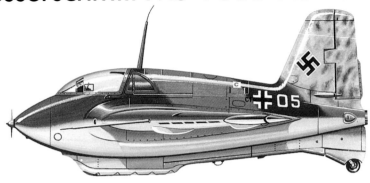

O f all the aircraft engaged in World War II the Me 163 was perhaps the most radical and futuristic. The concept of the short endurance high speed interceptor powered by a rocket engine was certainly valid and could have been more of a adversary than it was. The first flight of Dr Alex Lippisch's radical fighter, bereft of a horizontal tail and with an incredibly short fuselage, was made in glider form in the spring of 1941. To propel the aircraft, two extremely volatile liquids were employed, which ignited when they came into contact. To save weight the Komet took off from a wheeled trolley and landed on a sprung skid. The landing impact often caused any residual propellants to 'slosh' together causing a violent explosion. Many aircraft were lost this way, but nevertheless by May 1944 these tiny aircraft were regularly attacking US bomber formations. Unfortunately their high closing speeds meant that they scored few successes.

| | |
|---|---|
| Country of origin: | Germany |
| Type: | single-seat interceptor |
| Powerplant: | one 1700kg (3750lb) Walter HWK 509A-2 bi-propellant rocket burning concentrated hydrogen peroxide and hydrazine/methanol |
| Performance: | maximum speed at 10,000m (32,800ft) 960km/h (596mph); service ceiling 16,500m (54,000ft); range under 100km (62 miles); endurance about eight minutes in total |
| Weights: | empty 1905kg (4191lb); maximum loaded 4110kg (9042lb) |
| Dimensions: | wingspan 9.3m (30ft 7in); length 5.69m (18ft 8in); height 2.74m (9ft) |
| Armament: | two 300mm MK 108 cannon with 60 rounds each |

# Messerschmitt Me 262A-1a

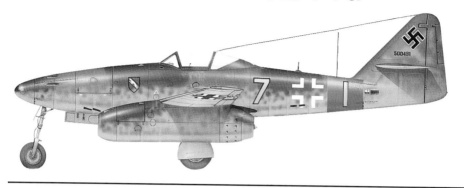

The Me 262 was undoubtedly the most advanced jet aircraft to see combat service during the World War II, and certainly the most successful in combat. Messerschmitt were somewhat late in getting off the mark in designing a jet combat aircraft. Heinkel were well advanced with the development of the He 280 prototype when in January 1939 Messerschmitt were ordered by the RLM to begin development of a similar type of aircraft. The turbojet engines then available lacked sufficient power to be used singly, and so the design mounted twin-turbojets in underwing nacelles. The Me 262 V7 was the immediate precursor to a production model, the Me 262A-1a. This aircraft was the standard interceptor version, and first flew in combat on October 3, 1944. The aircraft pictured is in the colours of the 9. Staffel Jagdgeschwader Nr. 7 based at Parchim in early 1945.

| | |
|---|---|
| Country of origin: | Germany |
| Type: | single-seat air-superiority fighter |
| Powerplant: | two 900kg (1984lb) Junkers Jumo 004B-1, 2, or -3 turbojets |
| Performance: | maximum speed at 6000m (19,685ft) 869km/h (540mph); service ceiling above 12,190m (40,000ft); range 1050km (652 miles) |
| Weights: | empty 3795kg (8,378lb); maximum take-off 6387kg (14,080lb) |
| Dimensions: | wingspan 12.5m (40ft 11½in); length 10.58m (34ft 9.5in); height 3.83m (12ft 7in); wing area 21.73sq m (234sq ft) |
| Armament: | four 30mm Rheinmetall-Borsig Mk 108A-3 cannon with 100 rounds for upper pair and 80 rounds for lower; provision for 12 R4M air-to-air rockets under each wing |

# Messerschmitt Me 262 A-2a

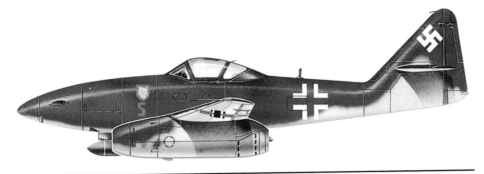

Allied air power during the North African and Italian landings effectively kept the Luftwaffe and German naval forces at bay, forcing a reappraisal of the role of the Me 262. Senior German commanders, Hitler included, were adamant that the new jet should be adapted to the role of fighter-bomber. By the autumn of 1943 of course, the outcome of the war was already decided, but nonetheless the decision was taken to convert many Me 262-A1a's in service to the later A-2a standard, by fitting Schloss 503A-1 bomb racks under the wings. The first unit to use the Me-262A-2a in battle was *Erprobugs-kommando Schenk,* led by Major Wolfgang Schenk, who formed at Lechfeld in July 1944. Four more fighter/bomber units were formed on January 30, 1945, although only I/KG(J)54, II/KG(J)54 and III/KG(J)6 saw any combat.

| | |
|---|---|
| Country of origin: | Germany |
| Type: | single-seat fighter-bomber |
| Powerplant: | two 900kg (1984lb) Junkers Jumo 004B-1, -2, or -3 turbojets |
| Performance: | maximum speed at 6000m (19,685ft) 869km/h (540mph); service ceiling above 12,190m (40,000ft); range 1050km (652 miles) |
| Weights: | empty 3795kg (8,378lb); maximum take-off 6387kg (14,080lb) |
| Dimensions: | wingspan 12.5m (40ft 11.5in); length 10.58m (34ft 9.5in); height 3.83m (12ft 7in); wing area 21.73sq m (234sq ft) |
| Armament: | two 30mm Rheinmetall-Borsig Mk 108A-3 cannon with 100rounds for upper pair and 80 rounds for lower; provision for two 250kg (551lb) bombs under the wings |

# Messerschmitt Me 262B-1a/U1

Consideration of the Me 262 in the night-fighting role stemmed from a series of trials performed in October 1944 at Rechlin. These trials were conducted with single-seat A-1a fitted with FuG 220 intercept radar and a four-pole *Hirschgeweih* antenna array. Successful testing led to the decision to adopt a modified two-seat B-1a conversion trainer, designated Me 262B-1a/U1, as an interim night fighter, prior to the availability of a specialised model (Me 262B-2a). The B-1a/U1 aircraft were fitted with FuG 218 *Neptun* V radar with a *Hirschgeweih* array, and FuG 350 ZC *Naxos* for homing onto the emissions from British H2S radar equipment. The first unit to receive the aircraft were *Kommando Welter* (later 10./NJG 11), a specialised unit staffed by experienced *Wild Sau* (night-fighting) personnel, who took delivery of fewer than a dozen Me 262B-1a/U1s during February–March 1945.

| | |
|---|---|
| Country of origin: | Germany |
| Type: | two-seat night fighter |
| Powerplant: | two 900kg (1984lb) Junkers Jumo 004B-1, -2, or -3 turbojets |
| Performance: | maximum speed at 6000m (19,685ft) 869km/h (540mph); service ceiling above 12,190m (40,000ft); range 1050km (652 miles) |
| Weights: | empty 3795kg (8,378lb); maximum take-off 6387kg (14,080lb) |
| Dimensions: | wingspan 12.5m (40ft 11.5in); length 10.58m (34ft 9.5in); height 3.83m (12ft 7in); wing area 21.73sq m (234sq ft) |
| Armament: | two 30mm Rheinmetall-Borsig Mk 108A-3 cannon with 100 rounds for upper pair and 80 rounds for lower |

# Messerschmitt Me 410 Hornisse

This multi-role warplane was evolved as successor to the unsuccessful Messerschmitt Me 210 heavy fighter and was an altogether more capable as well as more successful warplane. The failings of the Me 210 had in fact been solved just before the type's cancellation, and it was from this ultimately excellent type that the Me 410 was evolved with basically the same revised aerodynamic and structural features in combination with modified outer wing panels and the different powerplant of two Daimler-Benz DB 603A inverted-Vee piston engines. The Me 410 first flew in prototype form during autumn 1942, and there were 1137 production aircraft in variants such as the Me 410A (three major variants) and the Me 410B. Five major variants of the 410B were produced with the DB 603G engines. The B-5 anti-shipping torpedo bomber, the B-7 day reconnaissance and B-8 night reconnaissance aircraft were still in experimental stage at the war's end.

| | |
|---|---|
| Country of origin: | Germany |
| Type: | (Me 410A-1/U2) two-seat heavy fighter |
| Powerplant: | two 1750hp (1305kW) Daimler-Benz DB 603A 12-cylinder inverted-Vee engines |
| Performance: | maximum speed 624km/h (388mph); climb to 6700m (21,980ft) in 10 minutes 42 seconds; service ceiling 10,000m (32,810ft); range 1670km (1050 miles) |
| Weights: | empty 7518kg (16,574lb); normal take-off 9651kg (21,276lb) |
| Dimensions: | span 16.35m (53ft 7.75in); length 12.48m (40ft 11.5in); height 4.28m (14ft 0.5in) |
| Armament: | two 20mm fixed forward-firing cannon in the nose, two 20mm fixed forward-firing cannon in a ventral tray, two 7.92mm fixed forward-firing machine guns in the nose, and one 13mm machine |
| gun | in each of the two barbettes on the sides of the fuselage |

# Mikoyan-Gurevich MiG-1 and MiG-3

The MiG-1 and MiG-3 series of aircraft were placed in large-scale production largely because they possessed very high performance and despite the fact that they were extremely difficult to fly, not least because of a very short fuselage that resulted in a distinct lack of longitudinal stability. The MiG-1 was developed for an urgent Soviet air force requirement, issued early in 1938, for a high-altitude fighter, and first flew in prototype form in April 1940. Production totalled 100 aircraft, with the armament of one 12.7mm and two 7.62mm machine guns and either open or enclosed accommodation. These were followed by the improved MiG-3 of which 3322 were delivered up to spring 1942 with improved protective features, a rearward-sliding rather than side-hinged canopy, and increased dihedral. Pictured is a MiG-3 of an unidentified Soviet fighter unit operating on the Eatern Front in the summer of 1942.

| | |
|---|---|
| Country of origin: | USSR |
| Type: | (MiG-3) single-seat fighter and fighter-bomber |
| Powerplant: | one 1350hp (1007kW) Mikulin AM-35A 12-cylinder Vee engine |
| Performance: | maximum speed 640km/h (398mph); climb to 5000m (16,405ft) in 5 minutes 42 seconds; service ceiling 12,000m (39,370ft); range 1195km (742 miles) |
| Weights: | empty 2595kg (5721lb); maximum take-off 3350kg (7385lb) |
| Dimensions: | span 10.20m (33ft 5.5in); length 8.25m (27ft 0.8in); height 2.65m (8ft 8.33in) |
| Armament: | one 12.7mm and two 7.62mm fixed forward-firing machine guns in the upper part of the forward fuselage, plus an external bomb and rocket load of 200kg (441lb) |

# Mikoyan-Gurevich MiG-15 'Fagot'

No aircraft in history has had a bigger impact on the world scene than the MiG-15. Its existence was unsuspected in the West until American fighter pilots found themselves confronted by all-swept silver fighters that could fly faster, climb and dive faster, and turn more tightly. The development of the aircraft could be traced back to the decision of the post-war British government to send to the Soviet Union the latest British turbojet, the Rolls-Royce Nene, long before it was in service with any British service aircraft. This removed Mikoyan's problem of finding a suitable engine and by the end of December 1947 the prototype was flying, powered by an unlicensed version of the Nene. Losses in Korea were high, mainly because of pilot inexperience, but as late as 1960 the Mig-15 was still used as a fighter by 15 countries.

| | |
|---|---|
| Country of origin: | USSR |
| Type: | single-seat fighter |
| Powerplant: | one 2700kg (5952lb) Klimov VK-1 turbojet |
| Performance: | maximum speed 1100km/h (684 mph); service ceiling 15,545m (51,000ft); range at height with slipper tanks 1424km (885 miles) |
| Weights: | empty 4000kg (8820lb); maximum loaded 5700kg (12,566lb) |
| Dimensions: | wingspan 10.08m (33ft 0.75in); length 11.05m (36ft 3.75in); height 3.4m (11ft 1.75in); wing area 20.60msq m (221.74sq ft) |
| Armament: | one 37mm N-37 cannon and two 23mm NS-23 cannon, plus up to 500kg (1102lb) of mixed stores on underwing pylons |

# Mikoyan-Gurevich MiG-17F 'Fresco-C'

Although outwardly similar to the MiG-15, the -17 was in fact a completely different aircraft. Western observers believed the aircraft had been hastily designed to rectify deficiencies shown in the MiG-15s performance during the Korean War, particularly the instability at speed which made it a difficult gun platform. In fact design of the -17 began in 1949, and was probably the last aircraft design in which Mikhail I. Gurevich had a direct personal role. The most important aspect of the new design was the wing, with the thickness reduced, a different section and platform and with three fences high speed behaviour was much improved. With a new tail on a longer rear fuselage, the transformation was completed by complete revision of the avionics fit. Service deliveries commenced in 1952 to the Soviet Air Force, with total production in excess of 5000.

| Country of origin: | USSR |
|---|---|
| Type: | single-seat fighter |
| Powerplant: | one 3383kg (7,452lb) Klimov VK-1F turbojet |
| Performance: | maximum speed at 3000m (9,840ft) 1145km/h (711mph); service ceiling 16,600m (54,560ft); range at height with slipper tanks 1470km (913 miles) |
| Weights: | empty 4100kg (9040lb); maximum loaded 6,00kg (14,770lb) |
| Dimensions: | wingspan 9.45m (31ft); length 11.05m (36ft 3.75in); height 3.35m (11ft); wing area 20.60msq m (221.74sq ft) |
| Armament: | one 37mm N-37 cannon and two 23mm NS-23 cannon, plus up to 500kg (1102lb) of mixed stores on underwing pylons |

# Mikoyan-Gurevich MiG-19PM 'Farmer-D'

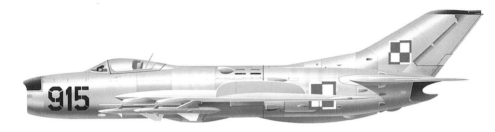

With the unveiling of the Mig-19 the Mikoyan-Gurevich bureau established itself at the forefront of the world's fighter design teams. The new fighter was in the preliminary design stage before the Mig-15 had been encountered over Korea, with five prototypes ordered in July 1951. The first flew in September 1953, powered by twin AM-5 engines. With afterburning engines the MiG-19 became the first supersonic engines in Soviet service. Steadily improved versions culminated in the MiG-19PM, with guns removed and pylons for four early beam-rider air-to-air missiles. In 1960 this simple, extremely potent aircraft was judged obsolete by Western observers. By 1970 the performance of the Chinese-built F-6 (MiG-19SF) in North Vietnamese and Pakistani service led to it being reappraised by NATO. It is now either retired or being retired in most countries that operate the type.

| Country of origin: | USSR |
| --- | --- |
| Type: | single-seat all-weather interceptor |
| Powerplant: | two 3250kg (7165lb) Klimov RD-9B turbojets |
| Performance: | maximum speed at 9080m (20,000ft) 1480km/h (920mph); service ceiling 17,900m (58,725ft); maximum range at high altitude with two drop tanks 2200km (1367 miles) |
| Weights: | empty 5760kg (12,698lb); maximum take-off 9500kg (20,944lb) |
| Dimensions: | wingspan 9m (29ft 6.5in); length 13.58m (44ft 7in); height 4.02m (13ft 2.25in); wing area 25sq m (269.11sq ft) |
| Armament: | underwing pylons for four AA-1 Alkali air-to-air-missiles, or AA-2 Atoll |

# Mikoyan-Gurevich MiG-21bis 'Fishbed-N'

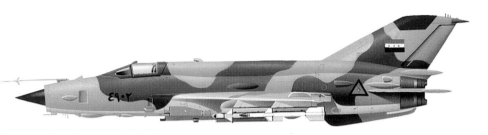

The MiG-21 established a reputation as one of the most versatile combat aircraft of the post-war era. With production totalling a figure estimated at more than 11,000 the 'Fishbed' has served with 39 air arms. The aircraft was developed in 18 months following the Korean War. At least 30 pre-production aircraft were manufactured, before service deliveries of the MiG-21F 'Fishbed-C' began in 1958. The MiG-21bis 'Fishbed-N' pictured here was an improved version of the MiG-21bis 'Fishbed-L', which first appeared in 1971 and introduced new advanced construction techniques, greater fuel capacity and updated avionics for multi role air combat and ground attack. In 1975 the 'Fishbed-N' was introduced and in addition to these improvements the 'N' had more powerful turbojets and further uprated avionics.

| Country of origin: | USSR |
|---|---|
| Type: | single-seat all-weather multi role fighter |
| Powerplant: | one 7507kg (16,535lb) Tumanskii R-25 turbojets |
| Performance: | maximum speed above 11,000m (36,090ft) 2229km/h (1385mph); service ceiling 17,500m (57,400ft); range on internal fuel 1160km (721 miles) |
| Weights: | empty 5200kg (11,464lb); maximum take-off 10,400kg (22,925lb) |
| Dimensions: | wingspan 7.15m (23ft 5.5in); length (including probe) 15.76m (51ft 8.5in); height 4.10m (13ft 5.5in); wing area 23sq m (247.58sq ft) |
| Armament: | one 23mm GSh-23 twin-barrell cannon in underbelly pack, four underwing pylons with provision for about 1500kg (3307kg ) of stores, including AA-2 Atoll or AA-8 Aphid air-to-air missiles, UV-16-57 rocket pods, napalm tanks, or drop tanks |

# Mikoyan-Gurevich MiG-21U 'Mongol'

The two-seat trainer version of the MiG-21F was known in the West by the NATO designated name 'Mongol'. Aside from the airframe modifications necessary to accommodate the instructor, the -21U is similar in configuration to the initial major production version, the -21F. The first prototype is reported to have flown in 1960. Variations from the single-seater include a one-piece forward airbrake, deletion of the cannon armament, repositioning of the pilot boom, adoption of larger mainwheels first introduced on the MiG-21PF. Further revisions were adopted on the -21US and -21UM models. These included vertical tail surfaces of revised design and a deeper dorsal spine. The aircraft is still used widely throughout in former Eastern Bloc countries and in India, were it was built under licence by HAL. This is one of the aircraft operated by the Finnish air force.

| | |
|---|---|
| Country of origin: | USSR |
| Type: | two-seat trainer |
| Powerplant: | one 5950kg (13,118lb) Tumanskii R-11F2S-300 turbojet |
| Performance: | maximum speed above 12,200m (40,025ft) 2145km/h (1333mph); service ceiling 17,500m (57,400ft); range on internal fuel 1160km (721 miles) |
| Weights: | not released |
| Dimensions: | wingspan 7.15m (23ft 5.5in); length (including probe) 15.76m (51ft 8.5in); height 4.10m (13ft 5.5in); wing area 23sq m (247.58sq ft) |

# Mikoyan-Gurevich MiG-23M 'Flogger-B'

Although undoubtedly a fine aircraft, the MiG-21 was hampered by limited payload/range performance. In 1965 a requirement was issued for a replacement to help try and rectify these problems. Mikoyan-Gurevich submitted two proposals, one for an enlarged version of the MiG-21, and an alternative which was later realised as the Ye-23-11/1 prototype. The aircraft formed the basis for the MiG-23 and was first publicly displayed at the 1967 Aviation Day flypast. Apart from the variable geometry wing, the other major variation on early MiG jet aircraft were side inlets to allow incorporation of search radar and allow for greater internal fuel capacity. The MiG-23M 'Flogger-B' was the first series production version, and entered service in 1972 with the USSR and later Warsaw Pact air forces.

| | |
|---|---|
| Country of origin: | USSR |
| Type: | single-seat air combat fighter |
| Powerplant: | one 10,208kg (22,485lb) Khachaturov R-29-300 turbojet |
| Performance: | maximum speed at altitude about 2445km/h (1520mph); service ceiling over 18,290m (60,000ft); combat radius on hi-lo-hi mission 966km (600 miles) |
| Weights: | empty 10,400kg (22,932lb); maximum loaded 18,145kg (40,000lb) |
| Dimensions: | wingspan 13.97m (45ft 10in) spread and 7.78m (25ft 6.25in) swept; length (including probe) 16.71m (54ft 10in); height 4.82m (15ft 9.75in); wing area 37.25sq m (402sq ft)spread |
| Armament: | one 23mm GSh-23L cannon, underwing pylons for AA-3 Anab, AA-7 Apex, and/or AA-8 Aphid air-to-air missiles |

# Mikoyan-Gurevich MiG-23 'Flogger-E'

Libya and a number of other Arab countries have purchased a much simplified export version of the MiG-23M 'Flogger-B', designated MiG-23 'Flogger-E'. The aircraft retains the same basic airframe as its predecessor, but is powered by the 10,000kg (22,046lb) Tumanskii R-27F2M-300 turbojet. It is also equipped with a far less capable version of the 'Jay Bird' radar in a shorter nose radome. This has search and tracking ranges of about 29km and 18km respectively and no look-down capability. The avionics suite is also simplified, with no Doppler navigation or IR sensor pod. Another version with slightly different equipment fit is also in service with numerous Arab countries. Both export models are considerably less capable than the aircraft in CIS service. This aircraft wears the Islamic green insignia adopted in 1978 in place of the red-white-black roundels shared with Egypt.

| | |
|---|---|
| Country of origin: | USSR |
| Type: | single-seat air combat fighter |
| Powerplant: | one 10,000kg (22,046lb) Tumanskii R-27F2M-300 turbojet |
| Performance: | maximum speed at altitude about 2445km/h (1520mph); service ceiling over 18,290m (60,000ft); combat radius on hi-lo-hi mission 966km (600 miles) |
| Weights: | empty 10,400kg (22,932lb); maximum loaded 18,145kg (40,000lb) |
| Dimensions: | wingspan 13.97m (45ft 10in) spread and 7.78m (25ft 6.25in) swept; length (including probe) 16.71m (54ft 10in); height 4.82m (15ft 9.75in); wing area 37.25sq m (402sq ft) spread |
| Armament: | one 23mm GSh-23L cannon with 200 rounds, six external hardpoints with provision for up to 3000kg (6614lb) of stores, including AA-2 Atoll air-to-air missiles, cannon pods, rocket launcher pods, large calibre rockets, and bombs |

# Mikoyan-Gurevich MiG-23BN 'Flogger-F'

The Mikoyan-Gurevich MiG-23BN/BM 'Flogger-F' are basically fighter-bomber versions of the MiG-23 for the export market. The aircraft have similar nose shape, the same laser rangefinder, raised seat, cockpit external armour plate, and low pressure tyres of the Soviet air forces' MiG-27 'Flogger-D', but retains the powerplant, variable geometry intakes and cannon armament of the MiG-23MF 'Flogger-B' interceptor (an improved version of the MiG-23M 'Flogger-B' detailed previously). The aircraft can be configured to carry the AS-7 Kerry air-to-surface missile, and was supplied to Algeria, Cuba, Egypt, Ethiopia, Iraq, Libya, Syria and Vietnam, as well as the Warsaw Pact versions. This aircraft was operated by a unit of the Czech air force based at Pardubice, 100km (62 miles) east of Prague, during the late 1970s.

| Country of origin: | USSR |
| --- | --- |
| Type: | single-seat fighter bomber |
| Powerplant: | one 10,000kg (22,046lb) Tumanskii R-27F2M-300 turbojet |
| Performance: | maximum speed at altitude about 2445km/h (1520mph); service ceiling over 18,290m (60,000ft); combat radius on hi-lo-hi mission 966km (600 miles) |
| Weights: | empty 10,400kg (22,932lb); maximum loaded 18,145kg (40,000lb) |
| Dimensions: | wingspan 13.97m (45ft 10in) spread and 7.78m (25ft 6.25in) swept; length (including probe) 16.71m (54ft 10in); height 4.82m (15ft 9.75in); wing area 37.25sq m (402sq ft) spread |
| Armament: | one 23mm GSh-23L cannon with 200 rounds, six external hardpoints with provision for up to 3000kg (6614lb) of stores, including AA-2 Atoll air-to-air missiles, AS-7 Kerry air-to-surface missiles, cannon pods, rocket launcher pods, large calibre rockets, and bombs |

# Mikoyan-Gurevich MiG-25P 'Foxbat-A'

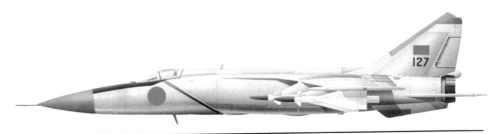

Reports of the development of a long-range high speed strategic bomber in the US in the late 1950s – the B-70 Valkyrie – prompted the Soviet authorities to give highest priority to the design and development of an interceptor that could be operational to meet the B-70s planned 1964 in-service date. Even when the B-70 programme was cancelled in 1961, work continued on the development of the interceptor known as the MiG-25 and was given the NATO reporting name 'Foxbat'. The aircraft was unveiled publicly at the 1967 Moscow Aviation Day. The prototypes blazed a trail of world records in 1965–67, and when the MiG-25P production aircraft entered service in 1970 it far outclassed any Western aircraft in terms of speed and height. This aircraft is also operated by Libya, Algeria, India, Iraq and Syria.

| | |
|---|---|
| Country of origin: | USSR |
| Type: | single-seat interceptor |
| Powerplant: | two 10,200kg (22,487lb) Tumanskii R-15B-300 turbojets |
| Performance: | maximum speed at altitude about 2974km/h (1848mph); service ceiling over 24,385m (80,000ft); combat radius 1130km (702 miles) |
| Weights: | empty 20,000kg (44,092lb); maximum take-off 37,425kg (82,508lb) |
| Dimensions: | wingspan 14.02m (45ft 11.75in); length 23.82m (78ft 1.75in); height 6.10m (20ft 0.5in); wing area 61.40sq m (660.9sq ft) |
| Armament: | external pylons for four air-to-air missiles in the form of either two each of the IR- and radar-homing AA-6 'Acrid', or two AA-7 'Apex' and two AA-8 'Aphid' weapons |

# Mikoyan-Gurevich MiG-25R 'Foxbat-D'

The MiG-25RB was later joined in service by two sub-variants, the MiG-25RBT with slightly different equipment fit and the MiG-25RBV with the SRS-9 Elint suite. Three further developments were deemed sufficiently different by NATO intelligence officers for them to be designated 'Foxbat D'. This series includes the MiG-25RBK, the MiG-25RBS, and the MiG-25RBSh (an upgraded version of the -25RBS). The Foxbat D series is used for non-optical reconnaissance and retains the limited bombing capability of the RB. The side of the nose has flush dielectric panels, and on the starboard side there is a large Side-Looking Airborne Radar that can record surface detail up to a range of 200km (124 miles). A development of the MiG-25 known as the E.266M still holds the world absolute height record for aeroplanes at 37,650m (123,524ft), which was set in 1977.

| Country of origin: | USSR |
| --- | --- |
| Type: | single-seat reconnaissance aircraft |
| Powerplant: | two 11,200kg (24,691lb) Tumanskii R-15BD-300 turbojets |
| Performance: | maximum speed at altitude about 3339km/h (2112mph); service ceiling 27,000m (88,585ft); operational radius 900km (559 miles) |
| Weights: | empty 19,600kg (43,211lb); maximum take-off 33,400kg (73,634lb) |
| Dimensions: | wingspan 13.42m (44ft 0.25in); length 23.82m (78ft 1.75in); height 6.10m (20ft 0.5in); wing area not disclosed |
| Armament: | six external pylons for six 500kg (1102lb) bombs |

# Mikoyan-Gurevich MiG-27 'Flogger-D'

The MiG-27 was a highly developed version of the MiG-23. The aircraft was designed from the outset as a dedicated ground attack aircraft and is optimised for operations over the battlefield. The most obvious difference is the nose, which was designed to give the pilot an enhanced view of the ground during approaches. Because it was only necessary to house a laser rangefinder and marked-target seeker in the nose, it was possible for the MiG designers to taper the nose steeply, as can be seen above. The pilot is protected from small-arms fire by armour plating on the side of the cockpit, and to enhance low-level performance, the variable geometry inlets and variable nozzle are replaced by lighter fixed units. The aircraft began to enter service in the late 1970s; improved versions are the MiG-27K and -27D 'Flogger-J'.

| | |
|---|---|
| Country of origin: | USSR |
| Type: | single-seat ground attack aircraft |
| Powerplant: | one 11,500kg (23,353lb) Tumanskii R-29B-300 turbojet |
| Performance: | maximum speed at 8000m (26,250ft) 1885km/h (1170mph); service ceiling over 14,000m (45,900ft); combat radius on lo-lo-lo mission with full weapon load and three tanks 540km (335 miles) |
| Weights: | empty 11,908kg (26,252lb); maximum loaded 20,300kg (44,750lb) |
| Dimensions: | wingspan 13.97m (45ft 10in) spread and 7.78m (25ft 6.25in) swept; length 17.07m (56ft 0.75in); height 5.0m (16ft 5in); wing area 37.35sq m (402sq ft) spread |
| Armament: | one 23mm GSh-23L cannon with 200 rounds, seven external hardpoints with provision for up to 4000kg (8818lb) of stores, Kh-29 air-to-surface missiles, AS-7 Kerry air-to-surface missiles, cannon pods, rocket launcher pods, large calibre rockets, napalm tanks, drop tanks, ECM pods, conventional and guided bombs |

# Mikoyan-Gurevich MiG-29 'Fulcrum-A'

In 1972 the Soviet Air Force began seeking a replacement for the MiG-21, -23, Sukhoi Su-15, and -17 fleets then in service. The MiG bureau submitted the winning entry and flight testing of the new fighter, designated 'Ram L' (later 'Fulcrum') by Western intelligence, began in October 1977. First deliveries of the aircraft were made to Soviet Frontal Aviation units in 1983 and the type became operational in 1985. A more detailed analysis of the aircraft was not possible until 1986, when a detachment of the aircraft visited Finland. The visit confirmed many estimates at to the size and configuration of the aircraft. More than 600 of the first production model, the 'Fulcrum-A', were delivered, with two important export orders to Syria and India. Deliveries to No. 28 Squadron and No. 47 Squadron of the Indian air force began in 1986.

| Country of origin: | USSR |
| --- | --- |
| Type: | single-seat air-superiority fighter with secondary ground attack capability |
| Powerplant: | two 8300kg (18,298lb) Sarkisov RD-33 turbofans |
| Performance: | maximum speed above 11000m (36,090ft) 2443km/h (1518mph); service ceiling 17,000m (55,775ft); range with internal fuel 1500km (932 miles) |
| Weights: | empty 10,900kg (24,030lb); maximum take-off 18,500kg (40,785lb) |
| Dimensions: | wingspan 11.36m (37ft 3.75in); length (including probe) 17.32m (56ft 10in); height 7.78m (25ft 6.25in); wing area 35.2sq m (378.9sq ft) |
| Armament: | one 30mm GSh-30 cannon with 150 rounds, eight external hardpoints with provision for up to 4500kg (9921lb) of stores, including six AA-11 'Archer' and AA-10 'Alamo' infra-red or radar guided air-to-air missiles, rocket launcher pods, large calibre rockets, napalm tanks, drop tanks, ECM pods, conventional and guided bombs |

# Mikoyan-Gurevich MiG-29M 'Fulcrum-D'

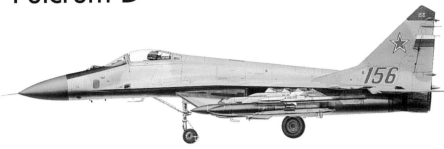

Work commenced on advanced versions of the MiG-29 at the end of the 1970s, with work concentrated on improving the range and versatility of the aircraft. One of the most significant changes was the incorporation of an advanced analog fly-by-wire control system, coupled with improved Head-Up and Head-Down displays. Physical appearance is similar, although the MiG-29M has an extended chord tailplane, and a recontoured dorsal fairing. Other changes are a more reliable and fuel efficient version of the Sarkisov turbofans, updated avionics with an advanced radar data processor four times the power of its predecessor, rearward shift in the centre of gravity to complement the fly-by-wire system, and two extra underwing hardpoints. The Russian air force has now decided to upgrade around 150 of its MiG-29s to MiG-29SMT standard with increased range and payload, a new glass cockpit, new avionics, improved radar and an refuelling probe.

| | |
|---|---|
| Country of origin: | USSR |
| Type: | single-seat air-superiority fighter with secondary ground attack capability |
| Powerplant: | two 9,409kg (20,725lb) Sarkisov RD-33K turbofans |
| Performance: | maximum speed above 11000m (36,090ft) 2300km/h (1,430mph); service ceiling 17,000m (55,775ft); range with internal fuel 1500km (932 miles) |
| Weights: | empty 10,900kg (24,030lb); maximum take-off 18,500kg (40,785lb) |
| Dimensions: | wingspan 11.36m (37ft 3.75in); length (including probe) 17.32m (56ft 10in); height 7.78m (25ft 6.25in); wing area 35.2sq m (378.9sq ft) |
| Armament: | one 30mm GSh-30 cannon with 150 rounds, six external hardpoints with provision for up to 3000kg (6614lb) of stores, including six AA-11 'Archer' and AA-10 'Alamo' infra-red or radar guided air-to-air missiles, rocket launcher pods, large calibre rockets, napalm tanks, drop tanks, ECM pods, conventional and guided bombs |

# Mikoyan-Gurevich MiG-31 'Foxhound-A'

The MiG-31 was developed during the 1970s from the impressive MiG-25 'Foxbat' to counter the threat from low-flying cruise missiles and bombers. A prototype first flew in September 1975, but it gradually became clear that the new aircraft was far more than a new-generation 'Foxbat'. In fact the MiG-31 was a vast improvement over its older stablemate, with tandem seat cockpit, IR search and tracking sensor, and the Zaslon 'Flash Dance' pulse-Doppler radar providing genuine fire-and-forget engagement capability against multiple targets flying at lower altitudes. The 'Foxhound-A' entered service in 1983 with the Voyska PVO. The aircraft pictured wears the colours of the former Soviet air force, based in the Arkhangel'sk district. Further development of the aircraft has been hampered by cut-backs in defence expenditure.

| Country of origin: | USSR |
| --- | --- |
| Type: | two-seat all weather interceptor and ECM aircraft |
| Powerplant: | two 15,500kg (34,171lb) Soloviev D-30F6 turbofans |
| Performance: | maximum speed at 17,500m (57,400ft) 3000km/h (1865mph); service ceiling 20,600m (67,600ft); combat radius with four AAMs and two drop tanks 1400km (840 miles) |
| Weights: | empty 21,825kg (48,415lb); maximum take-off 46,200kg (101,850lb) |
| Dimensions: | wingspan 13.46m (44ft 2in); length 22.68m (74ft 5.25in); height 6.15m (20ft 2.25in); wing area 61.6sq m (663sq ft) |
| Armament: | one 23mm GSh-23-6 cannon with 260 rounds, eight external hardpoints with provision for four AA-9 'Amos' and two AA-6 'Acrid' or four AA-8 'Aphid' air-to-air missiles, ECM pods, or drop tanks |

# Mitsubishi A5M 'Claude'

It is impossible to overstate the importance of the A5M carrierborne fighter in the development of Japanese industry and Japanese military capabilities in the mid-1930s. With this type Japan moved from dependence on Western imports and thinking to a completely indigenous product that was Japan's first carrierborne monoplane fighter and also in every way comparable in terms of performance and capabilities with the best of its Western equivalents. The first of six prototypes made the type's maiden flight in February 1935, and the A5M1 entered service in spring 1937. Production of the series, which departed first-line service in 1943, totalled 980 aircraft in the A5M1 to A5M4 series, the last with open rather than enclosed cockpits There were also 103 examples of the A5M4-K two-seat trainer development. In total it is estimated that nearly 1000 A5Ms were built, the aircraft proving very popular with naval pilots.

| | |
|---|---|
| Country of origin: | Japan |
| Type: | (A5M4) single-seat carrierborne and land-based fighter |
| Powerplant: | one 785hp (585kW) Nakajima Kotobuki 41 or Kotobuki 41 Kai nine-cylinder single-row radial engine |
| Performance: | maximum speed 435km/h (270mph); climb to 3000m (9845ft) in 3 minutes 35 seconds; service ceiling 9800m (32,150ft); range 1400km (870 miles) |
| Weights: | empty 1263kg (2874lb); maximum take-off 1822kg (4017lb) |
| Dimensions: | span 11.00m (36ft 1.13in); length 7.57m2 (4ft 9.88in); height 3.27m (10ft 8.75in) |
| Armament: | two 7.7mm fixed forward-firing machine guns in the upper part of the forward fuselage, plus an external bomb load of 60kg (132lb) |

# Mitsubishi G3M 'Nell'

Although it was already obsolescent when Japan entered World War II in 1941, the G3M belied this technical limitation by scoring a number of stunning successes in the opening phases of Japan's offensive onslaught. The lack of an adequate replacement meant that the 'Nell' was forced to soldier on into total obsolescence and suffered devastatingly heavy losses. First flown in July 1935, the G3M was designed to provide the Imperial Japanese Navy Air Force with the means to project its air power deep into the Pacific. The variant that entered service in 1937 was the G3M1, but these 34 aircraft were soon supplanted by an eventual 993 examples of the G3M2 (uprated engines and greater fuel capacity) and G3M3 (further uprated engines and increased fuel capacity). Some aircraft were also converted as L3Y armed transport aircraft. Pictured here is a G3M3 of the Takao Kokutai, 21st Koku Sentai, operating from Hanoi during March 1941.

| Country of origin: | Japan |
| --- | --- |
| Type: | (G3M2) seven-seat medium attack bomber |
| Powerplant: | two 1075hp (801.5kW) Mitsubishi Kinsei 41,42 or 45 14-cylinder two-row radial engines |
| Performance: | maximum speed 373km/h (232mph); climb to 3000m (9845ft) in 8 minutes 19 seconds; service ceiling 9130m (29,950ft); range 4380km (2722 miles) |
| Weights: | empty 4965kg (10,936lb); maximum take-off 8000kg (17,637lb) |
| Dimensions: | span 25m (82ft 0.25in); length 16.45m (53ft 11.63in); height 3.69m (12ft 1in) |
| Armament: | one 20mm trainable rearward-firing cannon in dorsal turret, one 7.7mm trainable machine gun in retractable dorsal turret, one 7.7mm machine gun in each beam position, and provision for one 7.7mm machine gun in cockpit, plus a bomb load of 800kg (1764lb) |

# Mitsubishi Ki-15 and C5M 'Babs'

**D**esigned for the high-speed reconnaissance and communications roles, the Ki-15 first flew in May 1936 and entered Imperial Japanese Army Air Force service in the late 1930s as the Ki-15-I with the 640hp (477kW) Nakajima Ha-8 (Army Type 94) radial engine. Production of the Ki-15 series totalled 435 aircraft, the later aircraft completed to Ki-15-II standard with an uprated engine. The same basic type appealed to the Imperial Japanese Navy Air Force, which acquired a development of the Ki-15-II with the designation C5M, of which 50 were delivered in the form of 20 C5M1 machines with the 875hp (652kW) Mitsubishi Zuisei 12 radial engine and 30 C5M2 aircraft with the 940hp (701kW) Nakajima Sakae 12 radial engine. Both army and navy models were relegated to second-line tasks from 1943, but were used for *kamikaze* attacks later in the war. Pictured is a Ki-15-I, operated by the 1sr Chuitai, 15th Hikosentai, of the Imperial Japanese Army air service.

| | |
|---|---|
| **Country of origin:** | Japan |
| **Type:** | (Ki-15-II) two-seat reconnaissance aeroplane |
| **Powerplant:** | one 900hp (671kW) Mitsubishi Ha 26-I (Army Type 99 Model 1) 14-cylinder two-row radial engine |
| **Performance:** | maximum speed 510km/h (317mph); climb to 5000m (16,405ft) in 6 minutes 49 seconds; service ceiling not available; range not available |
| **Weights:** | empty 1592kg (3510lb); normal take-off 2189kg (4826lb); maximum take-off 2481kg (5470lb) |
| **Dimensions:** | span 12.00m (39ft 4.5in); length 3.34m (28ft 6.5in); height 3.34m (10ft 11.5in) |
| **Armament:** | one 7.7mm trainable rearward-firing machine gun in the rear cockpit |

# Mitsubishi Ki-21 'Sally' and 'Gwen'

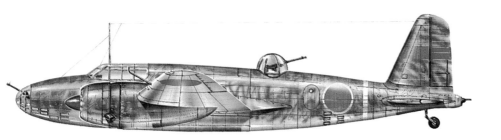

The best bomber that was available in significant numbers to the Imperial Japanese Army Air Force in World War II, the Ki-21 was yet another example of Japan's short-sighted policy of insisting on high speed and long range achieved only by sacrificing protection, defensive firepower and offensive warload. The type resulted from a February 1936 requirement for a modern bomber, and the first of eight prototypes made its maiden flight in December 1936. The Ki-21 entered service in mid-1938; production totalled 774 examples of the Ki-21-I with 850hp (634kW) Nakajima Ha-5 radial engines in three subvariants differentiated by their defensive armaments and fuel capacities, and 1278 examples of the Ki-21-II with a different and uprated powerplant in two subvariants. Some Ki-21-Is were converted as MC-21 unarmed civil transports. Pictured here is a Ki-21-IIb of the Imperial Japanese Army air service in 1944.

| Country of origin: | Japan |
| --- | --- |
| Type: | (Ki-21-IIb) five/seven-seat 'heavy' (actually medium) bomber |
| Powerplant: | two 1500hp (1118kW) Mitsubishi Ha-101 (Army Type 100) 14-cylinder two-row radial engines |
| Country | maximum speed 486km/h (302mph); climb to 6000m (19,685ft) in 13 minutes 13 seconds; service ceiling 10,000m (32,810ft); range 2700km (1678 miles) |
| Weights: | empty 6070kg (13,382lb); maximum take-off 10,610kg (23,391lb) |
| Dimensions: | span 22.50m (73ft 9.75in); length 16.00m (52ft 6in); height 4.85m (15ft 11in) |
| Armament: | one 12.7mm trainable machine gun in dorsal turret, one 7.7mm machine gun in nose position, one 7.7mm machine gun in ventral position, one 7.7mm machine gun in tail position, and one 7.7mm machine gun in each beam position; bomb load of 1000kg (2205lb) |

# Mitsubishi Ki-30 'Ann'

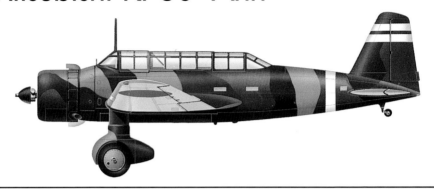

This aeroplane was the Imperial Japanese Army Air Force's first operational warplane with a double-row radial piston engine, variable-pitch propeller, internal weapons bay and split flaps. Despite these modern features, however, the Ki-30 was a basically undistinguished type that saw most of its service in the Chinese theatre, where lack of effective fighter opposition allowed it to operate generally without molestation. The origins of the type can be traced to the mid-1930s, when the Imperial Japanese Army Air Force launched an ambitious programme of expansion based on aircraft of Japanese design and manufacture. The first of 18 prototype and service trials aircraft flew in February 1937. There followed 686 production aircraft, of which the survivors were relegated to the crew training role from 1942. The aircraft shown here is a Ki-30 of the 2nd Chutai, 10th Hikosentai, Imperial Japanese Army air service in 1942.

| Country of origin: | Japan |
| --- | --- |
| Type: | two-seat light attack bomber |
| Powerplant: | one 950hp (708kW) Nakajima Ha-5 Kai (Army Type 97) 14-cylinder two-row radial engine |
| Performance: | maximum speed 432km/h (263mph); climb to 5000m (16,405ft) in 10 minutes 36 seconds; service ceiling 8570m (28,120ft); range 1700km (1056 miles) |
| Weights: | empty 2230kg (4916lb); maximum take-off 3322kg (7324lb) |
| Dimensions: | span 14.55m (47ft 8.75in); length 10.34m (33ft 11in); height 3.645m (11ft 11.5in) |
| Armament: | one 7.7mm fixed forward-firing machine gun in leading edge of the port wing, and one 7.7mm trainable rearward-firing machine gun in the rear cockpit, pus an internal bomb load of 400kg (882lb) |

# Mitsubishi Ki-46-I and Ki-46-II 'Dinah'

Oone of the finest machines of its type to see service in World War II and also one of the most elegant aircraft of all time, the Ki-46 was designed specifically as a high-altitude reconnaissance aeroplane to meet a 1937 requirement, and the prototype made its maiden flight in November 1939. Trials indicated excellent performance and handling, and there followed 34 Ki-46-I initial production aircraft with 900hp (671kW) Mitsubishi Ha-26-I radial engine before production switched to the first fully operational model, the Ki-46-II. Some 1093 examples of the Ki-46-II were delivered with an uprated powerplant and they proved virtually impossible to intercept. A number of these aircraft were later adapted to Ki-46-II Kai standard as radio and navigation trainers with an additional stepped cockpit above and behind the standard unit. The aircraft were an important asset in the early Pacific campaign, but as the capability of Allied fighters improved Ki-46-II losses mounted.

| | |
|---|---|
| Country of origin: | Japan |
| Type: | (Ki-46-II) two-seat high-altitude reconnaissance aeroplane |
| Powerplant: | two 1055hp (787kW) Mitsubishi Ha-102 (Army Type 1) 14-cylinder two-row radial engines |
| Performance: | maximum speed 604km/h (375mph); climb to 8000m (26,245ft) in 17 minutes 58 seconds; service ceiling 10,720m (35,170ft); range 2474km (1537 miles) |
| Weights: | empty 3263kg (7194lb); normal take-off 5050kg (11,133lb); maximum take-off 5800kg (12,787lb) |
| Dimensions: | span 14.70m (48ft 2.75in); length 11.00m (36ft 1in); height 3.88m (12ft 8.75in) |
| Armament: | one 7.7mm trainable rearward-firing machine gun in the rear cockpit |

# Mitsubishi A6M Reisen 'Zeke' and 'Zero'

The A6M was generally known in the West as the Zero, a name derived from its Japanese name Reisen (meaning zero fighter) that resulted from its adoption in the Japanese year 2600 (1940). The A6M rightly remains the most famous of all Japanese warplanes of World War II and in its heyday was a superb naval fighter. It is also important as the first carrierborne fighter anywhere in the world to achieve full parity with the best of its land-based contemporaries, but for lack of an adequate successor was maintained in development and production (11,280 aircraft) past its effective limits. The type reached its apogee as a dogfighting warplane in the A6M2, while the A6M3 had greater power but shorter range, the A6M5 heavier firepower, and the A6M6 better protection and greater fighter-bomber capability. When fitted with a drop tank the Zero had phenomenal range, afforded by a sophisticated engine/propeller management techniques.

| Country of origin: | Japan |
| --- | --- |
| Type: | (A6M2 Model 21) single-seat carrierborne and land-based fighter and fighter-bomber |
| Powerplant: | one 950hp (708kW) Nakajima NK1C Sakae 12 14-cylinder two-row radial engine |
| Performance: | maximum speed 534km/h (332mph); climb to 6000m (19,685ft) in 7 minutes 27 seconds; service ceiling 10,000m (32,810ft); range 3104km (1929 miles) |
| Weights: | empty 1680kg (3704lb); maximum take-off 2796kg (6164lb) |
| Dimensions: | span 12.00m (39ft 4.5in); length 9.06m (29ft 8.75in); height 3.05m (10ft) |
| Armament: | two 20mm fixed forward-firing cannon in the leading edges of the wing, and two 7.7mm fixed forward-firing machine guns in the forward fuselage, plus an external bomb load of 120kg (265lb) |

# Mitsubishi Ki-67 Hiryu 'Peggy'

The Ki-67 Hiryu (flying dragon) was without doubt the finest bomber to see service with the Imperial Japanese Army or Imperial Japanese Navy Air Forces in World War II, for it combined high performance with good defensive firepower, adequate offensive weapon load, and a structure that was sturdy and provided good protection for the crew and fuel supply. Mitsubishi submitted the winning design to a 1940 requirement and the flight of the first of 19 prototypes took place in in December 1942. Service entry of the Ki-67-I began in the summer of 1944 after a development programme that had been much protracted by the army's desire to develop the Hiryu in several variants exploiting its excellent performance and handling. Production totalled 698 aircraft, of which some were converted as explosives-laden *kamikaze* aircraft. Pictured is a Ki-67 of the Imperial Japanese Army Air Force.

| | |
|---|---|
| Country of origin: | Japan |
| Type: | (Ki-67-I) six/eight-seat 'heavy' (actually medium) bomber |
| Powerplant: | two 1900hp (1417kW) Mitsubishi Ha-104 (Army Type 4) 18-cylinder two-row radial engines |
| Performance: | maximum speed 537km/h (334mph); climb to 6000m (19,685ft) in 14 minutes 30 seconds; service ceiling 9470m (31,070ft); range 3800km (2361 miles) |
| Weights: | empty 8649kg (19,068lb); maximum take-off 13,765kg (30,347lb) |
| Dimensions: | span 22.50m (73ft 9.75in); length 18.70m (61ft 4.25in); height 7.70m (25ft 3in) |
| Armament: | one 20mm trainable cannon in dorsal turret, two 12.7mm trainable rearward-firing machine guns in tail position, one 12.7mm trainable machine gun in nose position, and one 12.7mm machine gun in each beam position, plus a bomb or torpedo load of 1070kg (2359lb) |

# Mitsubishi G4M1 'Betty'

The G4M was the ultimate expression of the Imperial Japanese Navy Air Force's desire to project land-based air power from its island garrisons deep into the Pacific Ocean for the destruction of enemy warships and the support of its own forces' amphibious operations. The G4M certainly possessed remarkable range but, as combat was to prove, this capability was purchased only at the expense of features that were just as important: crew protection, self-sealing fuel tanks and a sturdy structure able to absorb battle damage. Resulting from a 1937 requirement, the first of two G4M1 prototypes flew in October 1939, and the type entered service early in 1941. Production totalled 1200 G4M1 aircraft in variants such as the Convoy Fighter escort (five 20mm trainable cannon), Model 11 attack bomber and Model 12 attack bomber, the last with MK4E engines. Trainer and transport variants were then created as conversions. Pictured is a G4M1 of the 708th Kokutai.

| Country of origin: | Japan |
| --- | --- |
| Type: | (G4M1 Model 11) seven-seat medium attack bomber |
| Powerplant: | two 1530hp (1141kW) Mitsubishi MK4A Kasei 11 14-cylinder two-row radial engines |
| Performance: | maximum speed 428km/h (266mph); climb to 7000m (22,965ft) in 18 minutes; range 6033km (3749 miles) |
| Weights: | empty 6800kg (14,991lb); maximum take-off 9500kg (20,944lb) |
| Dimensions | span 25.00m (82ft 0.25in); length 20.00m (65ft 7.25in); height 6.00m (19ft 8.25in) |
| Armament: | one 20mm trainable rearward-firing cannon in the tail position, one 7.7mm trainable rearward-firing machine gun in the dorsal blister position, and one 7.7mm trainable lateral-firing machine gun in each of the two beam positions, plus an external bomb and torpedo load of 800kg (1764lb) |

# Mitsubishi G4M2 'Betty'

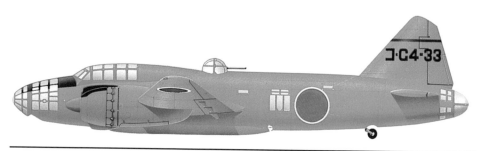

Following the G4M1, the G4M2 was built to the extent of 1154 aircraft for service from mid-1943 with an uprated powerplant, a laminar-flow wing, a larger tailplane, additional fuel capacity and heavier defensive armament for better overall capability but only at the cost of reduced agility. There were three attack bomber Model 22 subvariants (about 350 aircraft) with different armaments, and four attack bomber Model 24 subvariants (about 790 aircraft) with 1850hp (1379kW) MK4T engines and different armaments. A small number of aircraft were converted as engine test beds, and some machines were adapted as Model 24J carriers for the Yokosuka MXY7 Okha rocket-powered kamikaze warplane. The G4M2 remained in service right to the end of World War II. The delegation bringing the final declaration of surrender from the Japanese high command was brought to Ie-Shima in two 'Bettys'.

| | |
|---|---|
| Country of origin: | Japan |
| Type: | (G4M2 Model 22) seven-seat medium attack bomber |
| Powerplant: | two 1800hp (1342kW) Mitsubishi MK4P Kasei 21 14-cylinder two-row radial engines |
| Performance: | maximum speed 438km/h (272mph); climb to 8000m (26,245ft) in 30 minutes 24 seconds; range 6059km (3765 miles) |
| Weights: | empty 8160kg (17,990lb); maximum take-off 12,500kg (27,557lb) |
| Dimensions: | span 25.00m (82ft 0.25in); length 20.00m (65ft 7.25in); height 6.00m (19ft 8.25in) |
| Armament: | two 7.7mm trainable forward-firing machine guns in nose position, one 20mm trainable cannon in dorsal turret, one 20mm trainable lateral-firing cannon in each beam position, and one 20mm trainable rearward-firing cannon in tail position, plus a bomb and torpedo load of 800kg (1764lb) |

# Mitsubishi J2M Raiden 'Jack'

The Raiden ('Thunderbolt') was designed as land-based successor to the legendary A6M Reisen, but failed to live up to its initial promise, was very slow in development, and finally entered service with performance little better than that of its predecessor despite the use of a more potent engine. On the other side of the coin, however, the Allies assessed the Raiden as the best point interceptor available to the Japanese in the second half of World War II for its excellent blend of performance, stability, handling and field performance. First flown in March 1942, the J2M entered service only in the second half of 1943, and production totalled a mere 475 or so aircraft in variants such as the initial J2M2, the J2M3 – with heavier armament – and J2M4 – optimised for the high-altitude role. The aircraft pictured was on the strength of the 302nd Kokutai, Imperial Japanese Navy Air Force, based in Japan for the defence of the homeland in 1945.

| Country of origin: | Japan |
|---|---|
| Type: | (J2M3) single-seat interceptor fighter |
| Powerplant: | one 1870hp (1394kW) Mitsubishi MK4R-A Kasei 23a 14-cylinder two-row radial engine |
| Performance: | maximum speed 587km/h (365mph); climb to 6000m (19,685ft) in 6 minutes 14 seconds; service ceiling 11,700m (38,385ft); range 1899km (1180 miles) |
| Weights: | empty 2460kg (5423lb); normal take-off 3435kg (7573lb); maximum take-off 3945kg (8697lb) |
| Dimensions: | span 10.80m (35ft 5.25in); length 9.95m (31ft 9.75in); height 3.95m (12ft 11.25in) |
| Armament: | four 20mm fixed forward-firing cannon in the leading edges of the wing, plus an external bomb load of 120kg (265lb) |

# Mitsubishi T-2

To replace the T-1 tandem-seat trainer (Japan's first post-war military aircraft) a team led by Dr Kenji Ikeda designed the T-2, using the Anglo-French SEPECAT Jaguar as a basis. After flight trials had proved the validity of the design a single-seat version, the FST-2 - Kai was ordered (see F-1). The two aircraft are almost identical apart from the rear cockpit and addition of tubular passive warning radar aerial along the top of the fin. By mid-1975, orders had been placed for the T-2, powered by Ishikawajima-Harima built versions of the Rolls-Royce Turbomeca Adour turbofans. The aircraft entered service in 1976 with the 4th Air Wing at Mitsushima; its success in operational service has underlined the benefits of commonality with the F-1 fighter. This aircraft wears the colours of the 'Blue Impulse' aerobatic team of the JASDF, a component of the 4th Kokudan.

| Country of origin: | Japan |
|---|---|
| Type: | two-seat advanced flying, weapon and combat trainer |
| Powerplant: | two 3315kg (7308lb) Ishikawajima-Harima TF40-IHI-801A turbofans |
| Performance: | maximum speed at 10,675m (35,000ft) 1708km/h (1,061mph); service ceiling 15,240m (50,000ft); combat radius on hi-lo-hi mission with 1816kg (4000lb) load 350km (218 miles) |
| Weights: | empty 6307kg (13,904lb); maximum take-off 12,800kg (28,219lb) |
| Dimensions: | wingspan 7.88m (25ft 10.2in); length 17.86m (58ft 7in); height 4.39m (14ft 4.75in); wing area 21.17sq m (227.88sq ft) |
| Armament: | one 20mm JM61Vulcan six-barrell cannon with 750 rounds, five external hardpoints with provision for 2722kg (6000lb) of stores, including air-to-surface missiles, conventional and guided bombs, rocket-launcher pods, drop tanks, ECM pods; two wingtip pylons for air-to-air missiles |

# Mitsubishi F-1

Japan followed a somewhat unusual, but ultimately far-sighted route by developing the T-2 jet trainer before the F-1. Following the successful development of the T-2 Mitsubishi converted the second and third prototypes to single seat configuration, with the aim of producing a close-support fighter version. The first flight took place in 1975, and after evaluation by the JASDF Air Proving Wing at Gifu the aircraft was ordered into full time production. A total of 77 F-1S were ordered with deliveries commencing in September 1977. The final aircraft was received in March 1987, replacing the ageing North American F-86 Sabres then in service. This particular aircraft served with the 3rd Air Squadron of the 3rd Air Wing of the Japanese Air Self Defence Force (JASDF) at Misawa in the early 1980s.

| | |
|---|---|
| Country of origin: | Japan |
| Type: | close-support and anti-ship attack fighter |
| Powerplant: | two 3315kg (7,308lb) Ishikawajima-Harima TF40-IHI-801A turbofans |
| Performance: | maximum speed at 10,675m (35,000ft) 1708km/h (1,061mph); service ceiling 15,240m (50,000ft); combat radius on hi-lo-hi mission with 1816kg (4,000lb) load 350km (218 miles) |
| Weights: | empty 6358kg (14,017lb); maximum take-off 13,700kg (30,203lb) |
| Dimensions: | wingspan 7.88m (25ft 10.2in); length 17.86m (58ft 7in); height 4.39m (14ft 4.75in); wing area 21.17sq m (227.88sq ft) |
| Armament: | one 20mm JM61Vulcan six-barrell cannon with 750 rounds, five external hardpoints with provision for 2722kg (6000lb) of stores, including air-to-surface missiles, conventional and guided bombs, rocket-launcher pods, drop tanks, ECM pods; two wingtip pylons for air-to-air missiles |

# Morane-Saulnier MS.406

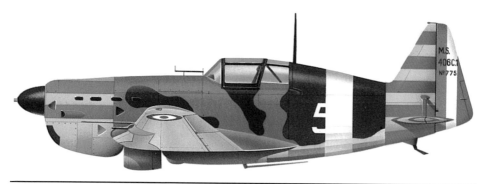

The MS.406 was France's first 'modern' monoplane fighter with a cantilever low-set wing, enclosed cockpit and tailwheel landing gear that included inward-retracting main units, but was obsolescent by World War II and suffered heavy losses in combat against the superior fighters fielded by the Luftwaffe. The type resulted from a 1934 requirement and was first conceived as the MS.405 that flew in prototype form during August 1935 and led to 15 MS.405C.1 pre-production fighters. There followed the MS.406C.1 production model of which an initial 1,000 examples were ordered in March 1938. The MS.406 was built on two production lines, and construction of 1077 aircraft was completed between June 1938 and June 1940. Exports were made to Switzerland and Turkey, and captured aircraft were passed to Croatia and Finland. Shown here is an MS.405C-1of the Escadron d'Entrainement, Vichy French Air Force, based at Toulouse in 1941.

| Country of origin: | France |
| --- | --- |
| Type: | (MS.406C.1) single-seat fighter |
| Powerplant: | one 860 hp (641kW) Hispano-Suiza 12Y-31 12-cylinder Vee engine |
| Performance: | maximum speed 490km/h (304mph); climb to 5000m (16,405ft) in 6 minutes 30 seconds; service ceiling 9400m (30,850ft); range 1500km (932 miles) |
| Weights: | empty 1872kg (4127lb); maximum take-off 2722kg (6000lb) |
| Dimensions: | span 10.62m (34ft 9.63in); length 8.17m (26ft 9.33in); height 3.25m (10ft 8in) with the tail up |
| Armament: | one 20mm fixed forward-firing cannon or 7.5mm fixed forward-firing machine gun in an engine installation, and two 7.5mm fixed forward-firing machine guns in the leading edges of the wing |

# Morane-Saulnier MS.760 Paris

The MS.760 is the more successful four-seater version of the MS.755 Fleuret, which made an unsuccessful bid to win the early 1950s Armée de l'Air competition for a jet trainer. The Morane-Saulnier company, which later became part of Potez in 1963, proceeded with development of the low-wing cabin monoplane and the first prototype flew in July 1954. Orders were received from both the Armée de l'Air and the Aeronavale as well as a number of overseas clients, including Brazil and Argentina. In 1961 production switched to the MS.760B Paris II, with more powerful engines, leading edge fuel tanks and improved baggage space. A total of 165 Paris Is and IIs were completed before production ended in 1964. A handful still serve as liaison aircraft with the Aeronavale and Argentina.

| | |
|---|---|
| **Country of origin:** | France |
| **Type:** | four/five-seat liason and light transport aircraft |
| **Powerplant:** | two 400kg (882lb) Turbomeca Marbore turbojets |
| **Performance:** | maximum speed at 7620m (25,000ft) 695km/h (432mph); service ceiling 12,000m (39,370ft); range 1740km (1,081 miles) |
| **Weights:** | empty 2067kg (4557lb); maximum take-off 3920kg (8642lb) |
| **Dimensions:** | wingspan 10.15m (33ft 6.75in); length 10.24m (33ft 7in); height 2.6m (8ft 6.5in); wing area 18sq m (193.76sq ft) |
| **Armament:** | none in liason/transport role; Argentina have used theirs in COIN role with two 7.62mm machine guns in nose, and two 50kg (110lb) bombs or four 90mm rockets under wings |

# Myasischev M-4 'Bison-C'

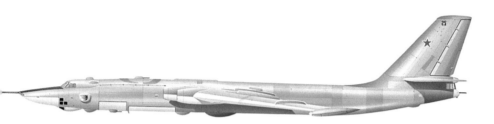

A single example of this large aircraft took part in the 1954 May Day parade over Moscow. It was expected to appear in large numbers in the inventories of the various Soviet air arms, but nothing was heard of it in the West for years. In fact the aircraft was produced in some numbers as the 'Bison-A' strategic bomber, and in 1959 a modified example set up new payload to height records. The Mya-4 bombers were subsequently adapted to the role of long-range strategic reconnaissance and ECM duties. In the 'Bison-C' sub-type a large search radar was fitted inside a lengthened and modified nose. The 'C' model was most frequently encountered on high- and low-level missions over the Arctic, and the Atlantic and Pacific oceans. Soviet bomber aircraft in operation during the 1960s wore a natural finish.

| | |
|---|---|
| Country of origin: | USSR |
| Type: | multi-role reconnaissance bomber |
| Powerplant: | four 13,000kg (28,660lb) Soloviev D-15 turbojets |
| Performance: | maximum speed 900km/h (560mph); service ceiling 15,000m (49,200ft); range with 4,500kg (9920lb) of electronic gear or bombs 11,000km (6835 miles) |
| Weights: | empty 80,000kg (176,400lb); maximum loaded 170,000kg (375,000lb) |
| Dimensions: | wing span 50.48m (165ft 7.5in); length 47.2m (154ft 10in); height 14.1m (46ft); wing area 309sq m (3,326.16sq ft) |
| Armament: | six 23mm cannon in two forward turrets and tail turret; internal bay with provision over 4500kg (10,000lb) of stores |

# Myasischev M-50 'Bounder'

Vladimir M. Myasishchev was involved in the design of a number of Soviet aircraft designs from 1924 before forming the design bureau that bears his name in 1951. His design for the M-50 was extremely advanced and was considered a considerable potential threat when details of its capabilities first became known. The aircraft was only ever built in prototype form, but it demonstrated extremely advanced design and construction techniques. A shoulder-mounted cropped delta wing was coupled with a conventional tail unit with all-swept surfaces. The fuselage was pressurised and incorporated a large weapons bay. The flight of the first prototype probably took place in 1957, and the last of several prototypes took part in the 1961 Aviation Day fly-past. This last prototype, designated M-52, differed from the others by having the two outer re-heated engines moved to the wing-tips.

| | |
|---|---|
| Country of origin: | USSR |
| Type: | prototype supersonic strategic bomber |
| Powerplant: | four wing-mounted 13,000kg (28,860lb) Soloviev D-15 turbojets |
| Performance: | (estimated) maximum speed at altitude 1950km/h (1,212mph) |
| Weights: | (not released) |
| Dimensions: | (not released) |
| Armament: | probably at least one cannon; internal bomb bay carrying stand-off nuclear weapons |

# Nakajima B5N 'Kate'

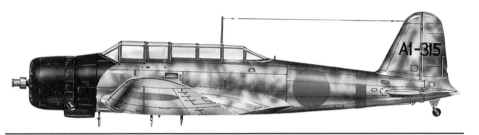

The B5N was the torpedo and level bomber counterpart of the Aichi D3A dive-bomber, and as such was a major weapon in the first part of the Japanese campaign in the Pacific theatre from December 1941. The type resulted from a 1934 requirement, and the first of two prototypes flew in January 1937. Successful development paved the way for the B5N1 initial production model with the powerplant of one 840hp (626kW) Nakajima Hikari 3 radial engine. Production of the B5N1 bomber was complemented by that of its B5N1-K advanced trainer derivative, and by 1941 the type had been replaced in first-line service by the improved B5N2 with a more potent engine. B5N production totalled 1147, and the B5N2 remained in first-line service up to mid-1944, thereafter being retasked to less demanding roles such as maritime reconnaissance. Shown here is a B5N2 of the Imperial Japanese Navy Air Force, based on the ill-fated carrier *Akagi* in 1941–42.

| | |
|---|---|
| Country of origin: | Japan |
| Type: | (B5N2) three-seat carrierborne and land-based torpedo and level bomber |
| Powerplant: | one 1000hp (746kW) Nakajima NK1B Sakae 11 nine-cylinder single-row radial engine |
| Performance: | maximum speed 378km/h (235mph); climb to 3000m (9845ft) in 7 minutes 40 seconds; service ceiling 8260m (27,100ft); range 1991km (1237 miles) |
| Weights: | empty 2279kg (5024lb); maximum take-off 4100kg (9039lb) |
| Dimensions: | span 15.52 m (50ft 11in); length 10.30m (33ft 9.5in); height 3.70m (12ft 1.75in) |
| Armament: | one 7.7mm trainable rearward-firing machine gun in the rear cockpit, plus an external torpedo and bomb load of 800kg (1764lb) |

# Nakajima B6N Tenzan 'Jill'

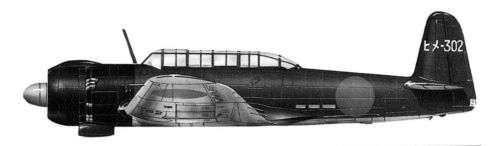

**D**esigned to a 1939 requirement for a B5N successor, the B6N Tenzan ('heavenly mountain') may be regarded as a extension of the design philosophy that inspired the B5N with considerably more power for significantly improved performance. The first of two prototypes flew in the spring of 1941, but the time needed to eradicate the problems that were encountered meant that the first of 133 B6N1 production aircraft entered service only late in 1943 with the 1870hp (1394kW) Nakajima NK7A Mamoru 11 radial engine. Further development of this engine was then cancelled, forcing Nakajima to develop the B6N2 with a different powerplant. Production of the B6N2 totalled 1133 aircraft in two subvariants, but little effective use could be made of these aircraft for lack of capable aircrew. The B6N3 was a purely land-based development that did not enter production. The aircraft pictured is a B6N2 of the Imperial Japanese Navy Air Force duirng 1944.

| | |
|---|---|
| Country of origin: | Japan |
| Type: | (B6N2) three-seat carrierborne and land-based torpedo bomber |
| Powerplant: | one 1850hp (1379kW) Mitsubishi MK4T Kasei 25 14-cylinder two-row radial engine |
| Performance: | maximum speed 481km/h (299mph); climb to 5000m (16,405ft) in 10 minutes 24 seconds; service ceiling 9040m (29,660ft); range 3045km (1892 miles) |
| Weights: | empty 3010kg (6636lb); maximum take-off 5650kg (12,456lb) |
| Dimensions: | span 14.89m (48ft 10.6in); length 10.87m (35ft 7.8in); height 3.80m (12ft 5.6in) |
| Armament: | one 7.7mm trainable rearward-firing machine gun in the rear of the cockpit, and one 7.7mm trainable rearward-firing machine gun in the ventral tunnel position, plus an external torpedo and bomb load of 800kg (1764lb) |

# Nakajima Ki-27 'Nate'

The Imperial Japanese Army Air Force's counterpart to the naval A5M, the Ki-27 was a cantilever low-wing fighter with fixed landing gear but advanced features such as an enclosed cockpit, and offered very creditable performance and a very high level of agility. The type first flew in October 1936 and was the army's standard fighter between 1937 and mid-1942. Production totalled some 3495 aircraft; the main variants were the Ki-27 pre-production type with a clear-view canopy, the Ki-27a production type with an uprated engine and a metal-faired canopy, and the Ki-27b definitive type with a clear-view canopy as well as provision for underwing bombs. After 1942 the Ki-27 was used mainly as a trainer, but numbers were expended as kamikaze attack warplanes in the closing stages of World War II. This particular aircraft was the personal mount of Lieutenant Colonel Toshio Katoh, commander of the 1st Sentai, based at Kagamigahara in June 1939.

| Country of origin: | Japan |
| --- | --- |
| Type: | (Ki-97b) single-seat fighter and fighter-bomber |
| Powerplant: | one 780hp (581.5kW) Nakajima Ha-1b (Army Type 97) nine-cylinder single-row radial engine |
| Performance: | maximum speed 470km/h (292mph); climb to 5000m (16,405ft) in 5 minutes 22 seconds; service ceiling 12,250m (40,190ft); range 1710km (1063 miles) |
| Weights: | empty 1110kg (2447lb); maximum take-off 1790kg (3946lb) |
| Dimensions: | span 11.31m (37ft 1.25in); length 7.53m (24ft 8.5in); height 3.25m (10ft 8in) |
| Armament: | two 7.7mm fixed forward-firing machine guns in the upper part of the forward fuselage, plus an external bomb load of 100kg (220lb) |

# Nakajima Ki-43 Hayabusa 'Oscar'

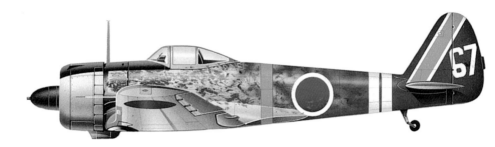

The Ki-43 Hayabusa ('Peregrine Falcon') was the most advanced fighter available to the Imperial Japanese Army Air Force in the opening phases of World War II, and as such the type came as a very considerable shock to the Allied air forces. The type was also the most important of all the Imperial Japanese Army Air Force's fighters in numerical terms, with production totalling more than 5900 aircraft right up to the end of the war, by which time the Ki-43 was decidedly obsolete in terms of firepower and protection. The main variants were the Ki-43-I (three subvariants) with the 980hp (731kW) Ha-25 engine driving a two-blade propeller, Ki-43-II (three subvariants) with an uprated engine driving a three-blade propeller, and the Ki-43-III (one subvariant) with the 1230hp (917kW) Ha-115-II engine. Shown here is a Ki-43IIb of the 3rd Chutai, 25th Sentai, Imperial Japanese Army air force, based at Hankow in China in January 1944.

| Country of origin: | Japan |
| --- | --- |
| Type: | (Ki-43-IIb) single-seat fighter and fighter-bomber |
| Powerplant: | one 1150hp (857kW) Nakajima Ha-115 (Army Type 1) 14-cylinder two-row radial engine |
| Performance: | maximum speed 530km/h (329mph); climb to 5000m (16,405ft) in 5 minutes 49 seconds; service ceiling 11,200m (36,750ft); range 3200km (1988 miles) |
| Weights: | empty 1910kg (4211lb); normal take-off 2590kg (5710lb); maximum take-off 2925kg (6450lb) |
| Dimensions: | span 10.84m (35ft 6.75in); length 8.92m (29ft 3.25in); height 3.27m (10ft 8.75in) |
| Armament: | two 12.7mm fixed forward-firing machine guns in the upper part of the forward fuselage, plus an external bomb load of 500kg (1102lb ) |

# Nakajima Ki-44 Shoki 'Tojo'

The Shoki ('Demon') was designed as a small and highly loaded fighter specifically for the interception role. The type was the only interceptor to serve with the Imperial Japanese Army Air Force, and after the start of strategic attacks on the Japanese home islands by American bombers the Shoki proved its worth as the fastest-climbing Japanese fighter. The Ki-44 entered service in the second half of 1942 as a type that was initially unpopular among pilots accustomed to more lightly loaded and agile fighters. Production of 1222 aircraft included the Ki-44-I (three subvariants) with the 1250hp (932kW) Ha-41 engine and machine gun armament, the Ki-44-II (three subvariants) with a m ore powerful engine and heavier armament. The Ki-44-III (two subvariants) had the 2000hp (1491kW) Ha-145 engine and armament of either four 20mm cannon (Ki-44-IIIa) or two 20mm and two 37mm cannon (Ki-44-IIIB). Shown here is a Ki-44-IIb.

| | |
|---|---|
| Country of origin: | Japan |
| Type: | (Ki-44-II) single-seat fighter |
| Powerplant: | one 1520hp (1133kW) Nakajima Ha-109 (Army Type 2) 14-cylinder two-row radial engine |
| Performance: | maximum speed 605km/h (376mph); climb to 5000 m (16,405ft) in 4 minutes 17 seconds; service ceiling 11,200m (36,745ft); range 1700km (1056 miles) |
| Weights: | empty 2106kg (4643lb); normal take-off 2764kg (6094lb); maximum take-off 2993kg (6598lb) |
| Dimensions: | span 9.45m (31ft); length 8.79m (28ft 9.9in); height 3.25m (10ft 8in) |
| Armament: | two 12.7mm machine guns in the upper part of the forward fuselage, and two 12.7mm fixed forward-firing machine guns in the leading edges of the wing, plus a bomb load of 200kg (441lb) |

# Nakajima Ki-49 Donryu 'Helen'

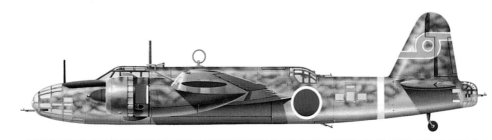

The Donryu ('Storm Dragon') was planned from 1938 as replacement for the Mitsubishi Ki-21 but proved so indifferent that it supplemented rather than replaced the older type. The first of three prototypes made its maiden flight in August 1939, and the evaluation of seven pre-production aircraft paved the way for the introduction from August 1941 of the Ki-49-I initial production variant, of which 129 were delivered with a powerplant of two 1250hp (932kW) Nakajima Ha-41 radial engines. There followed 667 examples of the Ki-49-II in two subvariants with an uprated and different powerplant, improved protection and heavier defensive firepower. There were also three prototypes of the Ki-58 escort derivative with no bombs but a trainable armament of five 20mm cannon and three 12.7mm machine guns. The inability of the Ki-49 to fulfill its intended role meant that the aircraft was increasingly relegated to secondary duties in the later stages of the war.

| Country of origin: | Japan |
|---|---|
| Type: | (Ki-49-IIa) eight-seat 'heavy' (actually medium) bomber |
| Powerplant: | two 1500hp (1118kW) Nakajima Ha-109 (Army Type 2) 14-cylinder two-row radial engines |
| Performance: | maximum speed 492km/h (306mph); climb to 5000m (16,405ft) in 13 minutes 39 seconds; service ceiling 9300m (30,510ft); range 2950km (1833 miles) |
| Weights: | empty 6530kg (14,396lb); maximum take-off 11,400kg (25,133lb) |
| Dimensions: | span 20.42m (67ft); length 16.50m (54ft 1.6in); height 4.25m (13ft 1.2in) |
| Armament: | one 20mm trainable cannon in dorsal turret, one 12.7mm machine gun in nose position, one 12.7mm machine gun in tail position, one 12.7mm machine gun in ventral position, and one 7.7mm machine gun in each beam position; bomb load of 1000kg (2205lb) |

# Nakajima Ki-84 Hayate 'Frank'

$D$esigned as successor to the Ki-43, the Hayate ('Gale') was one of the best fighters available to the Imperial Japanese Army Air Force in the closing stages of World War II. Its high level of basic capability was boosted by the fact that, unlike several other high-performance Japanese fighters, it was available in useful numbers and without the teething problems that affected many of these other types. Entering service in the first half of 1944, the Ki-84 was built to the extent of 3512 aircraft in two primary variants, namely the Ki-84-I (four subvariants distinguished by their steadily more capable armament) and the Ki-84-II (two subvariants) derivative of the Ki-84-I with a wooden rear fuselage and fittings in an effort to reduce the drain on Japan's dwindling reserves of strategic light alloys. The final variant was the Ki-116, a conversion by Mansyu from a standard Ki-84-1a with a lighter powerplant. Pictured is a Ki-84-1a of the 58th Shimbu-tai in August 1944.

| Country of origin: | Japan |
| --- | --- |
| Type: | (Ki-84-la) single-seat fighter and fighter-bomber |
| Powerplant: | one 1900hp (1417kW) Nakajima Ha-45 (Army Type 4) Model 23 18-cylinder two-row radial engine |
| Performance: | maximum speed 631km/h (392mph); climb to 5000m (16,405ft) in 5 minutes 54 seconds; service ceiling 10,500m (34,450ft); range 2168km (1347 miles) |
| Weights: | empty 2660kg (5864lb); normal take-off 3613kg (7955lb); maximum take-off 4170kg (9193lb) |
| Dimensions: | span 11.24m (36ft 10.5in); length 9.92m (32ft 6.5in); height 3.39m (11ft 1.25in) |
| Armament: | two 20mm fixed forward-firing cannon in the leading edges of the wing, and two 12.7mm fixed forward-firing machine guns in the forward fuselage, plus an external bomb load of 500kg (1102lb) |

# Nanchang Q-5 'Fantan'

The basic design of the Fantan close-support fighter was derived from the Mikoyan-Gurevich MiG-19. Design of the aircraft began in 1958, which retains a similar wing and rear fuselage configuration. Power is provided by two turbojets mounted side-by-side in the fuselage, with an attack radar mounted in the nose. Service deliveries began in 1970, and by 1980 approximately 100 were in service. Export customers have included Pakistan (52 A-5C), Bangladesh (20 A-5C), and North Korea (Q-5 IA). More than 900 of the aircraft now serve with the People's Liberation Army air force and navy. The Nanchang factory, based in Kiangsi province, has also developed a modernised version of the basic model pictured equipped with an Alenia FIAR Pointer 2500 ranging radar for export. This is designated A-5M.

| | |
|---|---|
| Country of origin: | China |
| Type: | single-seat close support fighter with secondary air combat capability |
| Powerplant: | two 3250kg (7165lb) Shenyang WP-6 turbojets |
| Performance: | maximum speed at 11,000m (36,090ft) 1190km/h (739mph); service ceiling 16,000m (52,500ft); combat radius on low level mission with maximum load 400km (249 miles) |
| Weights: | empty 6375kg (14,054lb); maximum take-off 11,830kg (26,080lb) |
| Dimensions: | wingspan 9.68m (31ft 9in); length (including probe) 15.65m (51ft 4.25in); height 4.33m (14ft 2.75in); wing area 27.95sq m (300.85sq ft) |
| Armament: | two 23mm Type 23-2K cannon with 100rpg; ten external hardpoints with provision for up to 2000kg (4409lb) of stores, including air-to-air missiles, fee-fall bombs, rocket launcher pods, napalm tanks, drop tanks and ECM pods |

# Naval Aircraft Factory N3N

The XN3N-1 prototype made its maiden flight in August 1935, and 179 N3N-1 production aircraft were delivered from June 1936 with provision for wheeled landing gear or float alighting gear. The first 159 had the 220hp (164kW) Wright R-790-8 radial engine, but later aircraft switched to the uprated R-760-8 engine. This unit was also used in the 816 examples of the N3N-3 delivered from 1938 with a vertical tail surface of revised shape, a modified main landing gear arrangement with a single strut on each side, and an uncowled engine installation that was retrospectively adopted for the N3N-1 in 1941 and 1942. The N3N series served with great utility throughout the period of World War II, but most of the surviving aircraft were sold to civil operators soon after the end of this conflict. A typically brightly coloured aircraft is pictured here, this example being a N3N-1 based at Pensacola in 1939.

| Country of origin: | USA |
|---|---|
| Type: | (N3N-3) two-seat primary flying trainer |
| Powerplant: | one 235hp (175kW) Wright R-760-2 Whirlwind seven-cylinder single-row radial engine |
| Performance: | maximum speed 203 km/h (126mph); initial climb rate 244m (800ft) per minute; service ceiling 4635m (15,200ft); range 756km (470 miles) |
| Weights: | empty 948kg (2090lb); maximum take-off 1266kg (2792lb) |
| Dimensions: | span 10.36m (34ft); length 7.77m (25ft 6in); height 3.30m (10ft 10in) |
| Armament: | none |

# Nieuport 11

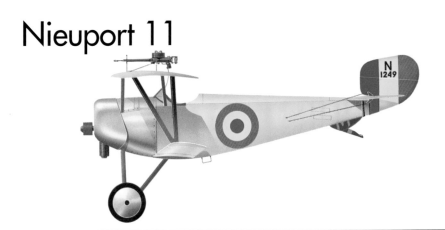

In January 1914 designer Gustave Delage joined the Etablissments Nieuport and started the series of aircraft that made him, and the company, famous. The first of these was the Nieuport 10, a small two-seat reconnaissance sesquiplane (with the lower wing much smaller than the upper). This aircraft was produced in two versions, one with the observer and gun in front of the pilot (10AV) and the other with the observer and gun behind (10AR). With only a Gnome-Rhône rotary engine to power them, the two-seaters proved underpowered and most were converted to single-seat scouts. A larger version was built as the Nieuport 12; production total for both types was 170. Concurrently with this programme, Delage designed and built the Nieuport Bébé for the Gordon-Bennett race, and developed this into the Type 11 scout. Hundreds were built for the RFC, RNAS, French and Belgian Aviation Militaire, and the Imperial Russian Air Service.

| | |
|---|---|
| Country of origin: | France |
| Type: | single-seat fighting scout |
| Powerplant: | one 80hp (60kW) Le Rhône 9C 9-cylinder rotary engine |
| Performance: | maximum speed 155km/h (97mph); service ceiling 4500m (14,765ft); endurance 2hrs 30mins |
| Weights: | empty 350kg (772lb); maximum take-off weight 480kg (1058lb) |
| Dimensions: | span 7.55m (24ft 9in); length 5.8m (19ft); height 2.45m (8ft); wing area 13 sq m (140 sq ft) |
| Armament: | one fixed forward-firing .303in Vickers machine gun |

# Nieuport 17

The Nieuport 17 was unquestionably one of the finest Allied combat aircraft of World War I. It bore a close physical resemblance to the Type 16, but was slightly larger and, to avoid the problems with wing-twist that had afflicted the XI at high speeds, the lower wing was considerably stiffened. The aircraft first flew in January 1916 and the first deliveries were made in May, helping to end the 'Fokker Scourge' of the previous months. The aircraft was highly manoeuvrable for its time, with a high rate of climb and good performance. Many hundreds were built for service with the RFC and RNAS, Aviation Militaire in France and Belgium, Russia, Holland, Italy, Finland and the USAAF. The fame of the Type 17 is due in no small part to the fact that it was the chosen mount of the Escadrille de Cicognes, Escadrille Lafayette and of the aces Nungesser, Guynemer, Ball and Bishop.

| Country of origin: | France |
| --- | --- |
| Type: | single-seat fighting scout |
| Powerplant: | 110hp (82kW) Le Rhône 9J rotary piston engine |
| Performance: | maximum speed 170km/h (106mph); service ceiling 1980m (6500ft); range 250km (155 miles) |
| Weights: | empty 374kg (825lb); maximum take-off weight 560kg (1235lb) |
| Dimensions: | span 8.2m (26ft 11in); length 5.96m (19ft 7in); height 2.44m (8ft); wing area 14.75 sq m (159 sq ft) |
| Armament: | one fixed forward-firing .303in Vickers machine gun |

# Nieuport 27

The most successful offshoot of the Type 17 was the Type 21, produced simply by substituting an 80hp (60kW) Le Rhône engine and enlarging the ailerons. Nearly 200 of these were produced, mostly for Russia and the USA, and in the years after the war it was the mount of a number of the barnstormers. A slightly heavier version was the Type 23 which had slightly enlarged tail surfaces and either an 80hp (60kW) or 120hp (89kW) Le Rhône engine. The Type 24 was yet another variant, with improved streamlining, fixed fin and a circular section fuselage, which was sold to the USA (124), Belgium, Italy and Japan. The Type 24-bis trainer had the original Type 17 tail unit, and the Type 25 was the Type 24 prototype fitted with the tailplane and skid seen on the Type 27. This had a 120hp (89kW) Le Rhône engine and was used by Sweden, the RFC and RNAS, and the USAAF. Pictured is a Nieuport 27 of No 1 Squadron, RFC, with French-style two-tone camouflage.

| Country of origin: | France |
|---|---|
| Type: | single-seat fighting scout |
| Powerplant: | 120hp (89kW) Le Rhône rotary piston engine |
| Performance: | maximum speed 185km/h (115mph); service ceiling 5550m (18,210ft); range 250km (155 miles) |
| Weights: | empty 380kg (838lb); maximum take-off weight 585kg (1289lb) |
| Dimensions | span 8.2m (26ft 11in); length 5.85m (19ft 2in); height 2.42m (7ft 11in); wing area 14.75 sq m (159 sq ft) |
| Armament: | one fixed forward-firing .303in Vickers machine gun; one fixed forward-firing .303in Lewis machine gun |

# Nieuport 28

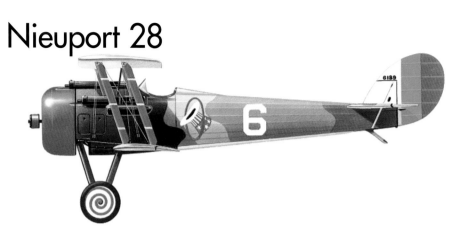

H aving exhausted all the possibilities for variations to the Type 17 airframe, Nieuport produced a totally new aircraft which it designated the Type 28. This marked a break from the V-strut sesquiplane configuration of the earlier Nieuport scouts, which was replaced by wings of almost equal proportion braced by parallel struts. The rectangular section fuselage was superseded by one of circular section, fitted around a new 160hp (119kW) Gnome-Le Rhône 9N engine. The Type 28 was ordered into production almost off the drawing board, but in service from March 1918 the Gnome engine proved to be its Achilles' heel, proving itself totally unreliable. A further failing was that at high speed any violent manoeuvre tended to rip the fabric from the upper wing. Notwithstanding these problems, the Type 28 happened to be the only fighter readily available to the US Expeditionary Force, the Pursuit Squadrons of which began arriving in France in early 1918.

| Country of origin: | France |
| --- | --- |
| Type: | single-seat fighter |
| Powerplant: | one 160hp (119kW) Gnome-Le Rhône 9N rotary piston engine |
| Performance: | maximum speed 195km/h (121mph); service ceiling 5200m (17,060ft); range 400km (248 miles) |
| Weights: | empty 532kg (1172lb); maximum take-off weight 740kg (1631lb) |
| Dimensions: | span 8m (26ft 3in); length 6.2m (20ft 4in); height 2.48m (8ft 2in); wing area 20 sq m (215 sq ft) |
| Armament: | two fixed forward-firing .303in Vickers machine guns |

# Nieuport-Delage Ni-D 29

Nieuport's last wartime fighter was first flown in prototype form in August 1918, and subsequent flight-testing confirmed the soundness of Gustave Delage's design. All the performance parameters were met with the exception of ceiling, and so for the second prototype a wing of increased span was constructed. In this form the Nieuport Ni-D 29 was ordered into quantity production at the beginning of 1920. Initial deliveries of an eventual 250 aircraft to the French Aviation Militaire were made in 1922 and the order book was soon filled with orders from Spain and Belgium, which took 30 (10 license-built) and 108 (87 license-built) aircraft respectively. French-built machines were supplied to both Sweden and Argentina. Japan was by far the biggest customer; an aircraft was purchased and using this as a pattern Nakajima built 608 for the Imperial Japanese Army as the Ko-4. Macchi in Italy built smaller numbers.

| Country of origin: | France |
| --- | --- |
| Type: | single-seat fighter |
| Powerplant: | one 300hp (224kW) Hispano-Suiza 8Fb 8-cylinder Vee piston engine |
| Performance: | maximum speed 235km/h (146mph); service ceiling 8500m (27,885ft); range 580km (360 miles) |
| Weights: | empty 760kg (1675lb); maximum take-off weight 1150kg (2535lb) |
| Dimensions: | span 9.7m (31ft 10in); length 6.49m (21ft 3in); height 2.56m (8ft 5in); wing area 26.7 sq m (287 sq ft) |
| Armament: | two fixed forward-firing .303in Vickers machine guns |

# Nieuport-Delage Ni-D 52

**G**ustave Delage's output before terminating his partnership with Nieuport in 1934 was prolific, evidenced by the fact that at the 1924 Paris Salon de l'Aéronautique, Nieuport-Delage unveiled no less than three new designs at a time when the military fighter market was severely depressed. Each of the designs bore the number 42, but each was quite different. One of the aircraft on display was one of two Ni-D 42 racers built for the 1924 Coupe Beaumont contest. Displayed alongside this was the Ni-D 42 C.1 single-seat and Ni-D 42 C.2 two-seat fighter. The former aircraft was operated in some numbers by the Aviation Militaire, and spawned a successful family of aircraft over the next decade. The Ni-D 52 of 1927 (pictured in the Spanish Republican Air Force colours) closely resembled the Ni-D 42 but was constructed of metal instead of wood. First flown in 1927, it won the 1928 Spanish fighter competition and was built under licence by Hispano until 1936.

| | |
|---|---|
| **Country of origin:** | France |
| **Type:** | single-seat fighter |
| **Powerplant:** | one 580hp (433kW) Hispano-Suiza 12Hb 12-cylinder Vee piston engine |
| **Performance:** | maximum speed 255km/h (158mph); service ceiling 7000m (2965ft); range 400km (249 miles) |
| **Weights:** | empty 1368kg (3016lb); maximum take-off weight 1837kg (4050lb) |
| **Dimensions:** | span 12m (39ft 4in); length 7.5m (24ft 7in); height 3m (9ft 10in); wing area 30.90 sq m (333 sq ft) |
| **Armament:** | two fixed forward-firing 7.62mm Vickers machine guns |

# North American B-25A/B Mitchell

One of the most important US tactical warplanes of World War II and built to the extent of 9816 aircraft, the Mitchell was a classic medium bomber that was also developed into a potent anti-ship warplane. The origins of the type can be found in 1938, when North American gambled that the US Army Air Corps would need a new attack bomber. In response work commenced on the NA-40 that first flew in January 1939 before conversion into the NA-40B to meet the definitive USAAC requirement issued in January 1939. The concept was then refined as the NA-62, subsequently ordered as 24 B-25 initial production aircraft which were delivered from February 1941. Later deliveries comprised 40 and 120 B-25A and B-25B aircraft, the former with self-sealing fuel tanks and the latter with dorsal and ventral turrets but no tail gun position. the B-25B was used in the 'Doolittle raid' of April 1942, when 16 aircraft lifted off from an aircraft carrier to bomb Tokyo.

| Country of origin: | USA |
|---|---|
| Type: | (B-25B) five-seat medium bomber |
| Powerplant: | two 1700hp (1267kW) Wright R-2600-9 14-cylinder two-row radial engines |
| Performance: | maximum speed 483km/h (300mph); service ceiling of 7175m (23,500ft); range 2172km (1350 miles) with a 1361kg (3000lb) bomb load |
| Weights: | empty 9072kg (20,000lb); maximum take-off 12,909kg (28,460lb) |
| Dimensions: | span 30.66m (67ft 7in); length 16.13 m (52ft 11in), height 4.80m (15ft 9in) |
| Armament: | one 0.3in trainable forward-firing machine gun in the nose position, two 0.5in trainable machine guns in the dorsal turret, and two 0.5in trainable machine guns in the ventral turret, plus an internal bomb load of 1361kg (3000lb) |

# North American P-51A /C Mustang

The Mustang was the finest all-round fighter of World War II, for it was a truly superb warplane that combined phenomenal performance, good acceleration, very good manoeuvrability, an extremely sturdy airframe and other operationally significant attributes in an aesthetically attractive package whose totality somehow seemed to be greater than the sum of its parts. The Mustang resulted from a British requirement and first flew in October 1940 with the Allison V-1710 engine, which was also used in the 1045 examples of the P-51 and P-51A (Mustang Mks I and II) that served from April 1942 in the low-level fighter and reconnaissance fighter roles. The P-51B and P-51C (1988 and 1750 aircraft respectively) then switched to the Packard V-1650 American-made version of a classic British engine, the Rolls-Royce Merlin. This transformed the Mustang from a mediocre aircraft into one of the most important fighters of World War II.

| Country of origin: | USA |
|---|---|
| Type: | (P-51B) single-seat fighter and fighter-bomber |
| Powerplant: | one 1400hp (1044kW) Packard V-1650-3 12-cylinder Vee engine |
| Performance: | maximum speed 708km/h (440mph); climb to 3050m (10,000ft) in 1 minute 48 seconds; service ceiling 12,800m (42,000ft); range 3540km (2,200 miles) |
| Weights: | empty 3103kg (6840lb); maximum take-off 5080kg (11,200lb) |
| Dimensions: | span 11.89m (37ft 0.25in); length 9.83m (32ft 3in); height 2.64m (8ft 8in) |
| Armament: | six 0.5in fixed forward-firing machine guns in the leading edges of the wing, plus an external bomb load of 907kg (2000lb) |

# North American P-51D to P-51K Mustang

The combination of the Mustang airframe and Merlin engine had proved ideal in the P-51B/C and paved the way for most later developments. The first of these was the definitive P-51D of which 7966 were completed with a cut-down rear fuselage and clear-view 'bubble' canopy, and later with increased fuel capacity and underwing provision for rocket projectiles as alternatives to bombs for the increasingly important ground-attack role. The P-51D was one of the decisive weapons of World War II, and was complemented by the P-51H lightweight model (555 aircraft) and the P-51K version of the P-51D with a different propeller (1337 aircraft). Variants of the P-51 series for other roles included the a-36A Apache dive-bomber and ground-attack model, and the F-6 series of photo-reconnaissance aircraft. Orders for 1700 P-51L aircraft and 1628 P-51M fighters were cancelled at VJ Day, but not before Mustang production had totalled 15,386.

| | |
|---|---|
| Country of origin: | USA |
| Type: | (P-51D) single-seat fighter and fighter-bomber |
| Powerplant: | one 1695hp (1264kW) Packard V-1650-7 12-cylinder Vee engine |
| Performance: | maximum speed 703km/h (437mph); climb to 6095m (20,000ft) in 7 minutes 18 seconds; service ceiling 12,770m (41,900ft); range 3703km (2301 miles) |
| Weights: | empty 3103kg (6840lb); maximum take-off 5493kg (12,100lb) |
| Dimensions: | span 11.28m (37ft 0.25in); length 9.84m (32ft 3.25in); height 4.16m (13ft 8in) with the tail down |
| Armament: | six 0.5in fixed forward-firing machine guns in the leading edges of the wing, plus an external bomb and rocket load of 907kg (2000lb) |

# North American FJ-1 Fury

The FJ-1 Fury was one of three jet-powered aircraft ordered for evaluation purposes by the US Navy. The three prototypes were heavily influenced by German wartime research; the North American NA-134, which was to become the FJ-1 Fury, flew in November 1946. One hundred production aircraft had been ordered in May 1945, but this was subsequently cut to 30. Production deliveries began in March 1948 to Naval Squadron VF-5A, who made the first carrier landings with the aircraft on the tenth day of that month on USS Boxer. Although it had a relatively undistinguished career the Fury was the first aircraft to complete an operational tour at sea, and paved the way for the more aesthetically pleasing F-86 Sabre. For a brief period it could also claim to be the fastest aircraft in US Navy service.

| Country of origin: | USA |
| --- | --- |
| Type: | single-seat carrier-borne fighter |
| Powerplant: | one 1816kg (4000lb) Allison J35-A-2 turbojet |
| Performance: | maximum speed at 2743m (9000ft) 880km/h (547mph); service ceiling 9754m (32,000ft); range 2414km (1500 miles) |
| Weights: | empty 4011kg (8843lb); maximum loaded 7076kg (15,600lb) |
| Dimensions: | wingspan 9.8m (38ft 2in); length 10.5m (34ft 5in); height 4.5m (14ft 10in); wing area 20.5sq m (221sq ft) |
| Armament: | six 0.5in machine guns |

# North American FJ-3M Fury

**B**oth Army and Navy contracts were awarded to North American in 1944 for a jet fighter, but the land-based programme moved fastest. After the land-based program had discarded the straight-wing configuration of the early design for an all-swept format, the naval team persisted with it and produced the unremarkable FJ-1 Fury. Before this aircraft had even entered service, the US Navy was seeking its replacement. This aircraft, the FJ-2, was in essence a navalised version of the company's land-based F-86E Sabre, with folding wings, strengthened landing gear and catapult hitches, and arrestor gear. Some 200 were produced and served with the US Marines. They were superseded by the FJ-3, which had a larger, more  powerful engine which necessitated increasing the depth of the fuselage, a new canopy, extended leading edge, and increased weapon load.

| | |
|---|---|
| **Country of origin:** | USA |
| **Type:** | single-seat fighter-bomber |
| **Powerplant:** | one 3648kg (7800lb) Wright J65-W-2 turbojet |
| **Performance:** | maximum speed at sea level 1091km/h (678mph); service ceiling 16,640m (54,600ft); range 1344km (835 miles) |
| **Weights:** | empty 5051kg (11,125lb); maximum loaded 9350kg (20,611lb) |
| **Dimensions:** | wingspan 11.30m (37ft 1in); length 11.43m (37ft 6in); height 4.47m (14ft 8.75in); wing area 27.76sq m (288sq ft) |
| **Armament:** | six 0.5 Colt-Browning M-3 with 267 rpg, underwing hardpoints for two tanks or two stores of 454kg (1000lb), plus eight rockets |

# North American F-86D Sabre

**O**ne of the most famous combat aircraft of the post war era, the Sabre was developed to meet a US Army Air Force requirement for a day fighter that could also be used as an escort fighter or dive-bomber. The F-86D was designed as an all-weather interceptor, and although development did not commence until 1949 the first prototype flew from Muroc Dry Lake on December 22 of that year. The F-86D was highly complex for its time, and introduced the new concept of gunless collision-course interception directed by a AN/APG-36 search radar above the nose intake and an autopilot. This was the most extensively built of all the Sabre series, with 2,054 completed. At the peak of its deployment in the 1950s some 20 Air Defence Command wings were equipped with the type. This aircraft was supplied to many NATO countries under the Military Aid Program.

| | |
|---|---|
| **Country of origin:** | USA |
| **Type:** | single-seat all-weather/night interceptor |
| **Powerplant:** | one 3402kg (7500lb) General Electric J47-GE-17B or -33 turbojet |
| **Performance:** | maximum speed at sea level 1138km/h (707mph); service ceiling 16,640m (54,600ft); range 1344km (835 miles) |
| **Weights:** | empty 5656kg (12,470lb); maximum take-off 7756kg (17,100lb) |
| **Dimensions:** | wingspan 11.30m (37ft 1in); length 12.29m (40ft 4in); height 4.57m (15ft); wing area 27.76sq m (288sq ft) |
| **Armament:** | 24 2.75in 'Mighty Mouse' air-to-air rocket projectiles in retractable tray under cockpit floor |

# North American F-86F Sabre

The F-86F Sabre was basically an uprated version of the F-84E, which had introduced the powered all-flying tailplane and slatted wing. The F-86F had further refinements, such as an extended leading edge, increased chord and a small wing fence. Both aircraft saw extensive service in the Vietnam conflict. The first Sabre units in Korea were equipped with the earlier 'A' model; the 'F' began to arrive in theatre with the 8th and 18th Fighter Bomber Wings in early 1953. The aircraft was flown brilliantly against the MiG-15. Despite having marginally inferior performance to the Russian aircraft, the disparity was more than matched by the superior training and experience of American pilots. Total production of the F-86F totalled 1079; from 1954 many were delivered to America's allies under the Military Aid Program.

| Country of origin: | USA |
| --- | --- |
| Type: | single-seat fighter-bomber |
| Powerplant: | one 2710kg (5970lb) General Electric J47-GE-27turbojet |
| Performance: | maximum speed at sea level 1091km/h (678mph); service ceiling 15,240m (50,000ft); range 1344km (835 miles) |
| Weights: | empty 5045kg (11,125lb); maximum loaded 9350kg (20,611lb) |
| Dimensions: | wingspan 11.30m (37ft 1in); length 11.43m (37ft 6in); height 4.47m (14ft 8.75in); wing area 27.76sq m (288sq ft) |
| Armament: | six 0.5 Colt-Browning M-3 with 267 rpg, underwing hardpoints for two tanks or two stores of 454kg (1000lb), plus eight rockets |

# North American F-100D Super Sabre

The resounding success of the Sabre made it only natural that North American would attempt to build a successor. This was planned from 1949 as a larger and more powerful machine able to exceed the speed of sound in level flight. After a very rapid development programme and with the first (479th) wing operational, the F-100A was grounded in November 1954 due to stability problems. After modifications to the wings and fin, the F-100 enjoyed a trouble-free and successful career. The 203 A fighter versions produced were followed by structurally strengthened C fighter-bombers, a flap and autopilot equipped D variant and a tandem seat F model. Total production was 2294, with many aircraft serving in Vietnam. The F-100D was an improved version with larger fin and rudder, increased external stores capacity, and for the first time, landing flaps.

| | |
|---|---|
| Country of origin: | USA |
| Type: | single-seat fighter-bomber |
| Powerplant: | one 7711kg (17,000lb) Pratt & Whitney J57-P-21A turbojet |
| Performance: | maximum speed at 10,670m (35,000ft) 1390km/h (864mph); service ceiling 14,020m (46,000ft); range with inernal fuel 966km (600 miles) |
| Weights: | empty 9525kg (21,000lb); maximum take-off 15,800kg (34,832lb) |
| Dimensions: | wingspan 11.82m (38ft 9.5in); length excluding probe 14.36m (47ft 1.25in); height 4.95m (16ft 3in); wing area 35.77sq m (385sq ft) |
| Armament: | four 20mm cannon; eight external hardpoints with provision for two drop tanks and up to 3402kg (7500lb) of stores, bombs, cluster bombs, dispenser weapons, rocket-launcher pods, cannon pods, and ECM pods |

# North American A-5A Vigilante

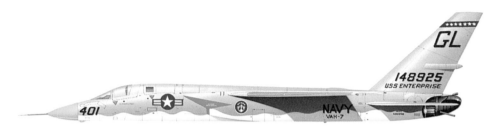

When it was introduced the Vigilante boasted some of the newest technology of any aircraft, including automatically scheduled engine inlets and nozzles, single surface vertical tail, differential slab tailplanes, linear bomb bay between the engines and a comprehensive radar-inertial navigation system. The aircraft was designed for carrier-based all-weather nuclear strike operations, and it became operational in this role in June 1961 with Navy Squadron VAH-7. The primary weapon of the A-5A was a free-fall nuclear weapon ejected rearwards from the bomb bay. The A-5A had only a short career as a strike aircraft as the US carrier force was relieved of its nuclear strike role; most were converted to reconnaissance aircraft. Total production was 57 aircraft, before the type was superseded by the improved A-5B.

| | |
|---|---|
| Country of origin: | USA |
| Type: | carrier-based attack aircraft |
| Powerplant: | two 7332kg (16,150lb) General Electric J79-2 turbojets |
| Performance: | maximum speed at altitude 2230km/h (1385mph); service ceiling 20,400m (67,000ft); range with drop tanks 5150km (3200 miles) |
| Weights: | empty 17,240kg (38,000lb); maximum loaded 36,285kg (80,000lb) |
| Dimensions: | wingspan 16.15m (53ft); length 23.11m (75ft 10in); height 5.92m (19ft 5in); wing area 70.05sq m (754sq ft) |
| Armament: | internal bomb bay with provision for nuclear weapons |

# North American RA-5C Vigilante

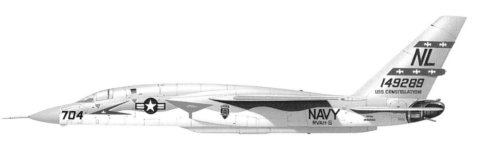

When the US Navy gave up its nuclear strike role, the 57 A-5A Vigilantes were followed into service by a reconnaissance version designated the RA-5C. These aircraft formed the airborne element of an integrated intelligence system serving the whole fleet and other forces. Originally designated A3J-3P, the RA-5C flew in prototype form in June 1962. Integrated into the aircraft were all the improvements in range and aerodynamic design that had been developed for the abandoned A-5B project. Fifty-five new production aircraft were built, and all but four of the original A-5A bomber aircraft were converted to RA-5C standard. RVAH-5, operating from USS *Ranger*, were the first unit to operate the aircraft. The aircraft pictured was operated by Heavy Recon Attack Squadron 6, known as the 'Fleurs'. The 'NL' tail code denotes the USS *Constellation*.

| | |
|---|---|
| Country of origin: | USA |
| Type: | carrier-based long-range reconnaissance aircraft |
| Powerplant: | two 8101kg (17,860lb) General Electric J79-GE-10 turbojets |
| Performance: | maximum speed at altitude 2230km/h (1385mph); service ceiling 20,400m (67,000ft); range with drop tanks 5150km (3200 miles) |
| Weights: | empty 17,009kg (37,498lb); maximum loaded 36,285kg (80,000lb) |
| Dimensions: | wingspan 16.15m (53ft); length 23.11m (75ft 10in); height 5.92m (19ft 5in); wing area 70.05sq m (754sq ft) |

# North American XB-70 Valkyrie

Unquestionably one of the most impressive aircraft ever built, the XB-70 was a large delta-wing Mach 3 strategic bomber designed to replace Strategic Air Command B-52s in service in the mid-1960s. The initial US Air Force requirement was issued in 1954, and the North American design was selected for development in 1957. Budgetary cut-backs meant that by 1959 the programme had been reduced to a single prototype, although this was partially restored in 1960 with a further $265 million made available for development. The first prototype flew in September 1964, with Mach 3 achieved just over 12 months later. Tragically, the second prototype was lost in a mid-air collision with an F-104 chase plane in June 1966. The surviving aircraft passed to NASA and the programme was terminated in 1969.

| Country of origin: | USA |
|---|---|
| Type: | long-range strategic bomber |
| Powerplant: | six 14,074kg (31,000lb) General Electric YJ93-GE-3 turbojets |
| Performance: | maximum speed at 24,400m (80,000ft) 3185km/h (1,980mph); service ceiling 24,400m (80,000ft); range 12,067km (7500 miles) |
| Weights: | maximum loaded 238,350kg (525,000lb) |
| Dimensions: | wingspan 32.03m (105ft); length 57.64m (189ft); height 9.15m (30ft); wing area 585.62sq m (6,297sq ft) |

# Northrop A-17

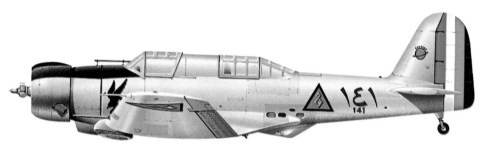

The A-17 was a development of the Gamma 2 transport for the attack role, and the first of 110 A-17 aircraft was delivered in July 1935. There followed 129 examples of the A-17A with an uprated engine and retractable landing gear, and two examples of the A-17AS three-seat command transport. All the American aircraft had been relegated to second-line tasks before the USA's entry into World War II, but a number of aircraft (built as DB-8s after Douglas's take-over of Northrop) were exported and some of these played a more active role. The exports included 102 (including licence-built) aircraft for Sweden as well as 17, 20, 36 and 10 for Iraq, the Netherlands, Norway and Peru respectively. Peru also ordered 34 other aircraft that were impressed for US service as A-33s. These aircraft were armed with six 7.62mm machine guns and had a potential bomb load of 816kg (1800lb). France and the UK received 32 and 61 aircraft respectively.

| | |
|---|---|
| Country of origin: | USA |
| Type: | (A-17A) two-seat attack warplane |
| Powerplant: | one 825hp (615kW) Pratt & Whitney R-1535-13 14-cylinder two-row radial engine |
| Performance: | maximum speed 354km/h (220mph); climb to 1525m (5000ft) in 3 minutes 54 seconds; service ceiling 5915m (19,400ft); range 1923km (1195 miles) |
| Weights: | empty 2316kg (5106lb); maximum take-off 3425kg (7550lb) |
| Dimensions: | span 14.55m (47ft 9in); length 9.65m (31ft 8in); height 3.66m (12ft ) |
| Armament: | four 0.3in fixed forward-firing machine guns in leading edges of the wing, and one 0.3in trainable rearward-firing machine in the rear of the cockpit with provision for its use in the ventral hatch position, plus an internal and external bomb load of 544kg (1200lb) |

# Northrop N-3PB

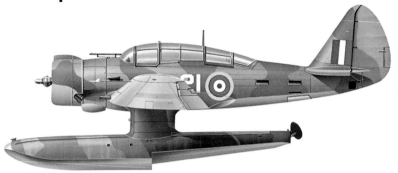

The N-3PB clearly owed much to the cantilever low-wing monoplanes that 'Jack' Northrop had designed while part of the Douglas Aircraft Company. In 1940 a Norwegian purchasing commission placed an order for 24 of the floatplanes, but shortly after this the Germans invaded the country and soon overran it. The Norwegian government-in-exile maintained its order for the N-3PB, and the first example flew in January 1941. By April 1941 all the aircraft had been delivered to 'Little Norway', the Norwegian base area in Canada. One squadron operated the type, flying 18 of the floatplanes from three bases in Iceland on convoy escort patrols under the auspices of an RAF unit. By the summer of 1942 it was clear that the N-3PB was unsuitable for the task and the aircraft were relegated to the training role. Pictured here is an N3-PB of the Royal Norwegian Naval Air Service, operating as No 330 Squadron RAF Coastal Command during 1941–42.

| | |
|---|---|
| **Country of origin:** | USA |
| **Type:** | (N-3PB) three-seat coastal reconnaissance and convoy escort floatplane |
| **Powerplant:** | one 1100hp (820kW) Wright GR-1820-G205A Cyclone nine-cylinder single-row radial engine |
| **Performance:** | maximum speed 414km/h (257mph); climb to 4570m (15,000ft) in 14 minutes 24 seconds; service ceiling 7315m (24,000ft); range 1609 km (1000 miles) |
| **Weights:** | empty 2808kg (6190lb); maximum take-off 4808kg (10,600lb) |
| **Dimensions:** | span 14.91m (48ft 11in); length 10.97m (36ft); height 3.66m (12ft) |
| **Armament:** | four 0.5in fixed forward-firing machine guns in leading edges of wing, one 0.3in machine gun in rear of cockpit, and one 0.3in machine gun in ventral position, plus a load of 907kg (2000lb) |

# Northrop P-61A Black Widow

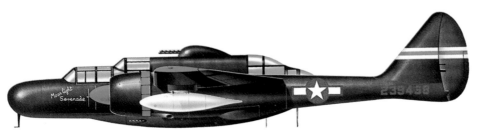

Although it did not possess the performance or the firepower of the German Heinkel He 219 Uhu, the Black Widow was still an immensely potent and impressive night-fighter with the additional advantage of being able to undertake the nocturnal intruder role with a very heavy disposable load. The first of two XP-61 prototypes made its maiden flight in May 1942 as very large twin-engined aircraft with a central nacelle for the crew, radar and armament, and the tail unit supported by the twin booms that were rearward extensions of the engine nacelles. There followed 13 YP-61 service test aircraft before the P-61A (200 aircraft) entered service in the summer of 1944. All the aircraft had a primary armament of four 20mm cannon, and the first 37 also featured a power-operated dorsal barbette carrying four 0.5in machine guns that was then omitted for reasons of buffet. P-61As began to enter service in the Pacific theatre in the first half of 1944.

| | |
|---|---|
| Country of origin: | USA |
| Type: | (P-61A) two/three-seat night-fighter |
| Powerplant: | two 2250 hp (1678kW) Pratt & Whitney R-2800-65 18-cylinder two-row radial engines |
| Performance: | maximum speed 594km/h (369mph); climb to 4570m (15,000ft) in 7 minutes 36 seconds; service ceiling 10,090m (33,100ft); range 3058km (1900 miles) |
| Weights: | empty 9510kg (20,965lb); maximum take-off 15,513kg (34,200lb) |
| Dimensions: | span 20.12m (66ft); length 14.91m (48ft 11in); height 4.46m (14ft 8in ) |
| Armament: | four 20mm fixed forward-firing cannon in the underside of the forward fuselage and, in the first 37 aircraft, four 0.5in trainable machine guns in a remotely controlled dorsal barbette |

# Northrop T-38A Talon

The T-38A trainer aircraft was derived from a requirement issued by the US government in the mid-1950s for a lightweight fighter to supply to friendly nations under the Military Assistance Program. The initial privately funded Northrop design formed the basis for a family of aircraft which also included the F-5A Freedom Fighter, to which the T-38 bears a strong physical similarity. Three YT-38 prototypes were ordered as part of a provisional contract awarded to Northrop in 1956. After three years of development, flight trials were undertaken to assess the performance of different powerplants, before service began with the USAF in March 1961. The aircraft has proved highly successful in service, with 1139 completed. Approximately 700 are still in service. An upgrade programme is in progress which will see their service life extended to 2020. Portugal and Turkey also use the aircraft and are likely to continue doing so for some years.

| | |
|---|---|
| Country of origin: | USA |
| Type: | two-seat supersonic basic trainer |
| Powerplant: | two 1746kg (3850lb) General Electric J85-GE-5 turbojets |
| Performance: | maximum speed at 10,975m (36,000ft) 1381km/h (858mph); service ceiling 16,340m (53,600ft); range with internal fuel 1759km (1093 miles) |
| Weights: | empty 3254kg (7174lb); maximum take-off 5361kg (11,820lb) |
| Dimensions: | wingspan 7.7m (25ft 3in); length 14.14m (46ft 4.5in); height 3.92m (12ft 10.5in); wing area 15.79sq m (170sq ft) |

# Northrop F-5A Freedom Fighter

In 1955, Northrop began the design of a lightweight fighter powered by two underslung J85 missile engines. This was yet another of the countless projects born during the Korean era when pilots were calling for lighter, simpler fighters with higher performance. The design team led by Welko Gasich refined the design, putting the engines in the fuselage and increasing their size. From this aircraft, the T-38 Talon, was developed the F-5A, which was largely a privately funded project by Northrop. In October 1962 the US Department of Defense decided to buy the aircraft in large numbers to supply to friendly countries on advantageous terms. More than 1000 were supplied to Iran, Taiwan, Greece, South Korea, Phillipines, Turkey, Ethiopia, Morocco, Norway, Thailand, Libya, and South Vietnam. The aircraft pictured is an F-5A of the 341 Mira, Hellenic (Greek) air force.

| | |
|---|---|
| Country of origin: | USA |
| Type: | light tactical fighter |
| Powerplant: | two 1850kg (4080lb) General Electric J85-GE-13 turbojets |
| Performance: | maximum speed at 10,975m (36,000ft) 1487km/h (924mph); service ceiling 15,390m (50,500ft); combat radius with maximum warload 314km (195 miles) |
| Weights: | empty 3667kg (8085lb); maximum take-off 9374kg (20,667lb) |
| Dimensions: | wingspan 7.7m (25ft 3in); length 14.38m (47ft 2in); height 4.01m (13ft 2in); wing area 15.79sq m (170sq ft) |
| Armament: | two 20mm M39 cannon with 280 rpg; provision for 1996kg (4400lb) of stores on external pylons, (including two air-to-air missiles on wingtip pylons), bombs, cluster bombs, rocket launcher pods |

# Northrop F-5E Tiger II

The F-5E Tiger II won a US industry competition in November 1970 for a follow-on International Fighter Aircraft to replace the F-5A. The improved aircraft is equipped with a more powerful powerplant, extending nosegear to improve short field performance, extra fuel in a longer fuselage, new inlet ducts, widened fuselage and wing, root extensions ad manoeuvring flaps. Deliveries began in 1972. The US Air Force operates the aircraft for aggressor training in the USA, UK and the Philippines. The aircraft pictured is operated by the US Navy's Fighter Weapons School at Naval Air Station Miramar in California. The manouevrability of the F-5 makes it a formidable opponent in air combat training. A two-seat trainer version is also produced with designation F-JF. Both aircraft retain full combat capability. The F-5E has also been supplied to the Royal Saudi Air Force.

| | |
|---|---|
| Country of origin: | USA |
| Type: | light tactical fighter |
| Powerplant: | two 2268kg (5000lb) General Electric J85-GE-21B turbojets |
| Performance: | maximum speed at 10,975m (36,000ft) 1741km/h (1082mph); service ceiling 15,790m (51,800ft); combat radius with maximum warload 306km (190 miles) |
| Weights: | empty 4410kg (9723lb); maximum take-off 11,214kg (24,722lb) |
| Dimensions: | wingspan 8.13m (26ft 8in); length 14.45m (47ft 4.75in); height 4.07m (13ft 4.25in); wing area 17.28sq m (186sq ft) |
| Armament: | two 20mm M39 cannon with 280 rpg; two air-to-air missiles on wingtip pylons, five external pylons with provision for 3175kg (7000lb) of stores, including air-to-surface missiles, bombs, cluster bombs, rocket launcher pods, ECM pods, and drop tanks |

# Northrop-Grumman B-2 Spirit

The B-2 has been developed from 1978 to a US Air Force requirement for a strategic penetration bomber to complement and replace the Rockwell B-1 Lancer and the Boeing B-52 Stratofortress. The aircraft was designed to incorporate low-observables (stealth technology), with Northrop as the prime contractor. The characteristic flying-wing stems from the extensive research carried out by the company in the 1950s. The B-2s radar reflectivity is very low because of smooth blended surfaces and the use of radiation-absorbent materials. Careful mixing of hot exhaust gases with cold airstream air reduces thermal and acoustic signals to a very significant extent. The original production order was cut from 132 to approximately 20 aircraft, partly because of the enormous unit costs (over $1 billion), and also because of the reduced threat from the former USSR.

| Country of origin: | USA |
|---|---|
| Type: | strategic bomber and missile-launch platform |
| Powerplant: | four 8618kg (19,000lb) General Electric F118-GE-110 turbofans |
| Performance: | maximum speed at high altitude 764km/h (475mph); service ceiling 15,240m (50,000ft); range on high level mission with standard fuel and 16,919kg (37,300lb) warload 11,675km (7255 miles) |
| Weights: | empty 45,360kg (100,000lb); maximum take-off 181,437kg (400,000lb) |
| Dimensions: | wingspan 52.43m (172ft); length 21.03m (69ft); height 5.18m (17ft); wing area more than 464.50sq m (5,000sq ft) |
| Armament: | two internal bomb bays with provision for up to 22,680kg (50,000lb) of stores; each bay can carry one eight-round Boeing Rotary launcher for a total of 16 1.1 megaton B83 thermonuclear free-fall bombs, 22 680kg (1500lb) bombs, or 80 227kg (500lb) free-fall bombs |

# PZL P.23 Karas

Stemming from the P.13 project for a six-passenger transport, the P.23 Karas (Crucian Carp) was a light bomber and army co-operation warplane. The P.23/I Karas was the first of three prototypes and flew in August 1934. A number of problems had to be overcome before the type was ordered into production as the P.23A trainer with the 590hp (440kW) Pegasus IIM2 engine and P.23B operational model with an uprated engine (40 and 210 aircraft respectively). With their fixed landing gear, indifferent performance, poor armament and cramped accommodation, the aircraft suffered very heavy losses in the German invasion of September 1939 before 31 survivors were flown to Romania. Another 54 aircraft were delivered to Bulgaria in two P.43 variants with Gnome-Rhòne radial engines. Pictured is a P.23B operated by No 42 Squadron, Polish Air Force attached to the Pomorze Army in September 1939.

| | |
|---|---|
| Country of origin: | Poland |
| Type: | (P.23B Karas) three-seat light reconnaissance bomber |
| Powerplant: | one 680hp (507kW) PZL (Bristol) Pegasus VIII nine-cylinder single-row radial engine |
| Performance: | maximum speed 300km/h (186mph); climb to 2000m (6560ft) in 4 minutes 45 seconds; service ceiling 7300m (23,950ft); range 1400km (870 miles) |
| Weights: | empty 1928kg (4250lb); maximum take-off 3526kg (7773lb) |
| Dimensions: | span 13.95m (45ft 9.25in); length 9.68m (31ft 9.25in); height 3.30m (10ft 10in) |
| Armament: | one 7.7mm fixed forward-firing machine gun in the forward fuselage, one 7.7mm trainable rearward-firing machine gun with 600 rounds in the rear cockpit, and one 7.7mm machine gun in the ventral position, plus an external bomb load of 700kg (1543lb) |

# PZL P.24

**P**oland's best fighter at the time of Germany's invasion in September 1939, the P.24 was a more powerfully engined development of the P.11, itself an upgraded Bristol Mercury-engined version of the P.7 with the Bristol Jupiter engine. All three types were therefore braced gull-wing monoplanes with fixed landing gear. As first flown in 1933, the P.24 introduced the more powerful Gnome-Rhône 14K engine, spatted main landing gear wheels, and a strengthened structure. Production totalled about 300 aircraft including export models, and the main variants were the P.24A with cannon and an enclosed cockpit, the P.24B with modified wheel spats, the P.24C development of the P.24A with machine gun armament, the P.24E with an uprated engine, and the P.24F and P.24G improved versions of the P.24A with cannon and machine gun armament respectively. The aircraft shown here is a P.24C of the 4th Regiment, Turkish Air Force, based at Kütaha in 1939.

| Country of origin: | Poland |
| --- | --- |
| Type: | (P.24F) single-seat fighter |
| Powerplant: | one 970hp (723kW) Gnome-Rhône 14N-07 14-cylinder two-row radial engine |
| Performance: | maximum speed 430km/h (267mph); climb to 5000m (16,405ft) in 5 minutes 40 seconds; service ceiling 10,500m (34,450ft); range 700km (435 miles) |
| Weights: | empty 1332kg (2937lb); maximum take-off 2000kg (4409lb) |
| Dimensions: | span 10.68m (35ft 0.75in); length 7.60m (24ft 11.5in); height 2.69m (8ft 10.25in) |
| Armament: | two 20mm fixed forward-firing cannon and two 7.92mm fixed forward-firing machine guns the leading edges of the wing, plus an external bomb load of 40kg (88lb) |

# PZL P.37 Los

The Los ('Elk') was the most modern Polish warplane at the time of the German invasion, and at a technical level compared favourably with the best medium bombers in service anywhere in the world. The P.37/I was the first of three prototypes and flew June 1936. The relatively swift solution to a number of early problems paved the way for orders for 180 production aircraft as the P.37A with 873hp (651kW) Pegasus XIIB engines, a single vertical tail surface and single-wheel main landing gear units, the P.37Abis with twin vertical surfaces, and the P.37B with an uprated powerplant, a redesigned cockpit, twin vertical surfaces and twin-wheel landing gear units: deliveries amounted to 10, 20 and about 60 aircraft respectively. Export aircraft with Gnome-Rhône engines were ordered by Bulgaria, Romania, Turkey and Yugoslavia, but none was completed. Pictured is a P.37B Los B of the Bomber Brigade, Dispositional Air Force, Polish Air Force, in September 1939.

| Country of origin: | Poland |
| --- | --- |
| Type: | (P.37B) four-seat medium reconnaissance bomber |
| Powerplant: | two 918hp (684.5kW) PZL (Bristol) Pegasus XX nine-cylinder single-row radial engines |
| Performance: | maximum speed 445km/h (277mph); service ceiling 9250m (30,350ft); range 1500km (932 miles) with a 2200kg (4850lb) bomb load |
| Weights: | empty 4280kg (9436lb); maximum take-off 8900kg (19,621lb) |
| Dimensions: | span 17.93m (58ft 10in); length 12.92m (42ft 4.7in); height 5.08m (16ft 8in) |
| Armament: | one 7.7mm trainable forward-firing machine gun in nose position, one 7.7mm trainable rearward-firing machine gun in the dorsal position, and one 7.7mm trainable rearward-firing machine gun in ventral position, plus an internal bomb load of 2580kg (5688lb) |

# PZL Mielec TS-11 Iskra-bis B

The Polish-designed TS-11 Iskra ('Spark') two-seat trainer was selected by the Polish air force for production in 1961, despite having lost a Soviet air force competition for such an aircraft to the Aero L-29. The aircraft became operational in 1964; improvements were made to the basic powerplant and production of the two-seat version continued until mid-1979. A single-seat reconnaissance version was also produced before this time. Production resumed in 1982 of an improved combat/reconnaissance version, and ceased in the late 1980s, with more than 600 aircraft completed. The aircraft was also produced for the Indian air force who took delivery of 50. The aircraft was being replaced in Polish service by the I-22 Iryda, but problems with the Iryda have led to a new competition for an advanced trainer. The IAF will gradually replace their aircraft with the BAe Hawk 115.

| Country of origin: | Poland |
| --- | --- |
| Type: | two-seat combat/reconnaissance trainer |
| Powerplant: | one 1100kg (2425lb) IL SO-3W turbojet |
| Performance: | maximum speed at 5000m (16,405ft) 770km/h (478mph); service ceiling 11,000m (36,090ft); range on internal fuel 1260km (783 miles) |
| Weights: | empty 2560kg (5644lb); maximum take-off 3840kg (8,66lb) |
| Dimensions: | wingspan 10.06m (33ft); length 11.15m (36ft 7in); height 3.5m (11ft 5.75in); wing area 17.50sq m (188.37sq ft) |
| Armament: | one 23mm cannon, four external hardpoints for a variety of weapons up to a total of 400kg (882lb) |

# PZL I-22 Iryda

The PZL I-22 Iryda was designed by a team at the Istytut Lotnictwa led by Alfred Baron to replace the TS-11 Iskra as the primary jet trainer of the Polish air force. The I-22 is a far more versatile aircraft, with the capability for advanced pilot training in roles such as ground attack, air combat and reconnaissance. The aircraft has a useful weapons load and can also undertake light attack missions. The aircraft is similar in both configuration and appearance to the Dassault/Dornier Alpha Jet, and has broadly similar performance. Pictured is one of the prototype aircraft; production deliveries to the Polish air force began in 1993, although with the dominance of the Aero L-29 in the inventories of former Eastern Bloc nations it was unlikely to enjoy major export success. In fact a series of problems led to the aircraft being grounded. The air force is now seeking a replacement trainer. The aircraft pictured is the first of the two prototypes, and first flew in March 1985.

| | |
|---|---|
| Country of origin: | Poland |
| Type: | two-seat multi-role trainer and light close-support aircraft |
| Powerplant: | two 1100kg (2425lb) PZL-Rzeszow SO-3W22 turbojets |
| Performance: | maximum speed at 5000m (16,405ft) 840km/h (522mph); service ceiling 11,000m (36,090ft); range with maximum warload 420km (261 miles) |
| Weights: | empty 4700kg (10,361lb); maximum take-off 6900kg (15,211lb) |
| Dimensions: | wingspan 9.6m (31ft 6in); length 13.22m (43ft 4.5in); height 4.3m (14ft 1.25in); wing area 19.92sq m (214.42sq ft) |
| Armament: | one 23mm GSh-23L cannon with 200 rds, four external hardpoints with provision for 1200kg (2645lb) of stores, including bombs, rocket launcher pods and drop tanks |

# Panavia Tornado GR1

A huge amount of planning went into the Tornado Multi-Role Combat Aircraft. Feasibility studies began in 1967, with the tri-national Panavia company formed in 1969 by collaboration between BAC, MBB and Aeritalia. The RB.199 turbofan was selected as the powerplant, to be built by the Turbo-Union (Rolls-Royce, MTU and Fiat) conglomerate. Each of the participating nations wanted different things from the aircraft, and the resolution of a design to meet the majority of these requirements in a single airframe represents a triumph for collaboration. The first prototype flew in August 1974, with service deliveries to the Tri-National Tornado Training Establishment at RAF Cottesmore in 1981. The RAF received 229 GR1 strike aircraft; the Lufwaffe received 212 which are used in a similar role; the Marineflieger (German naval air arm) ordered 112, and the Italian air force 100. The RAF's aircraft have now been updated to GR4 standard.

| | |
|---|---|
| Country of origin: | Germany, Italy and UK |
| Type: | multi-role combat aircraft |
| Powerplant: | two 7292kg (16,075lb) Turbo-Union RB.199-34R Mk 103 turbofans |
| Performance: | maximum speed above 11,000m (36,090ft) 2337km/h (1,452mph); service ceiling 15,240m (50,000ft); combat radius with weapon load on hi-lo-hi mission 1390km (864 miles) |
| Weights: | empty 14,091kg (31,065lb); maximum take-off 27,216kg (60,000lb) |
| Dimensions: | wingspan 13.91m (45ft 7in) spread and 8.6m (28ft 2.5in) swept; length 16.72m (54ft 10in); height 5.95m ( 19ft 6.25in); wing area 26.60sq m (286.3sq ft) |
| Armament: | two 27mm IWKA-Mauser cannon with 180 rpg, seven external hard-points with provision for up to 9000kg (19,840lb) of stores, including nuclear and JP233 runway denial weapon, ALARM anti-radiation missiles, air-to-air, air-to-surface and anti-ship missiles, conventional and guided bombs, cluster bombs, ECM pods and drop tanks |

# Panavia Tornado ADV

In the late 1960s the RAF saw the need to replace its McDonnell Douglas Phantom II and BAe Lighting interceptors, and ordered the development of the Tornado ADV (Air Defence Variant), a dedicated air-defence aircraft with all-weather capability, in based on the same airframe as the GR1 ground attack aircraft. It was realised early in the programme that to attain adequate fighter performance it would be necessary to recess the primary armament of the aircraft, the BAe Sky Flash air-to-air missile, under the fuselage centreline. Full development was authorised in March 1976, and the aircraft shares 80 percent commonality with its predecessor. Structural changes include a lengthened nose for the Foxhunter radar, and a slight increase in the fuselage length. Deliveries of 18 F2s to the RAF were followed by 155 F3 aircraft with Mk 104 engines. The aircraft was sold to Saudi Arabia and Italy has leased 24 ex-RAF F3s for air cover until the Eurofighter enters service.

| | |
|---|---|
| Country of origin: | Germany, Italy and UK |
| Type: | all-weather air defence aircraft |
| Powerplant: | two 7493kg (16,520lb) Turbo-Union RB.199-34R Mk 104 turbofans |
| Performance: | maximum speed above 11,000m (36,090ft) 2337km/h (1452mph); operational ceiling about 21,335m (70,000ft); intercept radius more than 1853km (1150 miles) |
| Weights: | empty 14,501kg (31,970lb); maximum take-off 27,987kg (61,700lb) |
| Dimensions: | wingspan 13.91m (45ft 7.75in) spread and 8.6m (28ft 2.5in) swept; length 18.68m (61ft 3in); height 5.95m ( 19ft 6.25in); wing area 26.60sq m (286.3sq ft) |
| Armament: | two 27mm IWKA-Mauser cannon with 180 rpg, six external hardpoints with provision for up to 5806kg (12,800lb) of stores, including Sky Flash medium-range air-to-air missiles, AIM-9L Sidewinder short range air-to-air missiles and drop tanks |

# Petlyakov Pe-2

The Pe-2 may be regarded as the Soviet counterpart of the de Havilland Mosquito and Junkers Ju 88, although it differed from its British and German counterparts in being optimised for the purely tactical role in a host of variants that were built to the extent of 11,427 aircraft. The origins of the design can be found in the VI-100 prototype for a high-altitude fighter that flew in 1939/40, but the design was then revised as the PB-100 dive-bomber with three rather than two crew members in unpressurised accommodation, a powerplant optimised for lower-altitude operations, and different armament including a lower-fuselage bomb bay. The PB-100 prototype was a conversion of the second VI-100, and first flew in June 1940. Later in the same month the decision was taken for the PB-100 to be placed in immediate production with a number of minor changes as the Pe-2. This proved to be the outstanding Soviet tactical bomber of World War II.

| | |
|---|---|
| Country of origin: | USSR |
| Type: | (Pe-2) three-seat multi-role attack bomber |
| Powerplant: | two 1100hp (820kW) Klimov VK-105RA 12-cylinder Vee engines |
| Performance: | maximum speed 540km/h (335mph); climb to 5000m (16,405ft) in 7 minutes; service ceiling 8800m (28,870ft); range 1500km (932 miles) with a 2205lb (1000kg) bomb load |
| Weights: | empty 5870kg (12,943lb); maximum take-off 8495kg (18,728lb) |
| Dimensions: | span 17.16m (56ft 3.7in); length 12.66m (41ft 6.5in); height 4.00m (13ft 1.5in) |
| Armament: | two 7.62mm fixed forward-firing machine guns in the nose, one 7.62mm trainable rearward-firing machine gun in the dorsal position, and one 7.62mm trainable rearward-firing machine gun in the ventral position, plus an internal and external bomb load of 1600kg (3527lb) |

# Petlyakov Pe-2FT

The original version of the Pe-2 was supplanted from the spring of 1942 by the Pe-2FT that featured improved defensive armament (single 7.62mm machine guns in a dorsal turret and either of two beam positions), removal of the underwing dive brakes, reduction of the nose glazing and, as availability permitted from February 1943, an uprated powerplant. Further development resulted in operational models such as the Pe-2R long-range photo-reconnaissance model with greater fuel capacity, the Pe-2UT dual-control trainer with a revised cockpit, and the Pe-3 multi-purpose fighter with a fixed forward-firing armament of two 20mm cannon and two 12.7mm machine guns, single 12.7mm trainable machine guns in the dorsal and ventral positions, and underwing provision for 132mm rockets. There were also many experimental developments. Pictured is a Pe-2FT of the Soviet Air Force, operating over the Eastern Front in the latter part of World War II.

| | |
|---|---|
| Country of origin: | USSR |
| Type: | (Pe-2FT) three-seat multi-role attack bomber |
| Powerplant: | two 1260hp (939.5kW) Klimov VK-105PF 12-cylinder Vee engines |
| Performance: | maximum speed 580km/h (360mph); climb to 5000m (16,405ft) in 9 minutes 18 seconds; service ceiling 8800m (28,870ft); range 1315km (817 miles) with a 1000kg (2205lb) bomb load |
| Weights: | empty 5950kg (13,119lb); maximum take-off 8520kg (18,783lb) |
| Dimensions: | span 17.11m (56ft 1.7in); length 12.78m (41ft 11in); height 3.42m (11ft 2.67in) |
| Armament: | two 7.62mm or one 7.62mm and one 12.7mm fixed forward-firing machine guns in nose, one 7.62mm machine gun in dorsal turret, one 7.62mm or 12.7mm trainable machine gun in ventral position, and one 7.62mm or 12.7mm trainable lateral-firing machine gun in window positions, plus a bomb load of 1600kg (3527lb) |

# Pfalz D.III

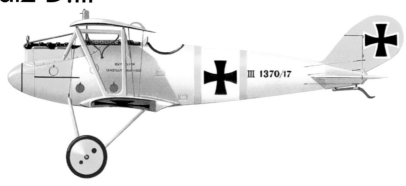

III 1370/17

The Pfalz Flugzeug-Werke GmbH began producing aircraft in 1913. At first it built Morane monoplanes and other types under licence. The D.III was a completely fresh design into which company designer Robert Thelen incorporated much experience gained in 1916-17 with the production of LFG-Roland fighters. Though fractionally inferior in performance to the best contemporary Albatros and Fokker scouts, the III and IIIa were strong and well-liked by pilots. The monocoque fuselage was well streamlined and owed much to Deperdussin construction principles. However production was delayed due to a lack of skilled workers. About 600 were built, the more powerful IIIa having rounded wings and tailplane, and the guns located on top of the nose to allow for easier maintenance. A single example of an experimental triplane version of the D.III was built, but this was never flown. Pictured is the D.III flown by Vzfw Hecht of Jasta 10 based near Courtrai.

| Country of origin: | Germany |
| --- | --- |
| Type: | single-seat fighter |
| Powerplant: | one 180hp (134kW) Mercedes D.IIIa inline piston engine |
| Performance: | maximum speed 165km/h (103mph); service ceiling 5180m (17,000ft); range 350km (217 miles) |
| Weights: | empty 750kg (1,653lb); maximum take-off weight 935kg (2061lb) |
| Dimensions: | span 9.4m (30ft 10in); length 6.95m (22ft 9 1/2in); height 2.67m (8ft 9in); wing area 22.1sq m (237.89sq ft) |
| Armament: | two fixed forward-firing 7.92mm LMG 08/15 machine-guns |

# Plage & Laskiewicz (Lublin) R-XIII

In the late 1920s the Polish Air Force and naval air arm were starting an expansion and upgrade programme involving the procurement of machines of Polish design and manufacture. One of the new types was the R-XIII liaison and observation aeroplane, a development of the R-XIV, and this was then produced in a complex series of variants with wheeled landing gear and float alighting gear. The prototype first flew in July 1931, and total manufacture of 273 aircraft included major variants such as the initial R-XIIIA and follow-on R-XIIIB with an improved gun mounting, the R-XIIIbis floatplane, the R-XIIIC improved R-XIIIB, the R-XIIID improved R-XIIIC, the R-XIIIter/hydro improved floatplane, and R-XIIIF with the 420hp (313kW) Skoda G.1620A Mors A engine. Although already obsolescent by the outbreak of war in 1939, the type equipped seven observation squadrons and suffered heavy losses, mainly to German ground fire.

| | |
|---|---|
| **Country of origin:** | Poland |
| **Type:** | (R-XIIID) two-seat observation and liaison aeroplane |
| **Powerplant:** | one 220hp (164kW) Skoda-built Wright Whirlwind J-5 seven-cylinder single-row radial engine |
| **Performance:** | maximum speed 195km/h (121mph); climb to 3000m (9845ft) in 15 minutes 50 seconds; service ceiling 4450m (14,600ft); range 600km (373 miles) |
| **Weights:** | empty 887kg (1956lb); normal take-off 1330kg (2932lb) |
| **Dimensions:** | span 13.20m (43ft 4in); length 8.46m (27ft 9.25in); height 2.76m (9ft 0.25in) |
| **Armament:** | one or two 7.7mm trainable rearward-firing machine guns in the rear cockpit |

# Polikarpov I-15

From a time early in 1933 Nikolai Nikolayevich Polikarpov planned the I-15 as successor to his I-5 biplane fighter with a gulled upper wing (intended to improve the pilot's forward fields of vision) and a powerplant of one Wright R-1820-F Cyclone radial piston engine, a US unit being imported in limited numbers pending the start of licensed production as the M-25. The I-15 (404 with the 480hp/358kW M-22 and 270 with the M-25 engine) entered service in 1934. These were complemented and supplanted by the I-15bis (otherwise I-152) that was manufactured to the extent of 2408 aircraft may of which were still in limited service at the time of Germany's June 1941 invasion of the USSR. The I-15bis had the improved M-25V engine in a longer-chord cowling, a conventional upper wing, greater fuel capacity, and doubled gun firepower. Pictured is one of the 186 I-15bis aircraft supplied to support Chinese nationalist forces in Manchuria in 1937-38.

| | |
|---|---|
| **Country of origin:** | USSR |
| **Type:** | (I-15bis) single-seat fighter |
| **Powerplant:** | one 750hp (559kW) M-25B nine-cylinder single-row radial engine |
| **Performance:** | maximum speed 370km/h (230mph); climb to 1000m (3280ft) in 1 minute 6 seconds; service ceiling 9000m (29,530ft); range about 530km (329 miles) |
| **Weights:** | empty 1310kg (2888lb); maximum take-off 1730kg (3814lb) |
| **Dimensions:** | span 10.20m (33ft 5.5in); length 6.33m (20ft 9.25in); height 2.19m (7ft 2.25in) |
| **Armament:** | four 7.62mm fixed forward-firing machine guns in the upper part of the forward fuselage, plus an external bomb load of 100kg (220lb) |

# Polikarpov I-153

Otherwise known as the I-15ter, the I-153 was first flown in 1938 as an attempt to modernise the I-15bis by reducing drag. In this capacity the two most important changes were a reversion to the type of gulled upper wing used on the I-15, and the introduction of manually operated retractable main landing gear units. The type was built to the extent of 3437 aircraft and entered service in time for participation in the border incident with Japan in the summer of 1939. The type was also heavily involved in the Russo-Finnish 'Winter War' of 1939-40, and in the first part of the German invasion of the USSR from June 1941. The surviving I-153 aircraft were relegated to training service from the middle of 1943, although the Finns used captured aircraft as first-line fighters into 1944. The aircraft was flown with some degree of success by experienced pilots, but in the hands of less experienced aviators it could be a handful.

| Country of origin: | USSR |
| --- | --- |
| Type: | (I-153) single-seat fighter and fighter-bomber |
| Powerplant: | one 1000hp (746kW) Shvetsov M-62 nine-cylinder single-row radial engine |
| Performance: | maximum speed 444km/h (276mph); climb to 3000m (9845ft) in 3 minutes; service ceiling 35,105ft (10,700m); range 880km (547 miles) |
| Weights: | empty 1348kg (2972lb); maximum take-off 2110kg (4652lb) |
| Dimensions: | span 10.00m (32ft 9.5in); length 6.17m (20ft 2.9in); height 2.80m (9ft 2.25in) |
| Armament: | four 12.7mm fixed forward-firing machine guns in the forward fuselage, plus an external bomb and rocket load of 200kg (441lb) |

# Polikarpov I-16

**D**esigned at much the same time as the I-15, the I-16 was an altogether more advanced fighter in its basic concept, for it was the USSR's first cantilever low-wing monoplane fighter with retractable main landing gear units (although the landing gear had to be retracted by pumping a handle no less than 100 times!). The type first flew in December 1933, and immediately revealed decidedly tricky handling characteristics, especially in the longitudinal plane as a result of its short fuselage. Even so the type entered large-scale production (7005 aircraft excluding about 1640 two-seat trainers) and saw operational service up to 1942, latterly suffering very heavy losses. The I-16 was produced in 10 main variants between the I-16 Tip 1 with the 480hp (358kW) M-22 radial engine and the definitive I-16 Tip 24 with an altogether more powerful engine as well as considerably heavier and more diverse armament.

| | |
|---|---|
| **Country of origin:** | USSR |
| **Type:** | (I-16 Tip 24) single-seat fighter and fighter-bomber |
| **Powerplant:** | one 1100hp (820kW) Shvetsov M-63 nine-cylinder single-row radial engine |
| **Performance:** | maximum speed 489km/h (304mph); climb to 5000m (16,405ft) in 4 minutes; service ceiling 9000m (29,530ft); range 700km (435 miles) |
| **Weights:** | empty 1490kg (3285lb); maximum take-off 2095kg (4619lb) |
| **Dimensions:** | span 9.00m (29ft 6.33in); length 6.13m (20ft 1.3in); height 2.57m (8ft 5in) |
| **Armament:** | two 7.62mm fixed forward-firing machine guns in the upper part of the forward fuselage and two 7.62mm fixed forward-firing machine guns or two 20mm fixed forward-firing cannon in the leading edges of the wing, plus an external bomb and rocket load of 500kg (1102lb) |

# Potez 25 A.2

**B**efore incorporation into SNCASE in 1935, Potez was among the largest French aircraft manufacturers. The giant Potez works at Meaulte was established in 1920 by Henri Potez and from it came a long and highly successful series of single-engine military and civil aircraft. The Potez 25 was one of the most famous and extensively built military aircraft of the interwar period. It was developed from the earlier Potez 24 A.2 prototype, designed by Louis Coroller and first flown in 1924. After modifications it was flown as the Potez 25. Two basic versions were offered, the A.2 two-seat fighter and B.2 two-seat bomber. In all, nearly 4100 were built in 87 different variants for domestic and foreign markets. Most came from the manufacturer, although 300 were license built in Poland, 200 in Yugoslavia, 70 in Romania and 27 in Portugal. Pictured is a Potez 25 A.2 of the 2do Escadron de Reconocimiento y Bombardio of the Paraguayan Air Force, during operations against Bolivia in 1933.

| Country of origin: | France |
| --- | --- |
| Type: | two-seat general-purpose military aircraft |
| Powerplant: | one 450hp (335kW) Lorraine-Dietrich 12-cylinder Vee piston engine |
| Performance: | maximum speed 220km/h (137mph); service ceiling 7200m (23,620ft); range 660km (410 miles) |
| Weights: | empty equipped 1510kg (3329lb); maximum take-off weight 2500kg (5512lb) |
| Dimensions: | span 14.19m (46ft 7in); length 9.19m (30ft 2in); height 3.65m (11ft 11in); wing area 47 sq m (506 sq ft) |
| Armament: | one fixed forward-firing .303in Vickers machine gun; two .303in Lewis machine guns on TO 7 ring mounting over observer's cockpit; underwing racks with provision for 200kg (441lb) of bombs |

# Potez 63.11

In 1934 the French air ministry issued a complex requirement for a multi-role warplane to be powered by two examples of the new small-diameter radial engines developed by Gnome-Rhône and Hispano-Suiza, to carry a fixed forward-firing armament that included at least one 20mm cannon, to carry sufficient radio equipment for the type to operate as a controller for single-seat fighters in running engagements with bomber formations, and to possess the capability for operation in three fighter roles. The winning design was the Potez 63 that was then developed in a number of forms including the Potez 63.11 for tactical reconnaissance and army co-operation. First flown in December 1938, the Potez 63.11 entered service in November of the same year, and about 925 Potez 63.11A.3 aircraft had been delivered by June 1940. After this the type was operated by both the Free French and Vichy French forces in North Africa and the Middle East.

| | |
|---|---|
| **Country of origin:** | France |
| **Type:** | three-seat multi-role warplane |
| **Powerplant:** | two 700hp (522kW) Gnome-Rhône 14M-4/5 radial engines |
| **Performance:** | maximum speed 425km/h (264mph); climb to 3000m (9845ft) in 6 minutes; service ceiling 8500m (27,885ft); range 1500km (932 miles) |
| **Weights:** | empty 3135kg (6911lb); maximum take-off 4530kg (9987lb) |
| **Dimensions:** | span 16.00m (52ft 6in); length 10.93m (35ft 10.5in); height 3.08m (10ft 1.25in) |
| **Armament:** | one 7.5mm machine gun under central fuselage, one 7.5mm machine gun in rear fuselage, and one 7.5mm machine gun in the rear cockpit, or in some aircraft three 7.5mm machine guns in nose and under fuselage, four 7.5mm machine guns in two two-gun underwing packs, three 7.5mm machine guns under fuselage, and two 7.5mm machine guns in cockpit; external bomb load of 300kg (661lb) |

# Potez 633

Resulting from a 1934 requirement for a multi-role warplane, the Potez 630 paved the way for a number of role-optimised variants. One of the first was a light bomber, which was evaluated from January 1937 as the Potez 632.01 prototype conversion of the Potez 630.02 night-fighter, and in May 1938 an order was placed for 125 examples (only six delivered) of the Potez 633B.2 production version that was basically similar to the Potez 631C.3 fighter except for its accommodation, armament, and the reintroduction of a glazed lower nose to provide a bombardier position. Other sales were made to China, Greece, Romania and Switzerland, and 30 of these aircraft were retained for French service. Another model was the Potez 637A.3 (60 delivered) three-seat attack and reconnaissance model with a ventral gondola and heavier armament. Pictured is one 21 aircraft supplied to Romania, which were used in the German campaign in the Ukraine.

| Country of origin: | France |
|---|---|
| Type: | (Potez 633B.2) two-seat light bomber |
| Powerplant: | two 700hp (522kW) Gnome-Rhòne 14M-6/7 14-cylinder two-row radial engines |
| Performance: | maximum speed 439km/h (273mph); climb to 4000m (13,125ft) in 8 minutes 30 seconds; service ceiling 8000m (26,250ft); range 1300km (808 miles) |
| Weights: | empty 2450kg (5401lb); maximum take-off 4500kg (9921lb) |
| Dimensions: | span 16.00m (52ft 6in); length 11.07m (36ft 4in); height 3.62m (11ft 10.5in) |
| Armament: | one 7.5mm fixed forward-firing machine gun in the upper starboard side of the forward fuselage, and one 7.5mm trainable rearward-firing machine gun in the rear cockpit, plus an internal bomb load of 400kg (882lb) |

# Reggiane Re.2000 Falco I

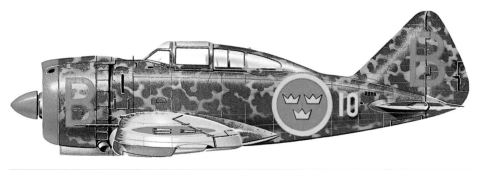

**F**irst flown in May 1939, this portly yet capable interceptor was the first fighter designed by Reggiane, a Caproni subsidiary, and bore a striking resemblance to the Seversky (later Sikorsky) fighters designed in the USA. Although it initially failed to win domestic orders the aircraft went into production as the Re.2000 Serie I to meet export orders from Sweden (60 aircraft) and Hungary (70 plus 191 licence-built aircraft with the Gnome-Rhòne 14K engine). Of the 27 aircraft retained in Italy, 10 were converted to Re.2000 Serie II shipborne fighter standard with the 1025hp (764kW) P.XIbis engine and the other 17 to the Re.2000 (GA) Serie III long-range fighter-bomber standard with the P.XIbis engine, greater fuel capacity and provision for 2000kg (4409lb) of bombs. The Swedish aircraft remained in service up to 1946. Pictured is an Re.2000 of the 1st Division, Flygflottilj 10, Royal Swedish air force, based at Angelholm early in 1945.

| | |
|---|---|
| **Country of origin:** | Italy |
| **Type:** | (Re.2000 Serie I) single-seat interceptor fighter |
| **Powerplant:** | one 985hp (734.5kW) Piaggio P.XI RC.40 14-cylinder two-row radial engine |
| **Performance:** | maximum speed 530km/h (329mph); climb to 6000m (19,685ft) in 6 minutes 10 seconds; service ceiling 10,500m (34,450ft); range 1400km (870 miles) |
| **Weights:** | empty 2080kg (4585lb); maximum take-off 2880kg (6349lb) |
| **Dimensions:** | span 11.00m (36ft 1in); length 7.99m (26ft 2.5in); height 3.20m (10ft 6in ) |
| **Armament:** | two 12.7mm fixed forward-firing machine guns in the upper part of the forward fuselage, plus an unspecified internal bomb load |

# Reggiane Re.2001 Falco II

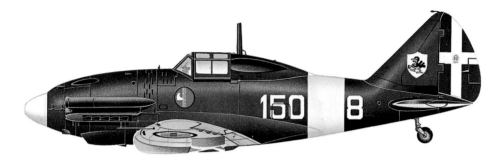

The Re.2000's potential could not initially be realised for lack of adequate power, Italy having ignored the advisability of developing potent Vee engines. The solution was found in the licensed production of German engines, and an early development was the Re.2001 Falco II, first flown in June 1940 as an Re.2000 development with the Alfa Romeo RA.1000 (Daimler-Benz DB 601) engine. Production then totalled 110 Serie I fighters and fighter-bombers, and 124 Serie II, III and IV night-fighters with heavier armament. The Re.2002 Ariete ('Ram'), of which 227 were completed, was a fighter-bomber development with the 1180hp (880kW) Piaggio P.XIX RC.25 radial engine, and the Re.2005 Sagittario ('Archer') was a fighter-bomber of which 37 were completed with the 1475hp (1100kW) Fiat RA.1050 (DB 605) engine. Pictured is an Re.2001 of the 150th Squadriglia, 2nd Gruppo 'Golletto', Regia Aeronautica, based at Pantellaria in August 1942.

| | |
|---|---|
| Country of origin: | Italy |
| Type: | (Re.2001 Serie III) single-seat night-fighter |
| Powerplant: | one 1175hp (876kW) Alfa Romeo RA.1000 RC.41-Ia Monsonie 12-cylinder inverted-Vee engine |
| Performance: | maximum speed 545km/h (339mph); climb to 5000m (16,405ft) in 6 minutes 20 seconds; service ceiling 11,000m (36,090ft); range 1100km (684 miles) |
| Weights: | empty 2460kg (5423lb); maximum take-off 3280kg (7231lb) |
| Dimensions: | span 11.00m (36ft 1in); length 8.36m (27ft 5in); height 3.15m (10ft 4in) |
| Armament: | two 12.7mm fixed forward-firing machine guns in the upper part of the forward fuselage and two 7.7mm fixed forward-firing machine guns in the leading edges of the wing |

# Republic P-47B to P-47G

The Thunderbolt is one of the classic warplanes of World War II, and remains an enduring example of the American predilection to 'think big' and produce an item that is visually impressive yet packed with equally impressive capability as a result of the careful combination of high power (a turbocharged engine) and clean design. The XP-47B prototype first flew in May 1941, but depite indications of impressive performance a number of serious design problems had to be resolved before the P-47B could enter combat service in April 1943. The 171 P-47B fighters and 602 generally similar P-47C fighter-bombers were powered by the 2000hp (1491kW) R-2800-21 engine, while the definitive P-47D introduced an uprated powerplant and, in its major subvariant, a clear-view 'bubble' canopy in place of the original framed canopy and 'razorback' rear fuselage. Production of the P-47D and generally similar P-47G 'razorback' model totalled 12,603 and 354 respectively.

| Country of origin: | USA |
| --- | --- |
| Type: | (P-47D) single-seat fighter and fighter-bomber |
| Powerplant: | one 2535hp (1890kW) Pratt & Whitney R-2800-59 18-cylinder two-row radial engine |
| Performance: | maximum speed 700km/h (435mph); climb to 4570m (15,000ft) in 5 minutes 36 seconds; service ceiling 12,800m (42,000ft); range 2776km (1725 miles) |
| Weights: | empty 4858kg (10,700lb); maximum take-off 7355kg (16,200lb) |
| Dimensions: | span 12.42m (40ft 9in); length 10.99m (36ft 1in); height 4.44m (14ft 7in) |
| Armament: | eight 0.5in fixed forward-firing machine guns in the leading edges of the wing, plus an external bomb and rocket load of 1134kg (2500lb) |

# Republic P-47M/N Thunderbolt

When the Germans started firing the Fieseler Fi 103 (or V-1) flying bomb at the southern part of the UK in June 1944, the USAAF decided to procure a 'sprint' version of the P-47D as the P-47M (130 built) with the R-2800-57(C) radial engine offering an emergency combat rating of 2800 hp (2088 kW). The last version of the Thunderbolt to be built was the P-47N, largest and heaviest of all Thunderbolt variants. The type was designed for operations in the Pacific theatre with particular emphasis on the maximum range with greater fuel capacity in a wing enlarged to a span of 42ft 7in (12.98m). P-47N production totalled 1816 aircraft with a maximum speed of 460mph (740km/h) and range of more than 2350 miles (3781km) after take-off at a maximum weight of 20,700lb (9390kg). In addition to service with the USAAF during the war the Thunderbolt was used by Brazil, the Free French Air Force, the British Royal Air Force and the Soviet Union.

| | |
|---|---|
| Country of origin: | USA |
| Type: | (P-47M) single-seat interceptor fighter |
| Powerplant: | one 2100hp (1566kW) Pratt & Whitney R-2800-57(C) 18-cylinder two-row radial engine |
| Performance: | maximum speed 756km/h (470mph); initial climb rate 1067m (3500ft) per minute; service ceiling not available; range 901km (560 miles) |
| Weights: | empty 4728kg (10,423lb); maximum take-off 7031kg (15,500lb) |
| Dimensions: | span 12.42m (40ft 9in); length 10.99m (36ft 1in); height 4.44m (14ft 7in) |
| Armament: | six or eight 0.5in fixed forward-firing machine guns in the leading edges of the wing |

# Republic F-84F Thunderstreak

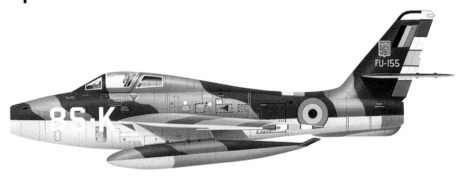

In 1944 Republic began development of the Thunderjet, an aircraft which they conceived as a replacement for the piston-engined P-47 Thunderbolt. The first of three prototype aircraft was flown at the Muroc Dry Lake test centre on February 28, 1946. The first production aircraft were designated F-84B and entered full-scale production for the USAF in May 1947. Total production was 224. Introduction of a swept wing began with the F-84F variant, which first flew in June 1950, although problems with the Allison powerplant delayed development and service deliveries. Some 2713 F-84Fs were completed, of which 1,301 were supplied to NATO forces. The aircraft continued in service with Air National Guard units until 1971. The aircraft pictured served with the Belgian air force during the 1960s.

| | |
|---|---|
| Country of origin: | USA |
| Type: | single-seat fighter-bomber |
| Powerplant: | one 3278kg (7220lb) Wright J65-W-3 turbojet |
| Performance: | maximum speed 1118km/h (695mph); service ceiling 14,020kg (46,000ft); combat radius with drop tanks 1304km (810 miles) |
| Weights: | empty 6273kg (13,830lb); maximum take-off 12,701kg (28,000lb) |
| Dimensions: | wingspan 10.24m (33ft 7.25in); length 13.23m (43ft 4.75in); height 4.39m (14ft 4.75in); wing area 30.19sq m (325sq ft) |
| Armament: | six 0.5in Browning M3 machine-guns, external hardpoints with provision for up to 2722kg (6000lb) of stores |

# Republic F-84G Thunderjet

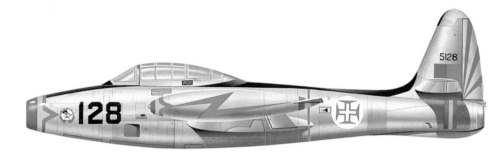

Last of the 'straight-wing' F-84 family, and the most numerous production version, was the F-84G, of which 3025 were built. This was the first single-seat US fighter aircraft capable of delivering nuclear weapons. The aircraft had provision for inflight refuelling and was equipped with an autopilot. In September 1954, using its refuelling capability, the F-84G became the first turbojet powered single-seat fighter to record a non-stop crossing of the Atlantic. Strategic Air Command retired its F-84Gs by 1956, although Tactical Air Command retained its aircraft for some time afterward. Of the total built, 1,936 were supplied to NATO air forces. Take-off with full weapons load was very long and often marginal, but the aircraft provided an effective foil to the Eastern Bloc in central Europe.

| | |
|---|---|
| **Country of origin:** | USA |
| **Type:** | single-seat fighter-bomber |
| **Powerplant:** | one 2542kg (5600lb) Wright J65-A-29 turbojet |
| **Performance:** | maximum speed 973km/h (605mph) at 1220m (4,000ft); service ceiling 12,353m (40,500ft); combat radius with drop tanks 1609km (1000 miles) |
| **Weights:** | empty 5203kg (11,460lb); maximum take-off 12,701kg (28,000lb) |
| **Dimensions:** | wingspan 11.05m (36ft 4in); length 11.71m (38ft 5in); height 3.9m (12ft 10in); wing area 24.18sq m (260sq ft) |
| **Armament:** | six 0.5in Browning M3 machine-guns, external hardpoints with provision for up to 1814kg (4000lb) of stores including rockets and bombs |

# Republic F-105B Thunderchief

Even before the F-84F Thunderstreak had entered service, Republic had begun studies on an aircraft which it was hoped would replace it in service. The primary mission of this new aircraft was perceived as the delivery of nuclear and conventional weapons in all weathers at high speeds and over long ranges. Contracts for two prototype aircraft were issued in 1954; the first flight was made in October 1955. No F105A production aircraft were built because of the availability of a more powerful powerplant, and the company subsequently built four YF-105B aircraft with these engines. The production F-105B entered service in August 1958 with the USAF's 335th Tactical Fighter Squadron, three years later than planned. Seventy-five were completed before the aircraft was superseded by the F-105D.

| | |
|---|---|
| Country of origin: | USA |
| Type: | single-seat fighter-bomber |
| Powerplant: | one 10,660kg (23,500lb) Pratt & Whitney J75 turbojet |
| Performance: | maximum speed 2018km/h (1254mph); service ceiling 15,850m (52,000ft); combat radius with weapon load 370km (230 miles) |
| Weights: | empty 12,474kg (27,500lb); maximum take-off 18,144kg (40,000lb) |
| Dimensions: | wingspan 10.65m (34ft 11.25in); length 19.58m (64ft 3in); height 5.99m (19ft 8in); wing area 35.8sq m (385sq ft) |
| Armament: | one 20mm M61 cannon with 1029 rounds; internal bay with provision for up to 3629kg (8000lb) of bombs; five external pylons for additional load of 2722kg (6000lb) |

# Republic F-105D Thunderchief

The major production version of the Thunderchief, the aircraft known to a generation of pilots as the 'Thud', was the F-105D. The aircraft represented a significant improvement over the -B with a more powerful version of the J75 turbojet and advanced avionics, including NASARR monopulse radar and Doppler navigation system. This gave the aircraft true all-weather strike capability. Deliveries to the 4th Tactical Fighter Wing began in May 1960, but it was in Vietnam that the Thud cemented its reputation. The aircraft operating in that theatre bore a huge burden throughout the war, and built up a solid reputation with the men who flew them. Nevertheless about half of those built were destroyed. About 350 of the 600 production aircraft were modified during the conflict to carry the T-stick (Thunderstick) all-weather blind attack bombing system.

| | |
|---|---|
| Country of origin: | USA |
| Type: | single-seat fighter-bomber |
| Powerplant: | one 11,113kg (24,500lb) Pratt & Whitney J75-19W turbojet |
| Performance: | maximum speed 2382km/h (1,480mph); service ceiling 15,850m (52,000ft); combat radius with 16 750lb bombs 370km (230 miles) |
| Weights: | empty 12,474kg (27,500lb); maximum take-off 23,834kg (52,546lb) |
| Dimensions: | wingspan 10.65m (34ft 11.25in); length 19.58m (64ft 3in); height 5.99m (19ft 8in); wing area 35.8sq m (385sq ft) |
| Armament: | one 20mm M61 cannon with 1029 rounds; internal bay with provision for up to 3629kg (8000lb) of bombs; five external pylons for additional load of 2722kg (6000lb) |

# Republic F-105G Thunderchief

The threat from Soviet-built SA-2 'Guideline' surface-to-air missiles operated by North Vietnamese forces led to the rapid development and introduction of the ECM equipped F-105F Wild Weasel. These aircraft were equipped with a large externally mounted pod containing electronics, RHAW (Radar Homing and Warning ), a missile-launch warning receiver, and other specialised avionics. The 86 aircraft thus configured were designated EF-105F. A more comprehensive modification was undertaken on 60 of these aircraft, which have the designation F-105G. The aircraft carried out the bulk of anti-SAM missions until 1973, before passing on to the Air National Guard units that operated them until 1984. This is one of the aircraft operated by the 561st Tactical Fighter Squadron of the 23rd Tactical Fighter Wing, based at McConnell AFB in Kansas.

| | |
|---|---|
| **Country of origin:** | USA |
| **Type:** | two-seat ECM aircraft |
| **Powerplant:** | one 11,113kg (24,500lb) Pratt & Whitney J75-19W turbojet |
| **Performance:** | maximum speed 2382km/h (1480mph); service ceiling 15,850m (52,000ft); ferry range 3486km (2390 miles) |
| **Weights:** | empty 12,890kg (28,393lb); maximum take-off 24,516kg (54,000lb) |
| **Dimensions:** | wingspan 10.65m (34ft 11¼in); length 21.21m (69ft 7.5in); height 6.15m (20ft 2in); wing area 35.8sq m (385sq ft) |
| **Armament:** | one 20mm M61 cannon with 1029 rounds; five external pylons for additional load of 2722kg (6000lb), including anti-radiation missiles, conventional and guided bombs, drop tanks and ECM pods |

# Rockwell T-2 Buckeye

The T-2 began service as the primary jet trainer of the US Navy in 1960, and after nearly 40 years is now being replaced by the T-45A Goshawk. The wing of the aircraft was derived from the FJ-1 Fury and the control system is similar to that employed on the T-28 Trojan. The first aircraft flew on January 31, 1958 and service deliveries began the following July. A total of 217 T-2As were supplied to the US Navy under the name Buckeye. A more powerful version designated T-2B was also produced. The final version was the T-2C with yet more powerful General Electric engines. Two hundred and seventy three were built, some of which were supplied to Venezuela and Greece. Pictured is one of the T-2C aircraft operated by VT-23 of Training Wing 2, US Navy. Some of the aircraft in US service have been converted for use as drone directors.

| | |
|---|---|
| Country of origin: | USA |
| Type: | two-seat multi-role jet trainer |
| Powerplant: | one 1338kg (2950lb) General Electric J85-GE-4 turbojets |
| Performance: | maximum speed at 7620m (25,000ft) 838km/h (521mph); service ceiling 13,535m (44,400ft); range 1465km (910 miles) |
| Weights: | empty 3681kg (8115lb); maximum take-off 5978kg (13,180lb) |
| Dimensions: | wingspan 11.63m (38ft 2in); length 11.79m (38ft 8in); height 4.51m (14ft 9.5in); wing area 23.70sq m (255sq ft) |

# Rockwell B-1B Lancer

The B-1B long-range penetration bomber was originally conceived in the 1965 USAF Advanced Manned Strategic Aircraft requirement. North American Rockwell, as it then was, were selected as the prime contractor for the new bomber, which was designated B-1. General Electric were selected to build the F101 engines to power it. Prototype contracts were awarded in June 1970, with planned service delivery of all 244 aircraft scheduled before 1981. The first prototype made its maiden flight on December 23, 1974, but the programme was cancelled in 1977 because of escalating costs. A contract for 100 aircraft derived from the B-1, with a revised role as a cruise missile carrier, awarded in 1982. The aircraft incorporated a variable-geometry configuration with stealth technology and advanced avionics. All aircraft now wear a dark low-visibility camouflage scheme.

| Country of origin: | USA |
|---|---|
| Type: | long-range multi-role strategic bomber |
| Powerplant: | four 13962kg (30,780lb) General Electric F101-GE-102 turbofans |
| Performance: | maximum speed at high altitude 1328km/h (825mph); service ceiling 15,240m (50,000ft); range on internal fuel 12,000km (7,455 miles) |
| Weights: | empty 87,090kg (192,000lb); maximum take-off 216,634kg (477,000lb) |
| Dimensions: | wingspan 41.67m (136ft 8.5in) unswept and 23.84m (78ft 2.5in) swept; length 44.81m (147ft); height 10.36m (34ft); wing area 181.16sq m (1,950sq ft) |
| Armament: | three internal bays with provision for up to 34,019kg (75,000lb) of weapons, plus eight underfuselage stations with a capacity of 26,762kg (59,000lb); weapons can include AGM-69 SRAMs, AGM-86B ALCMs, B-28, B-43, B-61 or B-83 nuclear bombs, and Mk 82 or Mk 84 conventional bombs |

# Rogozarski IK-3

**D**esigned as successor to the Ikarus IK-2 gull-wing monoplane fighter, the IK-3 was Yugoslavia's first 'modern' fighter of the cantilever low-wing type with an enclosed cockpit and retractable landing gear. The type first flew in private-venture prototype form in the spring of 1938 and, despite the loss of this aeroplane, the machine was ordered into production. The first 12 aircraft introduced considerable redesign of the cockpit enclosure and main landing gear, as well as a somewhat uprated engine and a strengthened airframe. The aircraft had all been delivered by July 1939, and were flown by the 161 and 162 Eskadrila of the 51 Grupa based at Zemun. After the German invasion of Yugoslavia in April 1941 they proved moderately successful, destroying 11 enemy aircraft before the surviving aircraft were destroyed on the emergency strip at Veliki Radnici to prevent their seizure by the victorious Germans.

| | |
|---|---|
| Country of origin: | Yugoslavia |
| Type: | (IK-3) single-seat fighter |
| Powerplant: | one 980hp (731kW) Avia-built Hispano-Suiza 12Ycrs 12-cylinder Vee engine |
| Performance: | maximum speed 527km/h (328mph); climb to 5000m (16,405ft) in 7 minutes; service ceiling 9460m (30,800ft); range 785km (488 miles) |
| Weights: | empty 2068kg (4560lb); maximum take-off 2630kg (5799lb) |
| Dimensions: | span 10.30m (33ft 9.75in); length 8.00m (26ft 3in); height 3.25m (10ft 8in) |
| Armament: | one 20mm fixed forward-firing cannon in an engine installation, and two 7.92mm fixed forward-firing machine guns in the upper part of the forward fuselage |

# Royal Aircraft Factory B.E.2c

**H**is Majesty's Balloon Factory at Farnborough diversified into heavier-than-air machines in 1909. Under the direction of Mervyn O'Gorman, Geoffrey de Havilland and F. M. Green built the B.E.1 (Blériot Experimental) tractor biplane in 1911 from the airframe of a Voisin pusher biplane. The following B.E.2 retained the same basic airframe and was the first military aircraft to be built as such in Britain. By mid-1913 it equipped 13 RFC squadrons. Production gave way to the B.E.2a with unequal-span wings, and the B.E.2b with revised decking around the cockpits and different aileron instead of wing-warping controls. The B.E.2c introduced the 90hp (66kW) RAF 1a engine and was the first to be armed with a machine gun. In wartime service the B.E.2 was a fine reconnaissance platform, but its stability proved lethal in aerial combat and many were lost during the 'Fokker Scourge' of 1915–16. Production certainly exceeded the 3535 for which records survive.

| | |
|---|---|
| **Country of origin:** | United Kingdom |
| **Type:** | two-seat reconnaissance/light bomber aircraft |
| **Powerplant:** | one 90hp (67kW) RAF 1a inline piston engine |
| **Performance:** | maximum speed 145km/h (90mph); service ceiling 2745m (9000ft); endurance 4hrs |
| **Weights:** | empty 649kg (1431lb); maximum take-off weight 953kg (2100lb) |
| **Dimensions:** | span 12.42m (40ft 9in); length 8.31m (27ft 3in); height 3.66m (12ft); wing area 33.44 sq m (360 sq ft) |
| **Armament:** | one.303in Vickers machine gun capable of being mounted on various upper centre wing and fuselage points |

# Royal Aircraft Factory F.E.2b

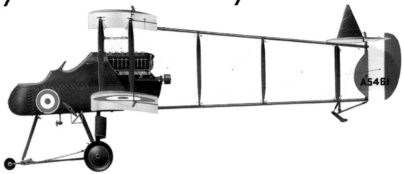

The first successful Fighter Experimental design from the Royal Aircraft Factory was ready to go into production in January 1914, and had it done so the RFC would have been able to match the Fokker monoplanes of the German Air Service on better terms. Instead, nearly a year elapsed after the first flight before a production order was even placed, and by this time the whole concept of a pusher biplane was rapidly becoming obsolete. The layout was due to the need to fire a machine gun, as in 1913 there was no way of safely firing ahead through a tractor propeller. The pilot therefore occupied the rear cockpit, although for night operations this was reversed. The first order for 12 F.E.2as was placed in August 1914, followed by the progressively more powerful F.E.2b and F.E.2c. Altogether some 1939 of these were built, as well as 386 long-span F.E.2d models.

| | |
|---|---|
| Country of origin: | United Kingdom |
| Type: | two-seat fighter |
| Powerplant: | one 120hp (89kW) Beardmore inline piston engine |
| Performance: | maximum speed 129km/h (80mph); service ceiling 2745m (9000ft); endurance 3hrs |
| Weights: | empty 904kg (1993lb); maximum take-off weight 1347kg (2970lb) |
| Dimensions: | span 14.55m (47ft 9in); length 9.83m (32ft 3in); height 3.85m (12ft 7in); wing area 45.89 sq m (494 sq ft) |
| Armament: | one or two .303in Lewis machine guns; plus up to 159kg (350lb) of bombs |

# Royal Aircraft Factory R.E.8

The 'Harry Tate', as it was dubbed by the RFC's Cockney contingent, was designed to meet an RFC requirement for a two-seat reconnaissance/artillery spotting aircraft. It resembled a scaled-up version of the B.E.2 and shared the same staggered biplane wing configuration, but it had a far sturdier fuselage and more substantial armament. Early tests revealed good all-round handling, encouraging the RFC to place a large order. The first aircraft were delivered in autumn 1916 but these were grounded after a series of mysterious accidents. As a result the tail was redesigned and the mass production of an eventual 4077 aircraft was resumed. However, like the earlier B.E.2, the aircraft's inherent stability proved to be a major handicap in aerial combat, and among the rank and file it was never a really popular machine.

| | |
|---|---|
| **Country of origin:** | United Kingdom |
| **Type:** | two-seat reconnaissance/artillery spotting aircraft |
| **Powerplant:** | one 150hp (112kW) RAF 4a 12-cylinder Vee piston engine |
| **Performance:** | maximum speed 164km/h (102mph); service ceiling 4115m (13,500ft); endurance 4hrs 15mins |
| **Weights:** | empty 717kg (1580lb); maximum take-off weight 1301kg (2869lb) |
| **Dimensions:** | span 12.98m (42ft 7in); length 6.38m (20ft 11in); height 2.9m (9ft 6in); wing area 22.67 sq m (444 sq ft) |
| **Armament:** | one fixed forward-firing .303in Vickers machine gun; one .303in Lewis machine gun on pivoted mounting over rear cockpit; plus a bomb load of up to 102kg (224lb) |

# Royal Aircraft Factory S.E.5a

Undoubtedly the best warplane to come from the Royal Aircraft Factory at Farnborough, the S.E.5 (Scout Experimental) was one of the great combat aircraft of World War I. It was designed around a new Hispano-Suiza engine (which somewhat ironically proved to be its lingering curse) by H. P. Folland with J. Kenworthy, and the first of three prototypes flew in November 1916. This and the second aircraft were lost in crashes. The third aircraft had a slightly modified radiator, cut-out in the upper wing, centre-section gravity tank, armament, and a windscreen that proved to be obstructive to the pilot's view. When the first S.E.5 aircraft were delivered to No 56 Squadron in March 1917 its pilots were dismayed to find that an even bigger screen had been added. Removal of these screens was expediently ordered before the unit was declared ready for combat. Pictured is one of the squadron's S.E.5a aircraft, built by the Austin Motor Company.

| | |
|---|---|
| **Country of origin:** | United Kingdom |
| **Type:** | single-seat fighting scout |
| **Powerplant:** | one 150hp (112kW) Hispano-Suiza 8a 8-cylinder inline piston engine |
| **Performance:** | maximum speed 177km/h (110mph); service ceiling 5185m (17,000ft); range 483km (300 miles) |
| **Weights:** | empty 639kg (1410lb); maximum take-off weight 902kg (1988lb) |
| **Dimensions:** | span 8.11m (26ft 7in); length 6.38m (20ft 11in); height 2.89m (9ft 6in); wing area 22.67 sq m (444 sq ft) |
| **Armament:** | one fixed forward-firing .303in Vickers machine gun, one .303in Lewis machine gun on Foster mount on upper wing |

# Royal Aircraft Factory S.E.5a

The engine problems of the S.E.5a were only fully resolved when Wolseley developed the Viper, a high-compression direct-drive version of the Hispano. There were further problems with the Constantinesco interrupter gear, but when all the shortcomings had been eliminated the true potential of the airframe was unleashed. The S.E.5a became increasingly popular with the aces of the day. Ball, who had first criticised the type, scored most of his victories on the aircraft, as did Beauchamp-Proctor, 'Billy' Bishop, Edward 'Mick' Mannock, and James McCudden. Some 5205 aircraft were built, including a small number of conversions as two-seat trainers. The Curtiss Aeroplane and Motor Company in the USA had plans to build 1000, and 56 kits of parts were sent to the there for assembly. The Armistice cut short these plans and only one 180hp (134kW) Wright-Martin engine was built. Pictured is an Austin-built S.E.5a of the 25th Squadron, US American Expeditionary Force.

| Country of origin: | United Kingdom |
| --- | --- |
| Type: | single-seat fighting scout |
| Powerplant: | one 200hp (149kW) Wolseley W.4a 8-cylinder Vee piston engine |
| Performance: | maximum speed 222km/h (138mph); service ceiling 5185m (17,000ft); range 483km (300 miles) |
| Weights: | empty 639kg (1410lb); maximum take-off weight 902kg (1988lb) |
| Dimensions: | span 8.11m (26ft 7in); length 6.38m (20ft 11in); height 2.89m (9ft 6in); wing area 22.67 sq m (444 sq ft) |
| Armament: | one fixed forward-firing .303in Vickers machine gun; one .303in Lewis machine gun on Foster mount on upper wing |

# SEPECAT Jaguar A

Developed jointly by BAC in Britain and Dassault-Breguet in France (Societé Européenne de Production de l'Avion Ecole de Combat at Appui Tactique), to meet a joint requirement of the Armée de l'Air and Royal Air Force, the Jaguar emerged from protracted development as a far more powerful and effective aircraft than originally envisaged. The original idea was for a light trainer and close-support machine with a 590kg (1300lb) load, but with British pressure, this was considerably upgraded. Power was provided by a turbofan developed jointly from the Rolls-Royce RB.172 by Rolls Royce and Turbomeca. The first French version to fly was the two-seat E, followed in March 1969 by the Jaguar A single-seat tactical support aircraft, which form the backbone of the French tactical nuclear strike force. Service deliveries began in 1973 with production of some 160 aircraft. The Jaguar was a notable success in the first Gulf war of 1990–91.

| | |
|---|---|
| Country of origin: | France and United Kingdom |
| Type: | single-seat tactical support and strike aircraft |
| Powerplant: | two 3313kg (7305lb) Rolls-Royce/Turbomeca Adour Mk 102 turbofans |
| Performance: | maximum speed at 11,000m (36,090ft) 1593km/h (990mph); combat radius on lo-lo-lo mission with internal fuel 557km (357 miles) |
| Weights: | empty 7000kg (15,432lb); maximum take-off 15,500kg (34,172lb) |
| Dimensions: | wingspan 8.69m (28ft 6in); length 16.83m (55ft 2.5in); height 4.89m (16ft 0.5in); wing area 24sq m (258.34sq ft) |
| Armament: | two 30mm DEFA cannon with 150 rpg; five external hardpoints with provision for 4536kg (10,000lb) of stores, including one AN-52 tactical nuclear weapon or conventional loads such as one AS.37 Martel anti-radar missile and two drop tanks, or eight 454kg (1000lb) bombs, or combinations of ASMs, drop tanks and rocket-launcher pods, and a reconnaissance pod |

# SOKO G-2A Galeb

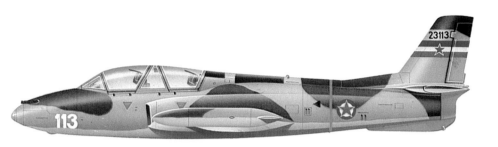

The SOKO company rose from the ashes of the Yugoslav aircraft industry, which had been comprehensively destroyed during the Second World War. In 1948 SOKO began licensed production of foreign designs before embarking on the design and construction of the G-2A Galeb trainer in 1957. This is a conventional low-wing monoplane of all-metal construction, retractable tricycle undercarriage, and turbojet power. The crew are seated in tandem seats in a heated and air-conditioned cockpit. The avionics suite is limited to a radio compass and communications transceiver, although full blind-flying system is standard. The first aircraft was flown in May 1961, and production for the Yugoslav air force under the designation G-2A Galeb began in 1963. Production of the uprated G-2A-E export model continued until 1983.

| | |
|---|---|
| **Country of origin:** | Yugolavia |
| **Type:** | basic trainer |
| **Powerplant:** | one 1134kg (2500lb) Rolls-Royce Viper 11 Mk 226 turbojet |
| **Performance:** | maximum speed at 6000m (19,685ft) 730km/h (454mph); service ceiling 12,000m (39,370ft); range with maximum standard fuel 1240km (771 miles) |
| **Weights:** | empty 2620kg (5776lb); maximum take-off 4300kg (9480lb) |
| **Dimensions:** | wingspan 9.73m (31ft 11in); length 10.34m (33ft 11in); height 3.28m (10ft 9in); wing area 19.43sq m (209.15sq ft) |
| **Armament:** | two 12.7mm machine guns with 80 rpg; underwing racks for 150kg (331lb) bomblet containers, 100kg (220lb) bombs, 127mm rockets, and 55mm rocket-launcher pods |

# SOKO G-4 Super Galeb

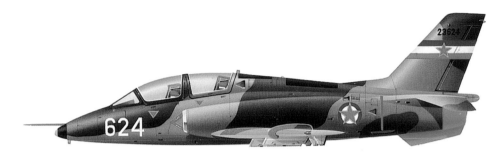

Studies began on an improved version of the G-2A Galeb to replace this aircraft and the Lockheed T-33 in basic and advanced training units of the Yugoslav air force. Despite having a name in common with its predecessor, the G-4 is in fact a wholly new design, with a swept wing and all-swept tail, and a far more modern cockpit, housing the student and instructor in tandem seats. The rear seat is slightly raised, in a style similar to the BAe Hawk. Avionics equipment on the G-4 is far more comprehensive, with Distance Measuring Equipment, radio altimeter, radio compass, VHF radio, very high frequency Omni-directional Range/Instrument Landing System. Although the aircraft is some 25 percent heavier than the G-2A, it can carry a greater weapons load. A small number of the large order for the Yugoslav air force had been delivered before the break-up of the country which halted the type's production.

| | |
|---|---|
| Country of origin: | Yugoslavia |
| Type: | basic trainer/light attack aircraft |
| Powerplant: | one 1814kg (4000lb) Rolls-Royce Viper Mk 632 turbojet |
| Performance: | maximum speed at 4000m (13,125ft) 910km/h (665mph); service ceiling 12,850m (42,160ft); range with internal fuel 1900km (1,80 miles) |
| Weights: | empty 3172kg (6993lb); maximum take-off 6300kg (13,889lb) |
| Dimensions: | wingspan 9.88m (32ft 5in); length 12.25m (40ft 2.25in); height 4.3m (14ft 1.25in); wing area 19.5sq m (209.9sq ft) |
| Armament: | one 23mm GSh-23L cannon with 200 rpg; four external hardpoints with provision for 2053kg of stores, including air-to-air missiles, bombs, cluster bombs, dispenser weapons, napalm tanks, large-calibre rockets, rocket-launcher pods, drop tanks and ECM pods |

# SOKO/Avioane IAR-93A

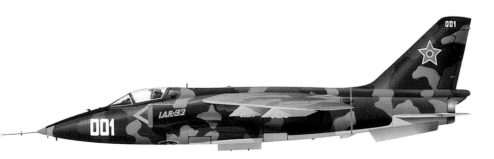

The J-22 was the result of a collaboration between the Romanian IAv (Intreprinderea De Avioane Bucuresti) company and SOKO of Yugoslavia, stemming from a common requirement in both countries for a twin-jet close-support and ground-attack aircraft. The initial design was contracted out to the Institute of Aviation in Romania and its counterpart in Yugoslavia. Each country constructed prototypes powered by two licence-built Rolls-Royce Viper Mk 632 41Rs, and the first flights took place simultaneously in October 1974. Production of the initial batch of 20 Romanian aircraft, which are designated IAR-93A, began in 1979, with SOKO commencing production of the similar J- 22 in 1980. An improved version with afterburning engines began production in 1984 and is designated J-22(M) or Orao 2, with production totalling 165 in both countries.

| Country of origin: | Yugoslavia |
|---|---|
| Type: | single-seat close-support/ground attack aircraft |
| Powerplant: | two 2268kg (5000lb) Turbomecanica (Rolls-Royce Viper Mk 633-47) turbojets |
| Performance: | maximum speed at sea level 1160km/h (721mph); service ceiling 12,500m (41,010ft); combat radius with four 250kg bombs and drop tanks 530km (329 miles) |
| Weights: | empty 5900kg (13,007lb); maximum take-off 10,100kg (22,267lb) |
| Dimensions: | wingspan 9.62m (31ft 6.75in); length 14.90m (48ft 10.75in); height 4.45m (14ft 7.25in); wing area 26sq m (279.87 q ft) |
| Armament: | two 23mm GSh-23L cannon with 200 rpg; five external hardpoints with provision for 2800kg (6173lb) of stores, including air-to-air missiles, air-to-surface missiles, bombs, cluster bombs, dispenser weapons, napalm tanks, rocket-launcher pods and drop tanks |

# SPAD S.VII (French)

J ust prior to World War I, the Société Pour les Appareils Deperdussin (SPAD) was
rescued from the mire of bankruptcy by the esteemed French aviator Louis Blériot, who
renamed it as the Société Pour l'Aviation et ses Dérivés, retaining the initials SPAD. The
new SPAD undertook the design and manufacture of one of the unremarkable 'A' series of
two-seat fighters, prior to the development from early 1915 of the SPAD S.V tractor biplane.
This was the company's first truly successful military aircraft and undisputedly one of the
greatest single-seat scouts of the war. The key to the design was the new Vee engine
designed in 1915 by Marc Birkgit, chief designer of Hispano-Suiza. This engine powered the
prototype when it first flew in April 1916, prompting the French authorities to place an
order for 268. The first of these began to arrive at the squadrons in September, with the
service designation S.VII. Later aircraft had a more powerful 180hp (134kW) 8Ac engine.

| Country of origin: | France |
|---|---|
| Type: | single-seat fighting scout |
| Powerplant: | one 150hp (112kW) Hispano-Suiza 8Aa 8-cylinder Vee piston engine |
| Performance: | maximum speed 192km/h (119mph); service ceiling 5334m (17,500ft); range 360km (225 miles) |
| Weights: | empty 510kg (1124lb); maximum take-off weight 740kg (1632lb) |
| Dimensions: | span 7.81m (25ft 8in); length 6.08m (19ft 11in); height 2.20m (7ft 2in); wing area 17.85 sq m (192 sq ft) |
| Armament: | one fixed forward-firing .303in Vickers machine gun |

# SPAD S.XIII

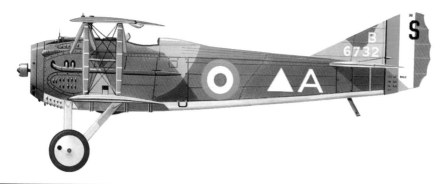

**B**oosted by the lobbying of Georges Guynemer and by the evolution of new German scouts, Louis Béchereau made strident efforts to improve the performance of the SPAD S.VII. The resulting SPAD S.XII Ca.1 was powered by a 200hp (134kW) Hispano-Suiza 8c engine and mounted a formidable 37mm Hotchkiss gun, fitted between the cylinder blocks and firing through the propeller block. Less than a hundred were built before production switched to the popular S.XIII, which had a 165hp (220kW) Hispano-Suiza 8Ba engine, twin Vickers machine guns, slightly larger wings, improved ailerons and an enlarged rudder. The prototype was first flown in April 1917 and series aircraft began entering service at the end of May. The S.XIII soon replaced the S.VII in service and its popularity spread far and wide. Orders for some 10,000 aircraft were cancelled at the end of the war. Pictured is an S.XIII of No 23 Squadron, RFC.

| | |
|---|---|
| **Country of origin:** | France |
| **Type:** | single-seat fighting scout |
| **Powerplant:** | one 220hp (164kW) Hispano-Suiza 8BEc 8-cylinder Vee piston engine |
| **Performance:** | maximum speed 224km/h (139mph); service ceiling 6650m (21,815ft); endurance 2hrs |
| **Weights:** | maximum take-off 845kg (1863lb) |
| **Dimensions:** | span 8.1m (26ft 7in); length 6.3m (20ft 8in); height 2.35m (7ft 8in) |
| **Armament:** | two fixed forward-firing .303in Vickers machine guns |

# Saab J21

S weden wished to ensure its continued neutrality through a policy of armed strength
during World War II but were effectively denied access to foreign weapons. In response
Sweden undertook an indigenous rearmament programme including an advanced fighter,
and for this task the Saab 21 was ultimately designed round a licence-produced version of
the Daimler-Benz DB 605B engine as a low-wing monoplane with tricycle landing gear,
heavy forward-firing armament, a pilot's ejection seat, and a twin-boom pusher layout that
later allowed the type's revision with a turbojet engine as the J 21R. The first of three J21
prototypes flew in July 1943, and 54 J21A-1 fighters were delivered from December 1945,
followed by 124 and 119 examples respectively of the J21A-2 with revised armament and
the J21A-3 fighter-bomber. Pictured is one of the aircraft operated by Flygflottilj 12 of
the Flygvapen.

| Country of origin: | Sweden |
|---|---|
| Type: | (J 21A-1) single-seat interceptor fighter |
| Powerplant: | one 1475hp (1100kW) SFA DB 605B 12-cylinder Vee engine |
| Performance: | maximum speed 645km/h (401mph); initial climb rate 850m (2789ft) per minute; service ceiling 11,000m (36,090ft); range 750km (466 miles) |
| Weights: | empty 3250kg (7165lb); maximum take-off 4413kg (9730lb) |
| Dimensions: | span 11.60m (38ft 0.75in); length 10.44m (34ft 3.25in); height 3.97m (13ft 3.25in) |
| Armament: | one 20mm fixed forward-firing cannon and two 13.2mm fixed forward-firing machine guns in the nose, and two 13.2mm fixed forward-firing machine guns in the front of the booms |

# Saab A21R

Frid Wanstrom's design is the only aircraft in the world to have seen front-line service with both piston and jet power. The aircraft was initially conceived in March 1941, in response to a Swedish request for a replacement for the miscellaneous obsolescent fighters then in service. The piston-engined version went into production with German Daimler-Benz 605B power in 1945. The conversion to jet power proved remarkably straightforward. The tailplane was carried high on altered fins and the landing gear was shortened. Power was provided by a single de Havilland Goblin 2 turbojet (J21RA), and later with a licence-built version of the same engine (J21RB). Thirty of each type were built and after a short career as fighter aircraft, they were converted to attack aircraft and redesignated A21R and A21RB respectively.

| | |
|---|---|
| Country of origin: | Sweden |
| Type: | single-seat fighter/attack aircraft |
| Powerplant: | one 1361kg (3000lb) de Havilland Goblin 2 turbojet |
| Performance: | maximum speed 800km/h (497mph); service ceiling 12,000m (39,400ft); range 720km (450 miles) |
| Weights: | empty 3200kg (7055lb); maximum take-off 5000kg (11,023lb) |
| Dimensions: | wingspan 11.37m (37ft 4in); length 10.45m (34ft 3in); height 2.90m (9ft 8in) |
| Armament: | one 20mm Bofors cannon and four 13.2mm M/39A, centreline pod housing eight 13.2mm guns, wing racks for 10 100mm or five 180mm Bofors rockets, or 10 80mm anti-tank rockets |

# Saab J32B Lansen

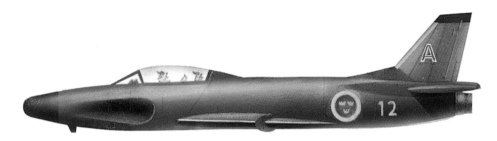

**D**esigned to replace the Saab 18 light-bomber in service with the Swedish air force, the Type 32 was a large all-swept machine of outstanding quality, designed and developed ahead of similar aircraft elsewhere in Western Europe. Owing to its not inconsiderable size, it was capable of development for three dissimilar missions. The A32A all-weather attack aircraft was the first into production in 1953, followed by the J32B all-weather and night fighter, and the S32C reconnaissance aircraft in mid-1958. The survivors of nearly 450 aircraft completed served well into the 1990s as aggressor aircraft, target tugs, and trials aircraft. The J32B pictured here had a more powerful licence-built Rolls-Royce engine than its predecessor, and S6 radar fire control for lead/pursuit interception. Between 1958 and 1970 seven squadrons were equipped with the type.

| Country of origin: | Sweden |
|---|---|
| Type: | all-weather and night fighter |
| Powerplant: | one 6890kg (15,190lb) Svenska Flygmotor (Rolls-Royce Avon) RM6A |
| Performance: | maximum speed 1114km/h (692mph); service ceiling 16,013m (52,500ft); range with external fuel 3220km (2000 miles) |
| Weights: | empty 7990kg (17,600lb); maximum loaded 13,529kg (29,800lb) |
| Dimensions: | wingspan 13m (42ft 7.75in); length 14.50m (47ft 6.75in); height 4.65m (15ft 3in); wing area 37.4sq m (402.58 q ft) |
| Armament: | four 30-mm Aden M/55 cannon; four Rb324 (Sidewinder) air-to-air missiles or FFAR (Folding Fin Air-launched Rocket) pods |

# Saab J35F Draken

The Draken was designed to a demanding Swedish air force specification for a single-seat interceptor which could operate from short air strips, have rapid time-to-height performance, and supersonic performance. The aircraft the Saab team, led by Erik Bratt, designed between 1949-51 is one of the most remarkable to arrive on the post-war aviation scene. The unique 'double-delta' is an ingenious method of arranging items one behind the other to give a long aircraft with small frontal area and correspondingly high aerodynamic efficiency. The aircraft was ten years in development, with the first J35A production models arriving in service in March 1960. Saab also offered the Draken for export under the designation Saab-35X, with increased fuel capacity and higher gross weight. Finland received 24 ex-Flyguapnet J34F single-seaters, one pictured here.

| | |
|---|---|
| **Country of origin:** | Sweden |
| **Type:** | single-seat all-weather interceptor |
| **Powerplant:** | one 7761kg (17,110lb) Svenska Flygmotor RM6C turbojet |
| **Performance:** | maximum speed 2125km/h (1320mph); service ceiling 20,000m (65,000ft); range with maximum fuel 3250km (2020 miles) |
| **Weights:** | empty 7425kg (16,369lb); maximum take-off 16,000kg (35,274lb) |
| **Dimensions:** | wingspan 9.4m (30ft 10in); length 15.4m (50ft 4in); height 3.9m (12ft 9in); wing area 49.20sq m (526.6sq ft) |
| **Armament:** | one 30mm Aden M/55 cannon with 90 rds, two radar-homing Rb27 and two IR-homing Rb28 Falcon air-to-air missiles, or two of four Rb24 Sidewinder AAMs, or up to 4082kg of bombs on attack mission |

# Saab 105

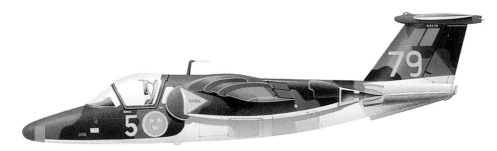

Saab established its reputation as a designer and manufacturer of first class jet aircraft with the Draken. The success of this aircraft encouraged the Swedish manufacturer to extend their range of aircraft by developing the privately-funded 105. This aircraft is a swept shoulder-wing monoplane with side-by-side cabin accommodation for either two or four crew. Power is provided by twin turbojets. The first prototype flew in June 1963, and after successful evaluation by the Swedish air force, orders were placed for 150 production aircraft. The type began to enter service in 1966, initially with the primary flying training school at Ljungbyhed air base. In Swedish air force use, the aircraft are designated Sk 60A; the armed close-support variant is the Sk 60B, and the photo-recce version is the Sk 60C. The aircraft is expected to serve until 2015.

| | |
|---|---|
| Country of origin: | Sweden |
| Type: | training/liason aircraft with secondary attack capability |
| Powerplant: | two 744kg (1640lb) Turbomeca Aubisque turbofans |
| Performance: | maximum speed at 6095m (20,000ft) 770km/h (480mph); service ceiling 13,500m (44,290ft); range 1400km (870 miles) |
| Weights: | empty 2510kg (5534lb); maximum take-off 4050kg (8929lb) |
| Dimensions: | wingspan 9.5m (31ft 2in); length 10.5m (34ft 5.375in); height 2.7m (8ft 10.25in); wing area 16.3sq m (175.46sq ft) |
| Armament: | six external hardpoints with provision for up to 700kg (1543lb) of stores, including two Saab Rb05 air-to-surface missiles, or two 30mm cannon pods, or 12 135mm rockets, or bombs, cluster bombs and rocket launcher pods |

# Saab AJ 37 Viggen

Until the arrival of the Panavia Tornado it may be argued that the Viggen was the most advanced combat aircraft ever produced in Europe. When it entered service in 1971 the AJ37 had a far more advanced radar, a greater speed range, and a more comprehensive avionics fit than most of its contemporaries. The Royal Swedish Air Board planned System 37 in 1958–61 as a standardised weapon system to be integrated with the Stril 60 air-defence environment of radars, computers and displays. Included in this system is a standard platform (the Viggen family) produced in five versions, each tailored for a specific task. The AJ37 is a dedicated all-weather attack aircraft which provides the Swedish air force with its ground-attack capability, and has an avionics suite optimised for this role. This aircraft is operated by Flygflottilj 15, of the Swedish air force, based at Soderhamn.

| | |
|---|---|
| Country of origin: | Sweden |
| Type: | single-seat all-weather attack aircraft |
| Powerplant: | one 11,800kg (26,015lb) Volvo Flygmotor RM8 turbofan |
| Performance: | maximum speed at high altitude 2124km/h (1320mph); service ceiling 18,290m (60,000ft); combat radius on hi-lo-hi mission with external armament 1000km (621 miles) |
| Weights: | empty 11,800kg (26,015lb); maximum take-off 20,500kg (45,194lb) |
| Dimensions: | wingspan 10.6m (34ft 9.25in); length 16.3m (53ft 5.75in); height 5.6m (18ft 4.5in); wing area 46sq m (495.16sq ft) |
| Armament: | seven external hardpoints with provision for 6000kg (13,228lb) of stores, including 30mm Aden cannon pods, 135mm rocket pods, Sidewinder or Falcon air-to-air missiles for self-defence, Maverick air-to-surface missiles, bombs, cluster bombs |

# Saab JA37 Viggen

The interceptor version of the Viggen, and an integral part of the System 37 series, was the single-seat JA37. Externally, the aircraft closely resembles the attack AJ37, although the fin is slightly taller and the interceptor has four elevon actuators under the wing instead of three as on other versions. A considerable amount of effort was made to optimise the Pratt & Whitney-designed Volvo turbofan for high altitude performance and high-stress combat manoeuvring, resulting in the RM8B unit fitted to the JA37. The other main area of development was the onboard avionics suite, most importantly the Ericsson UAP-1023 I/J-band long-range pulse-Doppler radar which provides target search and acquisition. Production of the JA37 totalled 149 aircraft with the last delivered in June 1990. The number 13 on the fuselage denotes Flygflottilz 13 of the Swedish air force.

| | |
|---|---|
| Country of origin: | Sweden |
| Type: | single-seat all-weather interceptor aircraft with secondary attack capability |
| Powerplant: | one 12,750kg (28,109lb) Volvo Flygmotor RM8B turbofan |
| Performance: | maximum speed at high altitude 2124km/h (1320mph); service ceiling 18,290m (60,000ft); combat radius on lo-lo-lo mission with external armament 500km (311 miles) |
| Weights: | empty 15,000kg (33,060lb); maximum take-off 20,500kg (45,194lb) |
| Dimensions: | wingspan 10.6m (34ft 9.25in); length 16.3m (53ft 5.75in); height 5.9m (19ft 4.25in); wing area 46sq m (495.16sq ft) |
| Armament: | one 30mm Oerlikon KCA cannon with 150 rds; six external hardpoints with provision for 6000kg (13,228lb) of stores, including two Rb71 Sky Flash and four Rb24 Sidewinder air-to-air missiles, or bombs and/or 135mm rocket pods |

# Saab JAS 39 Gripen

Saab has produced another excellent lightweight fighter in the form of the Gripen, and it is extremely surprising, given the outstanding performance demonstrated by the aircraft, that more export orders have not been forthcoming. The aircraft was conceived during the late 1970s as a replacement for the AJ, SH, SF and JA versions of the Saab 37 Viggen. Configuration follows Saab's tried and tested convention with an aft-mounted delta, and swept canard foreplanes. The flying surfaces are controlled via a fly-by-wire system. Advanced avionics, including pulse-Doppler search and acquisition radar, pod-mounted FLIR, head-up and -down displays (replacing normal flight instruments) and excellent ECM and navigation systems, give the aircraft multi-role all-weather capability. The JAS 39A became operational in 1995. It has been sold to South Africa and Hungary, and more export orders may be forthcoming.

| | |
|---|---|
| **Country of origin:** | Sweden |
| **Type:** | single-seat all-weather fighter, attack and reconnaissance aircraft |
| **Powerplant:** | one 8210kg (18,100lb) Volvo Flygmotor RM12 turbofan |
| **Performance:** | maximum speed more than Mach 2; range on hi-lo-hi mission with external armament 3250km (2020 miles) |
| **Weights:** | empty 6622kg (14,600lb); maximum take-off 12,473kg (27,500lb) |
| **Dimensions:** | wingspan 8m (26ft 3in); length 14.1m (46ft 3in); height 4.7m (15ft 5in) |
| **Armament:** | one 27mm Mauser BK27 cannon with 90 rounds, six external hardpoints with provision for Rb71 Sky Flash and Rb24 Sidewinder air-to-air missiles, Maverick air-to-surface missiles, Rb15F anti-ship missiles, bombs, cluster bombs, rocket-launcher pods, reconnaissance pods, drop tanks and ECM pods |

# Saro London Mk II

I n 1928 A. V. Roe bought a large share of S. E. Saunders Ltd and the company
subsequently built aircraft under the name of Saunders-Roe, more commonly known by
the abbreviated form of Saro. The A.27 London coastal patrol flying-boat was built to Air
Ministry Specification R.24/31 and was a development of the earlier A.7 Severn. The A.27
was slightly smaller, but in all other respects very similar to the A.7, with two 875hp
(652kW) Bristol Pegasus III radial engines. Ten aircraft were produced for RAF Coastal
Command as the Saro London Mk I, the first of them delivered in 1936. The following 20 Mk
IIs had up-rated powerplant in circular nacelles driving four-blade propellers, all Mk Is
being modified subsequently to this standard. Pictured is one of the aircraft operated by No
240 Squadron, which operated from Stranraer under No 15 Group in 1940.

| Country of origin: | United Kingdom |
|---|---|
| Type: | coastal patrol flying-boat |
| Powerplant: | two 1055hp (787kW) Bristol Pegasus X radial piston engines |
| Performance: | maximum speed 249km/h (155mph); service ceiling 6065m (19,900ft); range 1770km (1100 miles) |
| Weights: | empty 5035kg (11,100lb); maximum take-off weight 8346kg (18,400lb) |
| Dimensions: | span 24.38m (80ft); length 17.31m (56ft 9in); height 5.72m (18ft 9in); wing area 132.38 sq m (1425 sq ft) |
| Armament: | one .303in Lewis machine gun on pivoted mount in bow; one .303in Lewis machine gun on pivoted mount in each of two midships positions; underwing racks with provision for up to 907kg (2000lb) of bombs or depth charges |

# Savoia-Marchetti S.55SA

**D**espite its rather ungainly appearance (promulgated by its twin-catamaran hulls), the Savoia-Marchetti S.55 was one of the most advanced flying-boats of the interwar years and was an indispensable tool of the Regia Marina during the 1930s. It was designed in response to a request for a new multi-engine torpedo-bomber flying-boat, with the twin engines carried on a pylon above the thick cantilever wing carried at shoulder height on the twin-hulls. The centre wing section contained the pilot's cockpit, and extending from the rear of each hull was a boom to carry the tail unit, with two fins and three rudders. The prototype was flown in the summer of 1924, but military chiefs were critical of its unconventional design and limited performance. Savoia-Marchetti then developed a civil version as the S.55C. The military belatedly took an interest and ordered the first 14 S.55A aircraft in 1926. These were followed by the S.55M, S.55SA, and S.55X.

| | |
|---|---|
| **Country of origin:** | Italy |
| **Type:** | (S.55X) long-range bomber-reconnaissance flying-boat |
| **Powerplant:** | two 880hp (656kW) Isotta-Fraschini Asso 750 Vee piston engines |
| **Performance:** | maximum speed 279km/h (173mph); service ceiling 5000m (16,405ft); range 3500km (2175 miles) |
| **Weights:** | empty equipped 5750kg (12,677lb); maximum take-off weight 8260kg (18,210lb) |
| **Dimensions:** | span 24m (78ft 9in); length 16.75m (54ft 11in); height 5m (16ft 5in); wing area 93 sq m (1001 sq ft) |
| **Armament:** | two 7.7mm machine guns in nose position in each of the hulls; plus one torpedo or 2000kg (4409lb) of bombs |

# Savoia-Marchetti SM.79 Sparviero

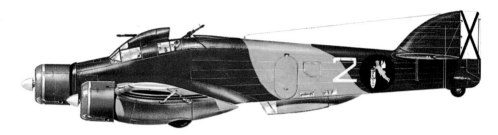

A rguably one of the finest torpedo bombers of World War II, the Sparviero ('Sparrowhawk') was notable for its three-engined layout and 'hunchback' fuselage. First flown in 1934 as the SM.79P civil transport prototype with eight-passenger seating, the type was then developed as a medium reconnaissance bomber and entered service as the SM.79-I with the uprated powerplant of three Alfa Romeo 126 radial engines and a large ventral gondola. The following SM.79-II was optimised for the anti-ship role with two 450mm torpedoes and a powerplant of three 1000hp (746kW) Piaggio P.XI RC.40 or 1030hp (768kW) Fiat A.80 RC.41 radial engines. The final Italian model was the SM.79-III improved SM.79-II with heavier defensive armament but no ventral gondola. Deliveries totalled 1230 aircraft. The aircraft continued in service after World War II as a transport with the Aeronautica Militare Italiana.

| | |
|---|---|
| Country of origin: | Italy |
| Type: | (SM.79-I) four/five-seat medium reconnaissance bomber |
| Powerplant: | three 780hp (582kW) Alfa Romeo 126 RC.34 9-cylinder single-row radial engines |
| Performance: | maximum speed 430km/h (267mph); climb to 5000m (16,405ft) in 19 minutes 45 seconds; service ceiling 6500m (21,325ft); range 1900km (1181 miles) with a 1250kg (2756lb) bomb load |
| Weights: | empty 6800kg (14,991lb); maximum take-off 10,480kg (23,104lb) |
| Dimensions: | span 21.20m (69ft 2.7in); length 15.62m (51ft 3.1in); height 4.40m (14ft 5.25in) |
| Armament: | one 12.7mm fixed forward-firing machine gun above cockpit, one 12.7mm trainable rearward-firing machine gun in dorsal position, one 12.7mm machine gun in ventral position, and one 7.7mm machine gun in two beam positions; bomb load of 2756lb (1250kg) |

# Savoia-Marchetti SM.81 Pipistrello

**D**eveloped in parallel with the SM.73 transport, with which it shared a basically common airframe, the Pipistrello ('Bat') was a dual-role bomber and transport that first flew in 1934 and entered service in 1935. The SM.81 was built to the extent of 535 aircraft in three subvariants that differed only in their powerplants, which could comprise any of three types of radial engine (two Italian and one French, the last from captured stocks). The SM.81 saw extensive service in the Italian conquest of Abyssinia in the mid-1930s and still proved moderately effective in the early part of the Spanish Civil War, but from the time of Italy's June 1940 entry into World War II was used increasingly in the dedicated transport role, although it did undertake night bombing raids in North Africa. The type survived the war in modest numbers and remained in Italian service to 1950. Pictured here is an SM.81 of the Gruppo Transporti 'Terraciano', air force of the Repubblica Sociale Italiana.

| Country of origin: | Italy |
|---|---|
| Type: | (SM.81) five/six-seat bomber and transport |
| Powerplant: | three 670hp (499.5kW) Piaggio P.X RC.35 nine-cylinder single-row radial engines, or 650hp (485kW) Alfa Romeo 125 RC.35 or 126 RC.34 nine-cylinder single-row radial engines, or 650hp (485kW) Gnome-Rhòne 14-K 14-cylinder two-row radial engines |
| Performance: | maximum speed 340km/h (211mph); climb to 3000m (9845ft) in 12 minutes; service ceiling 7000m (22,965ft); range 2000km (1243 miles) |
| Weights: | empty 6300kg (13,889lb); maximum take-off 10,055kg (22,167lb) |
| Dimensions: | span 24.00m (78ft 9in); length 17.80m (58ft 4.75in); height 6.00m (19ft 8.25in) |
| Armament: | two 7.7mm or one 12.7mm machine guns in dorsal turret, two 7.7mm machine guns in ventral turret, and one 7.7mm machine gun in beam positions, plus an internal bomb load of 4409lb (2000kg) |

# Seversky P-35

In May 1935 the US Army issued a requirement for a new fighter and the Seversky Aircraft Corporation created the SEV-2XP as its response. This was built with great speed and was developed via the SEV-1XP, SEV-7 and AP-1 stages with a higher-rated engine and a number of significant aerodynamic improvements before it was ordered as the P-35. These 77 aircraft were procured to maintain a production capability as the company (soon Republic) created more advanced types, and were delivered by August 1938. After the delivery of more capable fighters, the surviving P-35 machines became fighter trainers. Sweden ordered 120 of the EP-1 export version, but 60 of these were requisitioned by the USA for service as P-35A fighters, which were mostly lost in the Philippines to air attack in the hours after Japan's entry into the war. Pictured here is a 17th Pursuit Squadron P-35A, based at Nichols Field in the Phillipines during 1941.

| | |
|---|---|
| Country of origin: | USA |
| Type: | (P-35) single-seat fighter |
| Powerplant: | one 950hp (708kW) Pratt & Whitney R-1830-9 14-cylinder two-row radial engine |
| Performance: | maximum speed 452km/h (281mph); climb to 1525m (5000ft) in 2 minutes 3 seconds; service ceiling 9325m (30,600ft); range 1851km (1150 miles) |
| Weights: | empty 4315lb (1957kg); maximum take-off 2855kg (6295lb) |
| Dimensions: | span 10.97m (36ft); length 7.67m (25ft 2in); height 2.77m (9ft 1in ) |
| Armament: | one 0.5in fixed forward-firing machine gun and one 0.3in fixed forward-firing machine gun in the upper part of the forward fuselage, plus an internal bomb load of 159kg (350lb) |

# Short 184

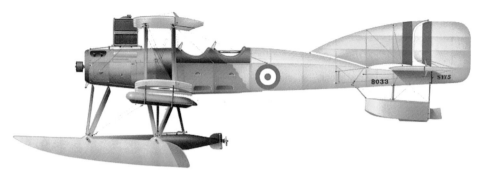

In 1908 Eustace and Oswald Short gained a licence to build the Wright Flyer, and at Leysdown on the Isle of Wight established the world's first factory for the construction of aircraft. The Type 184 was built in response to an Admiralty requirement for a torpedo-carrying seaplane and gave sterling service during World War I. Some 900 aircraft were built, with a variety of engines, but after achieving some spectacular early successes in its intended role the Type 184 was most commonly used for reconnaissance. The aircraft served in many theatres, from the Arctic Circle to the Indian Ocean. In 1916 one fitted with temporary wheels took off successfully from the seaplane-carrier *Campania*. Pictured is one of three aircraft attached to the famous seaplane-carrier HMS *Vindex*. The aircraft is shown here with a 14in torpedo. On 25 March 1916 this same aircraft was loaded with bombs and sent to attack the Zeppelin sheds at Tondern, but without success.

| Country of origin: | United Kingdom |
| --- | --- |
| Type: | two-seat torpedo-bomber/reconnaissance floatplane |
| Powerplant: | one 260hp (194kW) Sunbeam Maori Vee piston engine |
| Performance: | maximum speed 142km/h (88mph); service ceiling 2745m (9000ft); endurance 2hrs 45mins |
| Weights: | empty 1680kg (3703lb); maximum take-off weight 2433kg (5363lb) |
| Dimensions: | span 19.36m (63ft 6in); length 12.38m (40ft 7in); height 4.11m (13ft 6in); wing area 63.92 sq m (688 sq ft) |
| Armament: | one .303in Lewis machine gun on pivoted mount in rear cockpit; plus one 14in torpedo or up to 236kg (520lb) of bombs |

# Short Singapore

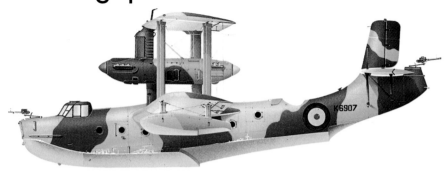

In 1926 Short produced the Singapore Mk I twin-engined flying boat that was built only in prototype form, and in 1931 developed this into the Singapore Mk II with a four-engined powerplant comprising two tandem pairs of tractor/pusher engines. The Singapore Mk II showed considerable promise, and in May 1934 the Air Ministry ordered four development machines, of which the first flew in July of the same year and soon received the designation Singapore Mk III. This paved the way for a further 33 boats, and all 37 machines had been delivered by June 1937 for use by five squadrons. The type was relegated to Far Eastern service in 1940–41, and in December 1941 the last four boats were handed over to the Royal New Zealand Air Force for continued service into 1942. Pictured here is one of the Mk III aircraft on the strength of No 203 Squadron, RAF, based at the British Middle East outpost of Aden in 1940.

| | |
|---|---|
| **Country of origin:** | United Kingdom |
| **Type:** | (Singapore Mk III) eight-seat maritime reconnaissance flying boat |
| **Powerplant:** | four 610hp (455kW) Rolls-Royce Kestrel VIII/XX 12-cylinder Vee engines |
| **Performance:** | maximum speed 219km/h (136mph); climb to 1525m (5000ft) in 7 minutes; service ceiling 4510m (14,800ft); range 1987 km (1235 miles) |
| **Weights:** | empty 9237kg (20,364lb); maximum take-off 14,692kg (32,390lb) |
| **Dimensions:** | span 27.43m (90ft); length 19.56m (64ft 2in); height 7.19m (23ft 7in) |
| **Armament:** | one 0.303in trainable forward-firing machine gun in bow position, one 0.303in trainable rearward-firing machine gun in dorsal position, and one 0.303in trainable rearward-firing machine gun in tail position, plus a bomb load of 590kg (1300lb) |

# Short Sunderland Mk I

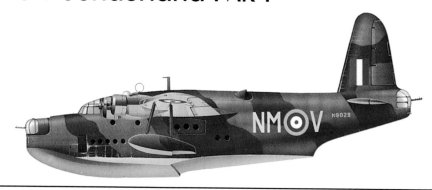

A 1933 requirement for a modern four-engined monoplane flying boat prompted designs from two companies including Short, which had an ideal starting point for its S.25 in the S.23 'Empire' class of civil flying boats. This proven lineage was a factor that contributed to the Air Ministry's order for 21 production examples of the S.25 in March 1936, some 18 months before the first prototype made its maiden flight in October 1937. The initial production model was the Sunderland Mk I that entered service in the summer of 1938 with an initial two squadrons. By the time World War II started in September 1939, another two British-based squadrons had converted onto the type, and the rising rate of production allowed another three to convert during the first months of the war. Sunderland Mk I production totalled 90 boats, 15 of them by the Blackburn Aircraft Company, all powered by 1010hp (753kW) Bristol Pegasus engines.

| | |
|---|---|
| Country of origin: | United Kingdom |
| Type: | (Sunderland Mk I) 10-seat maritime reconnaissance flying boat |
| Powerplant: | four 1010hp (753kW) Bristol Pegasus XXII nine-cylinder single-row radial engines |
| Performance: | maximum speed 336km/h (209mph); climb to 1525m (5000ft) in 7 minutes 12 seconds; service ceiling 4570m (15,000ft); range 4023km (2500 miles) |
| Weights: | empty 13,875kg (30,589lb); maximum take-off 22,226kg (49,000lb) |
| Dimensions: | span 34.38m (112ft 9.5in); length 26.00m (85ft 3.5in); height 10.52m (34ft 6in) |
| Armament: | two 0.303in trainable forward-firing machine guns in bow turret, four 0.303in trainable rearward-firing machine guns in tail turret, and one 0.303in machine gun in each beam position, plus an internal bomb, depth charge and mine load of 907kg (2000lb) |

# Short Sunderland MK III

**F**irst flown in June 1942, the Sunderland Mk III was the first major production model of the family and was in essence a late-production Sunderland Mk II with a revised planing bottom. Production of the 407 Mk IIIs lasted to late 1943. The Mk III was also converted for use as a long-range passenger aircraft and operated by British Overseas Airways Corporation from March 1943 on gradually extending routes. Operating alongside radar-equipped Catalinas, the RAF Short Sunderlands were extremely active in hunting for U-boats over the North Atlantic. When the latter received Metox passive receivers tuned to ASV Mk II they received ample warning of the presence of British aircraft and kills dropped dramatically. In response the RAF introduced the ASV Mk III, operating in the radar band well below 50cm (20in) and with the aerials neatly faired into blisters under the outer wings. When thus fitted the Sunderland became a Mk IIIa, of which 54 were built.

| | |
|---|---|
| **Country of origin:** | United Kingdom |
| **Type:** | 10-seat maritime reconnaissance flying-boat |
| **Powerplant:** | four 1065hp (794kW) Bristol Pegasus XVII 9-cylinder, single-row radial engines |
| **Performance:** | maximum speed 336km/h (209mph); service ceiling 4570m (15,000ft); range 4023km (2500 miles) |
| **Weights:** | empty 13,875kg (30,589lb); maximum take-off weight 22,226kg (49,000lb) |
| **Dimensions:** | span 34.38m (112ft 9in); length 26m (85ft 3in); height 10.52m (34ft 6in) |
| **Armament:** | two 0.303in trainable forward-firing machine guns in bow turret; two 0.303in trainable forward-firing machine guns in dorsal turret; four 0.303in trainable rearward-firing machine guns in tail turret; internal bomb, depth charge and mine load of 2000lb (907kg) |

# Short Stirling Mks I to V

The first four-engined heavy bomber to enter service with Bomber Command of the Royal Air Force during World War II, the Stirling was also the only British four-engined bomber to enter service after having been designed wholly as such, for the Avro Lancaster and Handley Page Halifax were both four-engined developments of two-engined designs. Even so, the Stirling was a workmanlike rather than inspired aeroplane largely as a result of the Air Ministry's demand for a span of less than 30.48m (100ft). The Stirling Mk I entered service in August 1940, and production of 2374 aircraft included 756 Mk I bombers with 1595hp (1189kW) Hercules XI engines, 875 Mk III bombers with a revised dorsal turret, 579 Mk IV paratroop and glider-towing aircraft without nose and dorsal turrets, and 160 Mk V unarmed transports. Pictured here is a Mk V of No 196 Squadron, RAF, based at Sheperd's Grove in the United Kingdom during 1946.

| | |
|---|---|
| Country of origin: | United Kingdom |
| Type: | (Stirling Mk III) seven/eight-seat heavy bomber |
| Powerplant: | four 1650hp (1230kW) Bristol Hercules XVI 14-cylinder two-row radial engines |
| Performance: | maximum speed 434km/h (270mph); initial climb rate 244m (800ft) per minute; service ceiling 5180m (17,000ft); range 3235km (2010 miles) with a 1588kg (3500lb) bomb load |
| Weights: | empty 21,274kg (46,900lb); maximum take-off 31,752kg (70,000lb) |
| Dimensions: | span 30.20m (99ft 1in); length 26.59m (87ft 3in); height 6.93m (22ft 9in) |
| Armament: | two 0.303in trainable forward-firing machine guns in the nose turret, two 0.303in trainable machine guns in the dorsal turret, and four 0.303in trainable rearward-firing machine guns in the tail turret, plus an internal bomb load of 6350kg (14,000lb) |

# Siemens-Schukert D.III

Siemens-Schukert Werke, a subsidiary of the vast Siemens electrical firm, began building experimental aircraft at the turn of the century and later, in 1916, built small numbers of the D.I, a copy of the French Nieuport 17. In 1917 the sister firm Siemens und Halske produced the remarkable Sh.III engine and this was installed in the various prototype D.II airframes of different span designed by Siemens-Schukert Werke's Chief Engineer Harald Wolff. The engine showed considerable promise, but suffered from imperfect development. The mid-span prototype went into production as the D.III, and demonstrated outstanding speed, climb and manoeuvrability. Service deliveries began in January 1918. However, the engine proved to be so troublesome that the entire fleet was withdrawn and re-engined with the Sh.IIIa, with the lower cowl cut away to improve cooling. Those aircrafft that made to the front mostly served with Jasta 15 of Jagdgeschwader II.

| Country of origin: | Germany |
| --- | --- |
| Type: | single-seat fighting scout |
| Powerplant: | one 200hp (150kW) Siemens und Halske Sh.IIIa rotary piston engine |
| Performance: | maximum speed 180km/h (112mph); service ceiling 8000m (26,245ft); endurance 2hrs |
| Weights: | empty 534kg (1177lb); maximum take-off weight 725kg (1598lb) |
| Dimensions: | span 8.43m (27ft 8in); length 6.7m (18ft 8in); height 2.8m (9ft 2in); wing area 203.44 sq m (19 sq ft) |
| Armament: | two fixed forward-firing 7.92mm LMG 08/15 machine guns |

# Sopwith Tabloid

In the summer of 1913 young T. O. M. (Tommy) Sopwith bought the lease on a former ice-skating rink in Kingston-upon-Thames, and set up the Sopwith Aviation & Engineering Company. He had hired Fred Sigrist to look after his yacht and now involved him in the design of aircraft, while Harry Hawker was taken on as a pilot and manager of the growing staff. From this came thousands of the greatest combat aircraft of World War I. One of the first to be built at the Sopwith works was a racing biplane, so small it was called the Tabloid. After Hawker had completed initial tests at Brooklands it was flown to Farnborough where it astonished everyone by reaching 148km/h (92mph) with a passenger and reaching 647m (1200ft) in one minute after leaving the ground. Thirty-six were subsequently built for the RFC and RNAS; RNAS machines mounted a series of famous attacks on the Zeppelin sheds in winter 1914. A float-equipped version was built as the Sopwith Schneider.

| | |
|---|---|
| **Country of origin:** | United Kingdom |
| **Type:** | single-seat maritime patrol and attack seaplane |
| **Powerplant:** | one 100hp (74.5kW) Gnow Monosoupape 9-cylinder rotary piston engine |
| **Performance:** | maximum speed 148km/h (92mph); service ceiling 4600m (15,000ft); range 510km (315 miles) |
| **Weights:** | empty 545kg (1200lb); maximum take-off weight 717kg (1580lb) |
| **Dimensions:** | span 7.77m (25ft 6in); length 7.02m (23ft); height 3.05m (10ft) |
| **Armament:** | Royal Naval Air Service seaplanes had one .303in Lewis machine gun |

# Sopwith 1½ Strutter

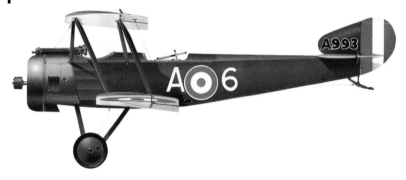

Deriving its nickname – by which it became universally known – from the '1½' sets of struts attaching the upper wing, the 1½ Strutter was the first military aircraft to be designed from the outset with a synchronised gun, and (apart from the Russian Sikorsky IM series) the first to equip a strategic bombing force. It included such unexpected features as a variable-incidence tailplane and airbrakes on the lower wing. The two-seat prototype was first flown in December 1915, and service deliveries of the first of an eventual 1513 machines were in April 1916. Most of the later versions were single-seat 9700 bombers and 'Ship Strutters' for the new Royal Navy aircraft carriers. About 4000 were built in France, and the aircraft was also operated with the air arms of Belgium, France, Japan, Latvia, Romania, and Russia, and with the American Expeditionary Force.

| | |
|---|---|
| Country of origin: | United Kingdom |
| Type: | two-seat multi-role combat aircraft |
| Powerplant: | one 130hp (97kW) Clerget rotary piston engine |
| Performance: | maximum speed 164km/h (102mph); service ceiling 3960m (13,000ft); range 565km (350 miles) |
| Weights: | empty 570kg (1260lb); maximum take-off weight 975kg (2149lb) |
| Dimensions: | span 10.21m (33ft 6in); length 7.7m (25ft 3in); height 3.12m (10ft 3in); wing area 32.14 sq m (346 sq ft) |
| Armament: | one fixed forward-firing .303in Vickers machine gun; plus up to four 25kg (56lb) bombs or an equivalent weight of smaller bombs |

# Sopwith Pup

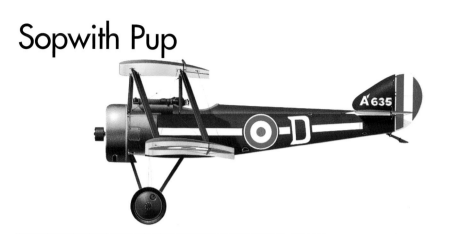

The Pup got its abiding nickname from its likeness to a scaled-down 1½ Strutter. It was first flown in February 1916 with an 80hp (60kW) Le Rhône rotary engine. Given the relatively small power output of this engine, the fact that the Pup was such a pleasure to fly speaks volumes of its design and construction. It was very small, simple and reliable, and its generous wing area gave it excellent performance at height. With only 80hp (60kW) on tap it soon became underpowered for combat with the more powerful Albatros and Halberstadt scouts, though compared with an Albatros it could turn twice for a single turn by the enemy. Sopwith built 170 Pups for the RNAS, and another 1600 were built for the RFC. Because of their exceptional time-to-height performance, many Pups were assigned to home defence units to counter the German bombing threat.

| | |
|---|---|
| Country of origin: | United Kingdom |
| Type: | single-seat fighting scout |
| Powerplant: | one 80hp (60kW) Le Rhône rotary piston engine |
| Performance: | maximum speed 179km/h (112mph); service ceiling 5334m (17,500ft); range 500km (310 miles) |
| Weights: | empty 358kg (790lb); maximum take-off weight 556kg (1225lb) |
| Dimensions: | span 8.08m (26ft 6in); length 5.89m (19ft 4in); height 2.87m (9ft 5in); wing area 23.60 sq m (254 sq ft) |
| Armament: | one fixed forward-firing .303in Vickers machine gun or one .303in Lewis aimed obliquely through cut-out in centre section of upper wing; anti-airship armament usually eight Le Prieur rockets launched from interplane struts |

# Sopwith Triplane

The lessons from early aerial combats over the Western Front emphasised the need for the highest possible rate of climb and manoeuvrability and, by fitting three slender planes to an airframe derived from the Pup, Sopwith designer Herbert Smith sought to exceed even this aircraft in these respects. The prototype flew in May 1916, and demonstrated an exceptional rate of climb, at only a small cost to manoeuvrability. The first aircraft entered service in November 1916 and over the following six months the Triplane gained almost complete ascendancy over enemy fighters. The German aircraft industry was launched into frenetic activity and by early 1917 almost every company was designing a triplane that could match it. Pictured here is the aircraft of Flight Lieutenant R. A. Little, No 8 (Naval) Squadron, RNAS, based in northern France in the spring of 1917.

| | |
|---|---|
| Country of origin: | United Kingdom |
| Type: | single-seat fighting scout |
| Powerplant: | one 130hp (97kW) Clerget 9B 9-cylinder rotary piston engine |
| Performance: | maximum speed 188km/h (117mph); service ceiling 6250m (20,500ft); endurance 2hrs 45mins |
| Weights: | empty 499kg (1101lb); maximum take-off weight 699kg (1541lb) |
| Dimensions: | span 8.08m (26ft 6in); length 5.74m (18ft 10in); height 3.2m (10ft 6in); wing area 21.46 sq m (231 sq ft) |
| Armament: | one or two fixed forward-firing .303in Vickers machine guns |

# Sopwith Camel F.1

The Triplane had only been in service for six months when its replacement, the Sopwith Camel, began to arrive in service. Perhaps the most famous aircraft of World War I, the Camel was so-called because of its distinctive 'humped' back, and between June 1917 and November 1918 it destroyed at least 3000 enemy aircraft, a greater total than that attained by any other aircraft. The Camel was a clear linear descendant of the Pup and Triplane, but its combat performance was achieved at some cost to the peerless handling of the earlier types. In inexperienced hands the Camel could bite, and the engine's torque was such that it had a nasty tendency to flip suddenly to the left on take off. Casualties among trainee pilots were high, but once mastered it was a superb dogfighter. Total production was in the order of 5490 aircraft, many of which served with foreign air arms.

| | |
|---|---|
| **Country of origin:** | United Kingdom |
| **Type:** | single-seat fighting scout |
| **Powerplant:** | one 130hp (97kW) Clerget rotary piston engine |
| **Performance:** | maximum speed 185km/h (115mph); service ceiling 5790m (19,000ft); endurance 2hrs 30mins |
| **Weights:** | empty 421kg (929lb); maximum take-off weight 659kg (1453lb) |
| **Dimensions:** | span 8.53m (28ft); length 5.72m (18ft 9in); height 2.59m (8ft 6in); wing area 21.46 sq m (231 sq ft) |
| **Armament:** | two fixed forward-firing .303in Vickers machine guns; plus up to four 11.3kg (25lb) bombs carried on fuselage sides |

# Sopwith Snipe

Designed as a successor to the Camel, the Snipe had a protracted development spanning six prototypes during which it was subjected to meticulous testing against such machines as the Bobolink and Nieuport B.N.1, before the Air Ministry finally decided to order it into production. All this was very much different from the experience of the Tabloid some four years previously, but in those four years much had been learned and the Snipe faced a horde of competitors. The Mk I had twin Vickers, the Lewis previously mounted on the upper plane having been found too difficult to aim, and electric heating and pilot oxygen for high-altitude flying. Deliveries to units in France began only eight weeks before the Armistice, but in the few aerial combats with the enemy the Snipe gave ample demonstration of its quality. Of the 4,515 ordered only 100 had been delivered by the Armistice; post-war production brought the total to 497, some remaining in front-line service until 1926.

| | |
|---|---|
| Country of origin: | United Kingdom |
| Type: | single-seat fighting scout |
| Powerplant: | one 230hp (172kW) Bentley B.R.2 rotary piston engine |
| Performance: | maximum speed 195km/h (121mph); service ceiling 5945m (19,500ft); endurance 3 hours |
| Weights: | empty 595kg (1,312lb); maximum take-off weight 916kg (2,020lb) |
| Dimensions: | span 9.17m (30ft 1in); length 6.02m (19ft 9in); height 2.67m (8ft 9in); wing area 25.08sq m (270sq ft) |
| Armament: | two fixed forward firing synchronised .303in Vickers machine-guns, plus up to four 11.3kg (25lb) of bombs on external racks |

# State Aircraft Factory Shenyang JJ-5

The physical similarity of the Shenyang JJ-5 to the MiG-15 is no coincidence. China benefited from considerable Soviet assistance when the communist government refurbished the Shenyang factory after the Second World War, and this extended to licensing machines of Soviet design to the new republic. The first turbojet-powered aircraft to be built in China were single-seat and two-seat versions of the MiG-15 'Fagot' and the MiG-17F. Chinese designers at the Chengdu factory (where the aircraft were built) developed an indigenous aircraft which incorporated features of both aircraft, and powered it with a Chinese built copy of a Soviet engine. The aircraft flew in prototype form in May 1966 and currently serves in the air arm of the PLA as its standard advanced trainer. An export model for Pakistan, Bangladesh, Sudan and Tanzania air force is designated FT-5.

| | |
|---|---|
| Country of origin: | China |
| Type: | two-seat advanced trainer |
| Powerplant: | one 2700kg (5952lb) Xian WP-5D turbojet |
| Perfomance: | normal operating speed 775km/h (482mph); service ceiling 14,300m (46,915ft); range with maximum fuel 1230km (764 miles) |
| Weights: | empty 4080kg (8995lb); maximum take-off 6215kg (13,702lb) |
| Dimensions: | wingspan 9.63m (31ft 7in); length 11.5m (37ft 8.75in); height 3.8m (12ft 5.5in) |
| Armament: | one 23mm Type 23-1 cannon in removable fuselage pack |

# State Aircraft Factory Shenyang J-6

The national aircraft company at Shenyang continued to assemble a version of the Mikoyan-Gurevich MiG-19S from knock-down kits supplied by the Soviet government until 1960. In that year, however, Sino-Soviet relations cooled and locally manufactured components were used instead. The Chinese-built MiG-19S was designated J-6 and entered service from mid-1962 with the Air Force of the People's Liberation Army and became its standard day fighter. The Nanchang Aircraft Manufacturing Company in Jiangxi province were also involved in the production of the aircraft, which numbered in their thousands. Pakistan was a major export customer for the F-6, many of which remain in service. These aircraft have been fitted with Western avionics, though this does not compensate for their overall obsolescence.

| | |
|---|---|
| Country of origin: | China |
| Type: | single-seat day fighter |
| Powerplant: | two 3250kg (7165lb) Shenyang WP-6 turbojets |
| Perfomance: | maximum speed 1540km/h (957mph); service ceiling 17,900m (58,725ft); range with internal fuel 1390km (864 miles) |
| Weights: | empty 5760kg (12,699lb); maximum take-off 10,000kg (22,046lb) |
| Dimensions: | wingspan 9.2m (30ft 2.25in); length 14.9m (48ft 10.5in); height 3.88m (12ft 8.75in); wing area 25sq m (269.11sq ft) |
| Armament: | three 30mm NR-30 cannon; four external hardpoints with provision for up to 500kg (1102lb) of stores, including air-to-air missiles, 250kg bombs, 55mm rocket-launcher pods, 212mm rockets or drop tanks |

# Sud-Ouest Aquilon 203

Although obviously derived from the de Havilland Venom, the Sud-Est Aquilon was significantly different and in many ways more capable than the carrier-based versions in service with the Royal Navy. The French company were suitably impressed with the proposed Sea Venom Mk 52, based on the Sea Venom FAW.Mk 20, to begin licensed production at Marignane, near Marseilles. This grew into an all-French family of aircraft using Westinghouse APQ-65 radar and Fiat-built de Havilland Ghost 48 engines. The single-seat Aquilon 203 had the pilot sitting slightly to starboard, a French APQ-65 radar and command-guidance Nord 5103 air-to-air missiles. Like the 202, it had full-air-conditioning (a source of much contention among British pilots), Martin-Baker ejector seat and Hispano 404 cannon. Forty were completed. This aircraft is painted in the colours of Aäronavale Flottila 16F.

| | |
|---|---|
| **Country of origin:** | France/United Kingdom |
| **Type:** | single-seat carrier-based fighter |
| **Powerplant:** | one 2336kg (5150lb) de Havilland Ghost 48 turbojet |
| **Performance:** | maximum speed 1030km/h (640mph); service ceiling 14,630m (48,000ft); range with drop tanks 1730km (1075 miles) |
| **Weights:** | empty 4174kg (9202lb); maximum loaded 6945kg (15,310lb) |
| **Dimensions:** | wingspan (over tip tanks) 12.7m (41ft 8in); length 10.38m (32ft 4in); height 1.88m (6ft 2in); wing area 25.99sq m (279.75sq ft) |
| **Armament:** | four 20mm Hispano 404 cannon with 150 rpg, two wing pylons for Nord 5103 (AA.20) air-to-air missiles |

# Sud-Ouest Vautour IIB

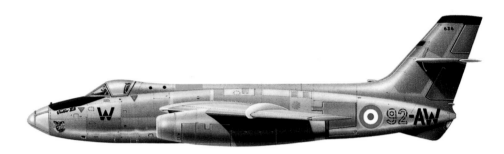

After World War II, the French aircraft industry strived to make up for five lost years, particularly in the new science of jet propulsion. By mid-March 1951 Sud-Ouest had flown the prototype of an advanced high-performance twin-jet bomber, designated the S.O. 4000. From this was developed the S.O. 4050. The S.O. 4050 differed quite considerably from its predecessor, with swept-wing surfaces and the engines mounted in nacelles beneath the wing. One of the three S.O. 4050 prototypes was completed as a two-seat bomber, with Armstrong Siddeley Sapphire turbojets and a glazed bomb-aiming position in the nose. The aircraft was designated S.O. 4050-3, and first flew on 5 December 1954. Evaluation of the aircraft led to production orders for 40, powered by the SNECMA Atar turbojet that was common to all variants.

| Country of origin: | France |
|---|---|
| Type: | two-seat medium bomber |
| Powerplant: | two 3503kg (7716lb) SNECMA Atar 101E-3 turbojets |
| Performance: | maximum speed 1105km/h (687mph); service ceiling more than 15000m (49,210ft) |
| Weights: | empty 10,000kg; maximum take-off 20,000kg (44,092lb) |
| Dimensions: | wingspan 15.09m (49ft 6in); length 15.57m (51ft 1in); height 4.5m (14ft 9in) |
| Armament: | internal bomb bay with provision for up to 10 bombs, and underwing pylons for two bombs up to 450kg (992lb), or two drop tanks |

# Sukhoi Su-2

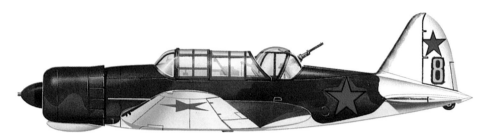

The Su-2 was designed in competition to the Ilyushin Il-2 as a means of providing the Soviet ground forces with potent close air support. Like the Il-2, therefore, the type's origins can be traced to the Soviet doctrine adopted in the mid-1930s that air power should be seen not as a means of projecting strategic capabilities deep into the enemy's rear areas and homeland but as a tactical adjunct of the ground forces. Pavel Sukhoi had previously worked as head of one of the design brigades in the Tupolev Design Bureau, where his last task had been the development of the ANT-51 tactical reconnaissance and ground-attack monoplane, and on being allowed to establish his own design bureau he set about the evolution of the ANT-51 into the BB-1 prototype, which entered production as the Su-2. Some 2000 aircraft were completed between 1940 and 1942, and this indifferent type was relegated to training use from 1943.

| | |
|---|---|
| Country of origin: | USSR |
| Type: | two-seat light attack bomber and reconnaissance warplane |
| Powerplant: | one 1000hp (746kW) Tumanskii M-88B 14-cylinder two-row radial engine |
| Performance: | maximum speed 460km/h (286mph); climb to 4000m (13,125ft) in 8 minutes 12 seconds; service ceiling 8800m (28,870ft); range 1200km (746 miles) |
| Weights: | empty 2970kg (6548lb); maximum take-off 4375kg (9645lb) |
| Dimensions: | span 14.30m (46ft 11in); length 10.46m (34ft 3.75in) |
| Armament: | between four and eight 7.62mm fixed forward-firing machine guns in the leading edges of the wings, and one 7.62mm trainable rearward-firing machine gun in the dorsal turret, plus an internal and external bomb and rocket load of 900kg (1984lb) |

# Sukhoi Su-7B 'Fitter-A'

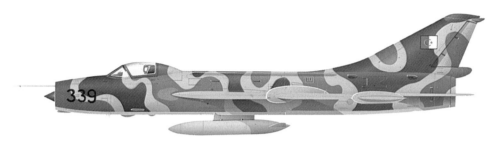

A large number of previously unknown Soviet aircraft were revealed at the 1956 Aviation Day at Tushino, among them a large swept-wing Sukhoi fighter (given the reporting name 'Fitter' by NATO). It has since become clear that the aircraft was planned as a fighter to intercept the North American F-100 and F-101 in service with the USAF, but subsequently became the standard tactical fighter-bomber of the Soviet air forces. The S-1 prototype aircraft was designed by Pavel Sukhoi after the re-establishment of Sukhoi OKB in 1953. Development work led to the S-2 and eventually to the S-22 pre-production aircraft. The Su-7B was ordered into production in 1958, and in a variety of sub-variants became the standard Soviet Bloc attack aircraft. Thousands were supplied to all Warsaw Pact nations and to Afghanistan, Algeria, Egypt, Cuba, India, Syria, Iraq and North Vietnam.

| | |
|---|---|
| **Country of origin:** | USSR |
| **Type:** | ground attack fighter |
| **Powerplant:** | one 9008kg (19,842lb) Lyulka AL-7F turbojet |
| **Performance:** | maximum speed at 11,000m (36,090ft) approximately 1700km/h (1056mph); service ceiling 15,150m (49,700ft); typical combat radius 320km (199 miles) |
| **Weights:** | empty 8620kg (19,000lb); maximum take-off 13,500kg (29,750lb) |
| **Dimensions:** | wingspan 8.93m (29ft 3.5in); length 17.37m (57ft); height 4.7m (15ft 5in) |
| **Armament:** | two 30mm NR-30 cannon with 70 rpg; four external pylons for two 750kg (1653lb) and two 500kg (1102lb) bombs, but with two tanks on fuselage pylons, total external weapon load is reduced to 1000kg (2205lb) |

# Sukhoi Su-17M-4 'Fitter-K'

Early Soviet research into 'swing-wing' technology concentrated on the Su-7. The basic wing of the aircraft was found to be unsuitable for conversion, and so a completely redesigned variable-geometry wing was tested on a prototype, designated Su-7IG, which first flew in August 1966. Fitted with a more powerful engine, the new aircraft was found to have far superior performance than even the most developed Su-7, especially for short-field operations. The aircraft entered service in 1971 and was widely used by the Soviet air arms. The ultimate development of the aircraft was the Su-17M-4. These are distinguishable by an airscoop for the cooling system on the leading edge of the tailfin root, but also incorporate advanced avionics. A centreline reconnaissance pod was also available. No longer in service with the Russian air force, it is being retired by its other user nations.

| Country of origin: | USSR |
|---|---|
| Type: | single-seat ground attack fighter |
| Powerplant: | one 11,250kg (24,802lb) Lyul'ka AL-21F-3 turbojet |
| Performance: | maximum speed above 11,000m (36,090ft) approximately 2220km/h (1380mph); service ceiling 15,200m (49,865ft); combat radius on hi-lo-hi mission with 2000kg (4409lb) load 675km (419 miles) |
| Weights: | empty 9,500kg (20,944lb); maximum take-off 19,500kg (42,990lb) |
| Dimensions: | wingspan 13.80m (45ft 3in) spread and 10m (32ft 10in) swept; length 18.75m (61ft 6in); height 5m (16ft 5in); wing area 40sq m (430sq ft) |
| Armament: | two 30mm NR-30 cannon with 80 rpg; nine external pylons with provision for up to 4250kg (9370lb) of stores, including tactical nuclear weapons, air-to-air missiles, air-to-surface missiles, guided bombs, cluster bombs, dispenser weapons, napalm tanks, large-calibre rockets, rocket-launcher pods, cannon pods, drop tanks and ECM pods |

# Sukhoi Su-15 'Flagon-A'

The Su-15 single-seat all-weather interceptor was developed to a requirement for a successor to the Sukhoi Su-11 (developed from the Su-7), and strongly resembles that aircraft in various aspects of its design. The most obvious similarities are the wings and tail. The initial T-5 prototype from which the Su-15 was developed was basically an enlarged version of the Su-11 with two engines, and the same pitot nose intake. The T-58 which followed had a solid radar nose housing Oriol-D radar and variable intakes on the fuselage sides. The 'Flagon A' entered IA-PVO Strany service in 1967, and some 1500 Sukhoi 15s in all versions are estimated to have been built. All these aircraft served with Soviet air arms, since the aircraft was never made available for export. The aircraft were often armed with the huge AA-3 'Anab' AAM.

| | |
|---|---|
| **Country of origin:** | USSR |
| **Type:** | single-seat all-weather interceptor |
| **Powerplant:** | two 6205kg (13,668lb) Tumanskii R-11F2S-300 turbojets |
| **Performance:** | maximum speed above 11,000m (36,090ft) approximately 2230km/h (1386mph); service ceiling 20,000m (65,615ft); combat radius 725km (450 miles) |
| **Weights:** | empty (estimated) 11,000kg (24,250lb); maximum take-off 18,000kg (39,680lb) |
| **Dimensions:** | wingspan 8.61m (28ft 3in); length 21.33m (70ft); height 5.1m (16ft 8.5in); wing area 36sq m (387.5sq ft) |
| **Armament:** | four external pylons for two R8M medium-range air-to-air missiles ouboard and two AA-8 'Aphid' short-range AAMs inboard, plus two under-fuselage pylons for 23mm UPK-23 cannon pods or drop tanks |

# Sukhoi Su-15TM 'Flagon-F'

A number of versions of the Su-15 were produced; the definitive Su-15TM 'Flagon-F' was designed in 1971 and introduced a low-drag ogival nose radome to cover the scanner for an uprated Typhoon M search radar for limited look-down/shoot-down capability, and more powerful engines. The Su-15TM entered service in 1975. By the mid-1990s only two PVO (Soviet home defence) units continued to operated the aircraft, and it has now been completely replaced in service by the Sukhoi Su-27 and Mikoyan-Gurevich MiG-31 from service. The aircraft achieved a degree of notoriety in 1983 when it was involved in the downing of a Korean Air Lines 747 passenger aircraft in the Sea of Japan, although it was for some time erroneously reported that this aircraft was an Su-21 – in fact this aircraft never even existed!

| | |
|---|---|
| Country of origin: | USSR |
| Type: | single-seat all-weather interceptor |
| Powerplant: | two 7200kg (15,873lb) Tumanskii R-13F2-300 turbojets |
| Performance: | maximum speed above 11,000m (36,090ft) approximately 2230km/h (1386mph); service ceiling 20,000m (65,615ft); combat radius 725km (450 miles) |
| Weights: | empty (estimated) 11,000kg (24,250lb); maximum take-off 18,000kg (39,680lb) |
| Dimensions: | wingspan 9.15m (30ft); length 21.33m (70ft); height 5.1m (16ft 8.5in); wing area 36sq m (387.5sq ft) |
| Armament: | four external pylons for two AA-3 'Anab' medium-range air-to-air missiles ouboard and two AA-8 'Aphid' short-range AAMs inboard, plus two under-fuselage pylons for 23mm GSh-23L two-barrell cannon pods or drop tanks |

# Sukhoi Su-24M 'Fencer-D'

In 1965, the Soviet government prompted Sukhoi to begin designing a new Soviet variable geometry attack aircraft comparable in performance to the F-111 due to enter service in the US. One of the primary requirements for the new aircraft was the ability to penetrate increasingly efficient radar defences by flying at very low-level and at supersonic speeds. It was also specified that the aircraft should be able to operate from short, unpaved airstrips. Initial development of a VTOL aircraft to meet these criteria was halted, and work began to develop the swing-wing aircraft, designated Su-24, which emerged to make its first flight in 1970. Service deliveries of the 'Fencer A' began in 1974. The 'Fencer D' (Su-24M), which entered service in 1986, is an improved version with inflight refuelling equipment, upgraded nav/attack systems, Kaira laser and TV designator and improved defensive aids.

| | |
|---|---|
| **Country of origin:** | USSR |
| **Type:** | two-seat strike and attack aircraft |
| **Powerplant:** | two 11,250kg (24,802lb) Lyul'ka AL-21F-3A turbojets |
| **Performance:** | maximum speed above 11,000m (36,090ft) approximately 2316km/h (1,439mph); service ceiling 17,500m (57,415ft); combat radius on hi-lo-hi mission with 3000kg (6614lb) load 1050km (650 miles) |
| **Weights:** | empty 19,000kg (41,888lb); maximum take-off 39,700kg (87,520lb) |
| **Dimensions:** | wingspan 17.63m (57ft 10in) spread and 10.36m (34ft) swept; length 24.53m (80ft 5in); height 4.97m (16ft 0.75in); wing area 42sq m (452.1sq ft) |
| **Armament:** | one 23mm GSh-23-6 six-barrelled cannon; nine external pylons with provision for up to 8000kg (17,635lb) of stores, including nuclear weapons, air-to-air missiles, air-to-surface missiles such as the AS-14 'Kedge', guided bombs, cluster bombs, dispenser weapons, large-calibre rockets, rocket-launcher pods, drop tanks and ECM pods |

# Sukhoi Su-25 'Frogfoot-A'

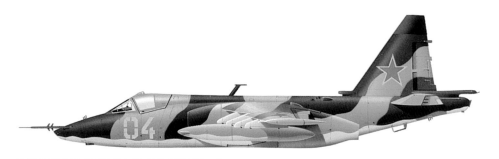

Western intelligence sources first identified the 'Frogfoot' at Ramenskoye test centre in 1977 and gave it the provisional US designation 'Ram-J'. The prototype first flew in 1975, and production of the single-seat close-support Su-25K (often compared to the Fairchild A-10 Thunderbolt II) began in 1978. The pilot sits in an armoured cockpit, and on the Su-25K had a Sirena-3 radar-warning system and tailcone mounted chaff/decoy flare dispenser to protect his aircraft. A nose-mounted laser range finder and marked target seeker reportedly allows bombing accuracy to within 5 meters over a stand-off range of 20km (12.5 miles). A trial unit was deployed to Afghanistan as early as 1980, followed by a full squadron, to support Soviet troops fighting in the mountainous country. The squadron worked closely with Mi-24 'Hind' gunships and the aircraft became fully operational in 1984.

| | |
|---|---|
| Country of origin: | USSR |
| Type: | single-seat close-support aircraft |
| Powerplant: | two 4500kg (9921lb) Tumanskii R-195 turbojets |
| Performance: | maximum speed at sea level 975km/h (606mph); service ceiling 7,000m (22,965ft); combat radius on lo-lo-lo mission with 4400kg (9700lb) load 750km (466 miles) |
| Weights: | empty 9,500kg (20,950lb); maximum take-off 17,600kg (38,800lb) |
| Dimensions: | wingspan 14.36m (47ft 1.5in); length 15.53m (50ft 11.5in); height 4.8m (15ft 9in); wing area 33.7sq m (362.75sq ft) |
| Armament: | one 30mm GSh-30-2 cannon with 250 rds; eight external pylons with provision for up to 4400kg (9700lb) of stores, including AAMs, ASMs, ARMs, anti-tank missiles, guided bombs, cluster bombs, dispenser weapons, large-calibre rockets, rocket-launcher pods, drop tanks and ECM pods |

# Sukhoi Su-27UB 'Flanker-C'

**D**evelopment of the Su-27 began in the mid-1970s, with the aim of producing a combat aircraft for Soviet forces comparable to the McDonnell Douglas F-15 Eagle. Given this seemingly daunting design brief, Sukhoi proceeded with impressive haste, and by the end of May 1977 the prototype Su-27 had flown. Development from prototype stage was somewhat longer and involved some fundamental design changes, necessitated by poor structural strength, excessive drag, flutter and excess weight. It was not until 1980 that full-scale production began and service entry started in 1984. The aircraft represents a significant advance over previous generations of Soviet aircraft and presented an outstanding potential for development. Advanced avionics make it a formidable fighter. The first variant was the Su-27UB 'Flanker-C' tandem-seat trainer, which retains full combat capability.

| | |
|---|---|
| **Country of origin:** | USSR |
| **Type:** | tandem-seat operational conversion trainer |
| **Powerplant:** | two 12,500kg (27,557lb) Lyul'ka AL-31F turbofans |
| **Performance:** | maximum speed at high altitude 2500km/h (1500mph); service ceiling 18,000m (59,055ft); combat radius 1500km (930 miles) |
| **Weights:** | maximum tak-off 30,000kg (66,138lb) |
| **Dimensions:** | wingspan 14.70m (48ft 2.75in); length 21.94m (71ft 11.5in); height 6.36m (20ft 10.25in); wing area 46.5sq m (500sq ft) |
| **Armament:** | one 30mm GSh-3101 cannon with 149 rds; 10 external hardpoints with provision for 6000kg (13,228kg) of stores, including AA-10A ('Alamo-A'), AA-10B ('Alamo-B'), AA-10C ('Alamo-C'), AA-11 ('Archer') or AA-8 ('Aphid') air-to-air missiles |

# Sukhoi Su-35

One of the ongoing developments of the Su-27 is the single-seat Su-35 all-weather air-superiority fighter (derived from the 'Flanker-B'). This aircraft, which has similar powerplant and configuration to the Su-27, is an attempt to provide a second-generation Su-27 with improved agility and operational capability. The program was severely delayed by problems with the radar and digital quadruplex fly-by-wire control systems, which replace the analogue system in the earlier aircraft. A new fire control system was incorporated, with air-to-ground and air-to-air modes, to improve the ground attack capability of the aircraft. This is linked to a new electro-optical complex incorporating laser and TV designation for air-to-surface missiles, as well as laser ranging. Inflight refuelling equipment is also fitted. The first of six Su-27M prototypes (as it was then known) made its maiden flight in 1988.

| | |
|---|---|
| **Country of origin:** | USSR |
| **Type:** | single-seat all-weather air superiority fighter |
| **Powerplant:** | two 12,500kg (27,557lb) Lyul'ka AL-31M turbofans |
| **Performance:** | maximum speed at high altitude 2500km/h (1500mph); service ceiling 18,000m (59,055ft); combat radius 1500km (930 miles) |
| **Weights:** | maximum take-off 30,000kg (66,138lb) |
| **Dimensions:** | wingspan 14.70m (48ft 2.75in); length 21.94m (71ft 11.5in); height 6.36m (20ft 10.25in); wing area 46.5sq m (500sq ft) |
| **Armament:** | one 30mm GSh-3101 cannon with 149 rounds; 10 external hardpoints with provision for 6,000kg (13,228kg) of stores, including AA-10A ('Alamo-A'), AA-10B ('Alamo-B'), AA-10C ('Alamo-C'), AA-11 ('Archer') or AA-8 ('Aphid') air -to-air missiles |

# Supermarine Southampton Mk I

In addition to its military aircraft designs, Supermarine produced a small number of commercial passenger-carrying amphibian flying-boats. The most successful of these was the single-engine Sea Eagle biplane of 1923, three of which were built for the British Marine Air Navigation company for service on its Southampton–Channel Islands routes. These were complemented in 1926 by a Supermarine Swan, from which was developed the elegant Southampton, designed by R. J. Mitchell. This five-crew biplane flying-boat first flew in March 1925 and deliveries began to the RAF a few months later. The Mk II had a Duralumin hull, which represented a considerable weight saving over the wooden-hulled Mk I. Production total was 68 aircraft. T he example pictured here is a Mk I of No 480 (Coastal Reconnaissance) Flight, RAF, based at Calshot during the mid-1920s.

| | |
|---|---|
| Country of origin: | United Kingdom |
| Type: | (Mk II) general reconnaissance flying-boat |
| Powerplant: | two 500hp (373kW) Napier Lion VA W-12 piston engines |
| Performance: | maximum speed 174km/h (108mph); service ceiling 4265m (14,000ft); range 1497km (930 miles) |
| Weights: | empty 4082kg (9000lb); maximum take-off weight 6895kg (15,200lb) |
| Dimensions: | span 22.86m (75ft); length 15.58m (51ft 1in); height 6.82m (22ft 4in); wing area 134.61 sq m (1449 sq ft) |
| Armament: | one .303in Lewis gun on pivoted mount in nose position; one .303in Lewis gun on pivoted mount in each of two midships positions, plus up to 499kg (1100lb) of bombs |

# Supermarine Walrus

In 1920 Supermarine flew its Channel flying boat, and in 1922 the Seagull Mk I development of this machine. There followed a development programme that led in June 1933 to the Seagull Mk V that introduced a predominantly metal structure. The Australian government ordered 24 of this type, and its success led to a British contract fore 12 catapult-capable 'boats that received the revised designation Walrus Mk I in 1935. Later orders increased the total to 556 boats (the later examples with air-to-surface radar) for service with the Fleet Air Arm and Royal Air Force in the reconnaissance and air/sea rescue roles with the 635hp (473.5kW) Pegasus IIM2 engine. The final model, of which 191 were delivered up to January 1944, was the Walrus Mk II with an uprated engine and a wooden hull. Pictured here is a Walrus Mk I of No 700 Squadron, Fleet Air Arm, based on HMS *Belfast* in the early 1940s.

| | |
|---|---|
| **Country of origin:** | United Kingdom |
| **Type:** | (Walrus Mk II) four-seat coastal and shipborne air/sea rescue, spotter and anti-submarine amphibian flying boat |
| **Powerplant:** | one 775hp (578kW) Bristol Pegasus VI nine-cylinder single-row radial engine |
| **Performance:** | maximum speed 217km/h (135mph); climb to 3050m (10,000ft) in 12 minutes 30 seconds; service ceiling 5640m (18,500ft); range 966 km (600 miles) |
| **Weights:** | empty 2223kg (4900lb); maximum take-off 3334kg (7350lb) |
| **Dimensions:** | span 13.97m (45ft 10in); length 11.58m (38ft); height 5.13m (16ft 10.5in) with the main landing gear units lowered |
| **Armament:** | one 0.303in trainable forward-firing machine gun in the bow position, and one or two 0.303in machine guns in the dorsal position, plus a bomb and depth charge load of 272kg (600lb) |

# Supermarine Spitfire Mk I to V

**R**.J. Mitchell began the design of the Spitfire in the mid-1930s, with a virtually free reign and unfettered by official specifications. The Type 300 was developed around the Rolls Royce Merlin engine, and the prototype was subsequently ordered into production in June 1936 as the Spitfire Mk 1. Service deliveries of 310 aircraft began in July 1938 to No 19 Squadron at Duxford. These were heavily engaged in the Battle of Britain, proving a better foil to the Bf 109 than the less manoeuvrable Hurricane. The Mk I was followed by 1566 IBs with twin 20mm cannon, the Mk IIA and IIB with Merlin XII, the one-off experimental Mk III with Merlin XX, the Mk IV (2 Griffon engines prototypes, and 229 photo reconnaissance versions of the Spitfire Mk V, and then by the Mk V with strengthened fuselage for Merlin 45 or Merlin 50, drop tank and bomb provision. Suffix LF designates an aircraft with the low-altitude clipped wing and F the standard wing. A,B, and C are different armament fits.

| | |
|---|---|
| **Country of origin:** | United Kingdom |
| **Type:** | (Spitfire Mk VA) single-seat fighter and fighter-bomber |
| **Powerplant:** | one 1,478hp (1102kW) Rolls-Royce Merlin 45 12-cylinder Vee engine |
| **Performance:** | maximum speed 594km/h (394mph); initial climb rate 1204m (3950ft) per minute; service ceiling 11,125m (36,500ft); range 1827km (1,135 miles) |
| **Weights:** | empty 2267kg (4998lb); maximum take-off 2911kg (6417lb) |
| **Dimensions:** | span 11.23m (36ft 10in); length 9.12m (29ft 11in); height 3.02m (9ft 11in) |
| **Armament:** | eight 0.303in fixed forward-firing machine guns in the leading edges of the wing |

# Supermarine Seafire

Faced with the technical and tactical obsolescence of its two-seat carrierborne fighters, the Royal Navy ordered the Seafire as a navalised version of the Spitfire for service from June 1942. The main variants were the Seafire Mk IB (166 conversions from Spitfire Mk VB standard), Seafire Mk IIC (372 aircraft in low- and medium-altitude fighter as well as reconnaissance fighter forms), and definitive Seafire Mk III (1220 aircraft in the same variants as the Seafire Mk II but with folding wings). There were also 30 Seafire Mk III (Hybrid) aircraft with fixed wings, these later being reclassified as Seafire Mk IIC machines, and the Seafire Mks XV, XVII, 45, 46 and 47 were post-war developments. The Seafire offered good performance, but was hampered for carrierborne operations by its long nose and narrow-track main landing gear units. Nevertheless the aircraft soldiered on after the war, seeing service in Korea with No 800 Sqn until final retirement from RNVR units in 1967.

| | |
|---|---|
| Country of origin: | United Kingdom |
| Type: | (Seafire LF.Mk III) single-seat carrierborne fighter and fighter-bomber |
| Powerplant: | one 1600hp (1193kW) Rolls-Royce Merlin 55M 12-cylinder Vee engine |
| Performance: | maximum speed 560km/h (348mph); climb to 1525m (5000ft) in 1 minute 54 seconds; service ceiling 7315m (24,000ft); range 890km (553 miles) |
| Weights: | empty 2814kg (6204lb); maximum take-off 3465kg (7640lb) |
| Dimensions: | span 11.23m (36ft 10in); length 9.21m (30ft 2.5in); height 3.42m (11ft 2.5in) |
| Armament: | two 20mm fixed forward-firing cannon and four 0.303in Browning fixed forward-firing machine guns in the leading edges of the wing, plus an external bomb and rocket load of 227kg (500lb) |

# Spitfire Mks IX and XVI

Entering service in June 1942 as a supposed 'interim' type to tackle the depredations of Focke-Wulf Fw 190 'hit-and-run' raiders over southern England, the Spitfire Mk IX was one of the most successful of all Spitfire variants and was in effect the airframe of the Spitfire Mk VC (Spitfire Mk V with two cannon and two machine guns and provision for carrying bombs ) with the uprated Merlin 60 series of engines. Production of the Spitfire Mk IX totalled 5665 aircraft in the low-, medium- and high-altitude subvariants that had been pioneered in the Spitfire Mk V model, and the Spitfire LF.Mk XVI (1054 aircraft) was a development with the 1580hp (1178kW) Packard Merlin 266. There were also the Spitfire PR.Mks IX, X and XI succeeding earlier Spitfire photo-reconnaissance adaptations: the PR.Mk IX was a Mk IX conversion, but the 16 and 471 PR.Mks X and XI were new-build aircraft with Merlin 61, 63 or 70 engines.

| | |
|---|---|
| Country of origin: | United Kingdom |
| Type: | (Spitfire F.Mk IX) single-seat fighter and fighter-bomber |
| Powerplant: | one 1565hp (1167kW) Rolls-Royce Merlin 61 or 1650hp (1230kW) Merlin 63 12-cylinder Vee engine |
| Performance: | maximum speed 655km/h (408mph); initial climb rate 1204m (3950ft) per minute; service ceiling 12,105m (43,000ft); range 1576km (980 miles) |
| Weights: | empty 2545kg (5610lb); maximum take-off 4309kg (9500lb) |
| Dimensions: | span 11.23m (36ft 10in); length 9.46m (31ft); height 3.85m (12ft 7.75in) |
| Armament: | two 20mm fixed forward-firing cannon and four 0.303in fixed forward-firing machine guns in the leading edges of the wing, plus an external bomb load of 454kg (1000lb) |

# Supermarine Spitfire Mks XII and XIV

**B**y the middle years of World War II the best way to wring yet more out of the Spitfire airframe appeared to be the application of considerably more power in the form of the Rolls-Royce Griffon engine. The first such variant was the Spitfire Mk XII, of which 100 were completed with a Griffon III or VI engine. However, the definitive variant was the Spitfire Mk XIV based on the Mk VII airframe but with the Griffon engine in a longer nose, a cut-down rear fuselage and 'clear-view' bubble canopy, a vertical tail surface of greater area, and the E-type wing that added provision for two 0.5in machine guns as alternatives to the four 0.303in weapons. The 527 F.Mk XIV aircraft were complemented by 430 FR.Mk XIV machines optimised for the reconnaissance fighter role with a fuselage-mounted camera. Production of the Spitfire Mk XIV totaled over 900 machines, and which helped to destroy over 300 German flying bombs.

| Country of origin: | United Kingdom |
|---|---|
| Type: | (Spitfire F.Mk XIV) single-seat fighter and fighter-bomber |
| Powerplant: | one 2050hp (1528.5kW) Rolls-Royce Griffon 65 12-cylinder Vee engine |
| Performance: | maximum speed 721km/h (448mph); climb to 6095m (20,000ft) in 7 minutes; service ceiling 13,565m (44,500ft); range 1368km (850 miles) |
| Weights: | empty 2994kg (6600lb); maximum take-off 3856kg (8500lb) |
| Dimensions: | span 11.23m (36ft 10in); length 9.96m (32ft 8in); height 3.86m (12ft 7.75in) |
| Armament: | two 20mm forward-firing cannon and either four 0.303 in or two 0.5in fixed forward-firing machine guns in the leading edges of the wing, plus an external bomb or rocket load of 227kg (500lb) |

# Supermarine Spitfire Mk XVIII

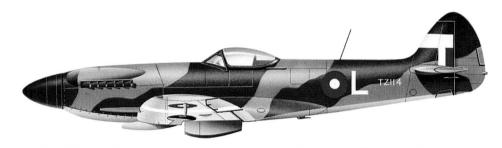

The success of the Spitfire Mk XIV made it sensible to continue this design trend further with the evolution of a longer-range variant with additional fuel tankage in the rear fuselage, even though this demanded some strengthening of the structure and main landing gear units. The wing was also redesigned, and the resulting type entered production as the Spitfire Mk XVIII, of which 300 examples were completed for service from the middle of 1945 as 100 F.Mk XVIII fighters and 200 FR.Mk XVIII reconnaissance fighters. There was also a Spitfire PR.Mk XIX of which 225 were completed as developments of the Mk XIV for the unarmed photo-reconnaissance role, mostly in tropical regions and with a pressurised cabin for operations at high altitude. These PR aircraft were used extensively after the war, making numerous flights over Chinese and Malaysian territory from bases in Hong Kong. In post-war service they were redesignated PR Mk 19.

| | |
|---|---|
| **Country of origin:** | United Kingdom |
| **Powerplant:** | one 2050hp (1528.5kW) Rolls-Royce Griffon 65 12-cylinder Vee engine |
| **Performance:** | maximum speed 721km/h (448mph); climb to 6095m (20,000ft) in 7 minutes; service ceiling 13,565m (44,500ft); range more than 1368km (850 miles) |
| **Weights:** | empty not available; maximum take-off 4990kg (11,000lb) |
| **Dimensions:** | span 11.23m (36ft 10in); length 10.14m (33ft 3.25in); height 3.86m (12ft 7.75in) |
| **Armament:** | two 20mm forward-firing cannon and two 0.5in fixed forward-firing machine guns in the leading edges of the wing, plus an external bomb and rocket load of 227kg (500lb) |

# Supermarine Scimitar F.Mk 1

The Scimitar had an extremely protracted gestation period, explained in part by the muddled procurement programme, which in 1945 asked for naval fighters without normal landing gear to land on a flexible deck. The first prototype, the Supermarine 508, was a thin straight-winged design with a butterfly tail. This was changed to a conventional swept layout with cruciform tail on the 525, and finalised in the 544 with blown flaps, slab tail, and area-ruled body. Three prototype Type 544 aircraft were constructed, the first of which flew in January 1956. Production aircraft were delivered from August 1957, and the type became operational in June 1958 with newly-formed No. 803 Squadron. A total of 76 were built, providing the Fleet Air Arm with a capable low-level supersonic attacker until the Scimitar was superseded by the Buccaneer from 1969.

| | |
|---|---|
| Country of origin: | United Kingdom |
| Type: | single-seat carrier-based multi-role aircraft |
| Powerplant: | two 5105kg (11,250lb) Rolls-Royce Avon 202 turbojets |
| Performance: | maximum speed 1143km/h (710mph); service ceiling 15,240m (50,000ft); range, clean at height 966km (600 miles) |
| Weights: | empty 9525kg (21,000lb); maximum take-off 15,513kg (34,200lb) |
| Dimensions: | wingspan 11.33m (37ft 2in); length 16.87m (55ft 4in); height 4.65m (15ft 3in); wing area 45.06sq m (485sq ft) |
| Armament: | four 30mm Aden cannon, four 454kg (1000lb) bombs or four Bullpup air-to-ground missiles, or four sidewinder air-to-air missiles, or drop tanks |

# Supermarine Swift FR.Mk 5

Designed by a Supermarine team that had cut its teeth on the Spitfire and the Attacker, the Swift had a problematic development which was matched by an unfulfilled service life. The prototype 541 Swift was deficient in many respects and spring-tab ailerons prohibited supersonic dives. Later geared-tab surfaces made transonic flight possible, but control was poor about all axes and dangerous above 25,000ft. The unsuitability of the Mk 1 and 2 as interceptor aircraft led to a decision to concentrate on development of the Swift as a a tactical reconnaissance aircraft. Sixty-two FR.Mk 5 were subsequently produced with lengthened nose to accommodate three cameras, a frameless canopy, and modified wing. The aircraft equipped both No.2 and No.79 Squadrons of the 2nd Allied Tactical Air Force in Germany.

| Country of origin: | United Kingdom |
| --- | --- |
| Type: | single-seat tactical reconnaissance aircraft |
| Powerplant: | one 4287kg (9450lb) Rolls-Royce Avon 114 turbojet |
| Performance: | maximum speed 1100km/h (685mph); service ceiling 13,690m (45,800ft); range 1014km (630 miles) |
| Weights: | empty 5800kg (12,800lb); maximum take-off 9,706kg (21,400lb) |
| Dimensions: | wingspan 9.85m (32ft 4in); length 12.88m (42ft 3in); height 3.8m (12ft 6in); wing area 45.06sq m (485sq ft) |
| Armament: | two 30mm Aden cannon plus provision for underwing rockets and bombs |

# Tupolev SB-2

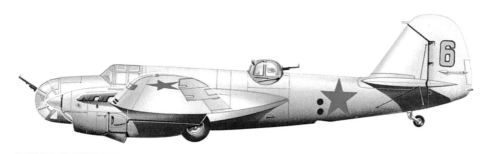

The SB-2 was almost certainly the most capable bomber serving anywhere in the world during the mid-1930s, in purely numerical terms was the most important bomber in the world during the late 1930s, and was also the first 'modern' aeroplane of the stressed-skin type to enter production in the USSR, an event that took place in 1935. The SB-2 was initially delivered with 730hp (544kW) M-100 engines driving fixed-pitch propellers, but then came the 860hp (641kW) M-100A engine in a wider nacelle and driving a variable-pitch propeller. SB-2 series production totalled 6967 aircraft, and the most important variant was the SB-2bis with uprated and different engines and greater fuel capacity. Other variants included 200 SB-RK dive-bombers with 1100hp (820kW) Klimov M-105R engines, and the 111 Czechoslovak licence-built B 71 bombers. Pictured is an SB-2bis of the Red Air Force, captured by the Germans late in 1941.

| Country of origin: | USSR |
|---|---|
| Type: | (SB-2bis) three-seat light bomber |
| Powerplant: | two 960hp (716kW) Klimov M-103 12-cylinder Vee engines |
| Performance: | maximum speed 450km/h (280mph); climb to 1000m (3280ft) in 1 minute 48 seconds; service ceiling 9000m (29,530ft); range 2300km (1429 miles) |
| Weights: | empty 4768kg (10,511lb); maximum take-off 7880kg (17,372lb) |
| Dimensions: | span 20.33m (66ft 8.5in); length 12.57m (41ft 2.75in); height 3.25m (10ft 8in) |
| Armament: | two 7.62mm trainable forward-firing machine guns in the nose position, one 7.62mm trainable rearward-firing machine gun in the dorsal turret, and one 7.62mm trainable rearward-firing machine gun in the ventral position, plus an internal bomb load of 600kg (1323lb) |

# Tupolev Tu-2

First flown in ANT-58 prototype form during January 1941, the Tu-2 was one of the best high-speed bombers to see service in World War II, but was built in larger numbers (2500 or more aircraft) after the end of the war than during the conflict. Developed via the ANT-59 and ANT-60 prototypes then the Tu-2 pre-production model, the Tu-2S initial production model was delivered from the spring of 1944 as a Tu-2 development with uprated engines and heavier offensive and defensive armament. The type proved to possess excellent operational capabilities in terms of its performance, strength and versatility in the attack bomber and ground-attack roles, and the only two other models to see significant combat service during World War II were the Tu-2D long-range model and the Tu-2R photo-reconnaissance model. The aircraft pictured is a Tu-2S of a Soviet bomber regiment operating on the Eastern Front in 1945.

| | |
|---|---|
| Country of origin: | USSR |
| Type: | (Tu-2S) four-seat medium attack bomber |
| Powerplant: | two 1850hp (1379kW) Shvetsov ASh-82FN 14-cylinder two-row radial engines |
| Performance: | maximum speed 547km/h (340mph); climb to 5000m (16,405ft) in 9 minutes 30 seconds; service ceiling 9500m (31,170ft); range 2100km (1305 miles) |
| Weights: | empty 7474kg (16,477lb); maximum take-off 11,360kg (25,044lb) |
| Dimensions: | span 18.86m (61ft 10.5in); length 13.80m (45ft 3.3in); height 4.56m (14ft 11in) |
| Armament: | two 20mm fixed forward-firing cannon in wing roots, one 12.7mm trainable rearward-firing machine gun in rear of the cockpit, one 12.7mm machine gun in dorsal position, and one 12.7mm machine gun in ventral position, plus an internal bomb load of 4000kg (8818lb) |

# Tupolev Tu-16 'Badger-A'

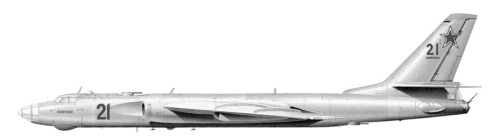

The 'Badger-A' was the first operational version of the Tu-16 medium bomber, which was designated Tu-88 in prototype form. The Tu-88 was first flown in the winter of 1952, and full-scale production commenced in 1953. Operational service with Soviet Long Range Aviation units commenced in 1955, making this perhaps the Soviet equivalent of the Boeing B-52. Technology throughout was derived directly from the Boeing B-29, which the Tupolev bureau had built in large numbers as the Tu-4. The new aircraft combined a swept wing, tricycle landing gear and indigenously produced Mikulin turbojets. The first 'Badger-A' version had a glazed nose, and is identifiable by a large radome under the nose covering the blind-bombing radar. The aircraft was supplied to Iraq, and license-built in China as the Xian H-6.

| Country of origin: | USSR |
| --- | --- |
| Type: | medium bomber |
| Powerplant: | two 9500kg (20.944lb) Mikulin RD-3M turbojets |
| Performance: | maximum speed at 6000m (19,685ft) 960km/h (597mph); service ceiling 15,000m (49,200ft); combat range with maximum weapon load 4800km (2983 miles) |
| Weights: | empty 40,300kg (88,846lb); maximum take-off 75,800kg (167,110lb) |
| Dimensions: | wingspan 32.99m (108ft 3in); length 34.80m (114ft 2in); height 10.36m (34ft 2in); wing area 164.65sq m (1772.3sq ft) |
| Armament: | one forward and one rear ventral barbette each with two 23mm NR-23 cannon; two 23mm NR-23 cannon in radar-controlled tail position; internal bomb bay for up to 9000kg (19,842lb) of free-fall bombs |

# Tupolev Tu-16R 'Badger-D'

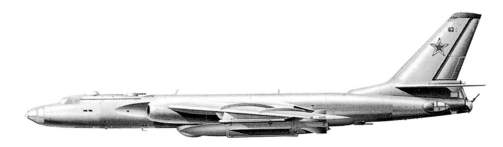

T he Tu-16R is a maritime/electronic reconnaissance version of the Tupolev medium
bomber. Two distinct types were developed. The first was based on the 'Badger-C',
which has the distinctive wide nose radome in place of the glazing (codenamed 'Puff Ball'
by NATO) and was the first of the anti-shipping versions. The 'Badger-D' has a similar nose
radome, an enlarged chin radome, and three radomes in tandem under the weapons bay.
The other Tu-16R variants, 'Badger-E' and '-F', realigned the glazed nose of the 'Badger-A'
aircraft on which they were based. 'Badger-E' has provision for a photo-reconnaissance
pallet in the weapons bay and passive Elint capability. 'Badger-F' is similar, but usually
carries underwing ESM (Electronic Signal Monitoring) pods. These aircraft were regularly
encountered over the Baltic by NATO interceptor squadrons.

| | |
|---|---|
| Country of origin: | USSR |
| Type: | medium bomber |
| Powerplant: | two 9500kg (20.944lb) Mikulin RD-3M turbojets |
| Performance: | maximum speed at 6000m (19,685ft) 960km/h (597mph); service ceiling 15,000m (49,200ft); combat range with maximum weapon load 4800km (2983 miles) |
| Weights: | empty 40,300kg (88,846lb); maximum take-off 75,800kg (167,110lb) |
| Dimensions: | wingspan 32.99m (108ft 3in); length 36.5m (120ft); height 10.36m (34ft 2in); wing area 164.65sq m (1772.3sq ft) |
| Armament: | one forward and one rear ventral barbette each with two 23mm NR-23 cannon; two 23mm NR-23 cannon in radar-controlled tail position |

# Tupolev Tu-22 'Blinder-A'

The 'Blinder-A' was produced in response to the growing capability of Western manned interceptors and surface-to-air missile systems in the early 1950. The planners in the Soviet aviation industry was convinced that the days of the Tupolev Tu-16 as a viable strategic bomber were numbered. The result was the Tu-22, the prototype of which is believed to have flown in 1959. Western analysts were completely unaware of this aircraft until 10 took part in the 1961 air display at Tushino in 1961. This ignorance is not really surprising, as at first glance the Tu-22 appears to be of similar basic configuration to the Tu-16 with a mid-set swept wing, all-swept tail surfaces and the main units of its tricycle landing gear retracting into wing pods. However, the wing differs considerably from that of the Tu-16 in having compound sweep on the leading edge and less anhedral.

| | |
|---|---|
| Country of origin: | USSR |
| Type: | medium bomber and missile-launch platform |
| Powerplant: | two 16,000kg (35,273lb) Koliesov VD-7M turbojets |
| Performance: | maximum speed 1487km/h (924mph); service ceiling 18,300m (60,040ft); range with maximum fuel 3100km (1926 miles) |
| Weights: | empty 40,000kg (88,185lb); maximum take-off 84,000lb (185,188lb) |
| Dimensions: | wingspan 23.75m (77ft 11in); length 40.53m (132ft 11.75in); height 10.67m (35ft); wing area 162sq m (1,722.28sq ft) |
| Armament: | one 23mm NR-23 cannon in tail turret; internal bomb bay with provision for up to 12,000kg (26,455lb) of conventional or nuclear bombs; or one AS-4 'Kitchen' air-to-surface missile semi-recessed under fuselage |

# Tupolev Tu-22R 'Blinder-C'

**F**irst identified at the 1961 Aviation Day at Tushino, asmentioned above, the Tu-22 was designed in the late 1950s to a Soviet air force requirement for a replacement for the Tu-16, which was effectively rendered obsolete by a new generation of Western interceptors and missile systems. The Tu-22 'Blinder' was designed to penetrate hostile airspace at high speed and high altitude. The rear-mounted engines reduce the aerodynamic drag penalties imposed by long inlet ducts. The aircraft entered service as the Tu-22, with the NATO reporting name 'Blinder-A', in the early 1960s. The Tu22R 'Blinder-C' was a dedicated maritime reconnaissance version of similar configuration to the 'A' with cameras and sensors in the weapons bay, inflight refuelling capability. Approximately 60 were built, but none now remain in service with naval aviation units.

| | |
|---|---|
| **Country of origin:** | USSR |
| **Type:** | long-range maritime reconnaissance/patrol aircraft |
| **Powerplant:** | two (estimated) 14,028kg (26,455lb) Koliesov VD-7 turbojets |
| **Performance:** | maximum speed 1487km/h (924mph); service ceiling 18,300m (60,040ft); combat radius with internal fuel 3100km (1926 miles) |
| **Weights:** | empty 40,000kg (88,185lb); maximum take-off 84,000kg (185,188lb) |
| **Dimensions:** | wingspan 23.75m (77ft 11in); length 40.53m (132ft 11.75in); height 10.67m (35ft); wing area 162sq m (1722.28sq ft) |
| **Armament:** | one 23mm NR-23 two-barrell cannon in radar-controlled tail barbette; internal weapons bay with provision for 12,000kg (26,455lb) of stores, including nuclear weapons and free-fall bombs, or one AS-4 carried semi-recessed under the fuselage |

# Tupolev Tu-28P 'Fiddler-B'

One of family of supersonic aircraft produced by Tupolev with technology explored with the 'Backfin' aircraft, the Tu-22 was designed as a long-range all-weather interceptor for the Soviet air force to counter the specific threat from Western long-range missile-carrying aircraft. The two prototype aircraft were first seen publicly in 1961 with the designation Tu-102 and identified by the NATO reporting name 'Fiddler-A'. These aircraft formed the basis for the Tu-128 which entered production in the early 1960s with the designation Tu-28P. These aircraft were not revealed until the 1967 Aviation Day, after which they were allocated the NATO name 'Fiddler-B'. The crew of two are accommodated in tandem cockpits, in what is still the largest interceptor aircraft ever built. All aircraft were replaced in service by 1992.

| | |
|---|---|
| Country of origin: | USSR |
| Type: | long-range all-weather interceptor |
| Powerplant: | two 11,200kg (24,690lb) Lyul'ka AL-21F turbojets |
| Performance: | maximum speed at 11,000m (36,090ft) 1850km/h (1,150mph); service ceiling 20,000m (65,615ft); combat range with internal fuel 5000km (3105 miles) |
| Weights: | empty 25,000kg (55,125lb); maximum take-off 40,000kg (88,185lb) |
| Dimensions: | wingspan 18.10m (59ft 4.5in); length 27.20m (89ft 3in); height 7m (23ft) |
| Armament: | four wing pylons for four AA-5 'Ash' long-range air-to-air missiles |

# Tupolev Tu-22M 'Backfire-A'

The Tu-22M 'Backfire' began life as a swing-wing derivative of the Tu-22 'Blinder' supersonic bomber and maritime patrol aircraft. The inability of this aircraft to fly strategic missions to the US (because of short range) led the Tupolev bureau to produce the 'Backfire-A' prototype (designated Tu-22M). Evaluation of this aircraft revealed that the aircraft fell far short of expectations, both in terms of speed and range, leading to the major design revisions incorporated on the Tu-22M-2. This aircraft entered service in 1975 and has the NATO reporting name 'Backfire-B'. Some 360 were produced in M-2 and M-3 configuration for Long Range Aviation and Naval Aviation units and were expected to remain in service, but it seems as if the M-2 aircraft have all been retired or placed in storage. The light-blue two-tone colour scheme was retained after the disbandment of the Soviet Union.

| | |
|---|---|
| Country of origin: | USSR |
| Type: | medium strategic bomber and maritime reconnaissance/patrol aircraft |
| Powerplant: | two (estimated) 20,000kg (44,092lb) Kuznetsov NK-144 turbofans |
| Performance: | maximum speed 2125km/h (1321mph); service ceiling 18,000m (59,055ft); combat radius with internal fuel 4000km (2485 miles) |
| Weights: | maximum take-off 130,000kg (286,596lb) |
| Dimensions: | wingspan 34.3m (112ft 6.5in) spread and 23.4m (76ft 9.25in) swept; length 36.9m (129ft 11in); height 10.8m (35ft 5.25in); unswept wing area 183.58sq m (1892 q ft) |
| Armament: | two 23mm GSh-23 two-barrell cannon in radar-controlled tail barbette; internal weapons bay with provision for 12,000kg (26,455lb) of stores, including nuclear weapons and free-fall bombs, or two AS-4 'Kitchen' missiles carried under the wings, or one AS-4 carried semi-recessed under the fuselage, or up to three AS-16 missiles |

# Tupolev Tu-160 'Blackjack-A'

**T**he most recent and undoubtedly formidable aircraft to have emerged from the Tupolev Design Bureau is the Tu-160 long-range strategic bomber. Comparable too although much larger than the Rockwell B1-B Lancer, the aircraft has variable-geometry outer wings and two pairs of afterburning turbofans in underwing nacelles. It is optimised for high-level penetration but also has a low-level terrain-following capability, and has a higher maximum speed and greater unrefuelled range than the B-1. Production of the aircraft, which entered service in 1988, has been curtailed by arms limitation agreements. Those in service have suffered from serviceability problems and flight control system difficulties. After the breakup of the Soviet Union, the aircraft were shared between Russia and the Ukraine. Only Russia now operates the Tu-160, but it is not clear how many remain in serviceable condition today.

| | |
|---|---|
| **Country of origin:** | USSR |
| **Type:** | long-range stategic penetration bomber and missile platform |
| **Powerplant:** | four 25,000kg (55,115lb) Kuznetsov NK-321 turbofans |
| **Performance:** | maximum speed at 11,000m (36,090ft) 2000km/h (1243mph); service ceiling 18,300m (60,040ft); combat range with internal fuel 14,000km (8699 miles) |
| **Weights:** | empty 118,000kg (260,140lb); maximum take-off 275,000kg (606,261lb) |
| **Dimensions:** | wingspan 55.70m (182ft 9in) spread and 35.60m (116ft 9.75in) swept; length 54.10m (177ft 6in); height 13.10m (43ft); wing area 360sq m (3875sq ft) |
| **Armament:** | provision for up to 16,500kg (36,376lb) of stores in two internal weapons bays and on hardpoints under wings; including nuclear and/or free-fall bombs, and/or missiles including up to 12 RK-55 (AS-15 'Kent') cruise missiles or 24 RKV-500B (AS-16 'Kickback') short-range attack missiles |

# Vickers Vimy Mk I

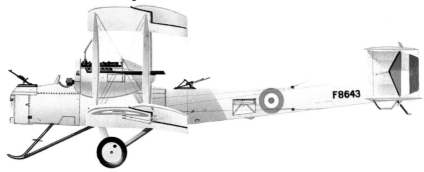

Vickers was already a large, well-established company when in 1911 it diversified into aircraft production. The F.B two-seat fighter/reconnaissance aircraft were used in large numbers, and in the closing stages of World War I Vickers produced a large biplane aircraft designed with the express purpose of attacking Berlin. The F.B.27 Vimy was designed by Rex Pierson to meet the same criteria as the Handley-Page V/1500 and de Havilland D.H.10 Amiens, and it too was ordered into largescale production for the newly formed Independent Bombing Force. By comparison with these two aircraft the Vimy was quite compact, and demonstrated exceptional handling qualities when flight-tested at Martlesham Heath during 1918 (lifting a greater load than the Handley-Page 0/400 on half the power). Production began of the Vimy Mk I but by the end of October 1918, the RAF had only three aircraft in service. Pictured is a Morgan-built Mk I of No 70 Squadron, based at Heliopolis in 1921.

| Country of origin: | United Kingdom |
| --- | --- |
| Type: | (Mk I) heavy bomber |
| Powerplant: | two 360hp (269kW) Rolls Royce Eagle VIII 12-cylinder Vee piston engines |
| Performance: | maximum speed 166km/h (103mph); service ceiling 2135m (7000ft); range 1464km (910 miles) |
| Weights: | empty 3221kg (7101lb); maximum take-off weight 5670kg (12,500lb) |
| Dimensions: | span 20.75m (68ft 1in); length 13.27m (43ft 6in); height 4.76m (15ft 7in); wing area 123.56 sq m (1330 sq ft) |
| Armament: | one .303in Lewis Mk III machine gun on pivoted mount in nose; one .303in Lewis Mk III machine gun on pivoted mount in dorsal position; one .303in Lewis Mk III machine gun on pivoted mount in ventral or each of two beam positions; internal bomb cells and underwing racks with provision for up to 2179kg (4804lb) of bombs |

# Vickers Vimy Mk II

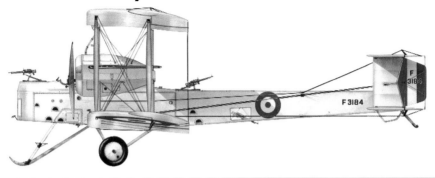

S ome 158 Vimys were completed to Mk I standard and there followed 74 other variants, and 55 variants of the Vickers Vernon. The Vimy Mk III (10 built by RAE at Farnborough) and Mk IV (25 built by Westland) had Rolls Royce Eagle engines and minor detail changes. The designation Vimy Mk II is most confusing, as it appears to have been given to many different types. To confuse matters further, the Mk III and Mk IV were redesignated Mk II in 1923, in an attempt to introduce some clarity! What is certain is that the Vimy was the standard heavy bomber of the RAF from 1919 to 1930, after which it began to be replaced by the Vickers Victoria. Most of the RAF aircraft were sent overseas to act as a tool of the RAF's air policing operations in the Middle East, where Nos 45, 58, 70 and 216 Sqns and No 4 Flying Training School were operating. The aircraft pictured served with No 70 Squadron in Egypt.

| Country of origin: | United Kingdom |
| --- | --- |
| Type: | heavy bomber |
| Powerplant: | two 360hp (269kW) Rolls Royce Eagle VIII 12-cylinder Vee piston engines |
| Performance: | maximum speed 166km/h (103mph); service ceiling 2135m (7000ft); range 1464km (910 miles) |
| Weights: | empty 3221kg (7101lb); maximum take-off weight 5670kg (12,500lb) |
| Dimensions: | span 20.75m (68ft 1in); length 13.27m (43ft 6in); height 4.76m (15ft 7in); wing area 123.56 sq m (1330 sq ft) |
| Armament: | one .303in Lewis Mk III machine gun on pivoted mount in nose; one .303in Lewis Mk III machine gun on pivoted mount in dorsal position; one .303in Lewis Mk III machine gun on pivoted mount in ventral or each of two beam positions; internal bomb cells and underwing racks with provision for up to 2179kg (4804lb) of bombs |

# Vickers Virginia Mk VII

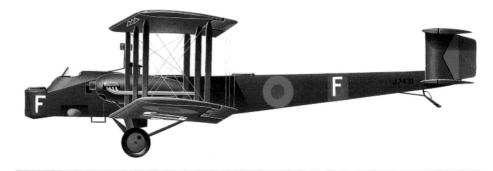

**D**esigned to replace the Vimy, from 1924 until 1937 the Vickers Virginia was the standard heavy bomber of the Royal Air Force. The prototype first flew in November 1922. It was large and heavy, and was constructed in much the same way as its predecessor, but in the event this proved something of a blessing as the aircraft's service career was progressively stretched far beyond its expected retirement date. The first major production version after a convoluted development programme was the Mk V, which had 468hp (349kW) Napier Lion II engines and a third (central) rudder in the tail unit to distinguish it. Some 114 newbuild aircraft followed, built to various standards. As each new type was introduced earlier aircraft were upgraded. Stealth was an unknown concept at this time, and the wooden screws driven by direct-drive Napier Lion engines could be heard from far and wide.

| | |
|---|---|
| **Country of origin:** | United Kingdom |
| **Type:** | heavy night-bomber |
| **Powerplant:** | two 580hp Napier Lion VB W-12 piston engines |
| **Performance:** | maximum speed 174km/h (108mph); service ceiling 4725m (15,500ft); range 1585km (985 miles) |
| **Weights:** | empty 4377kg (9650lb); maximum take-off weight 7983kg (17,600lb) |
| **Dimensions:** | span 26.72m (87ft 8in); length 18.97m (62ft 3in); height 5.54m (18ft 2in); wing area 202.34 sq m (2178 sq ft) |
| **Armament:** | one .303in Lewis machine gun in nose position; twin .303in Lewis machine guns in dorsal position; plus up to 1361kg (93,000lb) of bombs |

# Vickers Vildebeest Mk III

In 1927 the British Air Ministry began its search for a new light bomber to replace the Hawker Horsley torpedo/day bomber, which entered service that year. The Vickers Vildebeest was designed to this requirement, and was flown as the Type 132 prototype in April 1928. Development with a number of engines was followed by the initial Mk I production model with Bristol Pegasus I for service delivery in April 1933. The Mk II had the Pegasus IIM3, the Mk III had a revised rear cockpit for a third crew member. Production of the first three series amounted to 152 aircraft. In December 1937 the last of 57 Mk IVs, the last production series, was delivered. About 100 Vildebeest were still serving at the outbreak of World War II, and were used operationally in the Far East. Pictured is a Mk III of No 273 Squadron, Royal Air Force, stationed at China Bay in Ceylon in 1939. The squadron re-equipped with the Fairey Fulmar in March 1942.

| | |
|---|---|
| **Country of origin:** | United Kingdom |
| **Type:** | three-seat general-purpose aircraft |
| **Powerplant:** | one 660hp (492kW) Bristol Pegasus IIM3 sleeve-valve radial piston engine |
| **Performance:** | maximum speed 230km/h (142mph); service ceiling 5182m (17,000ft); range 2500km (1553 miles) |
| **Weights:** | empty 1918kg (4229lb); maximum take-off weight 3674kg (8100lb) |
| **Dimensions:** | span 14.94m (49ft in); length 11.17m (36ft 8in); height 5.42m (17ft 9in) |
| **Armament:** | one fixed forward-firing .303in Vickers machine gun; one.303in Lewis machine gun on pivoted mount in rear cockpit |

# Vickers Vincent

In the early 1930s the standard army cooperation warplanes operated by the Royal Air Force in overseas theatres were the Fairey IIIF and Westland Wapiti. Both these types were obsolescent, and in its search for a successor type the Air Ministry decided that the new Vildebeest torpedo bomber had the potential to be transformed into an effective general-purpose warplane. In 1932, therefore, a Vildebeest Mk I was converted as prototype of a general-purpose version, and successful evaluation of this conversion resulted in orders for 196 Vincent Mk Is completed between July 1934 and October 1936 as new aircraft or Vildebeest conversions. Some 171 of the aircraft served with the RAF (12 squadrons in India, the Middle East and East Africa), and they continued to serve in Iraq until 1941. Small numbers were transferred to Iraq and New Zealand. Pictured here is a Vincent of the Royal New Zealand Air Force in 1940.

| Country of origin: | United Kingdom |
| --- | --- |
| Type: | three-seat general-purpose warplane |
| Powerplant: | one 635hp (473.5kW) Bristol Pegasus IIM3 nine-cylinder single-row radial engine |
| Performance: | maximum speed 228.5km/h (142mph); initial climb rate 233m (765ft ) per minute; service ceiling 5180m (17,000ft); range 2012km (1,250 miles) |
| Weights: | empty 1918kg (4229lb); maximum take-off 3674kg (8100lb) |
| Dimensions: | span 14.94m (49ft); length 11.175m (36ft 8 in); height 5.41m (17ft 9in ) |
| Armament: | one 0.303in fixed forward-firing machine gun in the port side of the forward fuselage, and one 0.303in trainable rearward-firing machine gun in the rear cockpit, plus an external bomb load of 499kg (1100lb) |

# Vickers Wellesley

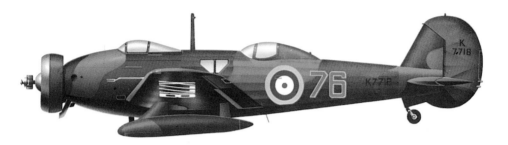

Designed in 1933 as a private venture to meet an official requirement for a general-purpose and torpedo bomber, the Wellesley was based on the novel geodetic structure and emerged for its first flight in June 1935 as a fabric-covered cantilever monoplane with a wing of high aspect ratio. Such were the capabilities of the prototype that the Air Ministry ordered an initial 96 Wellesley Mk I aircraft optimised for the medium bomber role with its bombs carried in two panniers under the wing. The Wellesley Mk I entered service in April 1937, and production up to May 1938 and totalled 176 aircraft, most of the later aircraft being completed (with the unofficial designation Wellesley Mk II) with a continuous 'glasshouse' canopy bridging the front and rear cockpits. The Wellesley saw useful service in East and North Africa during the first part of World War II. Pictured is a Wellesley Mk I of No 76 Squadron, based at Finningley in 1938.

| | |
|---|---|
| Country of origin: | United Kingdom |
| Type: | (Wellesley Mk I) two/three-seat general-purpose bomber |
| Powerplant: | one 835hp (622.5kW) Bristol Pegasus XX nine-cylinder single-row radial engine |
| Performance: | maximum speed 367km/h (228mph); climb to 6000m (19,685ft) in 17 minutes 30 seconds; service ceiling 7770m (25,500ft); range 4635km (2880 miles) with a 1060lb (481kg) bomb load |
| Weights: | empty 3066kg (6760lb); maximum take-off 5670kg (12,500lb) |
| Dimensions: | span 22.73m (74ft 7in); length 11.66m (39ft 3in); height 4.67m (15ft 3.5in) |
| Armament: | one 0.303in fixed forward-firing machine gun in the leading edge of the port wing, and one 0.303in trainable rearward-firing machine gun in the rear cockpit, plus an internal bomb load of 907kg (2000lb) |

# Vickers Wellington B.Mks I to X

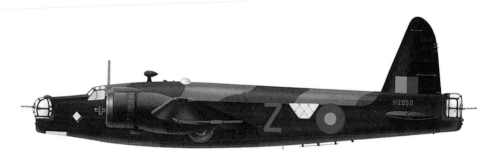

One of the most important warplanes in the British inventory at the beginning of World War II, the Wellington bore the brunt of the bomber effort until large numbers of four-engined heavy bombers became available in the later stages of 1941. The type then found an important second career in the maritime reconnaissance, transport and training roles until a time well after the end of the war. Total production was 11,461, the last machine not being delivered until October 1945. Entering service in October 1938, the initial model was the Wellington Mk I with 1000hp (746kW) Pegasus XVIII radial engines, and bomber development continued via the Mk III with Rolls-Royce Merlin Vee engines, Mk III with Hercules radial engines, Mk IV with Pratt & Whitney Twin Wasp radial engines, Mk VI with Merlin engines, and Mk X with Hercules engines. Wellingtons formed the major component of the first 1000-bomber raid.

| | |
|---|---|
| Country of origin: | United Kingdom |
| Type: | (Wellington Mk X) six-seat medium bomber |
| Powerplant: | two 1675hp (1249kW) Bristol Hercules XI or XVI 14-cylinder two-row radial engines |
| Performance: | maximum speed 410km/h (255mph); climb to 4570m (15,000ft) in 27 minutes 42 seconds; service ceiling 6705m (22,000ft); range 3033.5km (1885 miles) with a 680kg (1500lb) bomb load |
| Weights: | empty 10,194kg (22,474lb); maximum take-off 16,556kg (36,500lb) |
| Dimensions: | span 26.26m (86ft 2in); length 19.68m (64ft 7in); height 5.31m (17ft 5in) |
| Armament: | two 0.303in trainable forward-firing machine guns in nose turret, four 0.303in trainable rearward-firing machine guns in tail turret, and one 0.303in trainable lateral-firing machine gun in each beam position, plus an internal bomb load of 2041kg (4500lb) |

# Vickers Valiant B.Mk 1

Although designed to the same B.35/46 specification as the Avro Vulcan and Handley Page Victor, the prototype Vickers 660 did not fully meet the detailed requirements of that document. However, the fact that it could be rapidly put into production and represented a lower risk than the radical Vulcan or Victor encouraged the government to order it under the reduced specification B.9/48. The prototype 660 first flew in May 1951; the first pre- production aircraft flew in December 1953, and service deliveries commenced in August the following year. Most aircraft were finished in white anti-flash paint and had an extended tailcone housing avionics. The aircraft were active during the Suez campaign. They conducted all live trails with British air-dropped nuclear weapons, but were assigned to low-level missions in 1963. The whole fleet was scrapped a year later.

| Country of origin: | United Kingdom |
|---|---|
| Type: | strategic bomber |
| Powerplant: | four 4559kg (10,050lb) Rolls-Royce Avon 204 turbojets |
| Performance: | maximum speed at high altitude 912km/h (567mph); service ceiling 16,460m (54,000ft); maximum range 7242km (4,500 miles) |
| Weights: | empty 34,4191kg (75,881lb); maximum loaded with drop tanks 79,378kg (175,000lb) |
| Dimensions: | wingspan 34.85m (114ft 4in); length 33m (108ft 3in); height 9.8m (32ft 2in); wing area 219.43sq m (2,362sq ft) |
| Armament: | internal weapons bay with provision for up to 9525kg (21,000lb) of conventional or nuclear weapons |

# Vought SB2U Vindicator

Ordered in October 1934, the SB2U was the US Navy's first monoplane scout and dive-bomber, although it is worth noting that lingering doubts about the monoplane's high take-off and landing speed meant that an order was also placed for a single XSB3U-1 biplane prototype. The XSB2U-1 monoplane prototype made its maiden flight in January 1936. In October of the same year the US Navy ordered 54 SB2U-1 production aircraft with the 825hp (615kW) Pratt & Whitney R-1535-96 engine. The SB2U-1 was delivered from December 1937, and there followed 58 and 57 examples of the SB2U-2 with equipment changes and the SB2U-3 with heavier armament and enlarged fuel tankage. The SB2U was phased out of service in 1942. France and the UK bought 39 and 50 generally similar V-156F and Chesapeake Mk I aircraft. Pictured is the SB2U-2 aircraft operated by the 5th section leader of Bombing Squadron VB-2 deployed on the USS *Lexington* in July 1939.

| Country of origin: | USA |
| --- | --- |
| Type: | (SB2U-3) two-seat carrierborne and land-based scout and dive-bomber |
| Powerplant: | one 825hp (615kW) Pratt & Whitney R-1535-2 Twin Wasp Junior 14-cylinder two-row radial engine |
| Performance: | maximum speed 391km/h (243mph); initial climb rate 326m (1070ft) per minute; service ceiling 7195m (23,600ft); range 1802km (1120 miles) |
| Weights: | empty 2556kg (5634lb); maximum take-off 4273kg (9421lb) |
| Dimensions: | span 12.77m (41ft 10.9in); length 10.36m (33ft 11.75in); height 4.34m (14ft 3in) |
| Armament: | one 0.5in fixed forward-firing machine gun in the port upper part of the forward fuselage, and one 0.5in machine gun in the rear cockpit, plus an external bomb load of 454kg (1000lb) |

# Vought OS2U Kingfisher

Vought built the VS-310 Kingfisher floatplane reconnaissance aircraft to replace the O3U Corsair in service with the US Navy. It was first flown in prototype form in landplane configuration in March 1938 and underwent sea trials with float gear in May. A production order for the OS2U-1 Kingfisher followed, and the first of these entered service in August 1940. This was the first catapult-launched monoplane to enter service with the US Navy, and was a valuable asset to both the carrier air wings and the US Navy's inshore patrol squadrons. The type was also used by the Royal Navy as the Kingfisher Mk I, 100 being supplied under the Lend Lease Act. Eighteen of the 24 aircraft that were en route to the Dutch East Indies in 1942 were seconded to the Royal Australian Air Force. Pictured is a Mk I of the Antarctic Flight, Royal Australian Air Force, during 1947.

| | |
|---|---|
| **Country of origin:** | USA |
| **Type:** | two-seat observation floatplane |
| **Powerplant:** | one 450hp (336kW) Pratt & Whitney R-985-4 radial piston engine |
| **Performance:** | maximum speed 264km/h (164mph); service ceiling 3960m (13,000ft); range 1296km (805 miles) |
| **Weights:** | empty 1870kg (4123lb); maximum take-off weight 2722kg (6000lb) |
| **Dimensions:** | span 10.95m (35ft 11in); length 10.31m (33ft 10in); height 4.61m (15ft 1in); wing area 24.34 sq m (262 sq ft) |
| **Armament:** | one fixed forward-firing .3in Browning machine gun; one .3in Browning machine gun on pivoted mount in rear cockpit; underwing racks with provision for two 45kg (100lb) or 147kg (325lb) bombs |

# Vought F4U Corsair

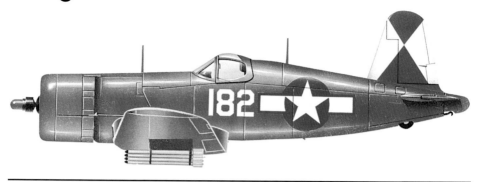

**D**esigned with an inverted-gull wing to keep span and main landing gear lengths as short as possible, the F4U Corsair was planned as a carrierborne fighter but matured as a superlative ground-attack and close support fighter that saw service mainly in the Pacific theatre against the Japanese, where it did sterling service in the grim battle of attrition against the Japanese. The type first flew in May 1940 and entered operational service in February 1943 in the land-based role as the type's carrierborne capabilities were initially thought suspect. Armed with bombs and rockets to supplement its fixed guns, the type remained in production until after World War II, but the main war-time variants were the F4U-1 (4399 aircraft in five subvariants), F4U-4 (2651 aircraft in five subvariants), 4006 Goodyear-built FG-1 aircraft in three subvariants, and 735 Brewster-built F3A-1 aircraft in three subvariants.

| | |
|---|---|
| Country of origin: | USA |
| Type: | (F4U-4) single-seat carrierborne and land-based fighter and fighter-bomber |
| Powerplant: | one 2250hp (1678kW) Pratt & Whitney R-2800-18W Double Wasp 18-cylinder two-row radial engine |
| Performance: | maximum speed 718km/h (446mph); initial climb rate 1180m (3870ft) per minute; service ceiling 12,650m (41,500ft); range 2511km (1560 miles) |
| Weights: | empty 4175kg (9205lb); maximum take-off 6149kg (13,555lb) as a fighter or 8845kg (19,500lb) as a fighter-bomber |
| Dimensions: | span 12.49m (40ft 11.75in); length 10.27m (33ft 8.25in); height 4.50m (14ft 9in) |
| Armament: | six 0.5in fixed forward-firing machine guns in the leading edges of the wing, plus an external bomb and rocket load of 907kg (2000lb) |

# Vought A-7D Corsair II

Though derived from the Vought F-8 Crusader, the Corsair is a totally different aircraft. By restricting performance to high subsonic speed it was possible to reduce structural weight dramatically, and correspondingly the range increased dramatically and weapon load multiplied by nearly four times. Development was impressively rapid; the first flight was made in September 1965 and just over two years later the first A-7A aircraft were used in action in the Gulf of Tonkin. During the Vietnam War the 27 squadrons equipped with the A-7 flew more than 90,000 combat missions. Although predominantly a naval aircraft, the USAF also decided to adopt the A-7. The A-7D was a version with a Rolls-Royce Spey derived Allison engine, M61 cannon armament, inflight refuelling capability, advanced nav/attack systems and (from 1978) laser tracker. The aircraft retired in 1993.

| | |
|---|---|
| **Country of origin:** | USA |
| **Type:** | single-seat attack aircraft |
| **Powerplant:** | one 6465kg (14,250lb) Allison TF41-1 (Rolls-Royce Spey) turbofan |
| **Performance:** | maximum speed at low-level 1123km/h (698mph); combat range with typical weapon load 1150km (4100 miles) |
| **Weights:** | empty 8972kg (19,781lb); maximum take-off 19,050kg (42,000lb) |
| **Dimensions:** | wingspan 11.8m (38ft 9in); length 14.06m (46ft 1.5in); height 4.9m (16ft 0.75in); wing area 34.84sq m (375sq ft) |
| **Armament:** | one 20mm M61 Vulcan with 1000 rounds, external pylons with provision for up to 6804kg (15,000lb) of stores, including guided and conventional bombs, cluster bombs, napalm tanks, air-to-surface missiles, and drop tanks |

# Vought F-8D Crusader

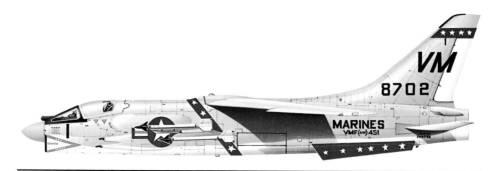

In 1955, Vought began the development of a totally new Crusader. Designated XF8U-3 Crusader III, the three prototypes of this aircraft were powered with various J75 engines developing up to 13,064kg (28,800lb) of thrust. The aircraft were able to fly at 2543km/h (1580mph) at a height of up to 21,335m (70,000ft), but to the eternal regret of many US Navy aviators, the potentially world-beating aircraft was rejected in favour of the Phantom II. Vought continued to take the F-8 through various stages of development, hardly altering the airframe at each stage, but steadily improved the aircraft so that it remained competitive. The most potent of all these versions was the F-8D, with J57-P-20 turbojet, extra fuel in place of the underfuselage Zuni rocket pack and new radar for a specially produced radar-homing AIM-9C Sidewinder air-to-air missile. A total of 152 F-8Ds were produced.

| | |
|---|---|
| Country of origin: | USA |
| Type: | single-seat carrier-based fighter |
| Powerplant: | one 8165kg (18,000lb) Pratt & Whitney J57-P-20 turbojet |
| Performance: | maximum speed at 12,192m (40,000ft) 1975km/h (1227mph); service ceiling about 17,983m (59,000ft); combat radius at high altitude 966km (600 miles) |
| Weights: | empty 9038kg (19,925lb); maximum take-off 15,422g (34,000lb) |
| Dimensions: | wingspan 10.72m (35ft 2in); length 16.61m (54ft 6in); height 4.8m (15ft 9in); |
| Armament: | four 20mm Colt Mk 12 cannon with 144 rpg, up to four Motorola AIM-9C Sidewinder air-to-air missiles; or two AGM-12A or AGM-12B Bullpup air-to-surface missiles |

# Vought F-8E (FN) Crusader

**D**espite failing to win export contracts for the F-8 Crusader from the Royal Navy, or for a two-seat version for the US Navy, Vought did manage to clinch a deal with the French Aéronavale for a version of the F-8E, even though her carrier's *Foch* and *Clemenceau* were thought to be too small for such aircraft. To create the F-8E (FN) Vought redesigned the wing and tail to provide greater lift and to improve low-speed handling. The first FN flew on June 26, 1964, and all 42 had been delivered by the following January. Nearly 25 years after entering service, *Clemenceau*'s aircraft were involved in the Gulf War. The aircraft were slightly modified during the mid-1990s to maintain their combat-capability until the Dassault Rafale-M entered service. They are no longer in service. The aircraft pictured was operated by Flottille 12F of the Aéronavale.

| | |
|---|---|
| **Country of origin:** | USA |
| **Type:** | single-seat carrier-borne interceptor and attack aircraft |
| **Powerplant:** | one 8165kg (18,000lb) Pratt & Whitney J57-P-20A turbojet |
| **Performance:** | maximum speed at 10,975m (36,000ft) 1827km/h (1135mph); service ceiling 17,680m (58,000ft); combat radius 966km (600 miles) |
| **Weights:** | empty 9038kg (19,925lb); maximum take-off 15,420kg (34,000lb) |
| **Dimensions:** | wingspan 10.87m (35ft 8in); length 16.61m (54ft 6in); height 4.80m (15ft 9in); wing area 32.51sq m (350sq ft) |
| **Armament:** | four 20-mm M39 cannon with 144 rpg; external pylons with provision for up to 2268kg (5000lb) of stores, including two Matra R530 air-to-air missiles or eight 5in rockets |

# Westland Lysander

**R**esulting from a 1934 battlefield reconnaissance and army co-operation requirement, the Lysander was designed to provide its two-man crew with the best possible fields of vision to the front and sides, especially toward the ground, and was therefore planned round a substantial fuselage carrying a large glazed cockpit under the high-set wing. The first of two prototypes flew in June 1936, and production (with totals) comprised the Lysander Mk I (169) for service from June 1938, Lysander Mk II (517) with the 905hp (675hp) Bristol Perseus XII engine, Lysander Mk III (517) with the Mercury XX engine, and Lysander Mk IIIA (347) improved version of the Mk III. From 1941 the type was increased used as a target-tug (100 new TT.Mk IIIA aircraft complementing 70 conversions) and for the delivery of agents into Europe. Pictured is a Lysander Mk II, one of 36 supplied to Turkey. This example was based at Yesilköy in 1940.

| | |
|---|---|
| Country of origin: | United Kingdom |
| Type: | (Lysander Mk I) two-seat tactical reconnaissance and army co-operation warplane |
| Powerplant: | one 890hp (664kW) Bristol Mercury XII nine-cylinder single-row radial engine |
| Performance: | maximum speed 369km/h (229mph); climb to 3050m (10,000ft) in 6 minutes 48 seconds; service ceiling 7925m (26,000ft); range 966km (600 miles) |
| Weights: | empty 1844kg (4065lb); maximum take-off 3402kg (7500lb) |
| Dimensions: | span 15.24m (50ft); length 9.30m (30ft 6in); height 3.35m (11ft) |
| Armament: | two 0.303in fixed forward-firing machine guns in the wheel fairings, and one 0.303in trainable rearward-firing machine gun in the rear of the cockpit, plus an external bomb load of 227kg (500lb) |

# Westland Whirlwind

The Whirlwind was the Royal Air Force's first single-seat twin-engined fighter, a layout conceived so that a fixed forward-firing battery of four 20mm cannon could be grouped in the nose. The powerplant was based on two examples of the Rolls-Royce Peregrine engine that was in essence a modernised version of the classic Kestrel, but this engine's teething problems (at a time when its manufacturer was more concerned with improving its great Merlin engine and maximising its production) meant that the future of the otherwise excellent Whirlwind was curtailed in terms of production and service life. Production totalled only 112 aircraft and they were in service for a short period between between June 1940 and June 1943. The type was flown by only two squadrons, and surviving Whirlwind Mk I fighters were later upgraded to Whirlwind Mk IA fighter-bomber standard. The aircraft also had a high landing speed, limiting its capacity for deployment.

| | |
|---|---|
| **Country of origin:** | United Kingdom |
| **Type:** | (Whirlwind Mk IA) single-seat long-range fighter-bomber |
| **Powerplant:** | two 765hp (570kW) Rolls-Royce Peregrine I 12-cylinder Vee engines |
| **Performance:** | maximum speed 579km/h (360mph); initial climb rate 396m (1300ft) per minute with two 227kg (500lb) bombs; service ceiling 30,000ft (9145m); range about 800 miles (1287km) |
| **Weights:** | empty 3769kg (8310lb); maximum take-off 5166kg (11,388lb) |
| **Dimensions:** | span 13.72m (45ft); length 9.83m (32ft 3in); height 3.20m (10ft 6in) |
| **Armament:** | four 20mm fixed forward-firing cannon in the nose, plus an external bomb load of 454kg (1000lb) |

# Xian H-6IV

The Xian H-6 is a direct copy of the Tu-16 'Badger-A', and forms the backbone of the Chinese bomber fleet. Plans were were well underway to license-build the aircraft in China until the political break with Moscow in 1960. The programme restarted in 1962 without Soviet assistance, but nevertheless deliveries of the Xian H-6 began in 1963 to the Chinese air force. The aircraft is powered by a copied version of the Mikulin RD-3M engine, built at Xian as the Wopen-8. The aircraft are configured primarily for air-dropping nuclear weapons, and were heavily involved in the Chinese nuclear test programme at Lop Nur. Avionics fit is different to Soviet aircraft, a large drum type chin radar is fitted and the fixed forward gun is deleted. The aircraft pictured is one of approximately 150 in service, painted in anti-flash white paint and carrying a pair of C-601 air-to-surface missiles.

| | |
|---|---|
| **Country of origin:** | China |
| **Type:** | medium bomber and missile-launch platform |
| **Powerplant:** | two 9500kg (20,944lb) Wopen-8 turbojets |
| **Performance:** | maximum speed 960km/h (597mph); service ceiling 15,000m (49,200ft); range with maximum load 4800km (2983 miles) |
| **Weights:** | empty 40,300kg (88,846lb); maximum take-off 75,800kg (167,110lb) |
| **Dimensions:** | wingspan 32.93m (108ft 0.5in); length 34.80m (114ft 2in); height 10.82m (35ft 6in); wing area 164.65sq m (1,772.34sq ft) |
| **Armament:** | six cannon; internal bomb bay with provision for up to 9000kg (19,842lb) of conventional or nuclear bombs; wing pylons for two C-601 air-to-surface missiles |

# Yakovlev Yak-1

First flown during January 1940, the Yak-1 lightweight fighter was one of the most important and successful fighters fielded by the USSR in the course of World War II and, like many of its Soviet contemporaries, was based on an airframe of mixed light alloy and wooden construction. In configuration the Yak-1 was of typical 'modern' fighter design with a cantilever low-set wing, enclosed cockpit and retractable main landing gear units, and entered production late in 1940 in a programme that saw the delivery of 8721 aircraft by the summer of 1943. The main models were the baseline Yak-1, the Yak-1B with a cut-down rear fuselage allowing the incorporation of a clear-view 'bubble' canopy, and the Yak-1M lightened model with a number of significant improvements. Developments were the Yak-3, Yak-7 and Yak-9. This series of fighters were the finest available to the Soviet air forces during the eastern campaign, and undoubtedly helped to turn the tide of the war.

| | |
|---|---|
| Country of origin: | USSR |
| Type: | (Yak-1 early production standard) single-seat fighter and fighter-bomber |
| Powerplant: | one 1100hp (820kW) Klimov M-105P 12-cylinder Vee engine |
| Performance: | maximum speed 600km/h (373mph); climb to 5000m (16,405ft) in 5 minutes 24 seconds; service ceiling 10,000m (32,810ft); range 700km (435 miles) |
| Weights: | empty 2347kg (5174lb); maximum take-off 2847kg (6276lb) |
| Dimensions: | span 10.00m (32ft 9.7in); length 8.48m (27ft 9.9in); height 2.64m (8ft 8in) |
| Armament: | one 20mm fixed forward-firing cannon in an engine installation, and two 7.62mm fixed forward-firing machine guns in the upper part of the forward fuselage, plus an external bomb and rocket load of 200kg (441lb) |

# Yakovlev Yak-26 'Mandrake'

**F**ew details of this secretive aircraft, the Soviet equivalent of the Lockheed U-2, have emerged despite the end of Cold War hostilities. Stemming directly from the Yak-25R reconnaissance aircraft, the two aircraft share a similar fuselage and radome. The tandem seat cockpit on the Yak-25 'Flashlight' was reconfigured to a single-seat and the 'Mandrake' has a completely new long, unswept wing that was obviously designed for high-altitude operations. Bicycle type undercarriage is employed with twin outriggers mounted in wing-tip pods. Service entry was around 1957, and the aircraft was involved in operations over Eastern Asia, the Middle East and along the borders of communist territory before being retired in the early 1970s. Its replacement was the MiG-25 'Foxbat'. The aircraft pictured is preserved at the Monino Museum outside Moscow.

| | |
|---|---|
| **Country of origin:** | USSR |
| **Type:** | single-seat high-altitude reconnaissance aircraft |
| **Powerplant:** | two 2803kg (6173lb) Tumanskii RD-9 turbojets |
| **Performance:** | maximum speed at altitude 755km/h (470mph); service ceiling about 19,000m (62,000ft); range 4000km (2500 miles) |
| **Weights:** | empty 8165kg (18,000lb); maximum take-off 13,600kg (30,000lb) |
| **Dimensions:** | wingspan 22m (71ft); length 15.5m (51ft); height 4m (13ft) |

# Yakovlev Yak-28P 'Firebar'

The Yak-28P two-seat all-weather interceptor has a generally similar configuration to the earlier Yak-25/26 family, but has a high shoulder-set wing with the leading edge extended further forward, a taller fin and rudder, revised powerplant in different underwing nacelles and different nosecone. The Yak-28 was designed in the late 1950s as a multi-role aircraft and was produced in tactical attack, ('Brewer-A, -B and -C), reconnaissance (Yak-28R 'Brewer-D'), electronic counter-measures (Yak-28E 'Brewer-E'), and trainer versions (Yak-28U 'Maestro') alongside the Yak-28P 'Firebar'. The suffix 'P' indicates that the design was adapted to the interceptor role, rather than designed only for it from the outset. After introduction of the type in 1962, approximately 60 remained in service in 1990 and all have now been withdrawn.

| | |
|---|---|
| Country of origin: | USSR |
| Type: | two-seat all-weather interceptor |
| Powerplant: | two 6206kg (13,669lb) Tumanskii R-11 turbojets |
| Performance: | maximum speed 1180km/h (733mph); service ceiling 16,000m (52,495ft); maximum combat radius 925km (575 miles) |
| Weights: | maximum take-off 19,000kg (41,890lb) |
| Dimensions: | wingspan 12.95m (42ft 6in); length (long-nose late production) 23m (75ft 7.5in); height 3.95m (12ft 11.5in); wing area 37.6 q m (404.74sq ft) |
| Armament: | four underwing pylons for two AA-2 'Atoll', AA-2-2 ('Advanced Atoll') or AA-3 ('Anab') air-to-air missiles |

# Yakovlev Yak-38 'Forger-A'

A part from the Harrier family of aircraft, the Yak-38 is the only other operational jet VTOL aircraft in the world, albeit a far less capable one. Development of the Yak-36MP prototype began in the late 1960s and operational service began in 1976. Unlike the Harrier, the Yak-38 uses two fixed turbojets mounted in tandem behind the cockpit for lift, which have auxiliary inlets on the top of the fuselage. These are augmented by a third vectoring thrust unit in the rear fuselage which is used for level flight. The wing folds at mid-span for carrier stowage, and at the tips there are reaction control jets. A small tailcone at the rear has a reaction control nozzle on either side. Although VTOL operations are possible, a short take-off run with both lift jets operative for the carriage of a useful weapon load. Production has been limited to about 90 aircraft, and as many as 37 of these have been lost in accidents. The aircraft is no longer in Russian service.

| Country of origin: | USSR |
|---|---|
| Type: | V/STOL carrier-based fighter-bomber |
| Powerplant: | two 3050kg (6724lb) Rybinsk RD-36-35VFR lift turbojets; one 6950kg (15,322lb) Tumanskii R-27V-300 vectored-thrust turbojet |
| Performance: | maximum speed at high altitude 1009km/h (627mph); service ceiling 12,000m (39,370ft); combat range on hi-lo-hi mission with maximum weapon load 370km (230 miles) |
| Weights: | empty 7485kg (16,502lb); maximum take-off 11,700kg (25,795lb) |
| Dimensions: | wingspan 7.32m (24ft); length 15.5m (50ft 10in); height 4.37m (14ft 4in); wing area 18.5sq m (199.14sq ft) |
| Armament: | four external hardpoints with provision for 2000kg (4409lb) of stores, including air-to-air missiles, air-to-surface missiles, bombs, rocket-launcher pods, cannon pods, and drop tanks |

# Zeppelin-Staaken R-series

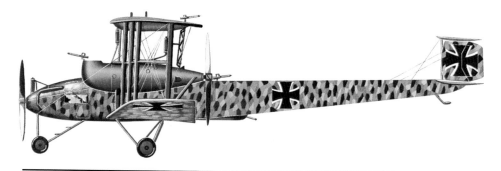

Thy largest aircraft used in World War I were the sluggish but capable *Riesenflugzeug* (giant aeroplane) series produced by the Zeppelin Werke Staaken. Originally this organisation had been Gotha, where the V.G.O.1 weighing 9000kg (19,850lb) first flew in April 1915 on the power of three 240hp (179kW) engines. Via several other one-off bombers, with three, four or five engines and different schemes of defensive armament, the design team of Baumann, Hirth and Klein eventually produced R.VI. Except for the V.G.O.I, which was lost in a crash, all of the giant bombers were used on the Eastern Front or against Britain. The VI went into production, one being built by the Staaken works, six by Aviatik, four by OAW, and seven by Schütte-Lanz. Three of the Aviatik machines had different noses, tails and Maybach engines. The VI was followed by an assortment of derivatives, mainly powered by five Maybach engines, with varied airframes.

| | |
|---|---|
| **Country of origin:** | Germany |
| **Type:** | heavy bomber |
| **Powerplant:** | four 245hp Maybach Mb.IV 6-cylinder inline piston engines |
| **Performance:** | maximum speed 130km/h (81mph); service ceiling 3800m (12,500ft); range 800km (500 miles) |
| **Weights:** | empty 7350kg (16,200lb); maximum take-off weight 11,460kg (25,265lb) |
| **Dimensions:** | span 42.2m (138ft 6in); length 22.1m (72ft 6in); height 6.3m (20ft 8in) |
| **Armament:** | one or two 7.92mm Parabellum machine guns in nose position; one or two 7.92mm Parabellum machine guns in dorsal cockpit; one 7.92mm Parabellum machine gun in rear position; internal bay with provision for up to 18 100kg (220lb) or one 1000kg (2205lb) bomb carried in semi-recessed position, up to a maximum load of 2000kg (4409lb) |

# Index

# Index

# Index

# Index

# Index

# Index

# Index

# Index

# Index

# Index